Student's t Distribution

d.f.	c → 0.750, α′ 0.125, α″ 0.250	0.800 / 0.100 / 0.200	0.850 / 0.075 / 0.150	0.900 / 0.050 / 0.100	0.950 / 0.025 / 0.050	0.980 / 0.010 / 0.020	0.990 / 0.005 / 0.010
1	2.414	3.078	4.165	6.314	12.706	31.821	63.657
2	1.604	1.886	2.282	2.920	4.303	6.965	9.925
3	1.423	1.638	1.924	2.353	3.182	4.541	5.841
4	1.344	1.533	1.778	2.132	2.776	3.747	4.604
5	1.301	1.476	1.699	2.015	2.571	3.365	4.032
6	1.273	1.440	1.650	1.943	2.447	3.143	3.707
7	1.254	1.415	1.617	1.895	2.365	2.998	3.499
8	1.240	1.397	1.592	1.860	2.306	2.896	3.355
9	1.230	1.383	1.574	1.833	2.262	2.821	3.250
10	1.221	1.372	1.559	1.812	2.228	2.764	3.169
11	1.214	1.363	1.548	1.796	2.201	2.718	3.106
12	1.209	1.356	1.538	1.782	2.179	2.681	3.055
13	1.204	1.350	1.530	1.771	2.160	2.650	3.012
14	1.200	1.345	1.523	1.761	2.145	2.624	2.977
15	1.197	1.341	1.517	1.753	2.131	2.602	2.947
16	1.194	1.337	1.512	1.746	2.120	2.583	2.921
17	1.191	1.333	1.508	1.740	2.110	2.567	2.898
18	1.189	1.330	1.504	1.734	2.101	2.552	2.878
19	1.187	1.328	1.500	1.729	2.093	2.539	2.861
20	1.185	1.325	1.497	1.725	2.086	2.528	2.845
21	1.183	1.323	1.494	1.721	2.080	2.518	2.831
22	1.182	1.321	1.492	1.717	2.074	2.508	2.819
23	1.180	1.319	1.489	1.714	2.069	2.500	2.807
24	1.179	1.318	1.487	1.711	2.064	2.492	2.797
25	1.178	1.316	1.485	1.708	2.060	2.485	2.787
26	1.177	1.315	1.483	1.706	2.056	2.479	2.779
27	1.176	1.314	1.482	1.703	2.052	2.473	2.771
28	1.175	1.313	1.480	1.701	2.048	2.467	2.763
29	1.174	1.311	1.479	1.699	2.045	2.462	2.756
30	1.173	1.310	1.477	1.697	2.042	2.457	2.750
35	1.170	1.306	1.472	1.690	2.030	2.438	2.724
40	1.167	1.303	1.468	1.684	2.021	2.423	2.704
45	1.165	1.301	1.465	1.679	2.014	2.412	2.690
50	1.164	1.299	1.462	1.676	2.009	2.403	2.678
55	1.163	1.297	1.460	1.673	2.004	2.396	2.668
60	1.162	1.296	1.458	1.671	2.000	2.390	2.660
90	1.158	1.291	1.452	1.662	1.987	2.369	2.632
120	1.156	1.289	1.449	1.658	1.980	2.358	2.617
∞	1.150	1.282	1.440	1.645	1.960	2.326	2.58

Student's t values generated by Minitab Version 9.2.

c is a confidence level:

α′ is the level of significance for a one-tailed test:

Right-tailed test

Left-tailed test

α″ is the level of significance for a two-tailed test:

Need some extra help with your statistics course?

With a little help from this specially designed study aid, you can prepare for tests and get the best grade possible.

A welcome companion to your statistics text!
The **Study and Solutions Guide** (0-669-39479-3) gives you a thorough second look at the concepts, techniques, and problems presented in your text. Each section features:

- Lesson-by-lesson review
- Problem-solving warm-up
- Critical thinking questions
- Answers to critical thinking questions
- Solutions to selected odd-numbered problems from the text

Look for this supplement in your bookstore.

If you don't find it, check with your bookstore manager or call D. C. Heath toll free at 1-800-334-3284. In Canada, call toll free at 1-800-268-2472. Shipping, handling, and state tax may be added where applicable (tell the operator you are placing a #1-PREFER order).

Understandable Statistics

Understandable Statistics

Concepts and Methods

Fifth Edition

Charles Henry Brase
Regis University

Corrinne Pellillo Brase
Arapahoe Community College

D. C. Heath and Company
Lexington, Massachusetts   Toronto

Address editorial correspondence to:

D. C. Heath and Company
125 Spring Street
Lexington, MA 02173

Acquisitions Editor:	Charles W. Hartford
Developmental Editor:	Philip Charles Lanza
Production Editor:	Carolyn Ingalls
Designer:	Kenneth Hollman
Photo Researcher:	Billie Porter
Art Editor:	Diane B. Grossman
Production Coordinator:	Lisa Merrill
Permissions Editor:	Margaret Roll

Photo Credits: Page 1, Courtesy, Museum of Fine Arts, Boston, Fenollosa-Weld Collection. Page 23, UPI/Bettmann Newsphotos. Page 107, Culver Pictures, Inc. Page 185, North Wind Picture Archives. Page 261, Fogg Art Museum, Cambridge, Mass. Page 325, Historical Pictures/Stock Montage. Page 401, Ralph Steiner. Page 443, © Topham/The Image Works. Page 529, Brown Brothers. Page 655, Hulton/Deutsch Collection, Ltd. Page 747, © Topham/The Image Works. Page 811, Keystone Press Agency, Inc.

Published simultaneously in Canada.

Printed in the United States of America.

International Standard Book Number: 0-669-35513-5

Library of Congress Catalog Number: 94-71569

10 9 8 7 6 5

This book is dedicated to the memory of
a great teacher, mathematician, and friend,

Burton W. Jones

Professor Emeritus, University of Colorado

P R E F A C E

This text is designed for students with a minimal background in mathematics. The same pedagogical features that made the first four editions of the text so readable are preserved in this fifth edition.

We have retained the *graduated approach to problem solving.* Our experience in class-testing this approach convinces us that the format we have adopted will work for a wide variety of students in an introductory statistics course. The exercises and problems touch on applications appropriate to a broad range of interests. Complicated calculations are simplified by using step-by-step tabular procedures well suited to simple calculators. Hints for using more sophisticated calculators are also given.

Continuing Key Features

- *Detailed Examples* that show students how to select and use appropriate procedures.

- *Guided Exercises* that immediately follow an example. Each guided exercise gives the student a chance to *work* with a new concept before another is presented. The student must examine and analyze characteristic features of a problem similar to the preceding example. Completely worked out solutions occur beside each exercise to give immediate reinforcement to the learning process.

- *Section Problems* that require the student to use all the new concepts mastered in the preceding section. The section problems reinforce the material of the examples and exercises, providing additional exercise in practical application of the principles considered. Extensively revised problem sets include a variety of *real-world* problems with data or settings from identifiable sources. These problems illustrate connections in statistics to a wide range of fields. *Key steps* to solutions of odd-numbered problems are contained in Appendix III of the text.

- *Chapter Problems,* comprehensive problems that appear at the end of each chapter and cover each topic introduced in the chapter. Many chapter problems require material and concepts from several sections. Most important, the student must decide what technique to apply to a problem. As in actual applications, the position of the problem does not indicate which section the student should look to for the method of solution.

- *Linking Concepts* that provide students the opportunity to extend their thinking and that look at statistical concepts from a broader perspective. This feature includes problems that ask the student to discuss and write brief essays about main concepts from the chapter and related topics from prior chapters.

New Features in the Fifth Edition

- *The extensive revision of Section Problems* includes many new problems, most based on *real-world* data or on situations with identifiable references. These problems come from a wide range of fields, including natural science, business, economics, medicine, social science, archaeology, and consumer interest.

- *Chapter Overviews* appear at the beginning of each chapter, providing brief previews of each section. These overviews are also useful reminders of section content for students as they review for exams.

- *Chapter Focus Problems* appear in the opening discussion of each chapter. They are interesting problems that demonstrate the type of questions that students can answer once they develop skills in the subject of the chapter.

- *Data Highlights* are problems based on real data from newspapers, magazines, and journals, or on general consumer questions. Appearing at the end of each chapter, they ask the student to apply appropriate statistical methods from the chapter.

- *Calculator Notes* give a general discussion regarding appropriate calculator use or give sample screens from the Texas Instruments TI-82 graphics calculator, showing how this calculator performs designated operations. The calculator notes are general enough to apply to a wide variety of calculators.

- *Using Technology sections* at the end of most chapters replace the former Using Computer sections. Computers and calculators are certainly powerful tools for the statistician. In many institutions it is possible to introduce the beginning statistics student to statistical software packages. The Using Technology sections feature published raw data and situations from a variety of fields. The problems in these sections can be solved using almost any appropriate statistical computer software package, and in many cases, by using a *graphing calculator*. We have tailored the exercises so that they can be completed easily by utilizing the software supplement package *ComputerStat* that accompanies this text. In addition, instructions for the popular commercial software package *Minitab* and for the *TI-82* graphing calculator are also included. Displays from Minitab, the TI-82, and ComputerStat are also included so that students who do not have direct access to these computing tools can see how such tools can be used.

- *A new four-color design* highlights the text's features, enhances its visual appeal, and provides additional strength to the text's pedagogy.

Content Changes to the Fifth Edition

With each new edition we evaluate again the scope, appropriateness, and effectiveness of the text's presentation, and reflect on extensive user feedback collected by the publisher. This thinking and research has resulted in the following content improvements in this edition:

- *Introduction to collecting data* is included in Chapter 1.

- *Topics from Quality Control* are given more emphasis. Pareto charts are included in Chapter 2, and expanded treatment of control charts is given in Chapter 6.

- *Poisson and Geometric Distributions* are included in Chapter 5.

- *Confidence Intervals for the Difference of Means and Proportions* is a new section at the end of Chapter 8.

- *Hypothesis Testing* is extensively revised. Traditional testing strategy is now done on the z or t distribution corresponding to the original data distribution. This is in keeping with most computer software packages which give the z or t value of the sample statistic. P values are introduced early. Students are shown how to compute the P value from the normal distribution and how to find an interval containing the P value from a Student's t distribution. All examples and guided exercises are done using the traditional method of hypothesis testing as well as by the P value method. Faculty may choose to omit P values entirely, introduce them briefly, or use them as extensively as they wish.

  In addition, Chapter 9, Hypothesis Testing, has been reorganized so that tests involving one parameter are at the beginning of the chapter and all tests involving the difference of parameters are at the end of the chapter. This organization permits greater flexibility in selecting tests of the mean, of proportions, or of differences in means or proportions if the syllabus does not give enough time to present the entire chapter.

- *Other revisions* include the addition of relative frequency tables and histograms, and ogives in Chapter 2, more discussion of EDA techniques, adjustment of hypothesis testing procedure in Chapters 10 and 11, and minor revisions in other chapters, such as the use of the symbol $\hat{p}$ for the point estimate of the sample proportion in a binomial experiment.

- *Bayes's Theorem* is included in Appendix I for courses that require an introduction to this important topic. The section is complete with examples and guided exercises.

- *The Hypergeometric distribution* is also included in Appendix I as a section complete with examples and guided exercises. This interesting topic could be included in a course or assigned as a special project.

Using Tools from Technology

Understandable Statistics supports student access to a wide range of activities for computers or graphing calculators. Students can simply look at displays of computer output and screens from the TI-82 graphing calculator contained in the Using Technology sections, or they can solve problems or complete projects utilizing ComputerStat, Minitab, other statistical software packages, or a graphing calculator such as the TI-82. Technology-based supplement support includes the following:

- *ComputerStat,* a computer software package designed to accompany this text. Institutions adopting the text may have a complimentary license to the software. ComputerStat is an interactive computer package, and it is designed to be very user friendly. The output is compatible with the results that the students obtain when they do a problem with pencil, paper, and calculator. However, the computer handles larger data sets with relative ease.

- *Technology Guide,* a new supplement that has activities and projects for students to explore utilizing the technology of computer software or graphing calculators. Specific instructions are given for using ComputerStat, Minitab, and the TI-82 graphing calculator to complete the activities. The activities and projects correlate with the text. This guide includes the ComputerStat software described previously.

Supplements

- *Instructor's Annotated Edition of Understandable Statistics: Concepts and Methods,* Fifth Edition. A special section in the front of the IAE provides answers to all even-numbered section problems and chapter problems. Answers to odd-numbered problems can be found in Appendix III. In addition, marginal comments appear throughout the IAE and offer to the instructor many different suggestions for using the text.

- *Instructor's Resource Guide.* This guide contains key steps and answers to even-numbered problems, two (revised) forms of chapter tests with solutions, and transparency masters for use with overhead projectors.

- *ComputerStat software,* a package of statistical programs designed and organized to accompany the text. This package is available without charge to institutions adopting the text.

- *Technology Guide* containing computer and graphing calculator activities coordinated with the text. Specific instructions for using ComputerStat, Minitab, and the TI-82 graphing calculator are included. ComputerStat software accompanies the guide.

- *Student Study and Solutions Guide* by Elizabeth Farber, Bucks County Community College. This guide offers comprehensive review per text section and additional practice. Thinking About Statistics questions with their solutions and detailed solutions to selected problems in the text are also included.

- *ESATEST III Computerized Testing* in MS-DOS and Macintosh formats. Instructors can custom-design tests from items in the test bank, add their own test items to the bank, or edit existing items. The program offers pull-down menus, dialogue boxes, pop-up windows, function keys, mouse support, and a graphical user interface.

- *Test Item File.* This supplement serves as a convenient printed guide of all items appearing in the computerized testing software package.
- *Data Sets Disk.* This software provides a useful bank of large data sets for additional experimentation with Minitab.

Alternate Routes Through the Text

Understandable Statistics: Concepts and Methods, Fifth Edition, is designed to be flexible. It offers the professor a choice of teaching possibilities. In most one-semester courses, it will not be practical to cover all the material in depth. However, depending on the emphasis of the course, the professor may choose to cover various topics. *A Table of Prerequisite Materials* follows this preface to aid in topic selection.

For a course with more *emphasis on descriptive statistics,* all of Chapters 2 and 3 may be included. For a course with more *emphasis on probability,* all of Chapter 4 may be included as well as the section on Bayes's Theorem in Appendix I.

For a streamlined course with an *emphasis on inferential statistics,* Section 2.1, Random Samples; Section 2.3, Histograms and Frequency Distributions; Section 3.1, Mode, Median, and Mean; and Section 3.2, Measures of Variation, comprise all that is essential from Chapters 2 and 3. A light treatment of probability including Section 4.1, What Is Probability?; part of Section 4.2, Some Probability Rules; and Section 4.4, Introduction to Random Variables and Probability Distributions, will enable the course to proceed quickly to Chapter 5, sections 5.1, 5.2, and 5.3 on the binomial distribution. Then topics from Chapter 8, Estimation, and Chapter 9, Hypothesis Testing, may be selected. Paired Data and Linear Regression in Chapter 10 may be presented at any time after Chapter 3. However, confidence intervals for predictions based on the linear regression model and multiple regression require some work from Chapter 8, Estimation, and Chapter 9, Hypothesis Testing.

To allow more time for Chi-square and ANOVA topics and for nonparametric statistics, Chapter 5 and later sections involving proportions may be omitted.

Acknowledgments

It is our pleasure to acknowledge the contributions of survey respondents, users of earlier editions, and prepublication reviewers of this new edition. All of their insights and comments have been very valuable to us. Reviewers of this edition include Bradford Crain of Portland State University; Stanley Fraser of the State University of New York at Canton; John Gazak of Herkimer County Community College; Stephen Gold of Cypress College; Larry Griffey of Florida Community College South; David Gurney of Southeastern Louisiana University; Raymond Guzman of Pasadena City College; Derek Hart of Dawson College, Montreal; Peter Knopf of Pace

University; Kitt Lumley of Columbus College; Carl Mancuso of William Patterson College; Peter Moloney of Madonna University; Diane L. Morris of Belmont Technical College; Charles Okeke of the Community College of Southern Nevada; Ronald Pierce of Eastern Kentucky University; Madelyn Smith of Gloucester County College; and Ellen Stutes of Louisiana State University. We also remain indebted to past reviewers for contributions that they made to the success of earlier editions.

We especially want to thank Dr. Diane Wagner of Regis University who read the manuscript carefully and solved all of the section and end-of-chapter problems. In addition to Patricia Hauss and Jack Pepper of Arapahoe Community College, we also want to thank Patrick Enright and James McCullough.

We also acknowledge the cooperation of Minitab, Inc., and Texas Instruments. The Minitab computer displays are from MINITAB Release 9. The graphing calculator displays are from the TI-82.

Charles Henry Brase
Corrinne Pellillo Brase

Table of Prerequisite Material

Chapter	Prerequisite Sections
1 Getting Started	None
2 Organizing Data	1.1
3 Averages and Variation	1.1, 2.1, 2.3
4 Elementary Probability Theory	1.1, 2.1, 2.3, 3.1, 3.2
5 The Binomial Probability Distribution and Related Topics	1.1, 2.1, 2.3, 3.1, 3.2, 4.1, 4.2, 4.4, with 4.3 useful but not essential
6 Normal Distributions	1.1, 2.1, 2.3, 3.1, 3.2, 4.1, 4.2, 4.4
7 Introduction to Sampling Distributions	
(omit 7.3)	1.1, 2.1, 2.3, 3.1, 3.2, 4.1, 4.2, 4.4, all of Chapter 6
(include 7.3)	5.1, 5.2, 5.3 also
8 Estimation	
(omit 8.3 and parts of 8.4 and 8.5)	1.1, 2.1, 2.3, 3.1, 3.2, 4.1, 4.2, 4.4, all of Chapter 6, 7.1, 7.2
(include 8.3 and parts of 8.4 and 8.5)	5.1, 5.2, 5.3, 7.3 also
9 Hypothesis Testing	
(omit 9.5 and part of 9.7)	1.1, 2.1, 2.3, 3.1, 3.2, 4.1, 4.2, 4.4, all of Chapter 6, 7.1, 7.2
(include 9.5 and all of 9.7)	5.1, 5.2 5.3, 7.3 also
10 Regression and Correlation	
(omit part of 10.2, 10.4, and 10.5)	1.1, 2.1, 3.1, 3.2
(include all of 10.2, 10.4, and 10.5)	4.1, 4.2, 4.4, Chapter 6, 7.1, 7.2, 8.1, 9.1, 9.2 also
11 Chi-Square and F Distributions	
(omit 11.3)	1.1, 2.1, 2.3, 3.1, 3.2, 4.1, 4.2, 4.4, Chapter 6, 7.1, 7.2, 9.1
(include 11.3)	8.1 also
12 Nonparametric Statistics	1.1, 2.1, 2.3, 3.1, 3.2, 4.1, 4.2, 4.4, Chapter 6, 7.1, 7.2, 9.1, 9.5

A USER'S GUIDE TO FEATURES

The new edition of **Understandable Statistics** includes a variety of features designed to enhance a student's understanding by providing overviews and summaries of concepts and methods, interesting real-world problems using real data sets, and information on using technology. In addition, the text has a **new four color design** which highlights important features and provides visual interest.

Key features of the text are listed below, along with brief descriptions of their purpose. Many new features have been added to this edition, and those found useful by students in the past have been retained.

Chapter Overview

This new feature provides more than just a list of topics to be covered—it includes a brief description of each section so that students move into the chapter with an overall sense of what they'll be studying.

Chapter Focus Problems

"What kinds of problems will this chapter help me solve?" These problems can motivate students by showing examples of the work they can do once they have developed the skills in the chapter. Chapter Focus Problems occur at the beginning of each chapter and are new to this edition.

XV

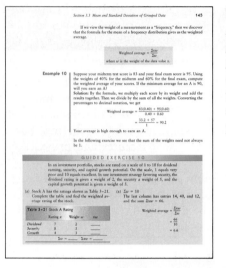

Guided Exercises

A continued unique feature of **Understandable Statistics** is the guided exercises following selected examples. Each guided exercise gives the student a chance to *work* with a new concept before another is presented by examining and analyzing a problem similar to the preceding example. Completely worked-out solutions occur beside each exercise to give immediate reinforcement in the learning process.

Real-World Exercises

Many interesting real-world problems lend themselves to the study of statistics. In this edition, great emphasis is placed on including interesting problems utilizing real data and real situations using identifiable sources. These problems come from a wide range of fields, including natural science, business, economics, medicine, social science, archaeology, and consumer interest.

Over a third of the problems in this edition are new. Real-World Exercises are identified with a distinctive icon.

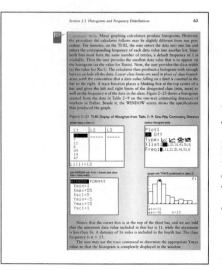

Calculator Notes

These notes are located throughout the book. They provide information regarding appropriate calculator use. New to this edition are sample screens from the Texas Instruments TI-82 graphing calculator showing how this calculator performs certain operations. The notes are general enough to apply to a wide variety of calculators.

End-of-Chapter Material includes a **Summary**, a listing of **Important Words and Symbols** with section references so that students who need additional review will be encouraged to read it in context, and **Chapter Review Problems.** Also included in the end-of-chapter presentation are the following features.

Data Highlights

These new problems can be solved by the student's using appropriate methods from that chapter. The **Chapter Focus Problems** show students what they'll be able to do, and the **Data Highlights Problems** provide them with additional opportunity to put their skills into action.

The sources for **Data Highlights Problems** include newspapers, magazines, and journals.

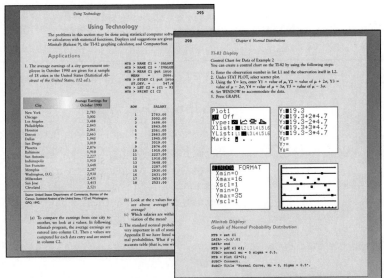

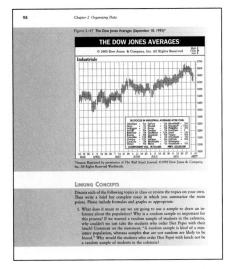

Linking Concepts

These questions help students extend and integrate their thinking, and develop a broader conceptual understanding of statistics. Students are asked to discuss and write about key concepts from the chapter and related topics from prior chapters.

Using Technology

All these sections have been revised for this edition to include information on using Minitab, the TI-82 graphing calculator, and ComputerStat to solve statistical problems.

CONTENTS

4 Elementary Probability Theory   185

Chapter Overview

5 The Binomial Probability Distribution and Related Topics   261

Chapter Overview

9 Hypothesis Testing   529

Chapter Overview

10 Regression and Correlation   655

Chapter Overview

11 Chi-Square and F Distributions 747

Chapter Overview

12 Nonparametric Statistics 811

Chapter Overview

Appendix I   Additional Topics   A1

Let us examine a listing of section titles with a short discussion of goals and objectives for the information we will learn in each section of this chapter.

Section 1.1

What Is Statistics?

Many, if not most, of life's really important questions involve incomplete information. The process of drawing good, reliable conclusions from incomplete information is central to the study of statistics. In this section we find that statistics is described as the study of how to collect, organize, analyze, and interpret information, especially numerical information. We introduce the terms *population* and *sample taken from a population.* Ways to gather data are introduced. We discuss how data can be classified by level of measurement.

Section 1.2

Calculators and Computers in Statistics

Computing numbers meaningful in statistical analysis sometimes may require quite a bit of calculation. In this section we present some information about using calculators and computer software to assist you in performing the calculations necessary for suitable statistical analysis.

Section 1.3

Where Will I Use Statistics?

Sociologists and economists speculate that we are leaving the industrial age and entering the information age. Every day we are bombarded by information, much of it statistical. Everyone needs to know some statistics simply to understand and evaluate the large amount of information that comes to us. In this brief section we list some fields of study where knowledge of statistics is essential, and we urge you to become aware of how your decisions are influenced by information from statistics.

Confucius (551–479 B.C.)

Confucius is China's renowned teacher, philosopher, and theorist. His influence has endured for over 2000 years.

Getting Started

To guess is cheap,
To guess wrongly is expensive,

Tell me, I'll forget.
Show me, I may remember.
But involve me and I'll understand.

Old Chinese Proverbs

Most of the important decisions in life involve incomplete information. Such decisions often involve so many complicated factors that a complete analysis is not practical or even possible. We are often forced into the position of making a guess based on limited information. However, as the first proverb implies, a blind guess is not the best solution. Statistical methods, such as you will learn in this book, can help you make the best "educated guess."

The authors of this book want you to understand and enjoy statistics. The reading material will *tell you* about the subject. The examples will *show you* how it works. To really understand, however, the second proverb says you must *get involved*. Guided exercises, calculator and computer applications, section and chapter problems, and writing exercises are all designed to get you involved in the subject. As you grow in your understanding of statistics, we believe you will enjoy learning a subject that has a world full of good applications. In fact, the applications of statistics are so numerous that in a sense you are limited only by your own imagination as to what areas in your life you may want to make use of the subject.

Focus Problem ▶ Where Have All the Fireflies Gone?

A feature article in the *Wall Street Journal* (September 3, 1993) discusses the alarming disappearance of fireflies. In the article, Professor Sara Lewis (of Tufts University) and other scholars and interested people around the world express real concern about the decline in the worldwide population of fireflies. So far, much of the evidence is anecdotal; however, a remarkable decline in

1

the population of fireflies has been reported from parks and suburbs of America to the once firefly-rich fields of Japan. In Japan there is a tradition that nighttime fireflies are a beautiful reminder of the souls of friends and family who have passed away. For reasons such as this, and possibly for the simple joy of watching fireflies, Japan has a number of special sanctuaries to protect the declining population of fireflies.

There are a number of possible explanations for the world decline in the firefly population.

1. We are in a normal worldwide 3-year cycle in which fireflies are on the decline. When the cycle hits bottom, the firefly population will start to come back in large numbers.

2. There is a general decline in the ecosystem. Too many chemicals and pesticides are killing fireflies all over the world.

3. A certain chemical company in St. Louis (mentioned in the *Wall Street Journal*) is willing to pay 1 cent for each firefly it receives from anyone anywhere. This use and other commercial uses of fireflies have resulted in their decline. In the *Wall Street Journal,* one family was quoted as making so much money from large-scale collection of fireflies that the family could send three children to college from the proceeds!

4. Woodlands, wetlands, and open fields have given way to cities and subdivisions. The habitat for fireflies has been reduced, and so the population is reduced.

5. Artificial nighttime lighting is used extensively across the United States as well as in Japan. This large-scale lighting is interfering with the Morse code–like mating ritual of the fireflies. If the fireflies have trouble mating, there will be fewer fireflies in the general population.

There are many other theories and possible explanations for the apparent worldwide decline in the population of fireflies.

What does any of this have to do with statistics?

The truth, at this time, is that no one really knows (1) how much the world firefly population has declined and (2) how to explain the decline *if* there is actually a significant decline in the firefly population. The population of all fireflies is simply too large to study in its entirety. If they are declining in the United States and Japan, are they declining in other places as well? In any study, we must rely on incomplete information from samples. Furthermore, we must draw realistic conclusions that have statistical integrity from these samples.

You may be sure that a number of very fine scholars in universities across the world are beginning to examine the possible world decline in fireflies. You also may be sure that these scholars will use statistical methods when they collect, analyze, and investigate their data about fireflies.

Section 1.1   **What Is Statistics?**

All of us have a built-in system of inference that helps us make decisions; without it we would be lost. Of course, we also have a built-in set of prejudices that affects our decisions. A definite advantage of statistical methods is that they can help us make decisions without prejudice. Moreover, statistics can be used for making decisions when we are faced with uncertainties. For instance, if we wish to estimate the proportion of people who will have a severe reaction to a new flu shot without giving the shot to everyone who wants it, statistics can provide appropriate methods.

The general prerequisite for statistical decision making is the gathering of *numerical* facts. Procedures for evaluating numerical data together with rules of inference are central topics in the study of statistics. In short, we may say that *statistics is the study of how to collect, organize, analyze, and interpret numerical information.*

The statistical procedures you will learn in this book should supplement your built-in system of inference—that is, the results from statistical procedures and good sense should dovetail. Of course, statistical methods in themselves have no power to work miracles. These methods can help us make some decisions, but not all conceivable decisions. Remember, a properly applied statistical procedure is no more accurate than the data, or facts, on which it is based. Finally, statistical results should be interpreted by one who understands not only the methods but also the subject matter to which they have been applied.

In any investigation it is important to ask the right kinds of questions. What are the key points of the problem and its solution? In this section we will examine a variety of problems. Then, thinking like statisticians, we will investigate some important concepts. As a start, let's look at a few important terms.

The term *population* refers to all measurements or observations of interest. For example, if we want to know the average height of people who have climbed Mt. Everest, then the population consists of the heights of all those people. Now suppose we want to know the average height of 20-year-old females in the United States. In this case, the population consists of the heights of *all* 20-year-old females in the United States.

It is interesting to note that the population is defined in terms of our *desire for knowledge.* The population can be thought of as measurements or observations for the entire group of objects or people about which information is desired. In this sense, a population can be an existing set of measurements, or it can be a set of measurements that is clear in our understanding but is not yet complete. The heights (in inches) of all U.S. presidents from George Washington to Bill Clinton can be thought of as an existing set of measurements. However, the set of heights of all presidents from George Washington on into the future is not yet complete. Nevertheless, we have a clear understanding of how this population is to be constructed. In a way, we can think of such an (incomplete) population as being open ended.

Often it is not feasible to study the entire population. How would you measure the height of every 20-year-old female in the United States? In such cases we look at samples. A *sample* is simply a part of the population. But not every sample is useful. The sample must represent the population. A *random sample* is such a representative sample; in the next chapter we will study these samples in much more detail. In the meantime, we can think of a random sample as a sample determined completely by chance.

Generally speaking, statistical problems are those which require us to draw a random sample of observations from a larger population. Then statistical methods are used to form conclusions about the population based on the information in the sample. Let's look at some examples of population and samples.

Example 1

The department of tropical agriculture is doing a study of pineapples in an experimental field. In this case the data under consideration are the individual weights of all pineapples in the field.

(a) The *population* is the weights of all the pineapples in the field.

(b) The random collection of 100 pineapples is taken from the field. Each pineapple is weighed. The 100 weights form a random *sample* from the population of all weights.

- *Comment:* When referring to a population or sample, be sure to give the *quantity* being measured or counted or the *quality* being observed. For instance, in Example 1 it is not sufficient to say that the population consists of all pineapples in the field. We also must state the quantity to be measured. Unless we do, we won't know whether to consider weight, diameter, length, sugar content, acidity level, time to mature, or any other of the many possible measurements that could be made on pineapples. On the other hand, we might be interested in a *quality* of the pineapple such as color, taste, or whether it is ripe or not.

Through this text you will encounter exercises embedded in the reading material. These guided exercises are included to give you an opportunity to work immediately with new ideas. Cover the answers on the right side (an index card will fit this purpose). After you have thought about or written down *your own response,* check the answers. If there are several parts to an exercise, check each part before you continue. You will be able to answer most of the exercise questions, but don't skip them—they are important.

GUIDED EXERCISE 1

Television station QUE wants to know the proportion of TV owners in Virginia who watch the station's new program at least once a week. The station asked a random group of 1000 TV owners in Virginia if they watch the program at least once a week.

(a) What is the population?

(a) The population consists of the response (does, or does not, watch the new program) from each TV owner in Virginia.

(b) What is the sample?

(b) The sample consists of the response of each of the 1000 TV owners in Virginia who were questioned.

Sometimes we do not have access to the entire population, and at other times the difficulties of working with an entire population are prohibitive. The benefit of statistical methods is that they allow us to draw conclusions about populations based only on information from samples. The handicap of these methods is that our conclusions are uncertain—probabilistic, if you will. Probabilism is one of the aspects of statistical thinking that may be unfamiliar to you, since you dealt with certainties in your previous mathematical experience. For instance, if you are asked to solve the equation $x + 2 = 5$, you know the solution is $x = 3$. There is no uncertainty; you can check the solution in the equation. We do not demand absolute certainty from statistical methods. That is generally too much to ask. However, we do have a measurable degree of probabilistic confidence that the conclusions of a method are valid.

In future work the probability attached to a conclusion will represent the amount of confidence we should have in the conclusion. Probability will be one of our basic tools in the study and application of statistical methods. In Chapter 4 we will study some elementary probability theory, but in the meantime, let's take an intuitive point of view. Thus, if the probability that some statement is true is 0.97, then the statement is true about 97% of the time. The statement is false about 3% of the time.

Now let's look at some examples and see where these new terms fit into place. These examples do not begin to cover the complete range of statistical applications, but they are an indication of the types of problems that can be solved using the methods of this book.

Example 2

If you travel a long distance by air, chances are that you will not have a direct flight. You usually need to change airplanes, and you will often change airlines in the process of making connections. Normally, an agent for your first airline makes arrangements for the connecting flights, and you pay this agent a lump sum for your ticket. If more than one airline company is involved, the companies decide among themselves how much money each should receive.

In the past, a great deal of clerical work was needed to apportion the monies. Then three airlines decide to use statistical methods to determine how total revenue should be split. During a 4-month trial period, they took random samples from the overall population of all interairline tickets. From that sample they determined the proportion of total revenues to be distributed to each airline. They were able to estimate that the degree of error in their statistical process was not more than 0.07%—that is, $700 in $1,000,000. On the basis of this work, more airlines have used statistical methods in settling interairline accounts. Some of the larger airlines estimate a clerical savings of more than $75,000 each year over the old methods.

Example 3

In 1778 Captain James Cook discovered what we now call the Hawaiian Islands. He gave the islanders a present of several goats, and over the years these animals multiplied into wild herds totaling several thousand. They eat almost anything, including the famous silver sword plant, which was once unique to Hawaii.

At one time the silver sword grew abundantly on the island of Maui (in Haleakala, a national park on that island, the silver sword can still be found), but each year there seemed to be fewer and fewer plants. The disappearance of these plants could have been due to many things (e.g., tourists picking them illegally), but a biologist hypothesized that the goats were mainly to blame.

To determine the effect of goats on the vegetation, the rangers set up stations in remote areas of Haleakala. Very few tourists came to these areas, but they were home to many goats. At each station the rangers found two plots with about the same area, plant count, soil, and climatic conditions. One plot was carefully fenced; the other was not. At regular intervals a plant count was made in each plot.

In this example, the population can be thought of as the plant count for the entire park. The samples are plant counts from the experiment stations. The claim is that goats are in fact detrimental to plant life in the park because they reduce the plant count by one fourth or more. Using statistical methods, the claim was confirmed with a high degree of confidence.

GUIDED EXERCISE 2

Mountain Joy Company produces ice axes, which are used by mountain climbers to catch themselves in case of a fall on a steep glacier. Most ice axes have a steel head and a fiberglass shaft. A problem with this piece of equipment is that the shaft sometimes breaks after a hard fall.

The specifications for manufacturing ice axes require that 99% of all ice axes made should hold at least 400 lb on the shaft. The production manager wants to be as certain as possible that under present production methods the shafts can support at least 400 lb. To test an ice ax, a force of 400 lb is applied to the shaft. If the shaft does not break, it passes the test. It is possible to weaken the shaft when the force is applied yet not break it. The manager does not wish to sell weakened ice axes, so she does not test them all.

(a) What does the manager wish to test?

(a) The manager wishes to test if 99% of ice axes made under present production methods hold at least 400 lb.

(b) What is the population?

(b) The population is the strength (in pounds) of each ice ax shaft produced under the present method.

(c) Since the manager does not wish to test *each* ice ax, what should she do?

(c) The manager should use a random sample of ice axes and test it.

Producing Data

Sampling

One very popular way to produce data is to *sample* an existing population. That is, we draw subsets from an existing population. There are many popular ways to sample a population. We will delay our discussion of sampling techniques until Section 2.1. However, we want to remember that the goal of sampling techniques is to gain an accurate picture of the population and disturb the population as little as possible by the act of sampling. Example 2, on the apportion of monies to the airlines, is an example of sampling.

Experiments

Another very popular way to produce data is to observe the outcome of an *experiment*. We are using the word *experiment* here in a very broad sense. In our context, we are using the term *experiment* to mean deliberately imposing some treatment on units or subjects in order to observe a given response. In Example 3, the rangers of Haleakala set up two vegetation plots. One received the treatment of being fenced. An experiment might be putting a given weight on a steel beam to measure how much it bends. An experiment might be done at the Colorado Shakespeare Festival in changing the costumes from Elizabethan to modern twentieth-century style and then observing the effect on ticket sales at performances.

Remember, the goal of experiments is to measure the effect of an intervention. To understand how nature (or a population) responds to a change, we must actually *impose* the change and measure the results. This is in contrast to sampling, where we try to describe or represent the population while making every effort *not* to change the population.

Simulation

Simulation is a numerical facsimile of real-world phenomena. Sometimes simulation is called a "dry lab" approach, in the sense that it is an arithmetic imitation of a real situation. Advantages of simulation are that arithmetic and statistical simulations can fit real-world problems extremely well. The researcher can explore procedures in simulation that might be very dangerous in real life. In the real world you might not want to introduce a high level of a drug into a diabetic person's bloodstream. However, you might want to simulate the injection statistically and study the results. You will harm no one, and the information gained may be of real medical value. Similarly, you might test the effect of wind sheer on an airplane wing in a simulated environment rather than with an actual airplane in flight.

Simulations usually require many, many calculations. Computers are a very practical tool for simulation. In this text we will see several uses of computer simulation such as computer-simulated random samples (end of Chapter 2), a computer simulation for tossing two dice (end of Chapter 4), and computer simulations of confidence intervals for proportions (Chapter 8) and the central limit theorem (Chapter 7).

Census

In a *census,* measurements from the *entire* population are used. The U.S. Department of Commerce, Bureau of the Census conducts a census every 10 years. An attempt is made to reach every resident of the United States. However, even in a census, some members of the population may be missed. For instance, it is difficult to contact homeless people. In other cases, some people may not respond. Statistical estimates for missing responses are often supplied.

GUIDED EXERCISE 3

Which technique (sampling, experiment, simulation, or census) for gathering
data do you think might be the most appropriate for the following studies?

(a) Study of the effect of stopping the cooling process of a nuclear reactor.

(a) Probably simulation, since you may not want to risk a nuclear meltdown.

(b) Study of the amount of time college students taking a full course load spend watching television.

(b) Sampling would work well. Notice that obtaining the information from a student will probably not change the amount of time a student spends watching television.

(c) Study of the effect of a calcium supplement given to young girls on bone mass.

(c) Experimentation. A study by Tom Lloyd reported in the *Journal of the American Medical Association* (August 18, 1993) utilized 94 young girls. Half were given a placebo, and half were given calcium supplements to bring their daily calcium intake up to about 1400 milligrams per day. The group getting the experimental treatment of calcium gained 1.3% more bone mass in a year than the girls getting less calcium.

(d) Study of the credit hours load of *each* student enrolled at your college at the end of the drop/add period this semester.

(d) Census. The registrar can obtain records for *every* student.

Surveys

Once you decide you are going to use sampling or experimentation, a common means to gather data about people is to ask them questions. This process is the essence of *surveying.* You are asked to participate in surveys in many ways. Teacher evaluations, market research conducted in shopping malls, telephone surveys, consumer questions asked on product warranties are all familiar surveys. In the design of a survey or questionnaire, the researcher must decide how the responses will be converted into numbers. Sometimes, as in some polls, the responses might be "agree," "disagree," or "no opinion." Then the researcher looks at the percentage of people who responded in each fashion.

A number of issues can arise in using a survey. Are the questions asked in a neutral way, or is conscious or unconscious bias built into the wording? How can you be sure the respondents are answering truthfully? Is your sample representative of the population? For instance, when conducting election polls, some studies use only registered voters because these are the only people eligible to vote. Other polls use only "likely" voters. They first inquire if the respondent is planning to vote. Other problems arise if the selected respondent refuses to participate.

Voluntary response samples often overrepresent people with strong opinions. A Denver newspaper that has wide circulation in Colorado decided to conduct a survey regarding the question, Should grazing fees for use of public lands be increased? Of the many people who responded, about 85% said, "No!" However, the results were misleading as an indicator of the opinions held by the population of *all* people in Colorado. The sample who responded were self-selected people. The sample consisted mainly of ranchers who felt strongly enough to write the newspaper. These people did not want their grazing fees increased on public land.

Many times negative opinions are especially overrepresented through voluntary response. A statistically designed opinion poll using a random sample from all (adult) Colorado residents later showed that only 34% responded no to the survey question about grazing fees. The random sample eliminated bias by giving all adult respondents an equal chance to be chosen.

Data from voluntary responses can be useful and interesting. However, the information given is anecdotal in nature. It would be questionable to generalize the results to the entire population of interest. Surveys must be designed and administered carefully for the results to generalize.

Hidden Bias

Whenever you gather data, whether by sampling a population, by results of experiment, or by simulation, you should view the data with a critical eye. The way the data are gathered may produce a *hidden bias.* This means that in reality you are not actually measuring what you hoped to measure. Care must be taken to deal with all units or subjects in the exact same way so that no (conscious or unconscious) preferential treatment or selection can occur.

Other Variables

Sometimes our goal is to understand the cause-and-effect relationships between two variables (as might occur in regression and correlation of two variables presented in Chapter 10). However, the effect of one variable on another can be hidden by other variables for which no data have been obtained. For instance, a study of ticket price and attendance at a sporting event might show that higher ticket prices and higher attendance are related, since events with higher ticket prices seem to have greater attendance. One might be led to conclude that if you want to increase attendance at an event, you should raise the price of the tickets. What is missing from this analysis is the variable of *event popularity*. A Super Bowl football game is so special that people are willing to pay higher prices just to be there. A preseason football game, however, does not have the drawing power and may need lower ticket prices to ensure a reasonable crowd at the game. Other variables such as the location of the game, weather, and record of the teams involved also might influence attendance.

The problem of other variables that influence one or both of the original variables can often be overcome if the researcher not only is familiar with statistics but also is well versed in the field of investigation.

Generalizing Results

Some researchers want to generalize their findings to a situation wider than that of the actual data setting. The true scope of a new discovery must be determined by repeated studies in various real-world settings. Just because statistical experiments showed that a drug had a certain effect on a collection of laboratory rats does not guarantee that the drug will have a similar effect on a herd of wild horses in Montana.

GUIDED EXERCISE 4

Comment on the usefulness of the data collected as described.

(a) A uniformed law officer interviews a group of 20 college freshmen. She asks each one his or her name and then if he or she has used an illegal drug in the last month.

(a) Respondents may not answer truthfully. Some may refuse to participate.

(b) Jessica saw some data that show that cities with more low-income housing have more homeless people. Does building low-income housing cause homelessness?

(b) There may be some other variables such as the size of the city. Larger cities may have more low-income housing and more homeless.

(c) A survey about food in the student cafeteria was conducted by having forms available for customers to pick up at the cash register. A drop box for completed forms was available outside the cafeteria.

(c) The voluntary response will likely produce more negative comments.

(d) Extensive studies on coronary problems were conducted using men over age 50 as the subjects.

(d) Conclusions for men over age 50 may or may not generalize to other age and gender groups. These results may be useful for women or younger people, but studies specifically involving these groups may need to be performed.

The process of gathering data is an essential component of good statistical practice. Sampling, experimental design, simulation, and survey design are all extensive studies. Treatises are written on these topics. In a serious statistical study, a great deal of attention is devoted to the process of gathering the data. Then appropriate statistical methods need to be applied. In this course we will explore some of these statistical methods, and you will be able to carry out many of them and use the terminology associated with the methods appropriately. Even with the best statistical methodology, the results need to be interpreted by someone who is an expert in the field. Good statistics and expertise in a given field must work together to give reliable results.

Levels of Measurement

When we collect data, it is common to classify the information obtained according to one of the following four *levels of measurement:*

> Nominal level
> Ordinal level
> Interval level
> Ratio level

Among these four levels of measurement, the *nominal* level is considered to be the *lowest*. This is followed by the *ordinal* level, the *interval* level, and finally the *ratio* level, which is the highest level of measurement.

Since the nominal level is the lowest level, let's examine it first. A dictionary meaning of the word *nominal* is "in name only." This is an easy way to remember the meaning of the nominal level of measurement. Data at this level of measurement consist of "names only," or qualities, with no implied criteria by which the data can be identified as greater than or less than other data items.

Nominal Level

Example 4

The following are examples of data at the nominal level of measurement.

(a) Aspen, Vail, and Breckenridge are names of three ski resorts from the population of names of all ski resorts in Colorado.

(b) Taos, Acoma, Zuni, and Cochiti are names of four Native American pueblos from the population of all names of Native American pueblos in Arizona and New Mexico.

(c) Smith Auto Dealers has a large supply of new T50 trucks on the lot. The colors of the trucks on the lot are red, white, silver, blue, and black.

It is clear that the nominal data in Example 4 are not intended for numerical calculation. The specific names or qualities do not contain any implied ordering or numerical significance.

The next level of measurement is the *ordinal level*. Data at the ordinal level may be arranged in some order, but actual differences between data values either cannot be determined or are meaningless.

Example 5 | The following are examples of data at the ordinal level of measurement.

(a) In a fishing tackle catalogue, there are 17 fishing reels advertised. Of these reels, 6 were rated as good quality, 4 were rated as better quality, and 7 were rated as best quality.

(b) In a travel guide to California, there are 416 bed-and-breakfast accommodations listed. Each bed-and-breakfast facility is given a rating from one to four stars, with four stars as the highest rating. Of the accommodations listed, 93 got one star, 115 got two stars, 172 got three stars, and 36 got four stars.

(c) In a high school graduating class of 319 students, Jim ranked 25th, June ranked 19th, Walter ranked 4th, and Julia ranked 10th.

(d) At one point in a recent baseball season, the Baltimore Orioles were ranked first, the Boston Red Sox were ranked second, and the Milwaukee Brewers were ranked third in the American League East.

In Example 5 we should not try to determine a specific quantitative difference between "good," "better," and "best." Nor should we try to determine an exact difference between a rating of two stars over three stars in the bed-and-breakfast rating system. The difference between June's and Jim's rank was 6, and this is the same difference that exists between Walter's and Julia's ranks. However, that difference doesn't really mean anything significant. For instance, if you look at grade point average, Walter and Julia may have had a big gap between them, whereas June and Jim may have been closer together. In any ranking system, it is only the relative standing that matters. Differences in ranks are meaningless.

In general, the ordinal level of measurement provides information about relative comparisons, but exact differences are not computed.

The *interval level of measurement* is like the ordinal level, but it has the additional property that meaningful differences between data values can be computed. However, interval-level data may not have an intrinsic zero or starting point. Consequently, differences are meaningful, but ratios of data values are not.

Example 6 | The following are examples of data at the interval level of measurement.

(a) Years in which Democrats won presidential elections.

(b) Body temperatures (in degrees Celsius) of trout swimming in the Yellowstone River.

Temperature readings in Celsius (or Fahrenheit) are examples of data at the interval level of measurement. Such values are certainly ordered, and we can compute meaningful differences. However, for Celsius-scale temperatures, there is not an inherent starting point. The value 0°C may seem to be a starting point, but the value of 0°C does not indicate the state of "no heat." Furthermore, it is not correct to say 20°C is twice as hot as 10°C. Calendar times are also interval measurements, since the date 0 AD does not signify "no time." However, a time lapse is at a higher level of measurement and is in fact an example of our top level of measurement, the *ratio level*.

Ratio Level

The *ratio level of measurement* is the highest level. The ratio level is similar to the interval level, but it includes an inherent zero as a starting point for all measurements. Consequently, at this level, both differences *and* ratios are meaningful.

Example 7

The following are examples of data at the *ratio level* of measurement.

(a) *The core temperatures of stars in the Milky Way when measured in degrees Kelvin.* Notice that in the Kelvin scale of measurement of 0°K means "no heat." This is a special temperature scale used primarily by scientists.

(b) *Time lapse between the deposit of a check into a bank account and the clearance of that check.* An out-of-state check that clears in 6 days takes twice as long as a local check that clears in 3 days.

(c) *Length of trout swimming in the Yellowstone River.* A trout 18 inches long is three times as long as a 6-inch trout. Observe that we can divide 6 into 18 to determine the *ratio* of the trout lengths.

In summary, there are four levels of measurement. The nominal is considered the lowest, and in ascending order we have the ordinal, interval, and ratio levels. In general, calculations based on one level of measurement should not be used for a lower level.

Level of Measurement	Suitable Calculation
Nominal	We can put the data in categories.
Ordinal	We can order the data from smallest to largest or "worst" to "best." Each data value can be *compared* with another data value.
Interval	We can order the data and also take the differences between data values. At this level, it makes sense to compare the differences between data values. For instance, we can say that one data value is 5 more than another or 12 more than another data value.
Ratio	We can order the data, take differences, and also find the ratio between data values. For instance, it makes sense to say that one data value is twice as large as another.

GUIDED EXERCISE 5

The following data describe different data associated with a state senator. For each data entry, indicate the corresponding *level of measurement*.

(a) The senator's name is Sam Wilson.

(a) Nominal level

(b) The senator is 58 years old.

(b) Ratio level

(c) The years in which the senator was elected to the senate are 1963, 1969, 1981, and 1994.

(c) Interval level

(d) His total taxable income last year was $278,314.19.

(d) Ratio level

(e) The senator sponsored a bill to protect water rights. Out of 1100 voters in his district, 400 said they strongly favored the bill, 300 said they favored the bill, 200 said they were neutral, 150 said they did not favor the bill, and 50 said they strongly did not favor the bill.

(e) The opinions about the bill are at the ordinal level.

(f) The senator is married now.

(f) Nominal level

(g) However, the senator was previously divorced in 1965 and again in 1982.

(g) Interval level

(h) A leading news magazine claims the senator is ranked seventh for his voting record on bills regarding public education.

(h) Ordinal level

In the next three chapters we will begin a more thorough study of random samples, populations, and ways to organize and summarize numerical information in samples and populations. The term *descriptive statistics* refers to this organization of data.

In Chapters 4, 5, 6, and 7 we cover elementary probability theory and some basic probability distributions. By Chapter 8 we will use the previous groundwork to begin *inferential statistics*—that is, methods of using a sample to obtain information about a population.

Section 1.1 Problems

1. *USA Today* reported that 44.9% of those surveyed (1261 adults) ate in fast-food restaurants from one to three times each week.
   (a) What is the implied population?
   (b) What is the sample?

2. What is the profile of students choosing to take a telecourse? A study conducted by Crane ("Student Uses of Annenberg/CPB Project Telecourses in the Fall of 1984") interviewed 200 students who were enrolled in various Annenberg/CPB telecourses on different campuses across the nation. She found that 62% of the students were female, 75% were working, and about half were over 35 years of age.

(a) What is the population for each stated profile quality?

(b) What is the sample for each stated profile quality?

3. The students at Eastmore College are concerned about the level of student fees. They took a random sample of 30 colleges and universities throughout the nation and obtained information about the student fees at these institutions. From this information they concluded that their student fees are higher than those of most colleges in the nation.

(a) What is the population?

(b) What is the sample?

4. The quality-control department at Healthy Crunch, Inc., wants to estimate the shelf life of all Healthy Crunch granola bars. A random sample of 10 of these bars was tested, and the shelf life was determined. From the sample results, a shelf life for all Healthy Crunch granola bars was estimated.

(a) What is the population?

(b) What is the sample?

5. An insurance company wants to determine the time interval between the arrival of an insurance payment check and the time that the check clears. A central payment office processes the payments for a five-state region. A random sample of 32 payment checks from this five-state region was received and processed. The time interval between receipt and check clearance was determined for each check. From this information the company estimated the time interval necessary for all checks sent to this office to clear.

(a) What is the population?

(b) What is the sample?

6. If you were going to apply *statistical methods* to analyze teacher evaluations, which question form, A or B, would be better?

Form A: In your own words, tell how this teacher compares with other teachers you have had.

Form B: Use the following scale to rank your teacher as compared with other teachers you have had.

1	2	3	4	5
worst	below average	average	above average	best

7. Categorize these measurements associated with student life according to level: nominal, ordinal, interval, or ratio.

(a) Length of time to complete an exam

(b) Time of first class

(c) Class category: freshman, sophomore, junior, senior

(d) Course evaluation scale: poor, acceptable, good

(e) Score on last exam (based on 100 possible points)

(f) Age of student

8. Categorize these measurements associated with a robotics company according to level: nominal, ordinal, interval, or ratio.
    (a) Salesperson's performance: below average, average, above average
    (b) Price of company's stock
    (c) Names of new products
    (d) Room temperature (°F) in CEO's private office
    (e) Gross income for each of past 5 years
    (f) Color of packaging

9. Which technique (sampling, experiment, simulation, or census) for gathering data do you think was used in the following studies?
    (a) A study reported in *USA Today* (October 13, 1993) of ages of General Motor's top management and the ages of members of the Rolling Stones rock group showed the average age of GM top executives to be 49.8 years, while it showed the average age of performers in the Rolling Stones rock group to be 50.6 years. Ages for *all* members of each group were used.
    (b) A sample of 82 healthy female and male subjects was recruited to participate in a study on pain (*Physical Therapy*, Vol. 70, No. 1). The subjects were divided into two groups. The experimental group received laser stimulation, and the control group received sham stimulation. Tests of pain tolerance were then conducted on each group.
    (c) Computer imaging of runners shows the effect of stride length on running efficiency.
    (d) Do the Chinese like chocolate? Gallup Chinese is conducting surveys in China to answer the question for the U.S. Chocolate Manufacturers Association. Gallup Chinese is surveying a portion of the Chinese population to determine whether there is a market for chocolate in China (*Wall Street Journal*, November 26, 1993).

10. Which technique (sampling, experiment, simulation, or census) for gathering data do you think was used in the following studies?
    (a) An analysis of a sample of 31,000 New York hospitals suggests that the poor and the elderly sue for malpractice at one-fifth the rate of wealthier patients (*Journal of American Medical Association*, October, 1993).
    (b) The effects of wind sheer on airplanes during both landing and take-off are studied by using complex computer programs that mimic actual flight.
    (c) A study of football scores attained through touchdowns and field goals was conducted by the National Football League to determine whether field goals account for more scoring events than touchdowns. Data from all regular season NFL football games from 1983 to 1992 were used (*USA Today*, October 12, 1993).
    (d) An Australian study included 588 men and women who already had some precancerous skin lesions. Half got a skin cream containing a sunscreen with a sun protection factor of 17; half got an inactive

cream. After 7 months, those using the sunscreen with the sun protection had fewer new precancerous skin lesions (*New England Journal of Medicine,* October 1993).

11. The *New York Times* did a special report on polling that was carried in papers across the nation (*Denver Post,* September 7, 1993). The article points out how readily the results of a survey can be manipulated. Some features that can influence the results of a poll include the following: the number of possible responses, the phrasing of the question, the sampling techniques used (voluntary response or sample designed to be representative), the fact that words may mean different things to different people, the questions that precede the question of interest, and finally, the fact that respondents can offer opinions on issues that they know nothing about.

(a) Consider the expression "over the last few years." Do you think that this expression means the same time span to everyone? What would be a more precise phrase?

(b) Consider this question: "Do you think fines for running stop signs should be doubled?" Do you think the response would be different if the question "Have you ever run a stop sign?" preceded the question about fines?

(c) Consider this question: "Do you watch too much television?" What do you think the responses would be if the only responses possible were yes or no. What do you think the responses would be if the possible responses were rarely, sometimes, or frequently?

Section 1.2   Calculators and Computers in Statistics

Calculators are a tremendous aid to statistics students. A simple four-function calculator with memory and square root key will be adequate, and in fact, examples in this text are presented in a fashion that allows you to use such a calculator. However, inexpensive calculators are now available that support both one- and two-variable statistics. These calculators have a statistics mode. Once you are in that mode, you enter your data and then select the desired statistical function from those available.

Graphing calculators have an even more extensive selection of statistical functions readily available. In addition, they produce some of the standard types of graphs that you will use as you analyze data. Many of these graphing calculators will order your data from smallest to largest as well. This feature alone saves a great deal of routine work. In addition, the larger screen size of the graphing calculator allows you to check all the data which you have entered so that you can be sure that you have not entered any data incorrectly.

Regardless of your choice of calculator, please keep the manual that comes with the calculator. Even calculators made by the same company have slightly different instructions from one model to the next. No one is an expert on all the available models. However, if you have your manual, a tutor, faculty member, or you yourself can usually determine how to operate the calculator.

Professional statisticians use computers, and there are many statistical software packages available. Displays from the widely used package MINITAB are presented in this text. A supplement written for this text guides you through the particular commands and features of MINITAB that are appropriate for the topics presented in an introductory statistics course. In addition, the authors of this text have developed an inexpensive and straightforward statistical package called ComputerStat as a supplement to this text. Disks and a user's manual are available from the publisher, D.C. Heath and Company, for DOS-based computers. Complimentary site licenses for ComputerStat are available to colleges using this text. The programs are designed for beginning statistics students with no computer experience.

Students should remember that although computers can process data efficiently, the user must determine which processes are appropriate and then interpret the results in a meaningful way.

In this text we do not attempt to explain how to use statistical software. That is best done in manuals and supplements for the particular software you are using. However, at the end of many chapters is a section called Using Technology. Real-world problems with data or situations from published sources are included in this section. The problems can be solved using any appropriate statistical software package or, in most cases, with a graphing calculator and tables.

Section 1.2 Problems

1. Review your calculator instructions manual so you can do calculations with confidence. Do some of the computation exercises in your manual that use the operations $+$, $-$, $\times$, $\div$, memory, and $\sqrt{}$.

2. If there are computer programs for statistics available to you, find out how you can use them. Plan to spend a little time reviewing the user's manual that goes with the software package.

3. If you have a graphing calculator, use the manual to determine how to use the statistics mode and how to enter data.

Section 1.3   Where Will I Use Statistics?

Open any newspaper or magazine, or turn on the TV. Before long you will see a chart of numbers, the results of an opinion poll, a graph, or some comment about how this year compares with last year with regard to crime rate, employment, availability of goods, and so forth. Sports reports are full of statistics. Even the ads tell you to use a certain toothpaste because four out of five dentists recommend it.

We are bombarded by statistical information. Important decisions about the allocation of funds or services are made based on statistical information. You need to know some statistics simply to understand and evaluate the statistical information you are given.

If you look at college catalogues, you will find that courses in statistics are required or recommended in such areas as psychology, sociology, computer science, biology, nursing, business, linguistics, economics, political science, education, premedicine, and prelaw.

In short, in almost any field you may find that you are required to present data in a meaningful way. You may be required to use some of the statistical methods you will learn about in this text. Even though you might not need to make statistical reports, you will more than likely read them or even be a subject in the report. For instance, in the year 2000, the U.S. Census Bureau will ask each of us to participate in creating a statistical profile of the United States by giving data about ourselves, our family, income, residence, and so on.

Section 1.3 Problems

1. Read a newspaper, and then take note of any articles or displays using statistics.
2. Next time you watch TV, listen to the ads and see how statistics are used to convince you to buy a product.
3. Go to the library and browse through a journal in a field that interests you. Note the use of statistics.
4. Next time someone asks you to respond to a survey, ask that person about the kinds of statistical reports that will be generated from the survey responses.

Summary

In this chapter we saw that statistics is the study of how to collect, organize, analyze, and interpret numerical information. We investigated some types of problems where statistics can be used. In these situations we saw examples of *populations* and *samples*. Methods of gathering data were introduced. We also examined levels of measurement. It is important to remember that the main role of inferential statistics is to draw conclusions about a population based on information obtained from a sample.

Important Words and Symbols

	Section*		Section
Statistics	1.1	Levels of measurement	1.1
Population	1.1	nominal	
Sample	1.1	ordinal	
Descriptive statistics	1.1	interval	
Inferential statistics	1.1	ratio	
Sampling	1.1		
Experiments	1.1		
Simulation	1.1		
Surveys	1.1		
Voluntary response	1.1		
Hidden bias	1.1		

*Indicates section of first appearance.

Chapter Review Problems

1. Find a newspaper article that uses statistics. Are the data from the entire population or just from a sample? What is the population? What is the sample?

2. A radio talk show asked listeners to respond either yes or no to the question, Is the candidate who spends the most on a campaign the most likely to win? Fifteen people called in and nine said yes. What is the implied population? What is the sample? Can you detect any bias in the selection of the sample?

3. In your own words, give a complete and careful description of the four levels of measurement. Which level is the highest? Which is the lowest? What are the different suitable uses for each of the levels of measurement?

4. Write a brief description of yourself in which you list your name, age, year of birth, height, Social Security number, color of your hair and eyes, address, phone number, place of birth, number of years of formal education, intended college major (if decided), distance you live from college, and so forth. In one column, list each item in the descriptions of yourself. In a second column to the right of the first, list the level of measurement corresponding to each item in the description.

5. *Class data project:* Make a statistical profile of your own statistics class. Items of interest might be
   (a) Height, age, gender, pulse, number of siblings, marital status
   (b) Number of college credit hours completed (as of beginning of term); grade point average
   (c) Major; number of credit hours enrolled in this term
   (d) Number of scheduled hours working per week
   (e) Distance from residence to first class; time it takes to travel from residence to first class
   (f) Year, model, and color of car usually driven

   What directions would you give to people answering these questions? For instance, how accurate should the measurements be? Should age be recorded as of last birthday?

Section 2.1

Random Samples

If we want to use information from a sample to draw conclusions about a population, the sample must represent the *entire* population. In this section you will learn how to construct a simple random sample using a random-number table. You also will learn to use random numbers to perform brief simulations such as a "random walk" of stock prices. Finally, we will discuss other frequently used and popular sampling techniques.

Section 2.2

Graphs

No matter what type of data we have, sample or population, it is important to be able to organize and present the data to other people. For this purpose, tables and graphs are indispensable. You will study bar graphs, pictograms, circle graphs, Pareto charts, and time plots for time series. Each type of graph has its own special features. For example, you will see that Pareto charts organize data by highlighting major categories from left to right, whereas circle graphs give a quick sense of comparative size.

Section 2.3

Histograms and Frequency Distributions

Frequency tables and histograms are used to condense raw data into more manageable and easy-to-read classes. Relative frequencies give us a good sense of the proportion of data in different classes. We will study relative frequency again in Chapter 4 in the context of probability distributions. Related topics of cumulative frequency and ogives are also presented.

Section 2.4

Stem-and-Leaf Displays

This is our first topic in the field of exploratory data analysis (EDA). These techniques are especially useful when we want to explore a data set and discover which data values, if any, are unusual, to ask questions we had not thought of before, or to pursue leads in different directions. EDA methods are fast to apply, they are robust in the sense that the analysis is not much influenced by extreme data values, and they are especially valuable because they require almost no assumptions about the nature of the data.

W. Edwards Deming

(1900–1993)
Deming is widely regarded for
his work and writing on the
statistics of business
management and economics.

Organizing Data

The wealth of a nation depends on its people, management, and government,
more than on its natural resources. The problem is where to find good
management.

W. Edwards Deming
Out of Crisis

W. Edwards Deming is a name that is almost synonymous with the study of
quality. He is described as one of the greatest American leaders of the postwar
era and the voice of quality worldwide. In his book *Out of Crisis* (MIT Press),
Dr. Deming writes in a clear and compelling style about management philosophy and its statistical relation to quality. The first step in any discussion
about quality is to gather and organize appropriate data. Gathering and organizing data are the central topics in this chapter.

Focus Problem ▶ Say It with Pictures

The graphs of Figure 2–1 each appeared in *USA Today*. The graphs have at-
tractive artwork included, but the basic graphs presenting the data are of types
you will study in this chapter. Examine each graph carefully. Then read this
chapter and answer the following questions: How do we categorize the type
of graph (bar, time plot, circle, Pareto chart, or pictogram)? How do we interpret each graph, and how can we make graphs like these? Also note the
references to the source of the data on which the graph is based. What kind
of sampling technique do you think was used?

Section 2.1   Random Samples

Eat lamb—20,000 coyotes can't be wrong!

This slogan is sometimes found on bumper stickers in the western United
States. The slogan indicates the trouble that ranchers have experienced in pro-
tecting their flocks from predators. Modern methods of predator control have

Figure 2–1 Some Types of Graphs Found in Chapter 2

USA SNAPSHOTS®   9/30/92

A look at statistics that shape your finances

A quality commitment

The Malcolm Baldrige National Quality Award will be announced in mid-October. How 700 executives answered a survey: Is your company committed to quality?

Type of firm	Percent who answered yes
Consumer products	**35%**
Pharmaceuticals	**23%**
Retail	**20%**
Banking	**15%**
Computer	**15%**

By Marcia Staimer, USA TODAY

(a)*

USA SNAPSHOTS®   9/30/92

A look at statistics that shape our lives

What time people go to work

Midnight - 6 a.m.   8.2

Workers in millions

6 - 9 a.m.   60.4

after 9 a.m.   18.3

Source: American Housing Survey for the Housing and Urban Development

By Elys A. McLean, USA TODAY

(b)*

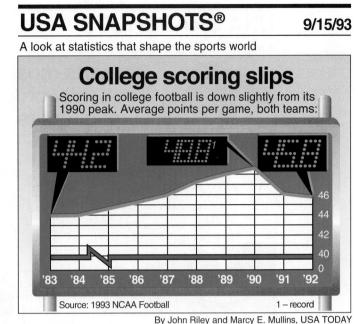

USA SNAPSHOTS® 9/15/93

A look at statistics that shape the sports world

College scoring slips

Scoring in college football is down slightly from its 1990 peak. Average points per game, both teams:

Source: 1993 NCAA Football   1 – record

By John Riley and Marcy E. Mullins, USA TODAY

(c)*

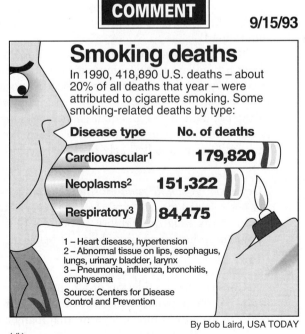

COMMENT 9/15/93

Smoking deaths

In 1990, 418,890 U.S. deaths – about 20% of all deaths that year – were attributed to cigarette smoking. Some smoking-related deaths by type:

Disease type	No. of deaths
Cardiovascular[1]	179,820
Neoplasms[2]	151,322
Respiratory[3]	84,475

1 – Heart disease, hypertension
2 – Abnormal tissue on lips, esophagus, lungs, urinary bladder, larynx
3 – Pneumonia, influenza, bronchitis, emphysema

Source: Centers for Disease Control and Prevention

By Bob Laird, USA TODAY

(d)*

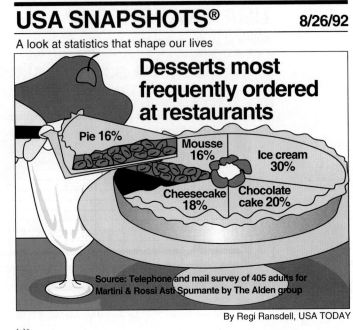

changed considerably from those of earlier days, and to a certain extent, the changes have come about through a closer examination of the sampling techniques used.

If we are to use information obtained from a sample to draw conclusions about a population, the sample must be representative of the *entire* population. A type of sample that is representative of the entire population is a *random sample*. One of the properties of a random sample is that each member of the population has an equal chance of being included in the sample. This is not enough, however. Another necessary condition is that *each* sample of the same size is equally likely to be selected.

Simple Random Samples

> **Definition:** A *simple random sample* of n measurements from a population is one selected in such a manner that every sample of size n from the population has equal probability of being selected, and every member of the population has equal probability of being included in the sample.

Consider the population of all coyotes in the western United States. The sample of the population that the ranchers observe is largely the coyotes that prefer to live near a ranch. It seems that many coyotes who choose to live near a ranch also like to eat lamb. In fact, most of the coyotes the ranchers observed appeared to be existing solely on sheep.

Based on their experience with this sample of the coyote population, the ranchers concluded that *all* coyotes are dangerous to their flocks. Coyotes should be eliminated! The ranchers used a special poison bait to get rid of the coyotes. Not only was this poison distributed on ranch land, but with government cooperation it also was distributed widely on public lands.

The ranchers found the results not very satisfactory. The overall coyote population dropped where the poison was applied, but the ranchers had almost as much trouble as ever. They were losing almost as many sheep to coyotes as before. Why?

GUIDED EXERCISE 1

(a) Do you think that the sample of coyotes the ranchers observed could be thought of as a random sample of the *entire* coyote population? Explain.

(a) No; the ranchers only observed coyotes near their ranches.

(b) If a sample is not chosen at random from the population, is it safe to use the results of that sample to describe the *entire* population?

(b) No.

(c) Do you think the idea of reducing the *entire* coyote population could be statistically justified on the basis of the ranchers' experience with the coyotes?

(c) We don't think it could be statistically justified one way or another because the sample of coyotes was not a true random sample.

(d) Biological field reports indicate that coyotes who eat sheep are fairly consistent in their preference for sheep, whereas the majority of coyotes who live in the wilderness stick to foods they find in the wild. When the poison was widespread, which group of coyotes would tend to get poisoned: those which ate sheep or those which ate what they could find in the wild?

(d) When there is poison bait scattered throughout the wilderness, it is the wilderness coyote that eats it; the sheep-eating coyote doesn't bother with it.

Today there is an effort to selectively hunt specific coyotes that are known sheep killers. The important thing to learn from the preceding discussion is that if statistical methods are to be reliable, we must have a *true random sample*.

GUIDED EXERCISE 2

Why don't the following procedures give a random sample for the entire population of New York City?

(a) Select every third woman entering a beauty shop.

(a) This sample is biased toward women who can afford to and like to go to beauty shops.

(b) Select every third man entering a bar.

(c) Select every third person coming out of a boxing match at Madison Square Garden.

(b) This sample is biased toward men who can afford to and prefer to visit bars.

(c) This sample is likely to be biased toward people who are sports-minded and can afford a ticket to Madison Square Garden.

In all cases there would probably be very few small children, elderly people, or poor people.

We've seen several sampling procedures that do not produce a random sample. How do we get random samples? Suppose you need to know if the emission system of the latest shipment of Toyotas satisfies pollution-control standards. You want to pick a random sample of 30 cars from this shipment of 500 cars and test them. One way to pick a random sample is to number the cars 1 through 500. Write these numbers on cards, mix up the cards, and then draw 30 numbers. The sample will consist of the cars with the chosen numbers. If you mix the cards sufficiently, this procedure produces a random sample.

Random-Number Table

An easier way to select the numbers is to use a random-number table. You can make one for yourself by writing the digits 0 through 9 on separate cards and mixing up these cards in a hat. Then draw a card, record the digit, return the card, and mix up the cards again. Draw another card, record the digit, and so on. However, Table 1 in Appendix II is a ready-made random-number table (adapted from Rand Corporation, *A Million Random Digits with 100,000 Normal Deviates*). Let's see how to pick our random sample of 30 Toyotas by using this random-number table.

Example 1

Use a random-number table to pick a random sample of 30 cars from a population of 500 cars.

Solution: Again, we assign each car a different number between 1 and 500. Then we use the random-number table to choose the sample. Table 1 in Appendix II has 50 rows and 10 blocks of five digits each; it can be thought of as a solid mass of digits that has been broken up into rows and blocks for user convenience.

You read the digits by beginning anywhere in the table. We dropped a pin on the table, and the head of the pin landed in row 15, block 2. We'll begin there and list all the digits in that row. If we need more digits, we'll move on to row 16, and so on. The digits we begin with are: 15560   27592
42089   99281   59640   15221   96079   09961   05371.
Since the highest number assigned to a car is 500, and this number has three digits, we regroup our digits into blocks of 3:   155   602   759
242   089   992   815   964   015   221   960
790   996   105   371.

To construct our random sample, we use the first 30 car numbers we encounter in the random-number table when we start at row 15, block 2. The first car will be number 155. There are no cars numbered 602 or 759, so we skip these numbers. The next car will be number 242. The next group of three digits is 089, which is the same as number 89, so we include car 89 in our sample. The other cars in our sample listed in row 15 are number 15, number 221, number 105, and number 371. To get the rest of the cars in the sample, we continue to the next line and use the random-number table in this fashion. If we encounter a number we've used before, we'll skip it.

- *Comment:* When we use the term *(simple) random sample,* we have very specific criteria in mind for selecting the sample. One proper method for selecting a simple random sample is to use a computer-based or calculator-based random-number generator or to use a table of random numbers as we have done in the example. The term *random* should not be confused with *haphazard!*

Simulation

Another important use of random-number tables is in *simulation.* We use the word *simulation* to refer to the process of providing arithmetic imitations of "real" phenomena. Simulation methods have been productive in studying nuclear reactors, cloud formation, cardiology (and medical science in general), highway design, production control, shipbuilding, airplane design, war games, economics, electronics, and in countless other studies. A complete list would probably include something from every aspect of modern life. In Example 2 and Guided Exercise 3 we'll perform a brief simulation.

Example 2

A well-known theory in stock market analysis is the "random walk" theory (see *A Random Walk Down Wall Street,* 4th Edition, Burton Malkiel, W. W. Norton & Co.). The term *random walk,* as applied to stock prices, means that short-term changes in stock prices cannot be predicted but rather are random. In particular, according to the random walk theory, the next move in price of a stock (up or down) is completely unpredictable on the basis of what price changes happened before.

Let's use a very simplified model to *simulate* the stock price changes of a hypothetical company, Fun Boards (maker of skate boards, surf boards, ski boards, and roller skates). Suppose the initial price of Fun Boards stock is $50 per share. Use the random-number table to simulate daily price changes for the next 15 trading days in the following way. Notice we are interested in price *changes.* Days during which the stock does not change price will be ignored.
Solution: The daily stock price change will be dictated by a number from the random-number table. When you encounter an even digit (0, 2, 4, 6, 8), increase the stock price by $1. When you encounter an odd digit (1, 3, 5, 7, 9), decrease the stock price by $1. Do this for a sequence of 15 trading days during which the price changed.

Beginning with line 6, block 2 in Table 1 of Appendix II, we see the 15 random digits

51709   94456   48396

Table 2–1 Simulated Price Moves of Fun Boards Stock

Price	50	49	48	47	48	47	46	47	48	47	48	49	50	49	48	49
Day	Initial	1	2	3	4	5	6	7	8	9	10	11	12	13	14	15
Digit		5	1	7	0	9	9	4	4	5	6	4	8	3	9	6

Since the first random digit is odd, we will decrease the price by $1 on the first day. In fact, the next two digits are also odd, so we will decrease the price again by $1 on day 2 and then again on day 3. The next digit is even, so we will increase the price by $1 on day 4. Table 2–1 shows the simulated price changes for the 15-trading-day period.

GUIDED EXERCISE 3

A single pollen grain is floating on a surface of water. Through a microscope we can observe the Brownian motion (random motion of the pollen grain caused by the impact of water molecules). As part of a project, Carlos is to chart the course of a pollen grain as it moves on a drop of water. Rather than watch it through a microscope and measure the direction of each movement (an almost impossible task without a slow-motion camera, because the pollen grain moves so rapidly), he is instructed to simulate the motion for seven motions.

Let's use a random-number table to simulate the observed direction of the pollen grain for seven position changes. For each position change, imagine the pollen grain to be in the center of a circle marked off in degree measure in such a way that 0° is east, 90° is north, 180° is west, and 270° is south (see Figure 2–2). An arrow pointing from the pollen grain indicates the direction of the pollen grain as it changes position.

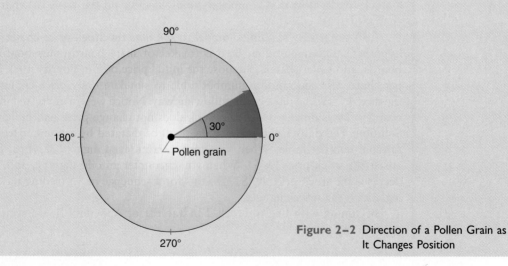

Figure 2–2 Direction of a Pollen Grain as It Changes Position

(a) Let's agree that measurement of the direction of the pollen grain to the nearest degree is accurate enough. Then our problem will be solved if we obtain seven random numbers, each of which is between 0 and 359. Since the highest possible number, 359, has three digits, we break up the digits in the random number table into blocks of _____ (one, two, three, or four) digits.

(b) Begin at row 5, block 7, and read the table row by row to find the seven random directions.

(a) Three

(b) The digits grouped in threes are 092 097 915   724   440   302   422, etc. The first numbers we use are 092 and 097. We skip numbers 915, 724, and 440 because we are interested in numbers between 0 and 359. The directions are then 92°, 97°, 302°, 351°, 64°, 169°, and 239°.

We have been reading the random-number table by rows, but there are other schemes we can follow when we use the random-number table. We can read the digits by column instead of by row, or we can read diagonally (Figure 2–3). But once we have picked the starting point, we must use a single scheme to read the random-number table until we have completed the sample. Use a consistent scheme in order to pick a random sample.

• *Comment:* Recall that the random samples we have been constructing so far are called *simple random samples*. Throughout this text we will use the term *random sample* to mean simple random sample. All the statistical methods in this text assume that a simple random sampling has been used to collect the data.

Other Sampling Techniques

Although we will always assume that (simple) random samples are used throughout this text, there are other methods of sampling that are also widely used. Appropriate statistical techniques exist for these sampling methods, but they are beyond the scope of this text.

Figure 2–3 Schemes by Which to Read the Random-Number Table

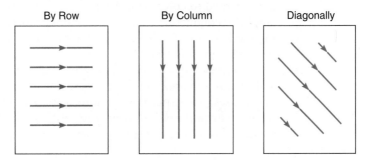

By Row   By Column   Diagonally

One of these sampling methods is called *stratified sampling.* Groups or classes inside a population that share a common characteristic are called *strata* (plural of *stratum*). For example, in the population of all undergraduate college students, some strata might be freshmen, sophomores, juniors, or seniors. Other strata might be men or women or instate students or out-of-state students, and so on. In the method of stratified sampling, the population is divided into at least two distinct strata. Then a (simple) random sample of a certain size is drawn from each stratum, and the information obtained is carefully adjusted or weighted in all resulting calculations.

The groups or strata are often sampled in proportion to their actual percentages of occurrence in the overall population. However, there are other (more sophisticated) ways to determine the optimal sample size in each stratum to give best results. In general, statistical analysis and tests based on data obtained from stratified samples are somewhat different from techniques discussed in an introductory course in statistics. Methods of stratified sampling will not be emphasized in this text.

Another popular method of sampling is called *systematic sampling.* In this method, it is assumed that the elements of the population are arranged in some natural sequential order. Then we select a (random) starting point and select every *k*th element for our sample. For example, to obtain a systematic sample of 20 students going through the cafeteria line at lunch, we could pick a random number between, say, 0 and 10. Then, between 12 noon and 12:10 (the actual time determined by our random number), we could begin the sampling process of taking, say, every fifth student in line.

The advantage of a systematic sample is that it is easy to get. However, there are dangers in using systematic sampling. When the population is repetitive or cyclic in nature, systematic sampling should not be used. For example, consider a fabric mill that produces dress material. Suppose the loom that produces the material makes a mistake every 17th yard, but we check only every 16th yard with an automated electronic scanner. In this case, a random starting point may or may not result in detection of fabric flaws before a large amount of fabric is produced.

Cluster sampling is a method used extensively by government agencies and certain private research organizations. In cluster sampling we begin by dividing the demographic area into sections. Then we randomly select sections and randomly select individuals in those sections. The resulting calculations are weighted to correct for disproportionate representation of groups. For example, in conducting a survey of school children in a large city, we could first randomly select 30 schools and then randomly select a certain number of children (perhaps 75) from each school.

Convenience sampling simply uses results or data that are conveniently and readily obtained. In some cases, this may be all that is available, and in many cases, it is better than no information at all. However, convenience sampling does run the risk of being severely biased. For instance, consider a newsperson who wishes to get the "opinions of the people" about a proposed seat tax to be imposed on tickets to all sporting events. The revenues from the seat tax will then be used to support the local symphony. The newsperson stands in front of a classical music store at noon and surveys the first five people coming out of the store who will cooperate. This method of choosing a sample will produce some opinions, and perhaps some human interest stories, but it certainly has bias. Hopefully, the city council will not use these opinions as the sole basis for a decision about the proposed tax. It is good advice to be very cautious indeed when the data come from the method of convenience sampling.

Our discussion of sampling methods is intended to be brief and general. This is not the place for an extensive treatment of theory and practice of sampling. However, the interested reader is referred to the book, *A Sampler on Sampling,* by Bill Williams, John Wiley and Sons, Inc.

Section 2.1 Problems

1. (a) In your own words, explain the meaning of the terms *random numbers* and *random samples*.
   (b) Why are random samples so important in statistics?

2. Use a random-number table to get a list of eight random numbers from 1 to 976. Explain your work.

3. Use a random-number table to get a list of six random numbers from 1 to 99. Explain your work.

4. Use a random-number table to get a list of five random numbers from 1 to 900. Explain your work.

5. Use a random-number table to get a list of seven random numbers from 1 to 500. Explain your work.

6. Use a random-number table to get a list of six random numbers from 324 to 6077. Explain your work.

7. Suppose you are given the number 1 and each of the other students in your statistics class calls out consecutive numbers until each person in class has his or her own number. Explain how you could get a random sample of four students from your statistics class.
   (a) Explain why the first four students walking into the classroom would not necessarily form a random sample.
   (b) Explain why four students coming in late would not necessarily form a random sample.
   (c) Explain why four students sitting in the back row would not necessarily form a random sample.
   (d) Explain why the four tallest students would not necessarily form a random sample.

8. Consider the population of all students at your school.
   (a) Explain how you could get a random sample of 10 students from this population.

(b) List some ways of getting samples from this population that are *not* random samples. Explain why each of these samples is *not* a random sample.

9. Lotto is the name of the Colorado lottery. The Lotto boards consist of 42 numbers (from 1 to 42). To play you select six distinct numbers. Every week a drawing machine randomly selects six numbered Ping-Pong balls. If one of your boards contains all six winning numbers, in any order, you've hit the jackpot! You can pick your numbers any way you wish. However, suppose you want to use a random-number table to pick your six numbers. Describe how you would do so, and list your selected numbers. (To play you must pay $1 to have your selections entered in a computer for a specified week's drawing.)

10. Quality control is an important component in manufacturing processes. Products are inspected during production, and equipment is adjusted to correct defects. It is usually not possible to examine every product, so a random sample is examined. For each of the following, give a detailed explanation of how you could get the requested random sample. Be sure to include the random numbers you use to get the random sample.
    (a) How would you draw a random sample of 6 of the next 500 stereo headsets coming off an assembly line?
    (b) How would you obtain a random sample of 10 men's dress shirts coming off an assembly line from 8 A.M. to 12 noon?
    (c) Serial numbers are placed on radios as they come off an assembly line. How could you get a random sample of nine radios with serial numbers from 21942 to 98756?
    (d) A truck has just delivered 800 cartons of eggs to a supermarket. How would you get a random sample of 12 cartons to check for broken eggs?

11. For each of the following, give a detailed explanation of how you would get the requested random sample. Be sure to include the random numbers you use to get the random sample.
    (a) You are a veterinarian. How would you get a random sample of 15 sheep to check for ticks on a farm that has 250 sheep?
    (b) You are a medical records technician. Patients from 1992 to the present were given file numbers starting at 1024 and ending with 8342. How would you get a random sample of 10 of these patients?
    (c) You are a security agent for an airline. How could you get a random sample of five pieces of luggage that are moving on a conveyor belt in the next 25 minutes?
    (d) You are conducting a survey for your sociology class project. How can you get a random sample of 12 adults walking past the information booth at a shopping center between 6 and 7 P.M.?

12. How do colds affect analytical thinking performance? Results of a study conducted by McGraw and Schleser were reported in *Psychology Today*. The study showed that under certain conditions, persons with colds do

better than their healthy colleagues. The study considered 62 subjects: 40 healthy men and women and 22 suffering from colds or flu. These subjects were divided into two groups, with each group containing both healthy and sick participants. The groups were told to solve anagrams. The first group was told to "focus on trying out systematically different combinations of letters," while the second group was told to "focus on remaining loose and relaxed as you complete the task." In the first group, after the second try, the sick participants who concentrated on their anagrams scored significantly better than the healthy ones in that group. In the second group, the sick people did slightly worse than the healthy ones on the anagram solving task. A key component in this study was the formation of two groups from the 62 participants. Describe how you could take these 62 participants and, using a random-number table, divide them into two groups of equal size.

13. A die is a cube with dots on each face. The faces have 1, 2, 3, 4, 5, or 6 dots. Use a random-number table is simulate the outcomes of tossing a die 20 times.

14. Use a random-number table to simulate the outcomes of tossing a quarter 25 times. Assume that the quarter is balanced (i.e., fair).

15. Use a random-number table to simulate drawing five cards (without replacement) from a standard bridge deck of 52 cards. The deck of cards consists of four suites: hearts, diamonds, clubs, and spades. Each suite contains the cards 2, 3, 4, 5, 6, 7, 8, 9, 10, jack, queen, king, and ace. First assign the numbers 1 through 52 to the cards. Then use the random-number table to simulate the outcome of the experiment of drawing 5 cards from the deck without replacement.

16. Suppose there are 30 people at a party. Do you think any two share the same birthday. Let's use the random-number table to simulate the birthdays of the 30 people at the party. Ignoring leap year, let's assume that the year has 365 days. Number the days, with 1 representing January 1, 2 representing January 2, and so forth, with 365 representing December 31. Draw a random sample of 30 days (with replacement). These days represent the birthdays of the people at the party. Were any two of the birthdays the same? Compare your results with those obtained by other students in the class. Would you expect the results to be the same or different?

17. Professor More is designing a multiple-choice test. There are to be 10 questions. Each question is to have five choices for answers. The choices are to be designated by the letters *a, b, c, d,* and *e.* Professor More wishes to use a random-number table to determine which letter choice should contain the correct answer for a question. Using the number correspondence 1 for *a,* 2 for *b,* 3 for *c,* 4 for *d,* and 5 for *e,* use a random-number table to determine the letter choice for the correct answer in each of the 10 questions.

18. Professor More also uses true–false questions. She wishes to place 20 such questions on the next test. To decide whether to place a true statement or false statement in each of the 20 questions, she uses a random-number table. She selects 20 digits from the table. An odd digit tells her to use a true statement. An even digit tells her to use a false statement. Use a random-number table to pick a sequence of 20 digits, and describe the corresponding sequence of 20 true–false questions. What would the test key for your sequence look like?

19. An important part of employee compensation is a benefits package that might include health insurance, life insurance, child care, vacation days, retirement plan, parental leave, bonuses, etc. Suppose you want to conduct a survey of benefit packages available in private businesses in Hawaii. You want a sample size of 100. Some sampling techniques are described below. Categorize each technique as *simple random sample, stratified sample, systematic sample, cluster sample,* or *convenience sample.*
    (a) Assign each business in the Island Business Directory a number, and then use a random-number table to select the businesses to be included in the sample.
    (b) Use the postal ZIP Codes to divide the state into regions. Pick a random sample of 10 ZIP Code areas and then pick a random sample of 10 businesses in each ZIP Code area.
    (c) Send a team of five research assistants to Bishop Street in downtown Honolulu. Let each assistant select a block or building and interview an employee from each business found. Each researcher can have the rest of the day off after getting responses from 20 different businesses.
    (d) Use the Island Business Directory. Number all the businesses. Select a starting place at random, and then use every 50th business listed until you have 100 businesses.
    (e) Group the businesses according to type: medical, shipping, retail, manufacturing, financial, construction, restaurant, hotel, tourism, other. Then select a random sample of 10 businesses from each business type.

20. Modern Managed Hospitals (MMH) is a national for-profit chain of hospitals. Management wants to survey patients discharged this past year to obtain patient satisfaction profiles. They wish to use a sample of such patients. Several sampling techniques are described below. Categorize each technique as *simple random sample, stratified sample, systematic sample, cluster sample,* or *convenience sample.*
    (a) Obtain a list of patients discharged from all MMH facilities. Divide the patients according to length of hospital stay (3 days or less, 3–7 days, 8–14 days, more than 14 days). Draw simple random samples from each group.
    (b) Obtain lists of patients discharged from all MMH facilities. Number these patients, and then use a random-number table to obtain the sample.

(c) Randomly select some MMH facilities from each of five geographic regions, and then take random samples from each of these hospital discharge lists.

(d) At the beginning of the year, instruct each MMH facility to survey every 500th patient discharged.

(e) Instruct each MMH facility to survey 10 discharged patients this week and send in the results.

21. *Sampling*—that's also a term used for eating food samples distributed at grocery stores. In an article appearing in the *USA Today Supplement,* it was reported that 75% of shoppers who sample a food item in a grocery store purchase it. Comment on some ways you could gather a sample of people who sample items in grocery stores in your area and determine the percentage of those who buy a sampled item. Suggest ways to draw the following:

(a) A simple random sample

(b) A stratified sample (consider strata based on food types sampled or age of customers)

(c) A cluster sample for a large metropolitan area

(d) A convenience sample

Section 2.2 Graphs

Tables

Millionaires are booming in the United States! One national news magazine recently published these figures: In 1948 there were 13,000 millionaires; in 1953 there were 27,000; in 1958, 52,000; in 1963 the number jumped to 75,000; by 1968 the number increased to 117,000; in 1973 there were 180,000; by 1978, 250,000; and by 1983, 475,000. In 1988 the number of millionaires was thought to exceed 1,000,000!

The last two sentences contain a mass of numbers that is difficult to read. No matter what type of data we have, sample or population, it is important to be able to organize and present the data to other people. A table is a far more effective way to present information than is a sentence full of numbers. A properly labeled table frees the reader from the task of scanning the text to discover what the table represents. The table caption and the column headings identifying the table entries make a table a self-contained body of information. How are the data organized within the table? Organization depends on the data and on what you are trying to show. In the case of our data about millionaires, it is natural to organize the table chronologically, or by year (Table 2–2). We will conservatively say that there were only 1,000,000 millionaires in 1988.

Apparently there were considerably more millionaires in 1988 than in 1948. However, the population has increased, too, from about 147 million to an estimated 246 million. If we list the percentage of millionaires in these years, we will take population growth into account as well as the growth in the number of millionaires.

Table 2–2 Americans Worth at Least One Million Dollars	
Year	Number of Millionaires
1948	13,000
1953	27,000
1958	52,000
1963	75,000
1968	117,000
1973	180,000
1978	250,000
1983	475,000
1988	1,000,000

GUIDED EXERCISE 4

Arrange the following information into a table with an appropriate caption and appropriate column headings. In 1948 the percentage of millionaires in the United States was about 0.01%; in 1953 the percentage was 0.02%; in 1958, 0.03%; in 1963, 0.04%; in 1968, 0.06%; in 1973, 0.08%; in 1978, 0.11%; in 1983, 0.21%; and in 1988, 0.41%.

(a) Make the table.

(a) The information telling us that the table gives the percentage of millionaires in the population of the United States for various years should be noted either in the table caption or in the column headings.

Table 2–3 Growing Percentage of U.S. Millionaires	
Year	Percentage of Population
1948	0.01
1953	0.02
1958	0.03
1963	0.04
1968	0.06
1973	0.08
1978	0.11
1983	0.21
1988	0.41

(b) Which 5-year interval shows the greatest increase in percentage?

(c) Inflation has reduced the purchasing power of one million dollars ($1,000,000) in 1948 to less than 21% of that amount ($210,000) in 1988. The 1988 millionaire would need more than 4.7 million dollars to have the same purchasing power as the 1948 millionaire. Does your table take the changing buying power into account?

(b) The years 1983–1988, because the percentage jumped from 0.21% to 0.41%, a change of 0.2%.

(c) No. We would need more information to take purchasing power into account.

Bar Graphs

Newspapers and magazines seem to prefer graphs to tables when they present information. Graphs make any trend more obvious. For instance, which information display in Figure 2–4 emphasizes the fact that there are almost *five* times as many widows as widowers among the millionaires set: *a* or *b*? The graph enables the reader to compare facts and figures quickly. Bar graphs, pictographs, and pie charts are frequently used graphs.

Let's first consider *bar graphs*. The bars can be vertical or horizontal, but they should be of *uniform width* and be *uniformly spaced*. The length of a bar represents the quantity we wish to compare under various conditions. In Figure 2–5 we are comparing the number of days a person can survive at 110°F temperature with various amounts of water. The length of the bar represents the number of days one can survive.

The following example shows you how to construct a bar graph.

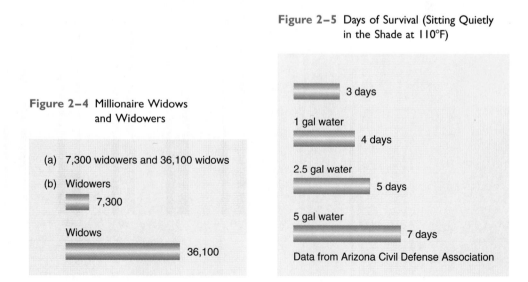

Figure 2–4 Millionaire Widows and Widowers

(a) 7,300 widowers and 36,100 widows

(b) Widowers
  7,300

Widows
  36,100

Figure 2–5 Days of Survival (Sitting Quietly in the Shade at 110°F)

3 days

1 gal water
  4 days

2.5 gal water
  5 days

5 gal water
  7 days

Data from Arizona Civil Defense Association

Example 3

Hikers are often cautioned to carry extra jackets so that they will be prepared for the effect of wind chill. Suppose you are hiking in 50°F temperature and a wind comes up. A breeze of 5 mph makes the effective temperature 48°F. If the wind picks up to 10 mph, then the temperature is equivalent to 40°F. A 15 mph wind drops the effective temperature to 36°F, and a 20 mph wind drops the temperature to freezing. A 25 mph wind makes the effective temperature only 30°F. Make a bar graph to display this information.

Solution: Before we make a bar graph of this information, we'll make a table of wind and effective temperature (Table 2–4). (Even though you may not want to exhibit the table, make one anyway to organize the data. Then the graph will be easier to make.)

To make the bar graph (Figure 2–6), we'll list the wind speed on the horizontal axis and the effective temperature on the vertical one. Each bar will be centered over its wind speed, and the height of the bar will represent the effective temperature. Note again that the bars have the same width and the spacing between all the bars is the same. Both axes are labeled and have scale markings.

Figure 2–6 Wind Chill at 50°F

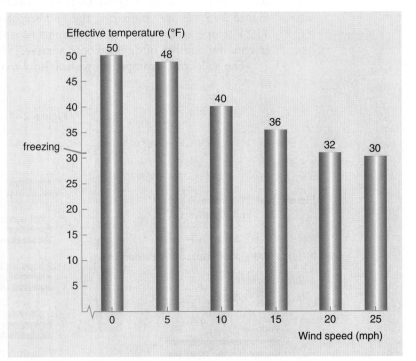

Table 2–4 Wind Chill at 50° F

Wind Speed (mph)	Equivalent Temperature (°F)
Calm	50
5	48
10	40
15	36
20	32
25	30

Source: Data from *Surviving the Unexpected Wilderness Emergency,* by Gene Fear, published by Survival Education Association, Tacoma, Washington.

GUIDED EXERCISE 5

Sunshine Travel Agency offers a rain insurance policy on their Hawaii tours. It costs an extra $100. If you buy the optional policy and it rains during more than 15% of the days of your trip, you will be reimbursed for meals and lodging during the extra rainy days (beyond the 15% and up to 5 days). You are planning a trip to Hawaii and you are debating about taking the insurance. You obtain the rainfall information in Table 2–5 from the U.S. National Oceanic and Atmospheric Administration.

Table 2–5 Average Monthly Rainfall in Honolulu, Hawaii (1941–1980)

Month	Jan.	Feb.	Mar.	Apr.	May	June	July	Aug.	Sept.	Oct.	Nov.	Dec.
Rainfall (inches)	4.40	2.46	3.18	1.36	0.96	0.32	0.60	0.76	0.67	1.51	2.99	3.64

(a) Make a bar graph of this information with month on the horizontal axis and rainfall on the vertical.

(b) There is the rainy season and there is the dry season. From the graph, which 6 months would you say make up the rainy season?

(c) Without the rain insurance, which winter month (November, December, January, or February) would be best for your trip?

(a) See Figure 2–7.

(b) October, November, December, January, February, and March.

(c) February, since it has the least average rainfall.

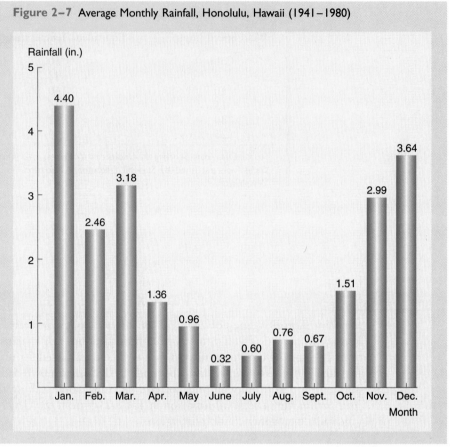

Figure 2–7 Average Monthly Rainfall, Honolulu, Hawaii (1941–1980)

When you read bar graphs, be careful of changing scales. For instance, in Figure 2–8 you see two graphs showing the life expectancy of a man born in 1920 and one born in 1990 (*Statistical Abstract of the United States,* Bureau of Census). The change in life expectancy over the 66-year period illustrated in Figure 2–8 is large: from 54 years to 72, an increase of 18 years. But part (a) makes it seem that the life expectancy has more than tripled. Notice the squiggle ⌇ at the bottom of the vertical axis. This is to inform you that the years 0 to 49 have been omitted. In the second bar graph, no years were skipped, and the picture immediately gives an accurate impression. Be on the alert—many magazine articles use a changing scale. You also should watch for omitted values. If you omit values, be sure to give the reader fair warning with a squiggle ⌇ at the beginning of the axis.

Pareto Charts

In his book *Out of the Crisis* (MIT Center for Advanced Engineering Study), W. Edwards Deming outlines many strategies for improving quality in

Figure 2–8 Male Life Expectancy from Birth

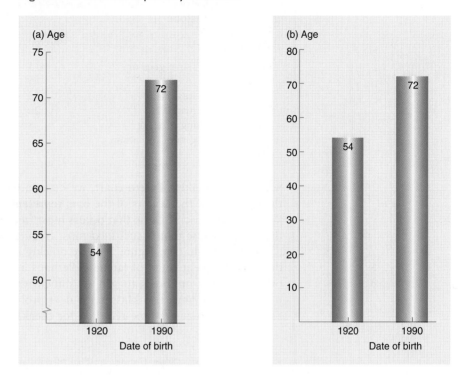

production and service industries. He recommends the use of some statistical methods to organize and analyze data from the industries so that sources of problems may be identified and then corrected. *Pareto charts* (pronounced "Pah-rāy-tōe") are among the many techniques used in quality-control programs. *The Deming Management Method,* by Mary Walton (Putman Publishing Group), lists Pareto charts among seven of the most helpful charts. Pareto charts are vertical bar graphs in which the height represents frequency. In addition, the bars are arranged according to height, with the tallest bar placed on the left. Pareto charts are often used to organize data about causes of problems so as to highlight major causes from left to right.

Example 4

This is an example adapted from *The Deming Management Method*. Suppose you want to arrive at the college 15 minutes before your first class so that you can feel relaxed when you walk into class. An early arrival time also allows room for unexpected delays. However, you always find yourself arriving "just in time" or slightly late. What causes you to be late? One student made a list of possible causes and then kept a checklist for 2 months. On some days more than one item was checked because several events occurred that caused the student to be late. Make a Pareto chart showing causes for lateness.

Table 2–6 Causes for Lateness (September–
          October)

Cause	Frequency
Snoozing after alarm goes off	15
Car trouble	5
Too long over breakfast	13
Last-minute studying	20
Finding something to wear	8
Talking too long with roommate	9
Other	3

Solution: To make a Pareto chart, we make a bar chart. The bars occur over the causes, and the heights of the bars represent the frequency of occurrence. We place the specific cause that occurs most frequently first and continue with the specific cause that occurs next most frequently, etc.

From the chart in Figure 2–9 we quickly see that last-minute studying is the most frequent cause of lateness. Perhaps a more realistic study plan is in order. Another option is to get up sufficiently early to allow for adequate morning study time. Breakfast is the next problem. Has there been a realistic assumption about the time required for breakfast? The second cup of coffee

Figure 2–9 Pareto Chart: Conditions That Might Cause Lateness

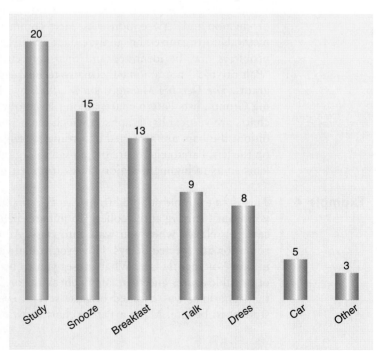

might not fit the schedule. The next cause is snoozing after the alarm goes off. Here a deliberate effort to get up immediately might help. The Pareto chart gives us a vehicle to organize our data and then attack the most frequent problems. Spending a lot of time and money on the car will not have much impact on arrival time at the college (assuming that the car does not get worse).

There are variations in Pareto charts. Sometimes the heights of the bars represent percentages rather than frequency. However, the bars are still arranged in order of decreasing height.

Pictograms

Sometimes pictures are used instead of solid bars. Such a graph is called a *pictogram.* A pictogram can give an accurate and sometimes more interesting display of data, but again, there are aspects that can mislead a reader who is not alert. If the size of the picture changes, the results can be quite misleading. For instance, in Figure 2–10 we see two pictograms of the same information.

The 1991 dollar was worth only 22% of the 1960 dollar, but part (b) of Figure 2–10 makes the situation look worse than it is. Not only did the width shrink by 78% to 22% of its original size, but the height did as well. The total area of the 1991 bill is much less than 22% of the 1960 dollar bill.

In pictograms, the pictures should all be the same size. The number of pictures rather than the size should be changed to indicate a changing quantity. In addition, the amounts represented by the pictograms should be labeled (e.g., $1.00) so that the reader does not have to count the number of pictures and to compensate for rounding off.

Circle Graphs

Another popular pictorial representation of data is the *circle graph,* or *pie chart.* It is relatively safe from misinterpretation and is especially useful for showing the division of a total quantity into its component parts. The total quantity, or 100%, is represented by the entire circle. Each wedge of the circle represents a component part of the total. These proportional segments are usually labeled with corresponding percentages of the total. Guided Exercise 6 shows how to make a circle graph.

Figure 2–10 The Shrinking United States Dollar (1960–1991)

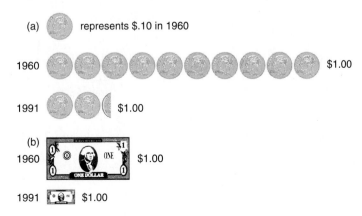

GUIDED EXERCISE 6

Homesweet College has no on-campus housing. However, there is a special housing service to help out-of-town students find approved living quarters. The current list includes 720 rental units as described in the first two columns of Table 2–7.

Table 2–7 Available Housing for Students

Unit	Number	Fractional Part	Percent	Number of Degrees Occupied in Circle
Room, no kitchen	360	$\frac{360}{720} = 0.5$	50%	$0.50 \times 360° = 180°$
Efficiency apartment	130	$\frac{130}{720} = 0.181$	18.1%	$0.181 \times 360° = 65°$
One-bedroom apartment	120	$\frac{120}{720} = 0.167$	16.7%	$0.167 \times \underline{\quad} = \underline{\quad}$
Two-bedroom apartment	90	$\frac{90}{720} = 0.125$	12.5%	$\underline{\quad} \times \underline{\quad} = \underline{\quad}$
Three-bedroom apartment	20	$\underline{\quad}$	$\underline{\quad}$	$\underline{\quad} \times \underline{\quad} = \underline{\quad}$
Total number = 720				

(a) Fill in the missing parts of Table 2–7. Remember the central angle of a circle is 360°.

(a)

Fractional Part	Percent	Number of Degrees
One-bedroom, $\frac{120}{720}$	16.7%	$0.167 \times 360° = 60°$
Two-bedroom, $\frac{90}{720}$	12.5%	$0.125 \times 360° = 45°$
Three-bedroom, $\frac{20}{720}$	2.8%	$0.028 \times 360° = 10°$

(b) Do the degrees in the last column add up to 360°?

(b) They always should; however, due to rounding errors, the sum might be slightly more or less than 360°.

(c) Fill in the missing degrees and percentages in the circle graph in Figure 2–11 (i.e., the degrees for one-bedroom apartments and for rooms).

(c) See Figure 2–12.

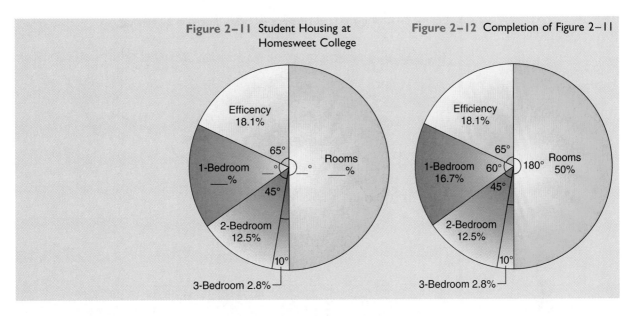

Figure 2–11 Student Housing at Homesweet College

Figure 2–12 Completion of Figure 2–11

Time Plot

Suppose you begin an exercise program that involves walking or jogging for 30 minutes. You exercise several times a week but monitor yourself by logging the distance you cover in 30 minutes each Saturday. How do you display these data in a meaningful way? Making a bar chart showing the frequency of distances you cover might be interesting, but it does not really show how the distance you cover in 30 minutes has changed over time. Are you covering more distance each week? We want to graph the distances against time.

We will use a *time plot*. A time plot is a graph showing the data measurements in time order. To make a time plot, we put time on the horizontal scale and the variable being measured on the vertical scale. For a basic time plot, we connect the data points by lines.

Example 5

Suppose you have been in the walking/jogging exercise program for 20 weeks, and each week you recorded the distance you covered in 30 minutes. Your data log follows in Table 2–8.

Table 2–8 Distance in Miles Walked/Jogged in 30 Minutes

Week	1	2	3	4	5	6	7	8	9	10
Distance	1.5	1.4	1.7	1.6	1.9	2.0	1.8	2.0	1.9	2.0
Week	11	12	13	14	15	16	17	18	19	20
Distance	2.1	2.1	2.3	2.3	2.2	2.4	2.5	2.6	2.4	2.7

Figure 2–13 Time Plot of Distance (in miles) Jogged in 30 Minutes.

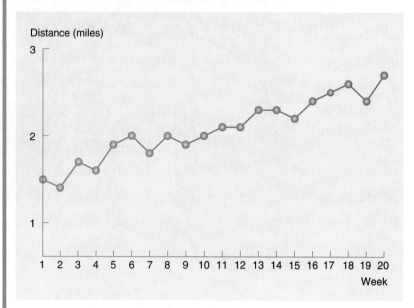

(a) Make a time plot.

   Solution: The data are appropriate for a time plot because they represent the same measure (distance covered in a 30-minute period) taken at different times. The measurements are also recorded at equal time intervals (every week). To make our time plot, we list the weeks in order on the horizontal scale. Above each week, plot the distance covered that week on a vertical scale. Then connect the dots. Figure 2–13 shows the time plot. Be sure the scales are labeled.

(b) Looking at Figure 2–13, can you detect any patterns?

   Solution: There seems to be an upward trend in distance covered. The distances covered in the last few weeks are about a mile further than those of the first few weeks. However, we cannot conclude that the trend will continue. Perhaps you have reached your goal for this training activity and now wish to maintain a distance of about 2.5 miles in 30 minutes.

Time Series

Data sets composed of similar measurements taken at regular intervals over time are called *time series*. Time series are often used in economics, finance, sociology, medicine, and any situation where we want to study or monitor a similar measure over a period of time. A time plot can reveal some of the main features of time series.

Figure 2–14 shows two time plots of the Dow Jones Industrial Average as presented in the *Wall Street Journal* on September 15, 1993. In one graph we see the averages plotted against months, beginning with March 1992

Figure 2–14 Markets Diary*

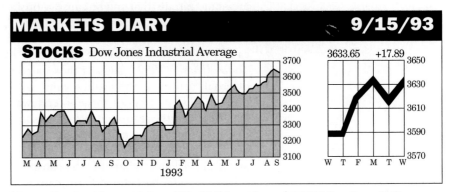

*Source: Reprinted by permission of *The Wall Street Journal,* ©1993 Dow Jones & Company, Inc. All Rights Reserved Worldwide.

through half of September 1993. The other time plot is over a much shorter period of time. It is a daily plot of the Dow Jones Industrial Average from Wednesday, September 8 through Wednesday, September 15, 1993.

In both graphs of Figure 2–14 we see an upward trend. However, there is a slight downward trend in September. By the time you read this material, you will be able to look back and see what the Dow Jones Industrial Average did next. Was there a dip in October 1993 as there was in 1992?

Section 2.2 Problems

1. It is costly in both time and money to go to college. Does it pay off? According to the *Conference Board Survey* by the Bureau of Census, the answer is yes. The average annual income (in thousands of dollars) of a household headed by a person with the stated education level is as follows: 16.5 if grade school is the top level of education achieved, 28.5 for high school graduates, 44.5 for college graduates, and 53.5 for completion of one or more years of postgraduate studies. Make a bar graph showing household income for each education level.

2. How much money do we as a nation make? The literal answer is given by the *Bank Note Reporter.* The number of U.S. bills printed and delivered during the 1989 fiscal year was as follows: 2.86 billion $1 bills, 835.2 million $5 bills, 777.2 million $10 bills, 1.53 billion $20 bills, 134.4 million $50 bills, and 201.6 million $100 bills. Make a bar graph showing the number of each denomination bill. (*Note:* 1 billion = 1000 million, so 2.86 billion = 2860 million and 1.53 billion = 1530 million.)

3. In an article entitled "How to Cure the Fear of Flying," *Fortune Magazine* gave the following information: The number of people who died in a calendar year while on a commercial flight, 33; in the bathtub, 318; by poisoning, 5900; as pedestrians, 6500; murdered by spouses, 7000; from falls, 12,400; in motor vehicle accidents, 33,800
   (a) Make a bar graph showing activities causing death.
   (b) Make a Pareto chart showing activities causing death.

4. Suppose you are interested in investing in a business corporation. What are some pitfalls that might cause a business corporation to fail? To answer this question, we can look at history. Buccino & Associates surveyed more than 1300 business professionals and asked them about leading causes of business failures in the 1980s. According to the report in *USA Today* (March 1992), 88% of those surveyed cited internal problems, not external factors, as the leading cause of business failure. Of the internal problems listed, 13% of those interviewed cited insufficient management experience as the leading cause of business failure, 13% cited poor business planning, 18% cited inadequate leadership, and 29% cited excessive debt.

   (a) Make a Pareto chart for the causes of business failure
   (b) Does your chart show *all* the causes for business failure cited by business professionals interviewed? Which internal cause was cited most frequently?

5. A survey of 1000 adults (reported in *USA Today*) uncovered some interesting housekeeping secrets. When unexpected company comes, where do we hide the mess? The survey showed that 68% of the respondents toss their mess in the closet, 23% shove things under the bed, 6% put things in the bath tub, and 3% put the mess in the freezer. Make a circle graph to display this information.

6. What meal are we most likely to eat in a fast-food restaurant? A survey of 1261 adults (reported in *USA Today*) revealed that 48.9% of the respondents are most likely to eat lunch at a fast-food restaurant; 7.7%, breakfast; 31.6%, dinner; 10%, a snack; and 1.8% answered "don't know." Display this information in a circle graph.

7. At Eastview College, faculty members in the Physical Education Department are required to keep records of injuries suffered by students in classes involving participation in sports. Of the 57 injuries that occurred last year, 23 involved the knee; 14, the ankle; 4, the elbow; 10, the wrist; and 6, other parts of the body. Make a pie chart showing the distribution of the injuries.

8. One dollar of tuition at Plattsburg College was distributed in the following way: 27 cents went to faculty salaries, 8 cents to the library and media center, 9 cents to the physical plant (including utilities, cleaning, etc.), 30 cents to general college administration, 11 cents to counseling and career services, 8 cents to records and admissions, and 7 cents to miscellaneous expenses such as equipment and duplicating services. Make a pie chart to show the distribution of the tuition dollar.

9. Electronic gadgets fill our homes. The U.S. Consumer Electronics Industry *Annual Review* reported that 98% of the U.S. households have a TV, 98% have radios, 90% have audio systems, 61% have VCRs, and 24% now have telephone answering machines. Display this information in a bar chart showing percentage of households owning each gadget. Could the information as reported be put in a circle graph? Why or why not?

10. Driving would be more pleasant if we didn't have to put up with bad habits of other drivers. *USA Today* reported the results of a Valvoline Oil Company survey of 500 drivers in which the drivers marked their complaints about other drivers. The top complaints turned out to be tailgating, marked by 22% of the respondents; not using turn signals, marked by 19%; 16% marked being cut off; 11% complained about other drivers driving too slowly; and 8% complained about other drivers being inconsiderate. Make a Pareto chart showing percentage of drivers listing each stated complaint. Could this information as reported be put in a circle graph? Why or why not?

11. The U.S. Department of Agriculture keeps track of agricultural land in the United States owned by foreign interest. Data provided by the Department of Agriculture listing the country of the foreign owner and the acreage owned (in thousands of acres) follow: Canada, 1971; Germany, 750; Netherlands, 370; Switzerland, 300; United Kingdom, 1800. Use a pictogram to represent these data. *Hint:* Select a convenient unit for the individual pictures, such as 100 (thousand acres).

12. The Social Security tax is computed as a percentage of a wage (up to a specified maximum wage). Over the years, the percentage has increased. In 1940 the percentage was 1%; by 1950 it increased to 1.5%; in 1960 it was 3%; in 1970 it was 4.8%; and by 1980 it was 6.13%. In 1990 it was 7.65%. Make a pictogram showing the percentages of taxable wages contributed to Social Security for the years given.

13. An important economic statistic is the amount of personal savings as a percentage of disposable income. These data are collected by the U.S. Department of Commerce. Make a time plot for the following data based on information from U.S. Department of Commerce, Bureau of Economic Analysis. Percent refers to personal savings as a percentage of disposable income.

Time	1980	1981	1982	1983	1984	1985
Percent	6	6.7	6.2	5.4	6.1	4.4

Time	1986	1987	1988	1989	1990	1991
Percent	4.1	3.2	4.2	4.6	5.1	5.2

14. The amount of money spent on medical care in the United States (billions of dollars) has grown over the following years. According to data from U.S. Department of Commerce, Bureau of Economic Analysis, the amount spent (in billions) on medical care in the United States for each of the years listed is as follows:

Year	1985	1986	1987	1988	1989	1990	1991
Dollars (billions)	327.5	357.6	399.0	487.7	536.4	595.9	656.0

Make a time plot showing this information.

15. Has the cost of long-distance telephone calls been changing over the years? Based on data from FCC (as analyzed by Dr. Robert E. Hall, Stanford University), the average cost per minute on the nation's three largest long-distance phone companies—AT&T, MCI, and Sprint—is as follows:

Year	1985	1986	1987	1988	1989	1990	1991	1992
Cost	41¢	33¢	26¢	24¢	21¢	17¢	16¢	14¢

Note: The cost is in constant 1993 figures. Make a time plot for this information.

16. How does average height for boys change as the boy gets older? According to *Physician's Handbook,* the heights at different ages are as follows:

Age (years)	0.5	1	2	3	4	5	6	7	8
Height (inches)	26	29	33	36	39	42	45	47	50

	9	10	11	12	13	14
	52	54	56	58	60	62

Make a time plot for average height for age 0.5 through 14 years.

Figure 2–15 The Booming On-Line Market*

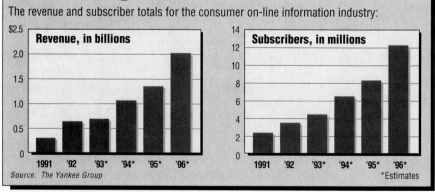

*Source: Reprinted by permission of *The Wall Street Journal,* ©1993 Dow Jones & Company, Inc. All Rights Reserved Worldwide.

17. The on-line information industry is growing. It provides computer access nationally and even internationally to information, e-mail, electronic bulletin boards, and so on. A *Wall Street Journal* special report on technology included Figure 2–15, The Booming On-Line Market.
    (a) What kinds of graphs are shown in Figure 2–15 (bar, Pareto, pie chart, pictogram, or time plot)?
    (b) Redisplay the revenue information in time-plot format.
    (c) Redisplay the subscriber information in time-plot format.

Section 2.3   Histograms and Frequency Distributions

Histograms

Healthy Crunch Cereal is about to take over sponsorship of the TV program "Space Voyage." The advertising manager has requested a report on the age distribution of the viewers so the spot ads can be tailored to appeal to the age groups with the most viewers. The viewer age report contains the graph in Figure 2–16 that was made from a random sample of viewers.

GUIDED EXERCISE 7

Use the graph of the viewer age distribution for the program "Space Voyage" (Figure 2–16) to answer the following questions.

Figure 2–16 Viewer Age for "Space Voyage"

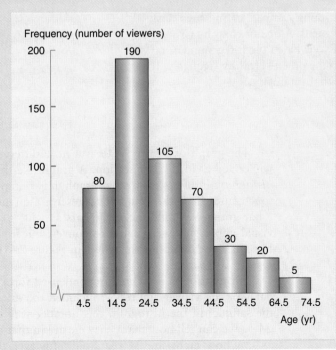

(a) What does the height of each bar represent? How many viewers are represented in this graph?

(b) What does the width of a bar represent?

(c) What ages are included in the group with the most viewers? Is this graph detailed enough to tell you exactly how many viewers are 21 years old?

(d) From the information in this graph about the ages of the viewers, which of the following ads do you think the manager might choose for "Space Voyage"?

Scene 1: A grandmother and first grader at the breakfast table. The grandmother says to the child, "Eat Healthy Crunch Cereal because it will make you grow."

Scene 2: A middle-aged man reading the stock report. An empty bowl is on the table with an open box of Healthy Crunch Cereal beside it. The man puts down the paper and puts his hands on the box of Healthy Crunch as he says, "I eat Healthy Crunch even *before* I read the stock report."

Scene 3: Two young campers eating breakfast in front of their tent. A box of Healthy Crunch Cereal is clearly visible in the foreground. One camper says to the other, "Healthy Crunch will help us climb that mountain."

(a) The height of each bar represents the number of viewers of that age group. To get the total number of viewers, add the heights of the bars. There are 500 viewers represented.

(b) The width represents the age group.

(c) The age group 14.5–24.5 has the most viewers. We cannot tell how many viewers are 21 years old. All we can say is that there are 190 viewers between the ages of 14.5 and 24.5 years.

(d) Since the largest age group is between 14.5 and 24.5, the ad about the campers would probably be the best. This age group would not necessarily be interested in food that makes a first grader grow or food that is eaten before one reads the stock market report.

The graph of Figure 2–16 is a little different from the other bar graphs we looked at in the last section. A graph like that of Figure 2–16 is called a *histogram*. It differs from a bar graph in two important ways: The bars always touch, and the width of a bar represents a quantitative value, such as age. In a bar graph we could make the bars as wide as we wished, according to the visual impression we wanted to convey, but in a histogram the width of the bar has a meaning. For instance, in Figure 2–16 the width of each bar represents 10 years.

Information is presented in condensed form in a histogram. The original data for the viewer age report included the *exact* number of 21-year-olds in the sample. In the histogram this number was grouped with the ages 14.5–24.5. We can tell how many viewers are in that age group, but we cannot tell exactly how many are 21 years old. However, the condensed information in the histogram can be assimilated more quickly than the same information in more detailed form.

If you are given many pieces of data, how do you condense the information to make a histogram? The task force to encourage car pools did a study of one-way commuting distances for workers in the downtown Dallas area. A random sample of 60 of these workers was taken. The commuting distances of the workers in the sample are given in Table 2–9.

The first thing to do is to decide how many bars or classes you want in the histogram. Five to 15 classes are usually used. If you use fewer than 5 classes, you risk losing too much information, but if you use more than 15 classes, the clarity of the diagram might be sacrificed for detail. Let the spread of the data and the purpose of the histogram be your guide when selecting the number of classes.

Next, find a convenient class width. To do this, find the difference between the largest and smallest data values and divide by the number of classes. If you want the class width to be a whole number, always *increase* the result to the next whole number so that the classes cover the data.

Class Width

1. Compute

$$\frac{\text{Largest data value} - \text{smallest data value}}{\text{Desired number of classes}}$$

2. Round the value computed to the next highest whole number

In this case, let's use 10 classes. The largest distance commuted is 47 miles and the smallest is 1 mile.

$$\frac{47 - 1}{10} = 4.6 \approx 5$$

The lowest and highest values that can fit in a class are called the *lower class limit* and *upper class limit*, respectively. The *class width* is the difference between the lower class limit of one class and the lower class limit of the next

Table 2–9 One-Way Commuting Distances in Miles for 60 Workers in Downtown Dallas

13	47	10	3	16	20	17	40	4	2
7	25	8	21	19	15	3	17	14	6
12	45	1	8	4	16	11	18	23	12
6	2	14	13	7	15	46	12	9	18
34	13	41	28	36	17	24	27	29	9
14	26	10	24	37	31	8	16	12	16

class. Each class should have the same width, although it is not uncommon to see either the first or the last class width a little longer or shorter than the others. The center of the class is called the *midpoint* (or *class mark*). This is found by adding the lower and upper class limits of one class and dividing by 2.

$$\text{Midpoint} = \frac{\text{lower class limit} + \text{upper class limit}}{2}$$

The midpoint is often used as a representative value of the entire class.

Now we can organize the commuting distance data into a *frequency table* (Table 2-10). Such a table shows the limits of each class, the frequency with which the data fall in a class, and the class midpoint. A tally will help us find the frequencies.

Now we're almost ready to make a histogram. But in a histogram we want the bars to touch. There is a space between the upper limit of one class and the lower limit of the next class. The halfway points of these intervals are called *class boundaries*. We use the class boundaries as the endpoints of the bars in the histogram. Then there is no space between the bars. Figure 2-17 is the histogram of commuter distances. The class boundaries are shown. (Sometimes only the class midpoints are labeled.)

Relative-Frequency Tables and Histograms

Other useful tools for organizing data are *relative-frequency tables* and *relative-frequency histograms*. Once we have made a frequency table, it is easy to construct a relative-frequency table. The relative frequency for a particular class is found by dividing the class frequency by the total of all frequencies (sample size).

Table 2-10 Frequency Table of One-Way Commuting Distances for 60 Downtown Dallas Workers (Data in Miles)

Class Lower Limit	Upper Limit	Tally	Frequency	Class Midpoint
1–5		‖‖ ‖ ‖	7	3
6–10		‖‖‖ ‖‖‖ ‖	11	8
11–15		‖‖‖ ‖‖‖ ‖‖‖	13	13
16–20		‖‖‖ ‖‖‖ ‖	11	18
21–25		‖‖‖	5	23
26–30		‖‖‖‖	4	28
31–35		‖‖	2	33
36–40		‖‖‖	3	38
41–45		‖‖	2	43
46–50		‖‖	2	48

Figure 2-17 One-Way Commuting Distances in Miles Driven by Downtown Dallas Workers

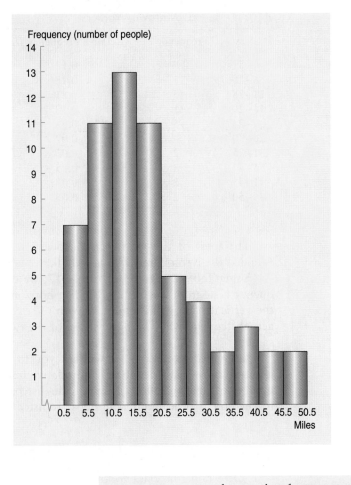

$$\text{Relative frequency} = \frac{f}{n} = \frac{\text{class frequency}}{\text{total of all frequencies}}$$

Table 2–11 shows the relative frequencies for the commuter data of Table 2–9. Since we already have the frequency table (Table 2–10), the relative-frequency table is easily obtained. The sample size is $n = 60$. Notice that the sample size is the total of all the frequencies. Therefore, the relative frequency for the first class (the class from 1 to 5) is

$$\text{Relative frequency} = \frac{f}{n} = \frac{7}{60} \approx 0.12$$

The symbol $\approx$ means "approximately equal to." We use the symbol because we rounded the relative frequency. Relative frequencies for the other classes are computed in a similar way.

Table 2–11 Relative Frequencies of One-Way Commuting Distances for 60 Downtown Workers

Class	Frequency f	Relative Frequency f/n
1–5	7	0.12
6–10	11	0.18
11–15	13	0.21
16–20	11	0.18
21–25	5	0.08
26–30	4	0.07
31–35	2	0.03
36–40	3	0.05
41–45	2	0.03
46–50	2	0.03

The total of the relative frequencies should be 1. However, since we rounded the results, our total is only 0.98.

Using Table 2–11 and Figure 2–17, we can quickly make a relative-frequency histogram (Figure 2–18). The horizontal scale will be the same, but the vertical scale will be marked with *relative frequencies f/n* instead of the actual frequencies *f*. The basic shape of the two graphs will otherwise be the same.

In Guided Exercise 8 we will ask you to make a frequency table, histogram, relative-frequency table, and relative-frequency histogram. There are a number of steps to follow. The individual steps are not difficult, but you need to keep them all in mind. The steps are listed for your convenience.

Frequency Table

1. Determine the class width.
2. Create the distinct classes. We use the convention that the *lower class limit* of the first class is the smallest data value. Add the class width to *this* number to get the *lower class limit* of the next class.
3. Tally the data into classes. Each data value should fall into exactly one class. Total the tallies to obtain each *class frequency*.
4. Compute the *midpoint* (class mark) for each class.
5. Determine the *class boundaries*.

Relative-Frequency Table

6. For each class, compute the *relative frequency f/n*, where *f* is the class frequency and *n* is the total sample size.

Figure 2–18 Relative-Frequency Histogram for Dallas Commuters: One-Way Commuting Distances

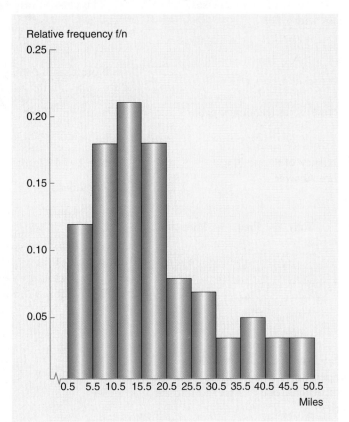

GUIDED EXERCISE 8

One irate customer called Dollar Day Mail Order Company 40 times during the last 2 weeks to see why his order had not arrived. Each time he called, he counted the number of rings before the phone was answered (Table 2–12).

Table 2–12 Number of Rings Before Phone Was Answered

17	10	8	7	3	5	15	6	9	5
6	18	13	18	1	17	10	17	2	6
4	17	16	9	3	18	15	8	14	17
17	7	14	6	3	17	2	14	4	11

(a) What are the largest and smallest values in Table 2–12? If we want five classes, what should the class width be?

(a) The largest value is 18; the smallest value is 1. The class width is

$$\frac{18-1}{5} = \frac{17}{5} = 3.4 \approx 4$$

Note that we must round *up* to 4.

(b) Complete the following frequency table.

(b)

Table 2–13 Frequency of Phone Rings Before Answer

Class Limits

Add class width

Lower	Upper	Tally	Freq.	Midpoint
1 – 4		———	———	———
5 – 8		———	———	———
9 – 12		———	———	———
13 –		———	———	———
— –		———	———	———

Table 2–14 Completion of Table 2–13

Class Limits

Lower	Upper	Tally	Freq.	Midpoint
1	4	༎༎༎ ༎༎༎	8	2.5
5	8	༎༎༎ ༎༎༎	10	6.5
9	12	༎༎༎	5	10.5
13	16	༎༎༎ ༎༎	7	14.5
17	20	༎༎༎ ༎༎༎	10	18.5

(c) Recall that the class boundary is halfway between the upper limit of one class and the lower limit of the next. Use this fact to find the class boundaries.

(c)

Table 2–15 Class Boundaries

Class Limits		Class Boundaries		Class Limits		Class Boundaries	
Lower	Upper	Lower	Upper	Lower	Upper	Lower	Upper
1	4	0.5	4.5	1	4	0.5	4.5
5	8	4.5	8.5	5	8	4.5	8.5
9	12	8.5	12.5	9	12	8.5	12.5
13	16	—	—	13	16	12.5	16.5
17	20	—	—	17	20	16.5	20.5

(d) Finish the histogram in Figure 2–19.

(d) See Figure 2–20.

Figure 2–19 Rings Before Answer

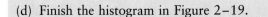

Figure 2–20 Completion of Figure 2–19

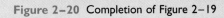
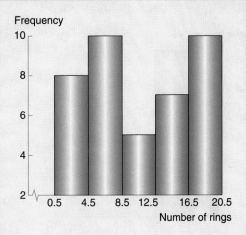

(e) Compute the relative class frequency *f/n* for each class.

(e)

Table 2–16 Relative Class Frequency

Class	*f/n*
1–4	8/40 = 0.20
5–8	10/40 = 0.25
9–12	_____
13–16	_____
17–20	_____

Table 2–17 Completion of Table 2–16

Class	*f/n*
1–4	0.20
5–8	0.25
9–12	0.13
13–16	0.18
17–20	0.25

(f) Finish the relative-frequency histogram in Figure 2–21.

(f) See Figure 2–22.

Figure 2–21 Rings Before Answer

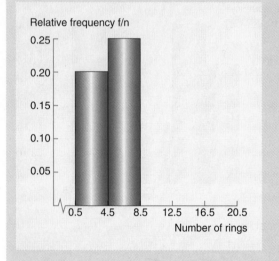

Figure 2–22 Completion of Figure 2–21

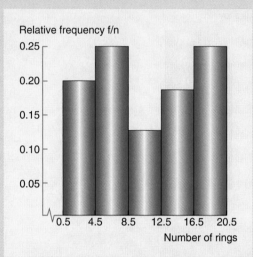

(g) Compare the histogram and relative-frequency histograms in this exercise.

(g) The horizontal axes are the same as are the shapes. The only difference is in the label of the vertical axis.

- *Comment:* The use of class boundaries in histograms assures us that the bars of the histogram touch and that no data fall on the boundaries. Both these features are important. However, a histogram displaying class boundaries looks somewhat awkward. For instance, the age range of 14.5 to 24.5 years shown in Figure 2–16 does not seem to be as convenient or natural a choice as an age range of 15 to 25 years. For this reason, many magazines and newspapers do not use class boundaries as labels on a histogram. Instead, some use lower class limits as labels, with the convention *that a data value falling on the class limit is included in the next higher class (class to the right of the limit).*

  When you use a computer program to create frequency tables and histograms, be sure to determine the convention that is being followed.

We will see relative-frequency distributions again when we study probability in Chapter 4. There we will see that if a random sample is large enough, then we can estimate the probability of an event by the relative frequency of the event. The relative-frequency distribution then can be interpreted as a *probability distribution.* Such distributions will form the basis of our work in inferential statistics.

Calculator Note Many graphing calculators produce histograms. However, the procedure the calculator follows may be slightly different from our procedure. For instance, on the TI-82, the user enters the data into one list and enters the corresponding frequency of each data value into another list. Since both lists must have the same number of entries, a default frequency of 1 is available. Then the user provides the smallest data value that is to appear on the histogram (as the value for Xmin). Next, the user provides the class width (as the value for Xscl). The calculator then produces a histogram with enough bars to include all the data. *Lower class limits are used in place of class boundaries, with the convention that a data value falling on a limit is counted in the bar to the right.* A trace function places a blinking box at the top center of a bar and gives the left and right limits of the designated class (min, max) as well as the frequency n of the data in the class. Figure 2–23 shows a histogram created from the data in Table 2–9 on the one-way commuting distances of workers in Dallas. Beside it, the WINDOW screen shows the specifications that produced the graph.

Figure 2–23 TI-82 Display of Histogram from Table 2–9: One-Way Commuting Distance

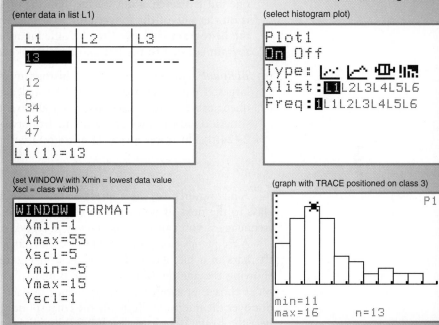

Notice that the curser box is at the top of the third bar, and we are told that the minimum data value included in this bar is 11, while the maximum is less than 16. A distance of 16 miles is included in the fourth bar. The class frequency is $n = 13$.

The user may use the trace command to determine the appropriate Ymax value so that the histogram is completely displayed in the window.

Distribution Shapes

Histograms are valuable and useful tools. If the raw data came from a random sample of population values, the histogram constructed from your sample values should have a distribution shape that is reasonably similar to that of the population.

There are several terms that are commonly used to describe histograms and their associated population distribution.

(a) *Symmetrical or Triangular:* These two terms refer to a histogram in which both sides are (more or less) the same when the graph is folded vertically down the middle. Figure 2–24(a) shows a typical histogram with a symmetrical shape.

(b) *Uniform or Rectangular:* These terms refer to a histogram in which every class has equal frequency. From one point of view, a uniform distribution is symmetrical with the added property that the bars are of the same height. Figure 2–24(b) illustrates a typical histogram with a uniform shape.

(c) *Skewed Left or Skewed Right:* These terms refer to a histogram in which one tail is stretched out longer than the other. The direction of skewness is on the side of the *longer* tail. So if the longer tail is on the left, we say the histogram is skewed to the left. Figure 2–24(c) shows a typical histogram skewed to the left and another skewed to the right.

(d) *Bimodal:* This term refers to a histogram in which the two classes with largest frequencies are separated by at least one class. The top two frequencies of these classes may have different values. Usually this type of situation indicates we are sampling from two different populations. Figure 2–24(d) illustrates a typical histogram with a bimodal shape.

Frequency Polygons

A histogram gives the impression that frequencies jump suddenly from one class to the next. If you want to emphasize the *continuous* rise or fall of the frequencies, you can use a *frequency polygon,* or *line graph.*

A frequency polygon is made by connecting in order the top midpoints of the bars in a histogram. For instance, in Figure 2–25 we have a histogram showing the age distribution of 1000 male diabetes patients 10 years old or older chosen at random. The frequency of each class is indicated by a heavy dot over the midpoint. To make the corresponding frequency polygon, we connect the heavy dots in order. In addition, we extend the lines on the left and on the right so that the polygon begins and ends with a frequency of zero. Place these left and right extensions one class width to the left and right of the first and last midpoints, respectively. The frequency polygon is shown in Figure 2–26.

A frequency polygon can be constructed without first drawing a histogram. Simply plot the class frequency over the class midpoint. Then connect the points in order.

Figure 2–24 Type of Histograms

(a) Typical symmetrical or triangular histogram

(b) Typical uniform or rectangular histogram

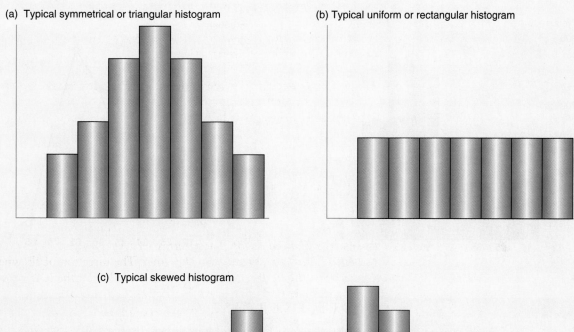

(c) Typical skewed histogram

Skewed left   Skewed right

(d) Typical bimodal histogram

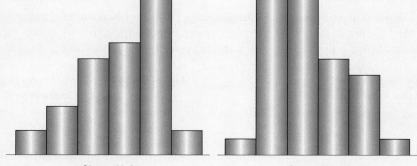

Figure 2–25 Age Distribution of Male Diabetes Patients 10 Years Old or Older

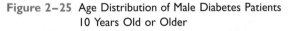
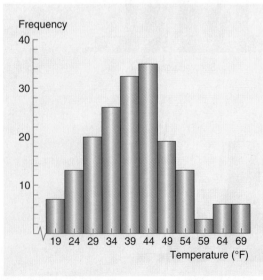

Figure 2–26 Frequency Polygon of Ages of Male Diabetes Patients

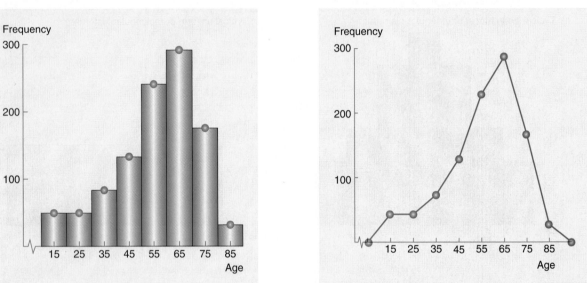

GUIDED EXERCISE 9

The ski season in Aspen, Colorado, lasts from mid-November through mid-May. Figure 2–27 shows the high temperatures during the ski season. Make a frequency polygon from the histogram (see Figure 2–28).

Figure 2–27 High Temperatures During the Ski Season, Aspen, Colorado (°F)*

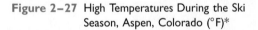

Figure 2–28 High Temperatures During the Ski Season, Aspen, Colorado (°F)*

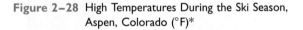
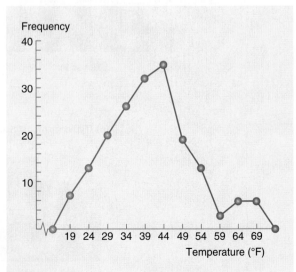

*Source: Temperatures from Climatological Data published by the U.S. Department of Commerce, 1973.

Frequency polygons are especially useful if you wish to compare two distributions. For instance, the president of Rainy Vail College is requesting a larger budget to pay 1950 part-time student workers. The request is based on the fact that under the newly approved salary schedule student workers will be paid more. Under the old salary schedule, a student was paid the same amount per hour no matter how many years he or she had been working. Under the new schedule, a student receives a raise of 25 cents per hour for every year of job-related experience. The president's request contains the graph in Figure 2–29 to support the request for increased budget.

The number of student workers is the same under each schedule. However, under the new schedule, more students receive wages between $4.50 and $5.75 per hour than under the old plan. Consequently, if students are to work the same number of hours as they have in the past, more money will be needed to pay them.

Cumulative Frequency Table

Sometimes we want to study *cumulative totals* instead of frequencies or relative frequencies. Cumulative totals can be used to determine how many scores are *above* or *below* a set level.

Figure 2–29 Hourly Wages for Part-Time Student Workers at Rainy Vail College

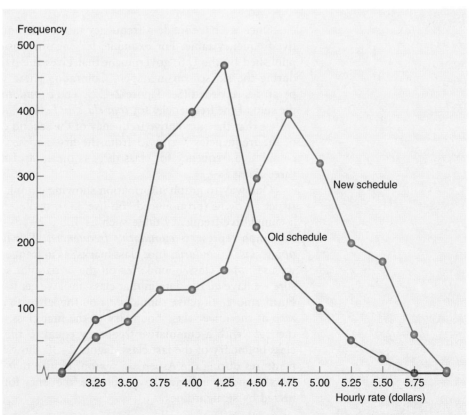

Table 2–18 High Temperatures During the Aspen Ski Season (°F)

Class Boundaries		Frequency	Cumulative Frequency
Lower	Upper		
16.5	21.5	7	7
21.5	26.5	13	20 (= 7 + 13)
26.5	31.5	20	40 (= 7 + 13 + 20)
31.5	36.5	26	66 (= 7 + 13 + 20 + 26)
36.5	41.5	32	98
41.5	46.5	34	132
46.5	51.5	19	151
51.5	56.5	13	164
56.5	61.5	3	167
61.5	66.5	6	173
66.5	71.5	6	179

Once we have made a frequency table, it is not hard to make a cumulative-frequency table. For example, let's again consider the climatologic data published by the U.S. government that gives the daily high temperatures (°F) during the ski season in Aspen, Colorado. There were 179 daily high temperatures recorded (See Figure 2–27). The *cumulative frequency* for a class is the sum of the frequencies for *that class and all previous classes.* In Table 2–18 we see that the cumulative frequency of the second class is 20. This is the sum of the frequencies 7 and 13 from the first and second classes. Likewise, the cumulative frequency for class three is the sum of the frequencies in the first three classes.

Ogives

One way to graph information showing cumulative frequencies is to construct an *ogive* (pronounced "ō-jīve"). To make an ogive, we first construct a cumulative-frequency table such as Table 2–18. Then the vertical scale of the graph represents *cumulative frequencies.* The horizontal scale represents *upper class boundaries* (not class marks, as in frequency polygons). The reason we use *upper* class boundaries on the horizontal scale is that we cannot be sure we have *all* the data in that class until we get to the upper class boundary. Furthermore, an ogive should *start* on the left with a cumulative frequency of zero at the *lower* class boundary of the first class. The ogive should end on the *right* with a cumulative frequency equal to the sample size at the upper class boundary of the last class. Figure 2–30 shows an ogive of the high temperatures during the Aspen ski season. Notice that heavy dots over the right class boundary indicate the cumulative frequency for a class. The dots are connected by straight lines.

Figure 2–30 Ogive for Daily High Temperatures (°F) During Aspen Ski Season

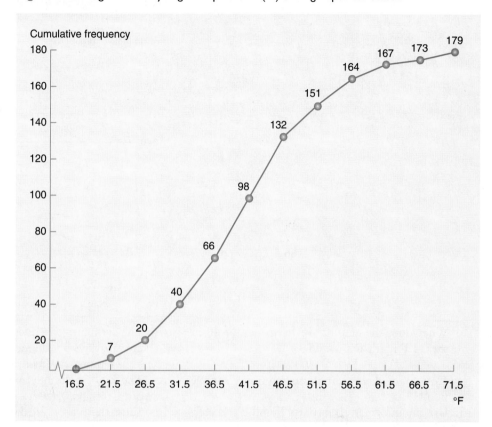

GUIDED EXERCISE 10

Ogives are helpful when we want to know how many of our scores are *above or below* some level. For instance, the Aspen-Ashcroft area is a world famous center for cross-country skiing on wilderness trails. If the daily high temperature is above 32°F, the snow tends to melt a little. Then at night it freezes again. This can result in a snow crust that makes cross-country skiing faster and more challenging. It also can increase avalanche danger. Let's use the ogive of Figure 2–30 to estimate the percentage of a typical ski season during which the daily high temperatures go above 32°F.

(a) Use Figure 2–30 and find 32°F on the horizontal scale. What is the cumulative frequency of number of days with high temperature less than 32°F?

(a) The upper class boundary for temperatures below 32°F falls at 31.5°F. The cumulative frequency corresponding to 31.5 is 40 (see Figure 2–31).

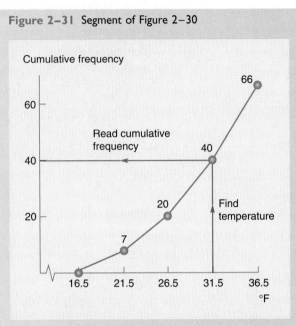

Figure 2–31 Segment of Figure 2–30

(b) What does the cumulative frequency of 40 at the 32°F mark tell us?

(c) How many days are represented in the sample in all?

(d) Use the information in parts b and c to determine how many days the daily high temperature equals or exceeds 32°F. What percentage of the season has temperatures at or above 32°F?

(b) The cumulative frequency 40 tells us that there are 40 days in the season during which the high temperature will be *below* 32°F.

(c) The highest cumulative frequency is 179 (see dot over 71.5).

(d) Since there are 179 days in all represented in the sample and 40 have daily high temperatures below 32°F, there are 179 − 40 = 139 days during which the daily high equals or exceeds 32°F. This means that 78% of the days have temperatures at or above freezing.

Section 2.3 Problems

For problems 1–8, use the specified number of classes to do the following:
(a) Find the class width.
(b) Make a frequency table showing class limits, class boundaries, midpoints, frequencies, relative frequencies, ~~cumulative frequencies.~~
(c) Draw a histogram.
(d) Draw a frequency polygon.
(e) Draw a relative-frequency histogram.
(f) Draw an ogive.

1. Selecting a computer printer? Dot-matrix printers are still very popular. Printing speed is often an important consideration in making a choice. *PC*

Magazine, in the 6th Annual Printer Issue (Vol. 8, No. 19), reported their speed test results of 312 printers of various kinds. A random sample of 44 dot-matrix printers rated for speed showed the following speeds in cps (characters per second):

93	115	46	173	133	124	60	53	99	258	111
100	91	145	195	247	72	86	37	102	128	154
138	141	105	163	138	111	154	136	131	100	150
14	157	111	173	147	89	89	133	150	157	173

Use five classes.

2. Recreational skiing is big business in some of the western and New England states. Many recreational skiers are beyond the beginning level and want intermediate or "more difficult" terrain (but not the most difficult). *Snow Country* described the 35 top-rated ski areas and gave the percentage of the skiing terrain that was at the more difficult level. The percentages follow:

36	54	51	49	30	43	40	46	35	40	52	28
57	51	40	40	45	40	60	20	25	50	40	65
58	43	59	49	55	30	33	60	30	46	65

Use five classes.

3. Tuitions at private colleges and universities vary quite a bit. *The 1990 Almanac* (Houghton-Mifflin Company) lists tuitions at all accredited U.S. senior colleges and universities. A sample of 49 private colleges and universities showed annual tuition (in hundreds) as follows:

69	91	144	93	97	43	38	126	96	93	110
62	77	83	126	94	66	84	68	63	75	119
106	132	141	131	63	78	141	58	113	122	138
62	63	74	39	51	60	45	51	64	87	48
52	73	104	72	88						

Use seven classes.

4. Franchise and Business Opportunities *Annual Report* contains information about franchise opportunities in the United States and Canada. A franchise fee is one of the expenses associated with owning a franchise. There are other expenses, such as startup, advertising, royalties, and so on. A large category of franchises is the fast-food business, which includes franchises such as baked goods, donuts, hamburgers, chicken, and hot-dogs. Franchise fees (in thousands of dollars) for the fast food category are as follows:

21	25	25	18	44	20	25	15	19	24	10
28	30	25	25	25	25	10	25	25	20	20
20	15	10	20	25	25	13	30	15	28	15
15	35	24	40	15	20	35	5	50	30	15

| 25 | 40 | 15 | 25 | 15 | 75 | 33 | 23 | 30 | 10 | 15 |
| 8 | 25 | 10 | 8 | 20 | 25 | 20 | 30 | | | |

Use five classes.

5. Nurses on the eighth floor of Community Hospital believe they need extra staffing at night. To estimate the night workload, a random sample of 35 nights was used. For each night the total number of room calls to the nurses' station on the eighth floor was recorded as follows:

68	70	86	18	90	100	101
95	80	70	73	82	71	37
102	87	46	58	62	63	92
70	69	85	84	86	90	77
60	74	83	86	75	71	88

Use five classes.

6. *The Baseball Encyclopedia*, 9th edition (Macmillan Publishing Co, New York) gives extensive data on baseball. The Player Register section gives statistics on all the players in the major leagues from 1876 to the present. One of the statistics given is the number of years a player has been on a major league team. A sample of 46 players taken from the Player Register (not including pitchers) shows the length of time (in years) that the player has been on a major league team to be as follows:

2	4	18	3	12	3	5	7	19	6	11
16	10	19	3	2	8	3	1	9	1	10
11	4	8	6	12	10	21	15	16	4	11
2	9	6	9	12	13	6	8	6	9	14
4	5									

Use five classes.

7. A random sample of 30 customers at the grand opening of a new clothing store gave the following information about the age of each customer:

43	33	18	23	19	16
51	54	18	26	25	21
17	30	28	27	27	17
32	21	35	40	39	36
48	47	38	41	50	19

Use seven classes.

8. The manager of a large plant wishes to estimate the amount of gasoline that the workers use to commute to and from work each week. A questionnaire was given to a random sample of 40 employees on the payroll. This questionnaire asked the employee to record his or her other gasoline usage to and from work for a designated week. Carpoolers split the total gasoline used by the number of people in the carpool. Here are the data in gallons of gasoline used per week:

10	4	25	15	17	6	8	14
5	20	21	16	3	30	17	14
8	12	24	15	23	18	12	7
9	11	10	17	21	13	18	13
18	14	22	6	12	16	19	26

Use six classes.

9. *Fortune* published statistics on its Fortune 500 companies. Forty-eight of the companies were categorized as food companies (including companies such as RJR Nabisco, Pillsbury, General Mills, Quaker Oats, Tyson Foods, Hershey Foods). For 39 of these companies, profits were given as a percentage of sales (with a negative number indicating a loss). The data follow:

2	8	3	2	7	4	5	1	6	5	7	6	5
6	11	6	2	0	8	3	1	4	2	3	0	2
4	2	-1	2	2	10	-3	6	4	1	0	0	1

Also listed in the Fortune 500 companies of 1989 were 45 electronic companies (including companies such as General Electric, Westinghouse Electronic, Texas Instruments). For 44 of these companies, profit as a percentage of sales was also given. The data follow:

7	7	5	6	-6	4	8	6	1	2	9	5	10	16	12
3	5	1	8	1	7	2	5	5	6	5	2	2	11	-3
2	3	5	6	4	-2	2	1	12	5	3	11	6	12	

(a) Make a frequency table and histogram for the food companies, and then make another frequency table and histogram for the electronic companies. Use five classes for each.

(b) By looking at the two histograms, can we determine which category (food or electronics) has the greatest profits as a percentage of sales? Discuss some of the problems involved in comparing these two distributions.

10. How do football teams stack up weight-wise? Let's look at two teams in the National Football League. *Lindy's Pro Football* guide gave the preseason player statistics for all the NFL teams. For the 70 players with the Miami Dolphins, the weights (in pounds) came in as follows:

242	220	224	200	220	222	222	185	223	192
225	196	208	193	202	232	200	225	226	220
198	185	193	190	190	210	192	240	238	227
235	228	237	264	228	235	221	275	275	289
280	275	280	275	295	290	282	295	290	282
295	277	248	182	175	184	234	190	180	238
240	260	270	275	255	280	265	273	280	249

For the 72 players with the San Diego Chargers, the weights were

213	196	185	119	208	205	203	222	220	214
198	195	180	192	170	200	185	202	198	184
207	223	212	188	206	240	255	242	242	236
246	230	230	230	275	278	280	310	260	280
293	310	295	275	270	275	230	265	305	248
248	165	210	195	188	277	184	300	259	291
237	245	267	271	209	170	285	279	233	195
200	205								

(a) Make frequency tables and histograms for each of the two teams using six classes.

(b) From the histograms, can you tell if either team seems to have the heavier distribution of players' weights? Discuss some of the problems involved in comparing these distributions.

11. The Kentucky Derby has been run annually since 1900 at Churchill Downs, Louisville, Kentucky. The distance is 1¼ miles. Since 1900, all

Figure 2–32 Seconds Over 2 Minutes for the Winning Times of the Kentucky Derby

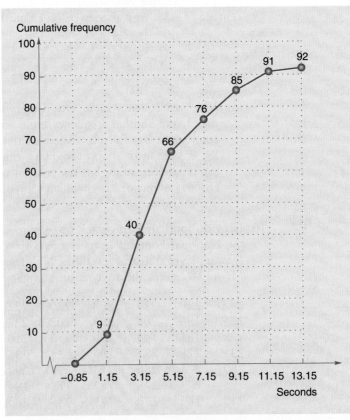

the winning times have been over 2 minutes, except for the record time of 1 minute and 59.2 seconds run by Secretariat in 1973. The ogive in Figure 2–32 shows the *seconds over 2 minutes* for the winning times. A winning time of 2 minutes and 8.4 seconds has a data entry of 8.4 seconds. Secretariat's record time of 1 minute and 59.2 seconds is a data entry of −0.8 second, since the time is *below* 2 minutes.

(a) Use Figure 2–32 to estimate the number of winning times less than 7.15 seconds (over 2 minutes). There are 92 data values represented. What percentage of the winning times are under 2 minutes and 7.15 seconds?

(b) Use Figure 2–32 to estimate the number of winning times *between* 5.15 and 11.15 seconds (over 2 minutes). What percentage of the winning times are between 2 minutes and 5.15 seconds and 2 minutes and 11.15 seconds?

12. Hospital costs vary from state to state. The Health Insurance Association of America *Source Book of Health Insurance Data* gave information about the average cost per day per patient in hospitals by state, including the District of Columbia. Figure 2–33 shows a histogram of these data.

(a) Use the information given in the histogram to construct an ogive.

Figure 2–33 Average Cost per Day for Hospital Stay in Each State (Including the District of Columbia)

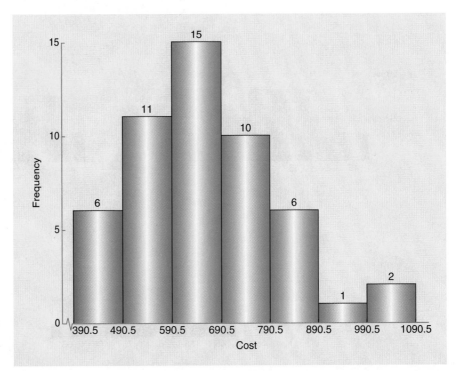

(b) How many states (including the District of Columbia) have average costs per day less than $690.50?

13. Professor Silva teaches anatomy and physiology. He has developed five different versions of a test on the same material. On giving each version to a different sample of 60 students, he discovered that the test score distributions looked like those shown in Figure 2–34.
    (a) Categorize the distribution shapes as uniform, symmetric, bimodal, skewed left, or skewed right.
    (b) Comment on some advantages or problems with each test version. As a student, which version might you prefer? Which version would you like the least?

Figure 2–34 Test Score Distributions

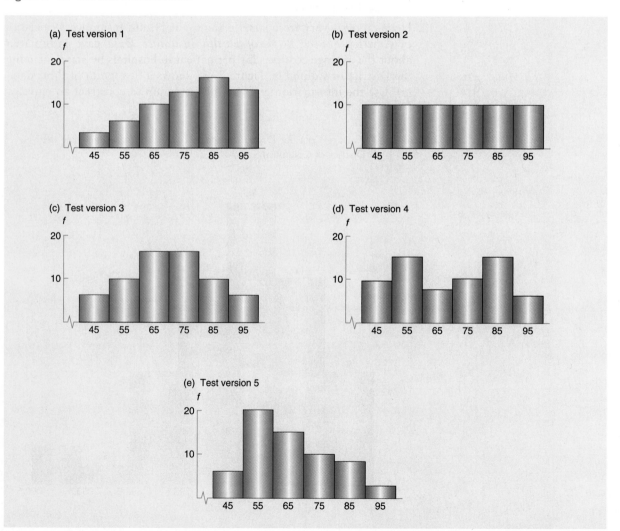

14. Many products come with owner registration or warranty cards. Usually the consumer is asked a few questions about his or her family and household income. Random samples of warranty or registration cards for the indicated product showed the household income distribution shown in Figure 2–35.
    (a) Categorize the distribution shapes as uniform, symmetric, bimodal, skewed left, or skewed right.
    (b) If you were in charge of advertising, how would you use income distribution information of present customers to target ads for the indicated product?
    (c) How valid do you think income information is on warranty cards?

Figure 2–35 Annual Household Income Shown on Product Warranty Card (in thousands of dollars)

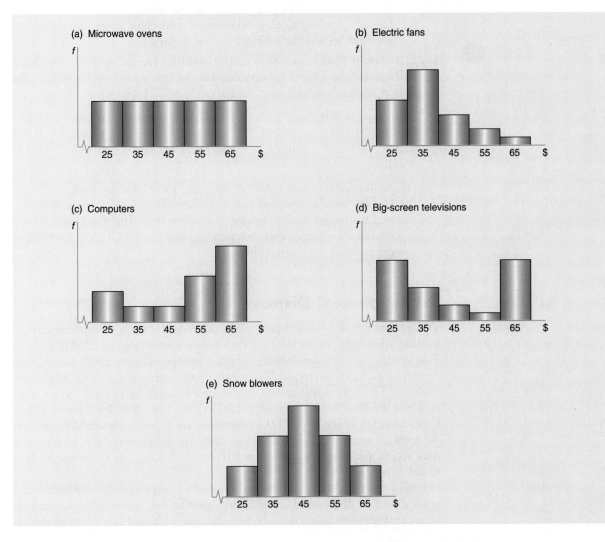

15. One minor but essential expense following a trip is the cost of developing film. Gary just returned from a trip to the South Seas and has 50 rolls of 35-mm film (36 slides each). He checks around town to find the price for developing the film and also explores mail order outlets. His findings for the price to develop one roll of film and mount the slides follow (data are given in dollars):

3.62	4.28	2.95	5.73	6.22	5.93	6.27	5.48
4.73	3.92	4.73	5.13	5.29	4.98	5.39	6.18
4.73	4.22	6.65	7.25	2.79	3.72	6.89	6.35
2.59	5.48	3.98	4.92	5.72			

(a) Multiply each data value by 100 to "clear" the decimals.
(b) Use the standard procedures of this section to make a frequency table and histogram with your whole-number data. Use six classes.
(c) Divide class limits, class boundaries, and class midpoints by 100 to get back to your original values (in dollars).

16. Elias Sports Bureau compiles season statistics for the major league base-ball teams. The 1989 final statistics for the Baltimore Orioles showed the season batting averages, as follows:

0.207	0.000	0.277	0.167	0.266	0.249	0.217
0.111	0.278	0.245	0.273	0.241	0.268	0.278
0.285	0.209	0.247	0.176	0.239	0.257	0.243
0.258						

(a) Multiply each data value by 1000 to "clear" the decimals.
(b) Use the standard procedures of this section to make a frequency table and histogram with your whole-number data. Use five classes.
(c) Divide class limits, class boundaries, and class midpoints by 1000 to get back to your original values.

Section 2.4

Exploratory Data Analysis

Stem-and-Leaf Displays

The stem-and-leaf display is just one of many useful ways of studying data in a field called *exploratory data analysis* (often abbreviated as EDA). John W. Tukey wrote one of the definitive books on the subject, *Exploratory Data Analysis* (Addison-Wesley, 1977). Another very useful reference for EDA techniques is the book, *Applications, Basics, and Computing of Exploratory Data Analysis,* by Paul F. Velleman and David C. Hoaglin (Duxbury Press, 1981). Exploratory data analysis (EDA) techniques are particularly useful for detecting patterns and extreme data values. They are designed to help us explore a data set, to ask questions we had not thought of before, or to pursue leads in many directions.

EDA techniques are similar to those of an explorer. An explorer has a general idea of destination but is always alert to the unexpected. An explorer needs to assess situations quickly and often simplify and clarify them. An explorer makes pictures—that is, maps showing the relationships of landscape features. The aspects of rapid implementation, visual displays such as graphs and charts, data simplification, and robustness (that is, analysis that is not influenced much by extreme data values) are key ingredients of EDA techniques. In addition, these techniques are good for exploration because they require very few prior assumptions about the data.

EDA methods are especially useful when our data have been gathered for general interest and observation of subjects. For example, we may have data regarding the age of applicants to graduate programs. We don't have a specific question in mind. We want to see what the data reveal. Are the ages fairly uniform or spread out? Are there exceptionally young or old applicants? If there are, we might look at other characteristics of these applicants, such as field of study. EDA methods help us quickly absorb some aspects of the data and then may lead us to ask specific questions for which we might apply methods of traditional statistics.

In contrast, when we design an experiment to produce data to answer a specific question, we focus on particular aspects of the data that are useful to us. If we want to determine the average highway gas mileage of a specific sports car, we use that model car in well-designed tests. We don't need to worry about unexpected road conditions, poorly trained drivers, different fuel grades, sudden stops and starts, etc. Our experiment is designed to control outside factors. Consequently, we do not need to "explore" our data as much. We can often make valid assumptions about the data. Methods of traditional statistics will be very useful to analyze such data and answer our specific questions.

Stem-and-Leaf Display

In this text we will introduce two of the EDA techniques: stem-and-leaf displays and, in Section 3.4, box-and-whisker plots. Let's first look at a stem-and-leaf display. We know that frequency distributions and histograms provide a useful organization and summary of data. However, in a histogram, we lose most of the specific data values. A stem-and-leaf display is a device that organizes and groups data but allows us to see as many of the digits in each data value as we wish. In the next example we will make a stem-and-leaf display.

Example 6

Many airline passengers seem weighted down with their carry-on luggage. Just how much weight are they carrying? The carry-on luggage weights for a random sample of 40 passengers returning from a vacation to Hawaii were recorded in pounds (see Table 2–19).

Table 2–19 Weights of Carry-On Luggage in Pounds

30	27	12	42	35	47	38	36	27	35
22	17	29	3	21	0	38	32	41	33
26	45	18	43	18	32	31	32	19	21
33	31	28	29	51	12	32	18	21	26

Figure 2–36 Weight of Carry-On Luggage

Stem	Leaves
0	3 0
1	2 7 8 8 9 2 8
2	7 7 2 9 1 6 1 8 9 1 6
3	0 5 8 6 5 8 2 3 2 1 2 3 1 2
4	2 7 1 5 3
5	1

To make a stem-and-leaf display, we break the digits of each data value into *two* parts. The left group of digits is called a *stem,* and the remaining group of digits on the right is called a *leaf.* We are free to choose the number of digits to be included in the stem.

The weights in our example consist of two-digit numbers. For a two-digit number, the stem selection is obviously the left digit. In our case, the tens digits will form the stems, and the units digits will form the leaves. For example, for the weight 12, the stem is 1, and the leaf is 2. For the weight 18, the stem is again 1, but the leaf is 8. In the stem-and-leaf display, we list each possible stem once on the left and all its leaves in the same row on the right.

Figure 2–36 shows a stem-and-leaf display for the weights of carry-on luggage. From the stem-and-leaf display in Figure 2–36, we see that two bags weighed 27 lb, one weighed 3 lb, one weighed 51 lb, and so on. We see that most of the weights were in the 30-lb range, only two were less than 10 lb, and six were over 40 lb. Note that the length of the leaves gives the visual impression that a sideways histogram would present.

Figure 2–37 Stem-and-Leaf Display of Carry-On Luggage Weights

leaf unit = 1 lb

3 | 2   represents 32

Stem	Leaves
0	3 0
1	2 7 8 8 9 2 8
2	7 7 2 9 1 6 1 8 9 1 6
3	0 5 8 6 5 8 2 3 2 1 2 3 1 2
4	2 7 1 5 3
5	1

As a final step, we need to indicate the scale. This is usually done by indicating the unit value of a leaf. In this case the unit value is 1 lb. Figure 2–37 includes the scale used in the stem-and-leaf display of the carry-on luggage weights presented in Figure 2–36.

Figure 2–37 shows a basic stem-and-leaf display. Sometimes you will see the leaves ordered from smallest to largest, but this is not necessary in a basic display. There are no firm rules for selecting the group of digits for the stem. But whichever group you select, you must list all the possible stems from smallest to largest in the data collection.

Sometimes we may want to spread the data even more. In such cases we can use two or more lines for each stem. For instance, we could put leaves 0 through 4 on one line and 5 through 9 on the next line, as shown in Figure 2–38. The asterisk indicates possible digits 0–4 for the leaves, and the raised dot indicates possible digits 5–9.

In this stem-and-leaf display, we see that the weight interval with the most data is between 30 and 34 lb. Depending on the data, each stem can be listed several times with various symbols designating the leaf range for the stem line.

Decimal points are usually omitted in the stems and leaves, but indicated in the unit designation as appropriate.

Figure 2–38 Multiple Lines per Stem for Carry-On
Luggage Weights

```
leaf unit = 1 lb

  3  |  2  represents 32

 0*  |  3   0

 0·  |

 1*  |  2   2

 1·  |  7   8   8   8   9

 2*  |  2   1   1   1

 2·  |  7   7   9   6   8   9   6

 3*  |  0   2   3   2   1   2   3   1   2

 3·  |  5   8   6   5   8

 4*  |  2   1   3

 4·  |  7   5

 5*  |  1
```

Tel-a-Message is experimenting with computer-delivered telephone advertisements. Of primary concern is how much of the 4-minute advertisement is heard. A study was done to see how long the advertisement ran before the listeners hung up. A random sample of 30 calls gave the information in Table 2–20.

Table 2–20 Time Spent Listening to Advertisement (in Minutes)

1.3	0.7	2.1	0.5	0.2	0.9	1.1	3.2
4.0	3.8	1.4	3.1	2.5	0.6	0.5	2.1
4.0	4.0	0.3	1.2	1.0	1.5	0.4	4.0
2.3	2.7	4.0	0.7	0.5	4.0		

(a) We'll make a stem-and-leaf display using the first digit as the stem and the second as a leaf. What is the leaf unit?

(a) The trailing digit is in the tenths position so

$$1 \text{ unit} = 0.1 \text{ min}$$

(b) List all the stem values.

(b) Stems: 0
1
2
3
4

(c) Complete the stem-and-leaf display including the unit designation. (*Note:* Order of leaves is not important and will depend on whether you read across rows or down columns. We read across the rows for the answer.)

(c) See Figure 2–39.

Figure 2–39 Time Before Hang-Up

leaf unit = 0.1 min

1 | 3 represents 1.3 min

0	7 5 2 9 6 5 3 4 7 5
1	3 1 4 2 0 5
2	1 5 1 3 7
3	2 8 1
4	0 0 0 0 0 0

(d) Looking at the stem-and-leaf display, what could you say about the time intervals before people hung up?

(d) Most people hung up before the end of the advertisement. Of those people, more hung up within the first minute than within any other 1-minute interval. There were people who listened to the entire advertisement.

In the example that follows, we show a stem-and-leaf display for data with three digits.

Example 7 What does it take to win at sports? If you're talking about basketball, one sports writer gave the answer. He listed the winning scores of the conference championship games over the last 35 years. The scores for those games follow below. To make a stem-and-leaf display, we'll use the first *two* digits as the stems (see Figure 2–40).

132	118	124	109	104	101
125	83	99	131	98	125
97	106	112	92	120	103
111	117	135	143	112	112
116	106	117	119	110	105
128	112	126	105	102	

Figure 2–40 Winning Scores of Conference Basketball Championship Games

leaf unit = 1 point

  08 | 3 represents 083 or 83

08	3
09	2 8 7 9
10	6 1 3 6 9 5 4 2 5
11	8 2 7 9 2 1 0 2 6 7 2
12	8 5 0 5 4 6
13	2 5 1
14	3

- *Comment:* Stem-and-leaf displays organize the data, let the data analyst spot extreme values, and are easy to create. In fact, they can be used to organize data so that frequency tables are easier to make. However, at this time, histograms are used more frequently in formal data presentations, whereas stem-and-leaf displays are used by data analysts to gain initial insights about the data.

Section 2.4 Problems

1. More and more people take fitness walks before or after work or during the lunch hour. They want comfortable walking shoes. *Consumer Reports* (February 1990) rated 25 walking shoes in both men's and women's styles. The prices for comfortable walking shoes follow (in dollars):

59	109	70	76	55
50	55	69	58	59
40	46	62	52	55
65	70	60	110	78
60	65	69	58	60

Make a stem-and-leaf display. Be sure to indicate the scale. How are the prices distributed? Is the distribution skewed? Are there any gaps?

2. Wetlands offer a diversity of benefits. They provide habitat for wildlife, spawning grounds for U.S. commercial fish, and renewable timber resources. In the last 200 years the United States has lost more than half its wetlands. *Environmental Almanac, 1993* gives the percentage of wetlands lost in each state in the last 200 years. For the lower 48 states, the percentage loss of wetlands per state is as follows:

46	52	46	72	85	42	59	50	49
87	91	90	46	87	50	89	49	67
27	23	60	81	20	73	59	35	50
35	38	42	38	56	39	74	56	31
48	36	27	54	52	30	33	28	35
37	24	9						

Make a basic stem-and-leaf display of these data. Be sure to indicate the scale. How are the percentages distributed? Is the distribution skewed? Are there any gaps?

3. Computer Services Incorporated offers customers a Computer Store option. Using a computer terminal and telephone modem, the customer contacts the service and can scan the catalogue and make orders from his or her own computer terminal. To use the service, the customer must pay a per-minute charge for the time connected. Last month a random sample of 60 customers using the Computer Store option had connect times as follows (in minutes):

5	20	7	30	18	10	12	15	65	25
8	3	17	15	21	27	15	25	42	37
51	12	14	5	10	8	21	19	16	31
30	57	61	12	22	26	24	18	17	43
62	47	16	19	20	37	40	58	61	19
18	61	12	72	17	26	31	29	33	15

Make a stem-and-leaf display of the connect times. Be sure to indicate the scale. How are the times distributed? Is the distribution skewed or more or less symmetrical? Are there any gaps?

4. Eastshore Community College requires all its students to take a basic math skills test before beginning any degree or certificate program. The scores range from 0 to 100. For 70 students interested in the associate of management degree the scores were as follows:

22	60	80	75	87	92	65	46	33	95
72	98	100	37	58	75	86	92	77	85
86	97	83	81	87	42	91	89	87	84
72	86	63	42	26	97	93	98	72	82
85	79	84	75	83	92	89	63	86	68
80	97	81	87	72	89	87	73	65	52
76	86	91	53	67	67	69	72	92	81

Make a stem-and-leaf display of the scores. If 70 is the minimal passing score, how many passed?

5. Making sure that patients get the prescribed medication in the correct dosage is an important task of the nurses at Memorial Community Hospital. A survey involving 50 patients was done at the hospital. The number of pills each patient was given per day was recorded as follows:

13	8	12	5	4	2	7	1	15	9
8	9	1	7	6	10	4	7	12	3
15	5	8	7	12	6	4	11	2	9
6	8	9	3	15	2	12	4	8	12
10	9	12	14	3	9	12	10	8	11

Make a stem-and-leaf display using two lines per stem. Be sure to indicate the scale. Comment on the distribution of pills. Is it skewed? symmetrical? Are there any gaps?

6. Management Efficiency Consultants are called on to help companies become more efficient in their operations. One of the first studies they conduct is to determine the amount of time executives spend in meetings. For one company the data for 25 executives were as follows (in hours per week):

12	9	6	7	15
18	26	13	21	10
5	7	24	12	2
17	3	8	9	10
11	10	6	25	19

Make a stem-and-leaf display using two lines per stem. Be sure to indicate the scale. Comment on the distribution.

7. The Boston Marathon is the oldest and best known U.S. marathon. It covers a route from Hopkinton, Massachusetts, to downtown Boston. The distance is approximately 26 miles. *The Universal Almanac, 1993* gives the winning times for the Boston Marathon. They are all over 2 hours. The following data are the minutes over 2 hours for the winning male runner.

Years 1953–1972

18	20	18	14	20	25	22	20	23	23
18	19	16	17	15	22	13	10	18	15

Years 1973–1992

16	13	9	20	14	10	9	12	9	8
9	10	14	7	11	8	9	8	11	8

(a) Make a stem-and-leaf diagram for the minutes over 2 hours of the winning times for the years 1953 to 1972. Use two lines per stem.

(b) Make a stem-and-leaf diagram for the minutes over 2 hours of the winning times for the years 1973 to 1992. Use two lines per stem.

(c) Compare the two distributions. How many times under 15 minutes are in each distribution?

8. The 1992 U.S. Open Golf Tournament was played at Pebble Beach, California, with a $1,525,000 purse. Par for the course is 72. The tournament consists of four rounds played on different days. The scores for each round of the 32 players who placed in the money are given in the *1993 Golf Almanac*. The scores for the first round were as follows:

71	73	70	71	70	70	73	72	74	69	74
72	66	74	72	70	72	68	74	77	74	70
71	71	70	73	76	73	73	74	77	67	

The scores for the fourth round for these players were as follows:

72	71	70	71	77	73	74	74	75	77	78
79	81	76	75	74	74	77	73	76	70	74
79	73	74	76	77	75	75	73	76	74	

(a) Make a stem-and-leaf diagram for the first-round scores. Use two lines per stem.

(b) Make a stem-and-leaf diagram for the fourth-round scores. Use two lines per stem.

(c) Compare the two distributions. How do the highest scores compare? How do the lowest scores compare?

9. Information in the *Environmental Almanac, 1993* gives the per capital energy use by state in millions of British thermal units (Btus). Rounded to the nearest 10 million Btus, the data by state are as follows:

Alaska	990	N.H.	220	La.	780
N. Dak.	470	Wyo.	790	Kans.	420
Tex.	570	Ind.	450	Ala.	390
W. Va.	420	Okla.	400	Miss.	360
Mont.	420	Ky.	380	Del.	350
Wash.	390	Tenn.	350	Nev.	340
Idaho	350	N. Mex.	350	S.C.	330
Ohio	350	Iowa	330	Oreg.	320
Nebr.	330	Ga.	320	Ill.	310

Ark.	330	Maine	310	Pa.	300
Utah	320	Minn.	310	N.J.	300
Va.	310	Mich.	300	S. Da.	280
N.C.	300	Wis.	290	Ariz.	260
Mo.	300	Md.	270	Fla.	240
Colo.	270	Hawaii	240	Mass.	230
Calif.	250	Vt.	230	N.Y.	200
Conn.	230	R.I.	220		

Make a stem-and-leaf display. Consider using the first digit as the stem and the next one as the leaf. It is permissible to simply omit the last digit if the scale on the diagram reflects the actual size of the numbers. Are there any unusual values?

10. The Commerce Department maintains statistics on per capita income state by state. For 1988 and for 1991, the per capita income (rounded to the nearest hundred dollars) by state follows:

State	1988	1991	State	1988	1991
Ala.	$12,900	$15,600	Mont.	$12,900	$16,000
Alaska	19,100	21,900	Nebr.	14,800	17,900
Ariz.	15,000	16,400	Nev.	17,500	19,200
Ark.	12,200	14,800	N.H.	19,400	21,000
Calif.	18,900	21,000	N.J.	22,000	25,400
Colo.	16,500	19,400	N. Mex.	12,500	14,800
Conn.	23,100	25,900	N.Y.	19,300	22,500
Del.	17,700	20,300	N.C.	14,300	16,600
Fla.	16,600	18,900	N. Dak.	12,800	16,100
Ga.	15,300	17,400	Ohio	15,500	17,900
Hawaii	16,800	21,300	Okla.	12,300	15,800
Idaho	12,700	15,400	Oreg.	14,900	17,600
Ill.	17,600	20,800	Pa.	16,200	19,100
Ind.	14,700	17,500	R.I.	16,900	18,800
Iowa	14,700	17,500	S.C.	12,900	15,400
Kans.	15,800	18,500	S. Dak.	12,800	16,400
Ky.	12,800	15,500	Tenn.	13,900	16,300
La.	12,300	15,100	Tex.	14,600	17,300
Maine	15,100	15,100	Utah	12,200	14,500
Md.	19,500	22,100	Vt.	15,300	17,700
Mass.	20,800	22,900	Va.	17,700	20,000
Mich.	16,600	18,700	Wash.	16,500	19,400
Minn.	16,700	19,100	W. Va.	12,700	14,200
Miss.	11,100	13,300	Wis.	15,500	18,000
Mo.	15,500	17,800	Wyo.	13,600	17,100

(a) Make a stem-and-leaf display of the 1988 per capita incomes. Consider using the first two digits as the stem and the next one as the leaf.

It is permissible to simply omit the last two digits if the scale on the diagram reflects the actual size of the numbers.

(b) Make a stem-and-leaf display of the 1991 per capita incomes. Use the same convention you followed in part a.

(c) Compare the distributions of per capita income for 1988 and 1991. Are they similarly shaped? Is the 1991 distribution shifted toward the higher incomes? Compare the low and high values of each distribution. Are there any unusual data in either distribution? Did they come from the same states in 1991 and 1988?

Summary

When a sample is taken, we must be careful to use a method of selection that will give us a sample that represents the entire population from which the sample is drawn. A random sample is taken in such a way that each member of the population has equal chance of being included in the sample, and each sample of the same size as our sample has equal chance to be drawn. The use of a random sample is essential in our later work in inferential statistics. However, other sampling techniques such as stratified sampling, systematic sampling, cluster sampling, and convenience sampling are also widely used.

Organizing and presenting data are the main purposes of that part of statistics called descriptive statistics. In this chapter we have studied tables, bar graphs, Pareto charts, pictograms, circle graphs, time plots, histograms, relative-frequency histograms, frequency polygons, ogives, and stem-and-leaf displays. From the viewpoint of future applications, histograms are the most important because the area under a bar can represent the likelihood of data values falling in that class. Histograms reveal distribution properties such as uniformity, symmetry, or skewness.

Important Words and Symbols

	Section		Section
Random sample	2.1	Pie chart or circle graph	2.2
Random number table	2.1	Frequency	2.3
Simulation	2.1	Frequency distribution	2.3
Stratified sample	2.1	Relative-frequency	
Systematic sample	2.1	distribution	2.3
Cluster sample	2.1	Class width	2.3
Convenience sample	2.1	Class, lower limit, upper	
Table	2.2	limit	2.3
Bar graph	2.2	Class mark	2.3
Pareto chart	2.2	Class midpoint	2.3
Pictograph	2.2	Histogram	2.3
Time series	2.2	Frequency polygon	2.3
Time plot	2.2	Cumulative frequency	2.3

	Section		Section
Ogive	2.3	Bimodal distribution	2.3
Uniform distribution	2.3	EDA	2.4
Symmetric distribution	2.3	Stem	2.4
Skewed left	2.3	Leaf	2.4
Skewed right	2.3	Stem-and-leaf display	2.4

Chapter Review Problems

1. At the beginning of Chapter 2 there is a Focus Problem asking you to categorize a number of graphs according to type and to comment on the nature of the sample. Using the tools and skills you learned in Chapter 2, complete the Focus Problem (on page 23).

2. The following time plot (Figure 2–41) appears in the book *Earth in Balance: Ecology and the Human Spirit*, by Al Gore. The time plot gives the carbon dioxide (CO_2) concentration in the atmosphere. The time plot is based on data gathered at the Mauna Loa Observation Station in Hawaii.

   (a) Estimate the range of CO_2 concentration for 1970.
   (b) Estimate the range of CO_2 concentration for 1988.

Figure 2–41 Concentration of CO_2*

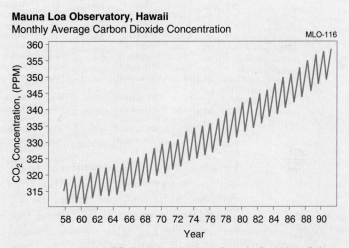

The concentration of CO_2 in the atmosphere from April 1958 until June 1991. In summer, the line goes down as vegetation in the Northern Hemisphere (with most of the earth's land area) breathes in vast quantities of CO_2. In winter, when the leaves have fallen, the line climbs again. The peak concentration has grown steadily higher because of such human activities as the burning of fossil fuels and the destruction of forests.

*Source: American Geophysical Union.

(c) Estimate the change in the highest levels of CO_2 concentration from 1970 to 1988.

3. The U.S. Office of Management and Budget gave the fiscal year 1991 budget outlay estimate to be $1,233.3 billion. Where will the money come from, and where will it go? The estimates follow: 43% from individual income taxes, 34% from social insurance receipts, 11% from corporate income taxes, 5% from borrowing, 3% from excise taxes, and 4% from other sources. As the budget is spent, 43% will go to direct benefit payments to individuals, 25% to national defense, 14% to net interest, 12% to grants to states, 6% for other federal operations.

(a) Make separate income circle graphs for both income source and income outlay.

(b) Estimate the amount of money the government is planning to borrow in fiscal year 1991.

(c) Estimate the amount of net interest the government is expected to pay in fiscal year 1991.

4. Driving under the influence of alcohol (DUI) is a serious offence. The following data give the ages of a random sample of 50 drivers arrested while driving under the influence of alcohol. This distribution is based on the age distribution of DUI arrests given in the *Statistical Abstract of the United States* (112th ed).

46	16	41	26	22	33	30	22	36	34
63	21	26	18	27	24	31	38	26	55
31	47	27	43	35	22	64	40	58	20
49	37	53	25	29	32	23	49	39	40
24	56	30	51	21	45	27	34	47	35

(a) Make a stem-and-leaf display of the age distribution.

(b) Make a frequency table using seven classes.

(c) Make a histogram showing class boundaries.

(d) Make an ogive. From the ogive, estimate the percentage of drivers who are age 29 or under and arrested while DUI.

5. How much do workers earn? The following data are based on information taken from *USA Today* (May 26, 1992). In the table, x represents earnings in thousands of dollars for workers 15 years of age and older. The relative frequency is the relative frequency of workers receiving these earnings. The first table is for males and the second is for females.

Males			
x	$12.5	$37.5	$62.5	$87.5
Relative Frequency	0.56	0.32	0.08	0.04

	Females			
x	$12.5	$37.5	$62.5	$87.5
Relative Frequency	0.81	0.16	0.02	0.01

Note: Earnings above $87.5 thousand are included in the $87.5 category.

(a) Make a relative-frequency histogram for males and one for females. Use the given incomes as class midpoints.

(b) Compare the distributions. Are the distributions skewed? Which is more skewed?

(c) The class boundaries fall halfway between the midpoints. Use this information to find the class boundaries. Use the fact that the classes all have the same width to find the left boundary of the first class and the right boundary of the last class.

(d) Make an ogive of relative frequencies for each of the distributions. About what percentage of males earns less than $25 thousand? About what percentage of females earns less than $25 thousand?

6. Many people say the civil-justice system is overburdened. Many cases center on suits involving businesses. The following data are based on a report appearing in the *Wall Street Journal* (December 3, 1993). Researchers conducted a study of lawsuits involving 1908 businesses ranked in the Fortune 1000 from 1971 to 1991. They found the following distribution of civil-justice case loads brought before the federal courts involving the businesses:

Case Type	Number of Filings (in thousands)
Contracts	107
General torts (personal injury)	191
Asbestos liability	49
Other product liability	38
All other	21

Note: Contracts involve disputes over contracts between business.

(a) Make a Pareto chart of the case loads. Which types of cases occur most frequently?

(b) Make a circle chart showing the percentage of cases in each type.

7. Based on information from the U.S. Bureau of the Census, *Current Population Survey* (May 1991), the percentage of the population in the United States having completed the indicated education level since 1940 is as follows:

Year	4 Years High School or More	4 Years College or More
1940	24.5	4.6
1950	34.3	5.2
1959	43.7	8.1
1970	55.2	11.0
1980	68.6	17.0
1987	75.6	19.9
1989	76.9	22.1
1991	78.4	21.4

Note: The percentage completing 4 years of high school or more includes those students who continued to college and completed 4 or more years of college.

(a) Make a time plot for percentage completing 4 or more years of high school and a time plot for percentage completing 4 or more years of college. Be sure to indicate the differing time intervals on your time plot. Use the same vertical scale.

(b) How do the two plots compare? Is one upward trend steeper than the other?

8. The following relative-frequency histogram is based on information from

Figure 2–42 High School Grade Point Average of Students Who Graduated from College in 1986

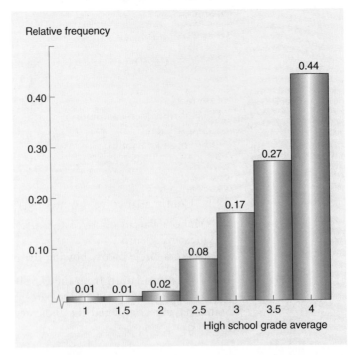

Statistical Abstract of the United States (112th ed.). In Figure 2–42, x = high school grade point average for a person who has received a bachelor's degree in 1986. We use a 4-point scale for grading, so A = 4, B+ = 3.5, B = 3, C+ = 2.5, C = 2, D+ = 1.5, and D = 1. The vertical axis gives the relative frequency for the high school grade point average of students who graduated from college in 1986.

(a) Comment on the shape of the distribution. Is it skewed? Is it symmetrical? Is it uniform?

(b) The class boundaries are halfway between the class midpoints. Find the class boundaries. *Hint:* Use the fact that the classes are all the same width to find the lower boundary of the first class and the upper boundary of the last class.

(c) Convert the relative frequencies into percentages. Then find the percentage of 1986 college graduates who had high school grade point averages of less than 3.25 (low B). What percentage had high school grade point averages of less than 3.75 (high B)?

9. The following data are based on information from *Statistical Abstract of the United States* (112th ed.). In Figure 2–43, the horizontal axis represents the age of hospital patients (from 5 years of age on). The vertical axis gives the relative frequencies.

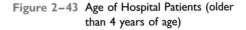

(a) Which age group is the most frequent?

Figure 2–43 Age of Hospital Patients (older than 4 years of age)

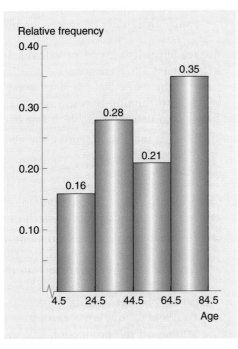

(b) Convert the relative frequencies into percentages. Then find the percentage of patients older than age 44. What percentage of patients is 44 years old or younger?

10. As a project for her statistics class, Laura was supposed to take a random sample of 30 cars in the student parking lot and determine the make and year of each car.

(a) Describe how Laura could use a random-number table to get a random sample of 30 cars in the parking lot. Suppose the lot is full and there are 950 parking places.

(b) After getting her random sample, Laura found that eight cars were Chevrolets, seven were Fords, five were Pontiacs, three were Toyotas, three were Chryslers, three were Oldsmobiles, and one was a Cadillac. Make a table for these data, and draw a bar graph. Draw a circle graph showing percentages of the total number of cars sampled.

(c) The model years for each of the 30 cars are shown here:

90	93	86	89	80	86	90	91	83	86
77	86	94	81	83	84	84	91	87	82
87	88	78	89	70	90	82	95	89	87

Make a frequency table, histogram, and frequency polygon for these data (use five classes). Describe the shape of the histogram.

(d) Consider the data types: nominal, ordinal, interval, or ratio. In part b, what type of data do we have? Could you make a histogram for these data? In part c, what type of data do we have? Could you organize these data in a circle graph?

11. At each Super Bowl, a Most Valuable Player award is given (in Super Bowl XII, two awards were given). According to the National Football League records, the MVP awards have gone to these positions: 14 to quarterbacks, 5 to running backs, 3 to wide receivers, 2 to defensive ends, and 1 each to a defensive tackle, a line backer, and a safety.

(a) Make a table representing the above information.
(b) Make a bar graph.
(c) Make a pictogram.

12. Categorize the type (simple random, stratified, systematic, cluster, or convenience) of sampling used in each of the following situations.

(a) To conduct a preelection opinion poll on the latest school bond election, samples of five households from each telephone prefix (first three digits of the phone numbers) in the voting district were called.

(b) To conduct a study on depression among the elderly, a sample of 30 patients in one nursing home was used.

(c) To maintain quality control in a brewery, every 20th bottle of beer coming off the production line was opened and tested.

(d) Subscribers to the magazine *Sound Alive* were assigned numbers. Then a sample of 30 subscribers was selected by using a random number table. The subscribers in the sample were invited to rate new compact disk players for a "What the Subscribers Think" column.

(e) To judge the appeal of a proposed television sitcom, a random sample of 10 people from each of three different age categories was selected and those chosen were asked to rate a pilot show.

13. *Forbes* (the eighth annual Forbes 400, October 1989) published an extensive report about the wealthiest people in the United States. Do you have to be old to be a billionaire? You can answer this question yourself by studying the following data. Ages of the billionaires profiled in *Forbes* are (in years) as follows:

75	59	66	65	46	60	61	66	59	67
63	65	93	60	52	77	58	57	71	45
44	41	50	50	43	58	53	49	80	70
71	64	58	51	58	54	50	90	41	46
80	81	73	63	66	73	72	43	46	33
49	76	61	33	53	64	55	73	74	83
76	44	70	59	66					

(a) Make a stem-and-leaf diagram.

(b) Make a histogram using seven classes. Describe the shape of the distribution (i.e., indicate if it is symmetrical, skewed, or bimodal.)

(c) Make an ogive. Estimate the percentage of billionaires age 50 or under.

DATA HIGHLIGHTS

1. Examine Figure 2–44, Bypassing Long Hours (*USA Today,* September 10, 1993). What is the name of this type of graph? The source, National Automobile Dealers Association, indicates that the graph might be constructed from population data. Comment on possible differences between sample data and population data. Do you think there might be a difference between rural areas with few dealerships and urban areas with many? There is an editorial comment in the upper left-hand corner about 75% of profit coming from repairs. How might this comment influence people's opinion as they read the graph? In a large county with 40 car dealerships, how many would you expect *not* to be open for repairs during weekend or evening hours?

2. Examine Figure 2–45, Complaint Business Growing (*USA Today,* September 15, 1993). Give a detailed explanation of why this is a combination of bar graph and Pareto chart. Is it a pictogram? Why or why not? In Section 1.1 we discussed the dangers of a voluntary response sample. How can such a sample be biased? Do you think people writing to the Better

Figure 2–44 Bypassing Long Hours*

USA SNAPSHOTS®   9/10/93

A look at statistics that shape your finances

Bypassing long hours

Although 75% of U.S. car dealers' profits come from repairs and parts sales, half of dealerships' service departments aren't open nights or weekends.

30% Weekend hours

Evening hours — **11.2%**

Both — **8.6%**

50.2% Neither

Source: National Automobile Dealers Association   By Cliff Vancura, USA TODAY

Figure 2–45 Complaint Business Growing*

USA SNAPSHOTS®   9/15/93

A look at statistics that shape the nation

Complaint business growing

Types of companies with the largest increase in complaints from 1991 to 1992 to the Better Business Bureau:

Percentage increase:

Hotels, motels, resorts — 132%

Mortgage/ escrow companies — 117%

Telemarketing, TV marketing — 116%

Mail magazine subscriptions — 76%

Computer sales/ service — 58%

Note: Categories with minimum of 1,000 complaints

Source: Better Business Bureau

By Chris Fruitrich and Cliff Vancura, USA TODAY

*Source: Copyright 1993, USA TODAY. Reprinted with permission.

Business Bureau to complain might constitute a voluntary response sample? Nevertheless, this graph only deals with *growth* in complaints. With this in mind, explain how the graph is probably an accurate representation of the growing public dissatisfaction with the given service industries.

3. Examine Figure 2–46, NYSE Volume (*Wall Street Journal*, September 10, 1993). This graph reports volume of sales from the New York Stock Exchange. Explain how this can be thought of as a bar graph. The market was closed on Good Friday (April), on Memorial Day (May), and on the Fourth of July, so there are some gaps in the graph. If we ignore these gaps, could the graph be thought of as a histogram? Explain.

4. Examine Figure 2–47, The Dow Jones Averages (*Wall Street Journal*, September 10, 1993). Explain why this could be considered a time plot. What is being plotted are intervals. The upper end is the high, the interior point is the close, and the bottom end is the low each day. So, in effect, we are looking at a time plot of (daily) range as well as closing. If you were a trader on the floor of the exchange, a broker in Miami, or just an individual who bought and sold stocks, how could this graph be useful to you? How could the table insert, which is a breakdown of the 30 industrials, be useful? Explain.

Figure 2–46 NYSE Volume (September 10, 1993)*

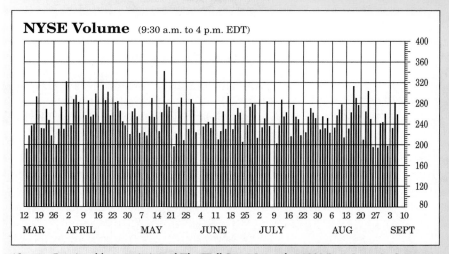

*Source: Reprinted by permission of *The Wall Street Journal*, ©1993 Dow Jones & Company, Inc. All Rights Reserved Worldwide.

Figure 2–47 The Dow Jones Averages (September 10, 1993)*

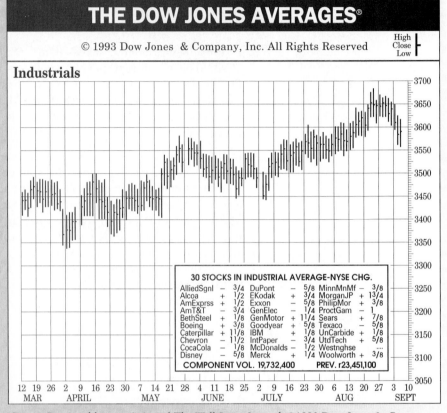

*Source: Reprinted by permission of *The Wall Street Journal*, ©1993 Dow Jones & Company, Inc. All Rights Reserved Worldwide.

LINKING CONCEPTS

Discuss each of the following topics in class or review the topics on your own. Then write a brief but complete essay in which you summarize the main points. Please include formulas and graphs as appropriate.

1. What does it mean to say we are going to use a sample to draw an inference about the population? Why is a random sample so important for this process? If we wanted a random sample of students in the cafeteria, why couldn't we just take the students who order Diet Pepsi with their lunch? Comment on the statement, "A random sample is kind of a miniature population, whereas samples that are not random are likely to be biased." Why would the students who order Diet Pepsi with lunch not be a random sample of students in the cafeteria?

2. In your own words, explain the differences among the following sampling techniques: simple random sample, stratified sample, systematic sample, cluster sample, convenience sample. Describe situations in which each type might be useful.

3. In your own words explain the differences among bar graphs, pictograms, circle graphs, time plots, Pareto charts, ogives, relative-frequency histograms, and histograms. If you have nominal data, which graphic displays might be useful? What if you have ordinal, interval, or ratio data?

4. What do we mean when we say a histogram is skewed to the left? to the right? What is a bimodal histogram? Discuss the following statement: "A bimodal histogram usually results if we draw a sample from two populations at once." Suppose you took a sample of weights of college football players and with this sample you included weights of cheerleaders. Do you think a histogram made from the combined weights would be bimodal? Explain.

5. Discuss the statement that stem-and-leaf displays are quick and easy to construct. How can we use a stem-and-leaf display to make the construction of a frequency table easier? How does a stem-and-leaf display help you spot extreme values fast?

6. Go to the library and pick up a current issue of the *Wall Street Journal, Newsweek, Time, USA Today,* or other news media. Examine each newspaper or magazine for graphs of the type discussed in this chapter. List the variables used, method of data collection, and general type of conclusion drawn from the graphs.

Using Technology

Professional statisticians in industry and research use computers to help them analyze and process statistical data. There are many computer programs available for statistics. Some commonly used statistical packages include Minitab®, SAS®, and SPSS.*

In addition, graphing calculators such as those available from Casio, Hewlett-Packard, Sharp, and Texas Instruments have built-in statistics routines, data editing, data sorting, and graphical support. These calculators can be programmed to perform statistical functions not included in the basic statistics modes.

ComputerStat is a software package specifically written to go with this text (it is available without charge to institutions using this text). The package is designed for the beginning statistics student with no previous computer experience. Users need only to enter data and select appropriate programs. Screen prompts guide the user through the software.

The problems in this section may be done using software or calculators with statistical functions. Displays and suggestions are given for Minitab (Release 9), the TI-82, and ComputerStat.

Random Number Generators

Statistical software packages and graphing calculators all have random number generators. Suggestions for using Minitab, the TI-82, and ComputerStat to generate random numbers follow.

Minitab

In Minitab, you can draw a random sample of integers between two values a and b and store the results in a specified column. The commands

```
MTB > RANDOM 50 C1;
SUBC> INTEGER a = 1 b = 500.
```

draw a random sample of size 50 from the numbers I to 500 and store the result in column C1.

TI-82

On the TI-82 the MATH PRB menu contains the selection *rand*. This selection generates a random number between 0 and 1. To generate a random number that is a whole number with up to 3 digits, multiply the random number by 1000 and take the integer part (*ipart* under MATH NUM). Then, each time you press ENTER, a random number with up to 3 digits is displayed.

---

*Minitab is a registered trademark of Minitab, Inc.; SAS is a registered trademark of SAS Institute, Inc. SPSS is a trademark of SPSS Inc.

```
iPart (rand*1000
)
                396
                864
                111
                 84
                649
■
```

ComputerStat

In ComputerStat select the program Random Samples found in the Descriptive Statistics menu. This program lets you select the range of integers from which you wish to draw random samples. It also gives you the option of sampling with or without replacement.

Application 1

Using the appropriate software or calculator that is available to you, do the following.

1. In a large condominium complex there are 473 condominiums numbered 1 to 473. You want to check the thermostat in a random sample of 50 different condominiums. Find the numbers of your 50 condominiums.

2. A theater is showing a new movie. After the movie you want to ask a random sample of 30 people for their opinions about the movie. As people buy their tickets you write a number on the back. Since 278 tickets are purchased, you will use the numbers from 1 to 278. Just before the movie begins, you announce that a small prize will be given to the people whose numbers are called and who respond to a questionnaire after the movie. Find the 30 different numbers you will call.

3. The phone book indicates that there are 83 sporting goods stores in Kansas City. Using the alphabetical order of their appearance in the phone book, you number the stores from 1 to 83. Find a random sample of 10 different sporting goods stores you will call.

4. You have a group of 18 people and you wish to split it into two groups for baseball teams. Use random numbers to assign players to the teams.

Histograms

Suggestions for creating histograms in Minitab (professional graphics), on the TI-82, in ComputerStat follow.

Minitab

In Minitab, after you enter the data make a histogram. You can control the number of classes by designating values for the class boundaries (called cutpoints). A basic outline of the process is given by the following command sequence:

```
MTB >   SET C1
DATA>   (enter the data)
DATA>   END
MTB >   HISTOGRAM C1;
SUBC>     CUTPOINT (list the class boundaries);
SUBC>     BAR.
```

TI-82

On the TI-82, enter the data in a list and select *histogram* in the STAT PLOT menu. In the WINDOW screen, make the following settings:

$$Xmin = \text{lowest class boundary}$$
$$Xmax = \text{highest class boundary}$$
$$Xscl = \text{class width}$$

ComputerStat

In ComputerStat, select Frequency Distribution under the Descriptive Statistics menu. Then follow the instructions given on the screen.

Application 2

Each business day the Dow Jones Information Retrieval Service gives closing price and volume of sales for all major stocks on the New York Stock Exchange. The phrase "volume leads price" is often heard in discussions about market activity. In fact, history has shown that an unusually high volume of sales of a stock generally indicates that an imminent change (either up or down) in stock price is about to take place. What is a high or low volume for a particular stock? What is an everyday or ordinary volume? How frequently do these volumes occur?

Perhaps the best way to answer these questions is to track the market activity of your stock over a period of time. In particular, a frequency table and histogram of volumes over, say, a ten-week period would help answer some of these questions about volume. Table 2–21 lists volume of IBM (International Business Machines) stock (in hundreds of shares sold) for a ten-week period from September 11, 1993 through November 17, 1993.

Using the appropriate available software or calculator, do the following.

1. Enter the given IBM volumes. Then make histograms with 3 classes; 5 classes; 8 classes; 10 classes.

2. Compare the effect of lumping all the data together in only three classes with the opposite effect of thinning the data out into as many as 10 classes. Both these extremes have drawbacks. Comment on them.

3. Looking at the histograms, what would you say is a high volume of sales? What is an everyday

Table 2–21*

Date	Volume (in hundreds)	Date	Volume (in hundreds)	Date	Volume (in hundreds)
09/09/93	17608	10/04/93	24145	10/27/93	43853
09/10/93	21647	10/05/93	15642	10/28/93	26625
09/13/93	13591	10/06/93	16425	10/29/93	19116
09/14/93	10896	10/07/93	10461	11/01/93	39631
09/15/93	19313	10/08/93	16071	11/02/93	102081
09/16/93	7885	10/11/93	5349	11/03/93	52244
09/17/93	31923	10/12/93	13379	11/04/93	30233
09/20/93	13300	10/13/93	11046	11/05/93	32996
09/21/93	18548	10/14/93	16785	11/08/93	18809
09/22/93	17091	10/15/93	32214	11/09/93	25178
09/23/93	19225	10/18/93	20682	11/10/93	20567
09/24/93	13052	10/19/93	19519	11/11/93	36834
09/27/93	16042	10/20/93	13033	11/12/93	31972
09/28/93	23739	10/21/93	24781	11/15/93	14534
09/29/93	21962	10/22/93	27192	11/16/93	33892
09/30/93	14644	10/25/93	22172	11/17/93	43807
10/01/93	33371	10/26/93	43519		

**Source:* Data obtained electronically from the *Dow Jones News Retrieval,* Dow Jones Historical Quotes, Princeton, 1993.

or ordinary volume? What is a low volume? What are the frequencies of days on which high, low, and ordinary volumes occur? In the given period of observation, which volumes (or volume ranges) seem to occur most frequently? Which occur least frequently?

Computer Displays

Different computer software packages follow slightly different procedures for generating and displaying histograms.

Figure 2–48 ComputerStat Histogram (for Problem 1 of Section 2.3), Version 4

```
FREQ.
  -
  -                  18
                   I      I
  -                I      I
              14
  -        I       I      I
  -        I       I      I
10+        I       I      I
  -        I       I      I
  -    5   I       I      I    5
  - I      I       I      I       I
                                     2
  - I      I       I      I       I
  +_I_ _ _ _ _I_ _ _ _ _I_ _ _ _ _I_ _ _ _ _I_ _ _ _ _I_
   13.5          CLASS WIDTH = 49  258.50000
```

Figure 2–49 Minitab Release 9.0 Histograms (for Data in Table 2–9)

Professional Graphics

```
MTB > NAME C1 'DISTANCE'
MTB > SET C1
DATA> 13 47 10 3 16 20 17 40 4 2 7 25 8 21 19 15 3 17 14 6
DATA> 12 45 1 8 4 16 11 18 23 12 6 2 14 13 7 15 46 12 9 18
DATA> 34 13 41 28 36 17 24 27 29 9 14 26 10 24 37 31 8 16 12 16
DATA> END
MTB > HISTOGRAM C1;
SUBC> MIDPOINT 3:48/5;
SUBC> BAR.
```

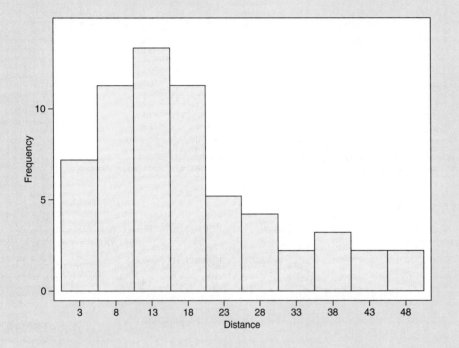

Character Graphics

```
 MTB > HISTOGRAM C1;
 SUBC> INCREMENT = 5;
 SUBC> START = 3.

 Histogram of DISTANCE    N = 60
 Midpoint    Count
     3.00        7   *******
     8.00       11   ***********
    13.00       13   *************
    18.00       11   ***********
    23.00        5   *****
    28.00        4   ****
    33.00        2   **
    38.00        3   ***
    43.00        2   **
    48.00        2   **
```

Minitab also generates stem-and-leaf displays. Notice that it automatically orders the leaves.

Figure 2–50 Minitab Release 9.0 Stem-and-Leaf Display (for Data in Table 2–20)

```
MTB >SET C1
DATA>1.3 0.7 2.1 0.5 0.2 0.9 1.1 3.2 4.0 3.8
DATA>1.4 3.1 2.5 0.6 0.5 2.1 4.0 4.0 0.3 1.2
DATA>1.0 1.5 0.4 4.0 2.3 2.7 4.0 0.7 0.5 4.0
DATA>END
MTB >STEM-AND-LEAF C1;
SUBC>INCREMENT=1.

      Stem-and-Leaf of C1        N=30
      LeafUnit=0.10

      10              0 2345556779
      (6)             1 012345
      14              2 11357
       9              3 128
       6              4 000000
```

Section 3.1

Mode, Median, and Mean

If you were to summarize the information from a collection of numerical data into just one number, you would do well to choose a number that somehow represents the *center* of the data set. There are many interpretations that can be given to the word *center*. We will see that mode, median, mean, and trimmed mean all attempt to summarize data into just one number as a kind of central data value. When you read an article or hear someone talk about an average, it is a good idea to ask *which* average is being used.

Section 3.2

Measures of Variation

Although the average attempts to describe the *center* of a data set, we need a measure of *variation* to describe the *spread* of the data. The range, variance, and standard deviation are useful for this purpose. The coefficient of variation expresses the standard deviation as a percentage of the center value $\bar{x}$ *or* μ. It is a unitless number, and for this reason, it is useful for comparing the data spread of two or more quite different populations. The spread of the data around the mean $\bar{x}$ or μ can be estimated using Chebyshev's theorem.

Section 3.3

Mean and Standard Deviation of Grouped Data

Means and standard deviations can be approximated quickly from grouped data. If we already have a frequency table, then a straightforward adjustment in the formulas for means and standard deviations permits a quick calculation of these quantities. If we want to assign more importance or weight to some numbers in a data set, then *weighted averages* are the tool to use. In this section we will present weighted averages with applications.

Section 3.4

Percentiles and Box-and-Whisker Plots

The standard deviation and variance are each sensitive to extreme data values (outliers). A more resistant description of spread is based on percentiles. The median is the 50th percentile and essentially divides the data in half. Quartiles (the 25th, 50th, and 75th percentiles) divide the data into quarters. A box-and-whisker plot is a graphic display that shows how the middle half of the data is spread around the median. This display is another of the exploratory data analysis tools.

CHAPTER THREE

*Sir Arthur Conan Doyle
(1859-1930)*

This British physician and
novelist is best known for
creating the brilliant fictional
detective Sherlock Holmes.

Averages and Variation

While the individual man is an insolvable puzzle,
in the aggregate he becomes
a mathematical certainty. You can,
for example, never foretell what any one man
will do, but you can say
with precision what an average number will be up to.

Arthur Conan Doyle, *The Sign of Four*

Sherlock Holmes spoke these words to his colleague Dr. Watson as the two were unraveling a mystery. The detective was commenting that if a single member is drawn at random from a population, we cannot predict *exactly* what that member will look like. However, there are some "average" features of the entire population that an individual is likely to possess. The degree of certainty with which we would expect to observe such average features in any individual depends on our knowledge of the variation among individuals in the population. Sherlock Holmes has led us to two of the most important statistical concepts: average and variation.

Focus Problem ▶ **Major League Baseball: How Much Do Players Earn?**

Averages are used in many different ways. Consider the information shown in Figure 3–1 about the salaries of the San Diego Padres (*USA Today*, August 6, 1993). Which average do you think is referred to in this diagram? Which average, mean, median, or mode is often used to describe *level* of income? If we estimate standard deviations to go with each average, how could we construct a range of salaries in which at least 75% of the starting pitchers would fall? How could the coefficient of variation be used to compare salaries of different positions such as pitcher and first base? How could a weighted average be used to compare salaries of one team with those of another?

Section 3.1 **Mode, Median, and Mean**

The average price of an ounce of gold is $385. The Zippy car averages 39 miles per gallon on the highway. A survey showed the average shoe size for women is size 8.

Figure 3–1 Salaries of Padres' Starters Compared with Major League Averages (August 6, 1993)

San Diego yard sale

To cut their payroll, the San Diego Padres traded several high-salaried players. In exchange, they received low-paid young prospects. Right fielder Tony Gwynn and right-handed starting pitcher Andy Benes are the only remaining Padres earning more than $800,000 a year. How salaries of Padres starters compare to the opening day major league average by position:

LEFT FIELD
Phil Plantier: $245,000
Position average: $1,305,791[1]

CENTER FIELD
Derek Bell: $165,000

RIGHT FIELD
Tony Gwynn:
$4,083,333

SHORTSTOP
Ricky Gutierrez:
$109,000
Position average:
$845,842

SECOND BASE
Tim Teufel:
$762,500
Position average:
$1,226,307

PITCHER
Andy Benes:
$2,050,000
Starters
average:
$1,175,916

THIRD BASE
Archi Cianfrocco:
$130,000
Position average:
$1,162,906

FIRST BASE
Guillermo Valasquez:
$109,000
Position average:
$1,490,378

CATCHER
Brad Ausmus:
$109,000
Position average:
$713,732

1– Major league average
for all outfielders

Source: USA TODAY research
Note: $109,000 is the Major League minimum salary.

USA TODAY

Source: Copyright 1993, USA TODAY. Reprinted with permission.

Table 3–1 Word Length of Paragraph Two	
Number of Letters in Word	**Number of Words**
1	1
Mode → 2	10 ← Greatest number of words
3	6
4	8
5	4
6	5
7	2
8	2
9	1
10	2

Table 3–2 Number of Minutes Spent by Professor Adams's Students Using the School Computer Terminals Last Wednesday Afternoon						
27	30	42	42	36	36	50

In each of the preceding statements, *one* number is used to describe the entire sample or population. Such a number is called an *average*. There are many ways to compute averages, but we will study only three of the major ones.

Mode

The easiest average to compute is the mode. The *mode* is the value or property that occurs most frequently in the data. For instance, if you count the number of letters in each word in the preceding paragraph, you will see that the mode is two letters. In other words, there are more words with exactly two letters than with any other number of letters (see Table 3–1).

Sometimes a distribution will not have a mode. If Professor Fair gives an *equal* number of A's, B's, C's, D's, and F's, then there is no modal grade. The data in Table 3–2 have no mode because no data value occurs more frequently than all the others.

GUIDED EXERCISE 1

On the first day of finals, 20 students at La Platta College were selected at random. They were asked how many hours they had slept the night before (rounded to the nearest hour). The results in hours were as follows:

8   6   5   6   4   3   5   8   7   7   5   6   2   0   5   7   6   6   7   8

(a) Complete the following table.

Table 3–3 Hours Slept Before Finals

Hours Slept	Number of Students
0	1
1	0
2	1
3	1
4	___
5	___
6	___
7	___
8	___

(b) Is there a mode?

(c) What is the modal number of hours slept?

(a)

Table 3–4 Completion of Table 3–3

Hours Slept	Number of Students
0	1
1	0
2	1
3	1
4	1
5	4
6	5
7	4
8	3

(b) Yes, there is one quantity that has the greatest frequency.

(c) The modal number of hours slept is 6 hours.

The mode is an easy average to compute, but it is not too stable. For example, if one of the students in Guided Exercise 1 had slept 5 hours instead of 6 on the night before the first finals, the mode would change to 5. However, if you are interested in the *most common* value in a distribution, the mode is appropriate to use.

Median

Another average is the *median,* or central value of an ordered distribution. When you are given the median, you know there are an equal number of values above and below it. To obtain the median, we order the data from the smallest value to the largest. Then we pick or construct the middle value.

The median of the following set of test scores for English literature is 75.

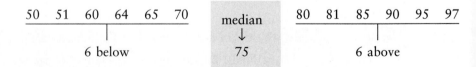

There are as many test scores above as below the median.

For an even number of test scores, the median must be constructed. It is not necessarily one of the given test scores. For instance, the following list has an even number of scores.

$$51 \quad 60 \quad 64 \quad 69 \quad 70 \qquad 75 \quad \boxed{?} \quad 78 \quad 80 \quad 85 \quad 90 \quad 91 \quad 95$$

median ↓

middle values

To construct the median of a set of data with an even number of entries, add the two middle values and divide by 2.

$$\text{Median} = \frac{\text{sum of two middle scores}}{2}$$

$$= \frac{75 + 78}{2} = 76.5$$

GUIDED EXERCISE 2

Belleview College must make a report to the budget committee about the average credit hour load a full-time student takes. (A 12 credit hour load is the minimum requirement for full-time status. For the same tuition, students may take up to 20 credit hours.) A random sample of 40 students yielded the following information (in credit hours):

17	12	14	17	13	16	18	20	13	12
12	17	16	15	14	12	12	13	17	14
15	12	15	16	12	18	20	19	12	15
18	14	16	17	15	19	12	13	12	15

(a) Organize the data from smallest to largest number of credit hours.

(a) 12 12 12 12 12 12 12 12 12 12
13 13 13 13 14 14 14 14 15 (15)
(15) 15 15 15 16 16 16 16 17 17
17 17 17 18 18 18 19 19 20 20

(b) Since there are an _____ (odd, even) number of values, we add the two middle values and divide by 2 to get the median. What is the median credit hour load?

(b) There are an even number of entries. The two middle values are circled in part (a).

$$\text{Median} = \frac{15 + 15}{2} = 15$$

(c) What is the mode of this distribution? Is it different from the median? If the budget committee is going to fund the school according to the average student credit hour load (more money for higher loads), which of these two averages do you think the college will use?

(c) The mode is 12. It is different from the median. Since the median is higher, the school will probably use it and indicate that the average being used is the median.

The median is a more stable average than the mode, but it does not indicate the range of values above or below it. For instance, the median is 20 for both the following groups of scores:

(a) 10   15   20   25   30

(b) 1   10   20   40   100

In the first group, all scores are within 10 points of the median; in the second group, one score is 80 points above the median. The median uses the *position* rather than the specific value of each data entry.

Mean

An average that uses the exact value of each entry is the *mean* (sometimes called the *arithmetic mean*). To compute the mean, we add the values of all the entries and then divide by the number of entries.

$$\text{Mean} = \frac{\text{sum of all the entries}}{\text{number of entries}}$$

The mean is the average usually used to compute a test average.

Example 1

To graduate, Linda needs at least a B in biology. She did not do too well on her first three tests; however, she did well on the last four. Here are her scores:

58   67   60   84   93   98   100

Compute the mean and determine if Linda's grade will be a B (80 to 89 average) or a C (70 to 79 average).

Solution:

$$\text{Mean} = \frac{\text{sum of scores}}{\text{number of scores}} = \frac{58 + 67 + 60 + 84 + 93 + 98 + 100}{7} = \frac{560}{7} = 80$$

Since the average is 80, Linda will get the needed B.

- *Comment:* When we compute the mean, we sum the given data. There is a convenient notation to indicate the sum. Let x represent any value in the data set. Then the notation

$$\Sigma x \text{ (read, the sum of all given } x \text{ values)}$$

means that we are to sum all the data values. In other words, we are to sum all the entries in the distribution. The symbol Σ means *sum the following* and is capital sigma, the S of the Greek alphabet.

The symbol for the mean of a sample distribution of x values is denoted by $\bar{x}$ (read, x bar). This symbol is simply an x with a bar over it. If we let the letter n represent the number of entries in the data set, we have

$$\text{Sample mean} = \bar{x} = \frac{\Sigma x}{n} \tag{1}$$

GUIDED EXERCISE 3

A fabric store manager is eager to see if the latest patterns for size 12 dresses show a longer hemline than last year's. If so, she can expect to sell more fabric because each pattern will call for more material. She took a random sample of 10 dress patterns and found the finished lengths from back of neck to bottom of hem (in inches) to be

| 41.5 | 42 | 39 | 44 | 43.5 | 45 | 43 | 45 | 42 | 46 |

(a) What is the value of n?

(b) How do you find Σx? What is the value of Σx?

(c) Compute the mean, $\bar{x}$.

(d) Last year the mean length of size 12 dresses was 36 in. How much longer is the mean length now? Can the manager expect to sell more material per dress?

(a) Since there are 10 data entries, $n = 10$.

(b) To find Σx, we add all the data entries together.

$$\Sigma x = 41.5 + 42 + 39 + 44 + 43.5 + 45$$
$$+ 43 + 45 + 42 + 46$$
$$= 431$$

(c) $\bar{x} = \dfrac{\Sigma x}{n} = \dfrac{431}{10} = 43.1$

(d) The difference is $43.1 - 36 = 7.1$ in. The manager can expect to sell more fabric for a dress.

Calculator Note It is very easy to compute the mean on *any* calculator: Simply add the data values and divide the total by the number of data. However, on calculators with a statistics mode, you place the calculator in that mode, *enter* the data, and then press the key for the mean, often designated $\bar{x}$. Once the data are entered under the statistics mode, other statistical measures are readily available. For instance, if you forget how many data values there are, you can press a key usually designated by the letter n. The number of data values appear. A Σx key tells you the sum of the data values.

Most *graphing* calculators will provide all the basic statistical measurements, and many will order the data for you through a *sort list* command. From the ordered list it is then easy to find or compute the median. Some graphing calculators such as the TI-82 actually give you the value of the median under the one-variable statistics calculation menu.

All these calculators are wonderful aids in analyzing data. *However, a measurement has no meaning if you do not know what it represents or how a change in data values might affect the measurement.* The defining formulas and procedures for computing the measures tell you a great deal about the measure. Even if you use a calculator to evaluate all the statistical measures, pay attention to the information the formulas give you about the components or features of the measurement.

Figure 3–2 shows the TI-82 displays for the data of Guided Exercise 2 on the average credit hour load of full-time students. The data are entered as list

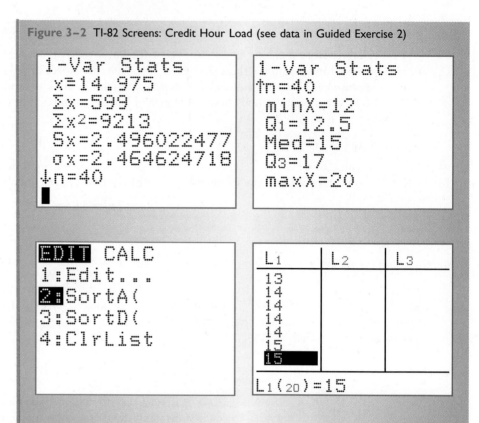

Figure 3–2 TI-82 Screens: Credit Hour Load (see data in Guided Exercise 2)

1 (L1). The command 1-Var Stats gives the summary statistics. Notice that $\bar{x}$ is given as well as the sum Σx. On the second screen, the median Med is given. The SortA(command sorts the data in ascending order. You can scan the sorted data to find the mode.

We have seen three averages: the mode, the median, and the mean. For later work, the mean is the most important of the averages. One disadvantage of the mean, however, is that it can be affected by exceptional values, as shown in the next guided exercise. In such cases, the median would better represent the general level of the distribution.

GUIDED EXERCISE 4

Rowdy Rho Fraternity is in danger of losing campus approval if they do not raise the mean grade point average of the entire group to at least 2.2 on a four-point scale. This term the averages of the members were

1.8   2.0   2.0   2.0   2.0   1.9   1.8   2.3   2.5   2.3   1.9   2.2   2.0   2.3

(a) What is the mean of the grade point averages?

(a) Mean $= \dfrac{\Sigma x}{n} = \dfrac{29.0}{14} = 2.07$

(b) Rod made a 2.0 average this term because he was in the hospital 6 weeks. He believes he would have made a 3.9 average if he had been well. Recompute the mean with the first 2.0 replaced by 3.9. Would Rod have saved the fraternity if he had made a 3.9 grade point?

(b) If we replace the first 2.0 by 3.9, the new mean is then

$$\text{Mean} = \frac{\Sigma x}{n} = 2.21$$

If Rod had made a 3.9 instead of a 2.0, the fraternity would have been saved.

(c) Suppose the college had required the fraternity to raise the *median* grade average to 2.2. Would Rod's potential 3.9 have saved the fraternity? What can you say about the effect of the exceptional value 3.9 on the median and mean?

(c) The median of both distributions is 2.00. If Rod had made a 3.9, the medians would still be the same, indicating that half the members were still below a 2.00 average. Rowdy Rho would lose campus approval either way. The exceptional value 3.9 changed the mean but did not change the median. In general, exceptional values will change the mean more than the median.

Resistant Measures

A *resistant measure* is one that is not influenced by extremely high or low data values. The mean is not a resistant measure of center because we can make the mean as large as we want by increasing the size of only one data value. The median, on the other hand, is more resistant. However, a disadvantage of the median is that it is not sensitive to the specific size of a data value.

Trimmed Mean

A measure of center that is more resistant than the mean but still sensitive to specific data values is the *trimmed mean*. To compute a 5% trimmed mean, order the data from smallest to largest, delete the bottom 5% of the data, and then delete the top 5% of the data. Finally compute the mean of the remaining 90% of the data. Trimming eliminates the influence of unusually small or large data values. Both 5% and 10% trimmed means are presented in the output of many statistical computer packages. The package MINITAB gives a 5% trimmed mean along with the mean and median of a data set.

Example 2

Barron's Profiles of American Colleges, 19th edition, lists average class size for introductory lecture courses at each of the profiled institutions. A sample of 20 colleges and universities in California showed class size for introductory lecture courses to be

| 14 | 20 | 20 | 20 | 20 | 23 | 25 | 30 | 30 | 30 |
| 35 | 35 | 35 | 40 | 40 | 42 | 50 | 50 | 80 | 80 |

Compute a 5% trimmed mean for this data set.

Solution: The data are already arranged in order. Since 5% of 20 = 1, we delete *one* data value from the bottom of the ordered data list and *one* data value from the top. The data values to be deleted are circled. Now we take the mean of the remaining 18 data values.

$$5\% \text{ trimmed mean} = \frac{\Sigma x}{n} = \frac{625}{18} = 34.7$$

The average you use depends on what you want to do with that average. If you want to know which value occurs most frequently in a distribution, use the mode. If a store wants to know which shirt size is requested most frequently, the mode is the proper average to use, and the store will know to carry more shirts of that size than any other. If you want to cut a distribution in half, use the median. A report showing the average salary of workers at Gator Tire Factory should show the median because the top-level administrative salaries will pull up the mean salary and make the production-line salaries look higher than they are. If you want each entry value in the data to enter into the average, use the mean. As we shall see in later chapters, we use the mean if we want to estimate population average from a sample average. The mean uses all the data entries, and the mean can be analyzed more conveniently by statistical methods.

- *Comment:* In Chapter 1 we examined four levels of data: nominal, ordinal, interval, and ratio. The mode (if it exists) can be used with all four levels, including nominal. For instance, the modal color of all passenger cars sold last year might be blue. The median may be used with data at the ordinal level or above. If we ranked the passenger cars in order of customer satisfaction level, we could identify the median satisfaction level. For the mean, our data need to be at the interval or ratio level (although there are exceptions in which the mean of ordinal-level data is computed). We can certainly find the mean model year of used passenger cars sold or the mean price of new passenger cars.

Section 3.1 Problems

Hw

1, 3, 5, 6, 11.

Read p 120 => 130

1. The average length of growing season is often measured in average number of frost-free days. The front range of Colorado (Fort Collins, Boulder, Denver, Colorado Springs, Pueblo) was studied by J. F. Benci and T. B. McKee, from the Department of Atmospheric Science at Colorado State University. Based on data from their Climatology Report No. 77-3 (1977), different locations in the Colorado front range had the following average number of frost-free days per year:

156	161	152	162	144	153
148	157	168	157	161	157

Compute the mean, median, and mode. Write a brief description of the meaning of these numbers from the point of view of a gardener.

2. Babe Ruth was the American League Home Run Champion 12 times (during the period from 1918 to 1931). The number of home runs he hit to earn the 12 titles were

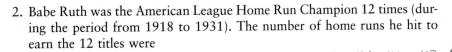

11	29	54	59	41	46
47	60	54	46	49	46

Find the mean, median, and mode of the number of home runs.

3. Gasoline excise tax is a source of revenue in all the states. *Significant Features of Fiscal Federalism,* 1992 edition, compiled the taxes in cents per gallon for each state. For the northeastern states, the taxes (in cents per gallon) were

Connecticut 26   Maine 19   Massachusetts 21
New Hampshire 18.6   New York 22.9   Rhode Island 26
Vermont 16

Find the mean, median, and mode of the taxes.

4. *Greater Yellowstone Today,* published by the Greater Yellowstone Coalition (1991), gave the following data about the number of grizzly bear mortalities (adult female) for the years 1973 to 1990. *Note:* Most bears died of natural causes, but some were (illegally) killed by humans near park boundaries.

6	4	1	1	6	1	1	1	5
4	2	1	3	2	2	2	0	5

Compute the mean, median, and mode. Explain the meaning of each number.

5. *The Universal Almanac* gives the scores for the first 26 Super Bowl football games. The margins of points by which the winning teams won are

25	19	9	16	3	21	7	17	10
4	18	17	4	12	17	5	10	29
22	36	19	21	4	45	1	13	

(a) Find the mean, median, and mode for the winning point margin.
(b) How many point margins were below the mean? How many point margins were below the median?
(c) Compute a 5% trimmed mean. (*Note:* Since 5% of 2 is 1.3 we round the result 1.3 to the nearest integer and eliminate only 1 data value from the bottom and one from the top.)

6. On Tuesday, October 5, 1993, the Nielson Ratings for all prime-time TV shows for major networks (ABC, NBC, FOX, CBS) were

15.7	8.0	5.4	11.3	15.1	8.5	5.0	20.4
9.3	6.0	18.5	8.0	15.4	10.0	8.0	11.0

(a) Compute the mean, median, and mode for the Nielsen Ratings.

(b) How many ratings were below the mean? How many ratings were below the median?

(c) If you were a producer, what would your reaction be if your show had the modal rating?

(d) The show with rating 20.4 was a special. As a producer of a regular show with a rating of 10, you want to know how your rating compares with other shows, excluding this special. Recompute the mean and median with the 20.4 rating excluded. How does the rating for your show compare with the mean and median ratings of all shows excluding the one with rating 20.4? Can you tell your sponsors that your show has an above-average rating?

(e) Compute a 5% trimmed mean for the ratings. (*Hint:* Round 5% of 18 to 1 and eliminate the lowest and highest data values.) How does this value compare with the result of part d?

7. Brookridge National Bank is a small bank in a rural Iowa town. The 12 people who work at the bank are the president, the vice president (his son-in-law), eight tellers, and two secretaries. The annual salaries for these people in thousands of dollars are:

President: 93
Vice President: 80
Tellers: 15, 25, 14, 18, 21, 16, 19, 20
Secretaries: 12, 13

(a) Compute the mean of all 12 salaries.

(b) Compute the median of all 12 salaries, and compare your answers with the mean of part a. Which average best describes the salaries of the *majority* of employees?

(c) Omit the salaries of the president and vice president. Calculate the mean and median for the remaining 10 people.

(d) Compare your answers from part c with those of parts a and b. Comment on the effect of extreme values on the mean and median.

8. A reporter for *Honolulu Star Bulletin* was doing a news article about car theft in Honolulu. For a given 10-day period, the police reported the following number of car thefts:

9   6   10   8   10   8   4   8   3   8

Then, for the next 3 days, for an unexplained reason, the number of car thefts jumped to 36, 51, and 30.

(a) Compute the mean, median, and mode for the first 10-day period.

(b) Compute the mean, median, and mode for the entire 13-day period.

(c) Comment on the effect of extreme values on the mean, median, and mode in this problem.

9. The College Astronomy Club has been counting meteoroids each night for the past week. Between the hours of 10:00 P.M. and 1:00 A.M., the meteoroid count for each night was

15   12   15   10   17   18   15

Then, for the next 2 nights there was a meteoroid shower, and the club counted 57 and 62 meteoroids.
(a) Compute the mean, median, and mode for the meteoroid counts on the first 7 nights.
(b) Compute the mean, median, and mode for all 9 nights.
(c) Comment on the effect of extreme values on the mean, median, and mode in this problem.

10. In a course entitled "Experimental Psychology" at Regis University, students train white rats to do various tasks based on a performance/reward theory (for rats).
(a) One event is the hurdles. Times in seconds for seven rats to run the hurdles were

    5.2   3.3   3.3   2.9   2.8   2.3   1.8

    Compute the mean, median, and mode
(b) Another event is the ladder climb. Times in seconds for eight rats to do the ladder climb were

    41.9   7.7   7.9   6.9   6.6   6.6   5.5   5.1

    Compute the mean, median, and mode for the ladder climb. The first time (41.9 seconds) was for a rat who got distracted in the middle of the performance. Omit the time for this rat, and recalculate the mean, median, and mode. Comment on the effect on the mean, median, and mode when we leave out the extreme value 41.9.

11. In an effort to estimate the size of elk herds spending the winter in Rocky Mountain Park, the rangers used a small airplane to spot count herds of elk in the park. They found 15 groups of elk and recorded the group sizes as follows:

    21   15   19   16   18   17   17   20
    25   7   16   10   16   18   12

    (a) Compute the mean, median, and mode of the group sizes.
    (b) In your own words, define the terms *mean, median,* and *mode.* Discuss how your definitions fit into the context of this problem. How do the mean, the median, and the mode each represent in a different way an estimate of the group size of elk wintering in Rocky Mountain Park?

12. Consider the following types of data that were obtained from a random sample of 49 credit card accounts. Identify all the averages (mean, median, or mode) that can be used to summarize the data.
    (a) Outstanding balance on each account.
    (b) Name of credit card (e.g., MasterCard, Visa, American Express, etc.)
    (c) Dollar amount due on next payment.

13. Consider the following types of data about courses obtained from a random sample of 35 student schedules. Identify all the averages (mean, median, or mode) that can be used to summarize the data.
    (a) Name of department in which each course is offered.
    (b) Number of credit hours each student is taking.
    (c) Starting time of earliest class on each schedule.

14. *Thriving on Chaos,* by Tom Peters, has some excellent cautions about utilizing measurements and averages. In discussing ways to provide superior service, he says, "The use of averages is downright dangerous." He illustrates with examples. Suppose a manufacturing company claims, "on average, we ship parts within 37 hours of order entry." But a careful look at data shows that for the "worst-off 10 percent of customers," the shipping time was within 89 hours of order entry. Peters' advice is to "focus attention on the worst-off 1, 5, 10, or 25 percent of customers" instead of on the average. Comment on this advice.

15. Consider a data set of 15 distinct measurements with mean A and median B.
    (a) If the highest number were increased, what would be the effect on the median and mean? Explain.
    (b) If the highest number were decreased to a value that is still larger than B, what would be the effect on the median and mean?
    (c) If the highest number were decreased to a value smaller than B, what would be the effect on the median and mean?

16. Create a data set with five numbers in which
    (a) the mean, median, and mode are all equal.
    (b) the mean is greater than the median.
    (c) the mean is less than the median.
    (d) the mode is higher than the median or mean.
    (e) all the numbers are distinct and the mean and median are both zero.

17. For the next week, record the length of time you spend on each telephone call you make or receive. Round the time to the nearest minute. Compute the mean, median, and mode. What accounts for some of your shorter phone calls (leaving messages, responding to marketing calls, etc.)?

Section 3.2   Measures of Variation

An average is an attempt to summarize a set of data in just one number. We have studied several averages. As some of our examples have shown, an average taken by itself may not always be very meaningful. We need a statistical cross-reference. This cross-reference should be a measure of the *variance,* or spread, of the data.

Range

The range is one such measure of variance. The *range* is the difference between the largest and smallest values of a distribution. For example, the distance between rows (in inches) in the various sections of Flicker Auditorium are

$$14 \quad 15 \quad 18 \quad 20 \quad 35$$

The range of these distances is

Range = largest value − smallest value

$$= 35 - 14 = 21 \text{ in.}$$

The range indicates the variation between the smallest and largest entries, but it does not tell us how much other values vary from one another. We need a different measure of variation, as the next example shows.

Example 3 You are trying to decide which compact disc club to join: Discount Disks or Selecta Disc. Both have the same bonuses for new members, and both require members to buy one compact disc a month from the monthly selections for at least 1 year. They both charge the same price for compact discs, and they both advertise that the number of compact discs in the monthly selections has mean 31 and range 79. The only advertised difference is that Discount Disks has no membership fee and Selecta Disc costs $25.00 to join. Which club would you join? Before you make up your mind, look at the additional information in Table 3–5.

Table 3–5 Compact Disc Selections Per Month

Month	Selecta Disc	Discount Disks
January	100	80
February	30	1
March	30	70
April	30	2
May	21	70
June	23	1
July	21	1
August	21	70
September	24	3
October	21	70
November	30	2
December	21	2
	Mean = 31	Mean = 31
	Range = 79	Range = 79

Solution: The mean and range are not enough to tell you how much the number of monthly disc selections varies from the advertised mean. Discount Disks could be a disappointment because some months they give you only one selection. Selecta Disc is more consistent in their offerings; you always have at least 21 compact discs from which to choose.

Sample Standard Deviation

A measurement that will give you a better idea of how the data entries differ from the mean is the *standard deviation*. The formula for the standard deviation differs slightly depending on whether you are using an entire population or just a sample. At the moment, we will compute the standard deviation for sample data only. When we have sample data, we use the letter s to denote the standard deviation. The formula for the sample standard deviation is

$$\text{Sample standard deviation} = s = \sqrt{\frac{\Sigma(x - \bar{x})^2}{n - 1}} \qquad (2)$$

where x is any entry in the distribution, $\bar{x}$ is the mean, and n is the number of entries.

Notice that the standard deviation uses the difference between each entry x and the mean $\bar{x}$. This quantity $(x - \bar{x})$ will be negative if the mean $\bar{x}$ is greater than the entry x. If you take the sum

$$\Sigma(x - \bar{x})$$

then the negative values will cancel the positive values, leaving you with a variation measure of 0 even if some entries vary greatly from the mean.

In the formula for the standard deviation, the quantities $(x - \bar{x})$ are squared before they are summed. This device eliminates the possibility of having some negative values in the sum. So, in the formula, we have the quantity

$$\Sigma(x - \bar{x})^2$$

Then we divide this sum by $n - 1$ to get the quantity under the square root sign:

$$\frac{\Sigma(x - \bar{x})^2}{n - 1}$$

If we had the *entire* population, we would divide by N, the population size, and would thus have the mean of the values $(x - \mu)^2$, where μ represents the mean of a population. However, a random sample may not include the extreme values of a population, so to make the standard deviation computed from the sample larger, we divide by the smaller value $n - 1$. Then the sample standard deviation is the best estimate for the standard deviation of the entire population.

These three steps have given us a quantity called the *variance* of a sample, denoted by s^2:

$$\text{Sample variance} = s^2 = \frac{\Sigma(x - \bar{x})^2}{n - 1} \qquad (3)$$

The compact disc data in Example 3 initially described the number of selections per month, but the variance s^2 of these data would be in *square number of selections*. Square number of selections—what's that? We need to take the square root of the variance to return to number of selections per month. This brings us to the standard deviation of a sample.

$$\text{Sample standard deviation} = s = \sqrt{\frac{\Sigma(x - \bar{x})^2}{n - 1}}$$

The next example shows how to use this formula.

Example 4

Big Blossom Greenhouse was commissioned to develop an extra large rose for the Rose Bowl Parade. A random sample of blossoms from hybrid A bushes yielded these diameters (in inches) for mature peak blossoms:

2   3   4   5   6   8   10   10

Find the standard deviation.

Solution: There are several steps involved in computing the standard deviation, and a table will be helpful (see Table 3–6). Since $n = 8$, we take the total sum of the entries in the first column of Table 3–6 and divide by 8 to find the mean $\bar{x}$.

$$\bar{x} = \frac{\Sigma x}{n} = \frac{48}{8} = 6.0$$

Table 3–6 Diameter of Rose Blossoms (in inches)

Column I	Column II	Column III
x	$x - \bar{x}$	$(x - \bar{x})^2$
2	$2 - 6 = -4$	$(-4)^2 = 16$
3	$3 - 6 = -3$	$(-3)^2 = 9$
4	$4 - 6 = -2$	$(-2)^2 = 4$
5	$5 - 6 = -1$	$(-1)^2 = 1$
6	$6 - 6 = 0$	$(0)^2 = 0$
8	$8 - 6 = 2$	$(2)^2 = 4$
10	$10 - 6 = 4$	$(4)^2 = 16$
10	$10 - 6 = 4$	$(4)^2 = 16$
$\Sigma x = 48$		$\Sigma(x - \bar{x})^2 = 66$

Using this value for $\bar{x}$, we obtain Column II of the table. We square each value in the second column to obtain Column III, and then we add the values in Column III. To get the variance, we divide the sum of Column III by $n - 1$. Since $n = 8$, $n - 1 = 7$.

$$s^2 = \frac{\Sigma(x - \bar{x})^2}{n - 1} = \frac{66}{7} = 9.43$$

Now obtain the standard deviation by taking the square root of the variance.

$$s = \sqrt{s^2} = \sqrt{9.43} = 3.07$$

(Generally you can use a calculator to compute a square root.)

GUIDED EXERCISE 5

Big Blossom Greenhouse gathered another random sample of mature peak blooms from hybrid B. The eight blossoms had these widths (in inches):

$$5 \quad 5 \quad 5 \quad 6 \quad 6 \quad 6 \quad 7 \quad 8$$

(a) Again, we will construct a table so we can find the mean, variance, and standard deviation more easily. In this case, what is the value of n? Find the sum of Column I in Table 3–7, and compute the mean. Complete Columns II and III of the table.

(a) $n = 8$. The sum of Column I is $\Sigma x = 48$, so the mean is

$$\bar{x} = \frac{48}{8} = 6 \text{ in.}$$

Table 3–7

I	II	III
x	$x - \bar{x}$	$(x - \bar{x})^2$
5	_____	_____
5	_____	_____
5	_____	_____
6	_____	_____
6	_____	_____
6	_____	_____
7	_____	_____
8	_____	_____
$\Sigma x = $ _____	_____	$\Sigma(x - \bar{x})^2 = $ _____

Table 3–8 Completion of Table 3–7

I	II	III
x	$x - \bar{x}$	$(x - \bar{x})^2$
5	−1	1
5	−1	1
5	−1	1
6	0	0
6	0	0
6	0	0
7	1	1
8	2	4
$\Sigma x = 48$		$\Sigma(x - \bar{x})^2 = 8$

(b) What is the value of $n - 1$? Divide the total sum of Column III by $n - 1$ to find the variance.

(b) $n - 1 = 7$

$$\text{Variance} = s^2 = \frac{\Sigma(x - \bar{x})^2}{n - 1} = \frac{8}{7} = 1.14$$

(c) Use a calculator to find the square root of the variance. Is this the standard deviation?

(c) $\sqrt{\text{variance}} = \sqrt{s^2} = \sqrt{1.14} \approx 1.07$ in. The square root of the variance *is* the standard deviation. (*Note:* We say $\sqrt{1.14} \approx 1.07$. The symbol $\approx$ means approximately equal. We use $\approx$ since 1.07 is not exactly equal to $\sqrt{1.14}$.)

Let's summarize and compare the results of Guided Exercise 5 and Example 4. The greenhouse found the following blossom diameters for hybrid A and hybrid B:

Hybrid A: mean, 6.0 in.; standard deviation, 3.07 in.
Hybrid B: mean, 6.0 in.; standard deviation, 1.07 in.

In both cases, the means are the same: 6 in. But the first hybrid has a larger standard deviation. This means that the blossoms of hybrid A are less consistent than those of hybrid B. If you want a rosebush that occasionally has 10-in. blooms and 2-in. blooms, use the first hybrid. But if you want a bush that consistently produces roses close to 6 in. across, use hybrid B.

Computation Formula for s

There is another formula for the standard deviation that gives the same results as those of Formula (2). It is easier to use with a calculator, since there are fewer subtractions involved.

The computation formula depends on the facts that

$$\Sigma(x - \bar{x})^2 = \Sigma x^2 - \frac{(\Sigma x)^2}{n}$$

which can be proved with the aid of some algebra. The expression $\Sigma(x - \bar{x})^2$ is a sum of squares. Using the notation SS_x to indicate this sum of squares, we get the relation

$$SS_x = \Sigma(x - \bar{x})^2 = \Sigma x^2 - \frac{(\Sigma x)^2}{n}$$

Then the computation formula for the standard deviation s is

Computation Formula for the Sample Standard Deviation s

$$s = \sqrt{\frac{SS_x}{n - 1}} \tag{4}$$

where $SS_x = \Sigma x^2 - \frac{(\Sigma x)^2}{n}$

To compute Σx^2, we *first square* all the x values and then take the sum. To compute $(\Sigma x)^2$, we *first sum* the x values and then square the total.

The next exercise shows you how to use the computation formula. The expression SS_x will be used later, both in the chapter on regression and correlation and in the section on ANOVA.

GUIDED EXERCISE 6

Rockwood Library was having difficulty because some books were being kept out long after the due date. The original late fine was 25¢ per day. The mean overdue time was found to be 10.8 days, with a standard deviation of 5.02 days. The librarian decided to change the late-fine rate to $1.00 per day. Table 3–9 contains data from a random sample of overdue books under the new fine system.

(a) Complete Table 3–9.

(a) See Table 3–10.

Table 3–9 Number of Days Books Are Overdue

x	x^2
5	25
5	25
6	___
6	___
6	___
7	___
7	___
8	___
9	___
10	___
$\Sigma x = $ ___	$\Sigma x^2 = $ ___

Table 3–10 Completion of Table 3–9

x	x^2
5	25
5	25
6	36
6	36
6	36
7	49
7	49
8	64
9	81
10	100
$\Sigma x = 69$	$\Sigma x^2 = 501$

(b) Evaluate SS_x.

(b) Since $SS_x = \Sigma x^2 - \dfrac{(\Sigma x)^2}{n}$, we need to find the values of Σx^2 and $(\Sigma x)^2$. From the total of the second column, we see that $\Sigma x^2 = 501$. By squaring the total of the first column, we get

$$(\Sigma x)^2 = (69)^2 = 4761$$

$$SS_x = \Sigma x^2 - \frac{(\Sigma x)^2}{n}$$

$$= 501 - \frac{4761}{10}$$

$$= 501 - 476.1$$

$$= 24.9$$

(c) Evaluate the sample standard deviation by using the formula

$$s = \sqrt{\frac{SS_x}{n-1}}$$

(c) Since $n = 10$, $n - 1 = 9$ and

$$s = \sqrt{\frac{24.9}{9}}$$

$$\approx \sqrt{2.77}$$

$$\approx 1.66$$

(d) Does the new fine system appear to have lowered the mean overdue time? Does it appear to have reduced the standard deviation? Under which fine system does it appear that the overdue times cluster more closely about the mean?

(d) The new fine system appears to reduce both the mean and standard deviation of overdue times. The overdue time seems more closely clustered about the mean of the new fine system since that system appears to have a much smaller standard deviation.

Population Mean
and Standard
Deviation

In almost all applications of statistics we work with a random sample of data rather than the entire population of *all* possible data values. However, if we do in fact have data for the entire population, we can compute the *population mean μ* (lowercase Greek letter mu, pronounced *mew*) and *population standard deviation σ* (lowercase Greek letter sigma) using the following formulas:

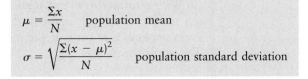

$$\mu = \frac{\Sigma x}{N} \qquad \text{population mean}$$

$$\sigma = \sqrt{\frac{\Sigma(x - \mu)^2}{N}} \qquad \text{population standard deviation}$$

where N is the number of data values in the population, and x represents the individual data values of the population. We note that the formula for μ is the same as the formula for $\bar{x}$ (the sample mean) and the formula for σ is the same as the formula for s (the sample standard deviation), except that N is used instead of $n - 1$ and μ is used instead of $\bar{x}$ in the formula for σ.

In the formulas for s and σ we use $n - 1$ to compute s and N to compute σ. Why? The reason is that N (capital letter) represents the population size, while n (lowercase letter) represents the sample size. Since a random sample usually will not contain extreme data values (large or small), we divide by $n - 1$ in the formula for s to make s a little larger than it would have been had we divided by n. Courses in advanced theoretical statistics show that this procedure will give us the best possible estimate for the standard deviation σ. In fact, s is called the *unbiased estimate* for σ. If we have the population of all data values, then the extreme data values are, of course, present, so we divide by N instead of $N - 1$.

Calculator Note The computation formula for standard deviation (4) using Σx and Σx^2 is fairly easy to implement on any calculator. You compute SS_x, divide by $n - 1$ or n depending on whether you are computing a sample or population standard deviation, and then take the square root of the result. If your calculator has a statistics mode, you set the mode and enter the data. Pressing a key usually designated by s_x or σ_{n-1} provides the sample standard deviation, while pressing a key designated σ_x or σ_n produces the population standard deviation. If your calculator has a Σx^2 key, pressing it will provide that value. Most graphing calculators provide the same information within options provided by pressing a STAT key.

Example 5 In Hawaii there is a species of goose called the *Nene goose*. Before Captain Cook discovered Hawaii in 1778, the Nene goose was abundant. However, after guns were introduced, the Nene goose population decreased severely. A few of these geese were sent to the London Zoo just before the Nene goose became extinct in Hawaii. In effect, the London Zoo had the population of *all* Nene geese. If eight Nene geese were all the zoo had and the weights (in pounds) of these birds were

12.7   15.2   19.4   8.2   16.4   10.8   14.6   23.5

find the population mean μ and the population standard deviation σ of weights of Nene geese.

Solution:

(a) *With a calculator in a statistics mode:* Using a calculator that has a statistics mode, set the calculator in that mode. Then enter the eight data values. Press the keys that provide the mean and the population standard deviation. The result should be

$$\mu = 15.1 \text{ lb} \quad \text{and} \quad \sigma = 4.51 \text{ lb}$$

Figure 3–3 shows the mean and population standard deviation σ displayed on the TI-82 calculator. *Note:* Since $\bar{x}$ and μ are computed with the same formula, the calculator gives only the $\bar{x}$ value.

Figure 3–3 TI-82 Display Showing $\bar{x}$ and σ

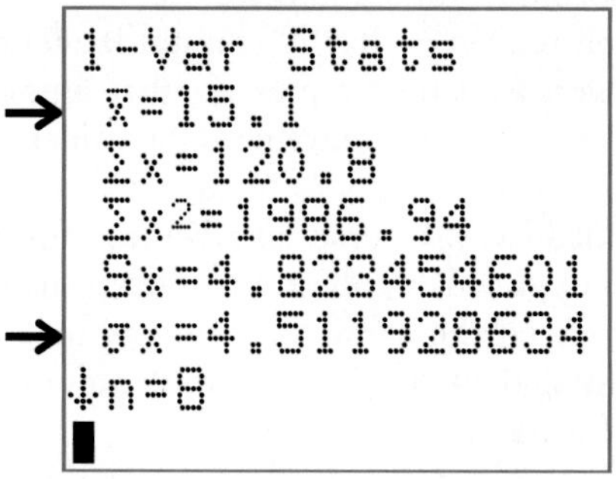

```
1-Var Stats
  x̄=15.1
  Σx=120.8
  Σx²=1986.94
  Sx=4.823454601
  σx=4.511928634
↓n=8
```

(b) *By computation table:* Using a computation table (Table 3–11), we proceed as follows:

Table 3–11 Weights of Nene Geese

x	$x - \mu$	$(x - \mu)^2$
12.7	−2.40	5.76
15.2	0.10	0.01
19.4	4.30	18.49
8.2	−6.90	47.61
16.4	1.30	1.69
10.8	−4.30	18.49
14.6	−0.50	0.25
23.5	8.40	70.56
$\Sigma x = 120.8$		$\Sigma(x - \mu)^2 = 162.86$
$N = 8$		

$$\mu = \frac{\Sigma x}{N} = \frac{120.8}{8} = 15.1 \text{ lb}$$

$$\sigma = \sqrt{\frac{\Sigma(x - \mu)^2}{N}} = \sqrt{\frac{162.86}{8}} = \sqrt{20.36} \approx 4.51 \text{ lb}$$

In the late 1950s, the London Zoo had a much larger population of Nene geese, and some of these geese were sent back to national parks in Hawaii. Today the Nene goose is protected, and visitors to the islands can see Nene geese in Haleakala National Park on Maui.

Rounding Note Rounding errors cannot be completely eliminated, even if a computer or calculator does all the computations. However, software and calculator routines are designed to minimize the error. If the mean is rounded, the value of the standard deviation will change slightly depending on how much the mean is rounded. If you do your calculations "by hand" or reenter intermediate values into a calculator, try to carry one or two more digits than occur in the original data. If your resulting answers vary slightly from those in this text, do not be overly concerned. The text answers are computer- or calculator-generated.

We've seen that the standard deviation (sample or population) is a measure of data spread. We will use the standard deviation extensively in later chapters. In Chapter 6 we will use it to study standard z values and areas under normal curves. In Chapters 8 and 9 we will use it to study the inferential statistics topics of estimation and testing. The standard deviation will appear again in our study of regression and correlation.

For now, though, we will show you two immediate applications of the standard deviation. The first is the coefficient of variation and the second is Chebyshev's theorem.

Coefficient of Variation

A disadvantage of the standard deviation as a comparative measure of variation is that it depends on the units of measurement. This means it is difficult to use the standard deviation to compare measurements from different populations. For this reason, statisticians have defined the *coefficient of variation*, which expresses the standard deviation as a percentage of what is being measured relative to the sample or population mean.

If $\bar{x}$ and s represent the sample mean and sample standard deviation, then the *coefficient of variation* CV is defined to be

$$CV = \frac{s}{\bar{x}} \cdot 100$$

If μ and σ represent the population mean and standard deviation, then the coefficient of variation CV is defined to be

$$CV = \frac{\sigma}{\mu} \cdot 100$$

Notice that the numerator and denominator in the definition of CV have the same units, so CV itself has no units of measurement. This gives us the advantage of being able to directly compare the variability of two different populations using the coefficient of variation.

Example 6

In the stock market the "volatility" of a stock is often measured by the coefficient of variation of the stock. In this way it is possible to directly compare the volatility of one stock against that of another or against that of a known index such as the Dow Jones Industrial Average (DJIA). The data for this example were obtained from Dow Jones News Retrieval Service.

During July 1989, the daily closing of the DJIA, International Business Machines (IBM), and Disney (DIS) gave the following information:

	Stock or Index		
	DJIA	*IBM*	*Disney*
Mean closing values for July 1989	2254.03	113.58	101.30
Standard deviation of			
closing values for July 1989	61.39	1.22	4.51

(a) For each stock or index, compute the coefficient of variation.
   Solution:

$$\text{For DJIA:} \quad CV = \frac{61.39}{2554.03} \cdot 100 = 2.40$$

$$\text{For IBM:} \quad CV = \frac{1.22}{113.58} \cdot 100 = 1.07$$

$$\text{For Disney:} \quad CV = \frac{4.51}{101.30} \cdot 100 = 4.45$$

(b) If we take the point of view that the coefficient of variation represents volatility or the level of activity of a stock, then comment on the results of part a.
   Solution: Using the Dow Jones Industrial Average as a measure of overall market activity, we see that stocks with a coefficient of variation below 2.40 were less active than the market in general, whereas a stock with coefficient of variation above 2.40 would be more active. July 1989 was

a rather slow month for high-tech stocks, and IBM had a coefficient of variation much below that of the overall market. However, compared with the overall market, Disney was very active in July 1989. Since the market was moving up and Disney also was moving up with the market, this was especially good news for Disney stockholders.

GUIDED EXERCISE 7

For August 1989, both the Dow Jones Industrial Average and Disney increased. In August the mean for Disney was 115.8, while the standard deviation was 2.4.

(a) Compute the coefficient of variation for Disney in August.

    (a) $CV = \left(\dfrac{2.4}{115.8}\right) \cdot 100$
           $= 2.07$

(b) How does the relative variability of Disney stock compare for July and August?

    (b) In July, the relative variability was higher. This means the stock was more active in July.

Chebyshev's Theorem

From our earlier discussion about standard deviation, we recall that the spread or dispersion of a set of data about the mean will be small if the standard deviation is small, and it will be large if the standard deviation is large. If we are dealing with a symmetrical bell-shaped distribution, then we can make very definite statements about the proportion of the data that must lie within a certain number of standard deviations on either side of the mean. This will be discussed in detail in Chapter 6 when we talk about normal distributions.

However, the concept of data spread about the mean can be expressed quite generally for *all data distributions* (population or sample) by using the remarkable theorem of Chebyshev:

> **Chebyshev's Theorem:** For *any* set of data (either population or sample) and for any constant k greater than 1, the proportion of the data that must lie within k standard deviations on either side of the mean is *at least*
>
> $$1 - \frac{1}{k^2}$$

P. L. Chebyshev was a famous Russian mathematician who lived from 1821 to 1894. He was a professor at the University of St. Petersburg, where he did a great deal of important work in both pure and applied mathematics.

The most surprising aspect of Chebyshev's theorem is that it applies to any and all distributions of data values!

In ordinary words, Chebyshev's theorem says the following about sample or population data:

1. Start at the mean.
2. Back off k standard deviations below the mean and then advance k standard deviations above the mean.
3. The fractional part of the data in the interval described will be at least $1 - 1/k^2$ (we assume $k > 1$). (See Figure 3–4.)

If we convert $1 - 1/k^2$ from a fraction to a percent, we obtain the results of Table 3–12 for various values of k.

Table 3–12 Minimal Percentage of Data Falling Within k Standard Deviations of the Mean

k	2	3	4	5	10
$(1 - 1/k^2) \cdot 100\%$	75%	88.9%	93.8%	96%	99%

Table 3–12, combined with Figure 3–4, gives us estimates for the smallest percentage of data we expect to find in intervals centered about the mean of *any* set of data.

Example 7

Students Who Care is a student volunteer program in which college students donate work time in community centers for homeless people. Professor Gill is the faculty sponsor for this student volunteer program. For several years Dr. Gill has kept a careful record of x = total number of work hours volunteered by a student in the program each semester. For students in the program, the mean number of hours was $\bar{x} = 29.1$ hours each semester, with a standard deviation $s = 1.7$ hours each semester.

(a) Find an interval A to B for the number of hours volunteered in which at least 75% of the students in this program would fit.

Figure 3–4 Chebyshev's Theorem

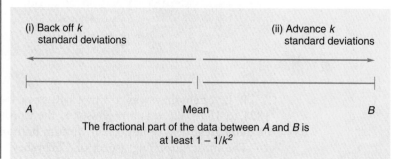

(i) Back off k standard deviations

(ii) Advance k standard deviations

A Mean B

The fractional part of the data between A and B is at least $1 - 1/k^2$

Solution: From Table 3–12 we see that 75% would correspond to $k = 2$ standard deviations on each side of the mean. (We also could solve the equation $1 - \dfrac{1}{k^2} = 0.75$ to get $k = 2$.)

Figure 3–5 Interval in Which at Least 75% of Data Fall

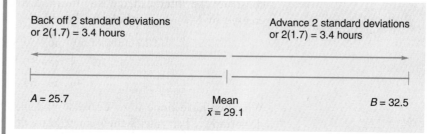

We conclude from Chebyshev's theorem that *at least* 75% of the students would fit in the group that volunteered from 25.7 hours to 32.5 hours.

(b) The interval from 20.6 to 37.6 hours represents the interval within 5 standard deviations on either side of the mean for the distribution of volunteered hours. Find the minimal percentage of students who volunteer from 20.6 to 37.6 hours.

   Solution: We could look up the result in Table 3–12 or simply compute it directly from the formula given in Chebyshev's theorem:

$$(1 - 1/k^2) = (1 - 1/5^2) = (1 - 1/25) = 0.96, \text{ or } 96\%$$

GUIDED EXERCISE 8

The *East Coast Independent News* periodically runs ads in its own classified section offering a month's free subscription to those who respond. In this way, management can get a sense about the number of subscribers who read the classified section each day. Over a period of 2 years, careful records have been kept. The mean number of responses is $\bar{x} = 525$ with standard deviation $s = 30$.

(a) Using Table 3–12, determine the interval about the mean in which at least 88.9% of the data fall.

(a) Using Table 3–12, we see that at least 88.9% of the data fall within 3 standard deviations of the mean. The interval goes from $525 - 3(30)$ to $525 + 3(30)$ or from 435 to 615.

(b) What is the smallest percentage of data we expect to fall within 2 standard deviations of the mean (that is, between 465 and 585)?

(b) By Chebyshev's theorem, we expect $1 - 1/k^2 = 1 - 1/2^2 = 0.75$, or 75%, of the data to fall within 2 standard deviations of the mean.

- *Comment:* Is there a relation between the coefficient of variation CV and Chebyshev's theorem? Yes. The coefficient of variation expresses the standard deviation as a percentage of the mean. For example, if we had a sample mean $\bar{x} = 50$ with sample standard deviation $s = 2$, the coefficient of variation would be $CV = 4$. The CV tells us that the standard deviation is 4% of the mean. If we decrease and increase the mean by 2CV or 8%, we would construct the interval from 46 (mean decreased by 8%) to 54 (mean increased by 8%). In symbols, we have

$$50 - (8\% \text{ of } 50) \quad \text{to} \quad 50 + (8\% \text{ of } 50)$$

$$50 - 4 \quad \text{to} \quad 50 + 4$$

$$46 \quad \text{to} \quad 54$$

What we have done is to decrease and increase the mean by 2 standard deviations. Chebyshev's theorem tells us this interval will contain at least 75% of the sample data. In general, if we decrease and increase the mean by kCV percent, Chebyshev's theorem tells us that at least $1 - 1/k^2$ of the collected data will fall in such an interval. Basically, the CV allows us to think in terms of a percentage change of mean rather than raw data.

Section 3.2 Problems

1. By sampling different landscapes in Mesa Verde National Park over a 2-year period, the number of deer per square kilometer was determined (*The Mule Deer of Mesa Verde National Park*, by G. W. Mieran and J. L. Schmidt, published by Mesa Verde Museum Association, 1981). The results were (deer per square kilometer)

| 30 | 20 | 5 | 29 | 58 | 7 |
| 20 | 18 | 4 | 29 | 22 | 9 |

   (a) Compute the range, sample mean, sample variance, and sample standard deviation.
   (b) Compute the coefficient of variation. Is the coefficient of variation a fairly large number? Would you say there was a considerable variation in the distribution of deer from one section of the park to another? Explain.

2. *USA Today* (September 16, 1993) reported the estimated total number of people watching prime-time TV each day of the week, Monday through Sunday. The results in millions of viewers starting with Monday are

   91.9   89.8   90.6   93.9   78.0   77.1   87.7

   (a) Compute the range and mean. Compute the variance and standard deviation. (*Hint:* Because we have data for each day of the week and there are only 7 days of the week, we have population data.)
   (b) Compute the coefficient of variation. Write a brief explanation of the meaning of this number.

3. *The 1990 Almanac* (Houghton Mifflin Company) lists the Broadway shows with the longest runs. A sample of seven of these shows had runs lasting the following number of years:

9   4   4   13   7   6   3

(a) Find the range of the runs (in years).
(b) Find the sample mean of the runs (in years).
(c) Find the sample standard deviation of the runs (in years).

4. For the past 10 years, the daily high temperature on New Year's Day in the mountain town of Tin Cup, Colorado, was (in °F)

3°   25°   −8°   17°   −2°   10°   −12°   21°   4°   6°

(a) Find the range.
(b) Find the sample mean.
(c) Find the sample standard deviation.

5. A museum curator examined the Crown of Charlemagne and found the seven rubies to have the following weights (in carats):

19.8   43.8   36.1   52.4   63.1   20.7   46.3

(a) Find the range.
(b) Since these numbers represent the *population* of all rubies in the crown, find the *population mean.*
(c) Find the *population standard deviation.*

6. The *Wall Street Journal* (September 27, 1993) gave the average monthly performance of the Dow Jones Industrial Average. These averages are based on the period from 1915 to 1993 and are given as a percentage gain or loss. Starting with January, the average monthly performance as a percentage gain or loss was

1.38   0.03   0.44   1.06   −0.06   0.72
1.58   1.40   −0.90   −0.19   0.37   1.36

(a) Compute the range and mean. Compute the variance and standard deviation. (*Hint:* Because there are only 12 months in the year and we have data for each month, we have population data.)
(b) Compute the coefficient of variation. Is this a fairly large number? Why would you expect it to be so by looking at the data? Explain.

7. *Consumer Reports* (February 1990) rated 20- and 13-inch televisions. For the top five rated 20-inch sets, the list prices (in dollars) were

470   390   470   327   430

For the top five-rated 13-inch sets, the list prices (in dollars) were

213   225   249   260   298

(a) Compute the range, sample mean, and sample standard deviation of prices for the 20-inch sets.

(b) Compute the range, sample mean, and sample standard deviation of the prices for the 13-inch sets.

(c) Compare the answers for parts a and b. Comment on the differences. Next, compute the coefficient of variation for the price distribution of the 20-inch sets and then for the price distribution of the 13-inch sets. Comment on the relative price variation.

8. June purchased a new home computer and has been having trouble with voltage spikes on the power line. Such voltage jumps can be caused by the operation of appliances such as clothes dryers and electric irons or just by a power surge on the outside power line. Her friend Jim is an electronics technician and has obtained the following data about voltages when certain electric appliances are turned on and off. Remember, the normal line voltage is 110 volts. All measurements are taken from the line and measured in volts.

73   140   78   142   80   140   90   133

(a) Compute the sample mean, sample standard deviation, coefficient of variation and range.

Jim advised June to buy a device called a *power surge protector* which protects the computer from strong voltage spikes. Using the power surge protector, Jim again measured voltages to the computer when the same appliances were turned on and off. The results in voltage were

100   120   108   114   105   117   103   114

(b) Compute the sample mean, sample standard deviation, coefficient of variation and range of the voltages using the power surge protector.

(c) Compare your answers for parts a and b. Were the means about the same? Were the voltage distributions different with and without the power surge protector? How did the standard deviation, coefficient of variation and range reflect this when the mean did not? Explain your answer.

9. A certain brand of nylon monofilament fishing line is known to deteriorate in very cold temperatures. A spool of 10-pound test monofilament line was left out overnight at Fairbanks, Alaska, when temperatures dropped to $-35°F$. A random sample of six pieces of line gave the following breaking strengths (in pounds):

10.1   6.2   9.8   5.3   9.9   5.7

(a) Compute the sample mean, sample standard deviation, coefficient of variation and range.

A second spool of this line that had not been subjected to extreme cold temperatures gave the following breaking strengths (in pounds) for a random sample of six pieces of line:

10.2   9.7   9.8   10.3   9.6   10.1

(b) Compute the sample mean, sample standard deviation, coefficient of variation and range for these values.

(c) Compare your answers for parts a and b and comment on the observed differences. Which line had the more consistent performance? How was this reflected in the sample standard deviations and in the coefficients of variation? In the ranges?

10. Ralph and Gloria did a 4-H project to demonstrate ways to get better gasoline mileage. They kept the car windows rolled up to prevent air drag, used only moderate acceleration from a standstill, and kept their speed down in general. Ralph recorded the mean miles per gallon for 5 days selected at random from the period in which he drove the car. Gloria did the same. The results are shown below.

Ralph	22.3	21.2	20.8	19.8	23.8
Gloria	25.2	19.1	18.0	24.4	20.3

(a) Find the range for Ralph and for Gloria.

(b) Find the mean, sample standard deviation, and coefficient of variation for each.

(c) Who consistently seems to have gotten better mileage: Ralph or Gloria? Who had the smaller coefficient of variation?

11. The National Aeronautics and Space Administration (NASA) has studied data on sun spot cycles collected for the years 1745 to the present. During this time, the mean length of a cycle (maximum to maximum) was 11.01 years, with a standard deviation 2.17 years.

(a) Use Chebyshev's theorem to find an interval centered about the mean for the cycle length in which you would expect at least 75% of the cycles to fall.

(b) Use Chebyshev's theorem to find an interval centered about the mean for the cycle length in which you would expect at least 93.8% of the cycles to fall.

12. The U.S. Weather Bureau has provided the following information about the total annual number of reported tornados in the United States for the years 1956 to 1975.

504	856	564	604	616	697	657	464	704	906
585	926	660	608	653	888	741	1102	947	918

(a) Use a calculator with mean and standard deviation keys to verify that the mean number of tornados per year is 730, with a sample standard deviation of 172 tornados.

(b) Use Chebyshev's theorem to find an interval centered about the mean for the annual number of tornados in which you would expect at least 75% of the years to fall.

(c) Use Chebyshev's theorem to find an interval centered about the mean in which you would expect at least 88.9% of the years to fall.

Table 3–13 Closing Values of the Dow Jones Industrial Average (DJIA) and Other Stocks, July 22 to August 25, 1993

DJIA	Sears	Delta Air	AT&T	Kodak	McDonald's
3525.22	49.88	51.00	63.88	51.00	48.75
3546.74	50.38	52.00	63.50	51.50	48.63
3567.70	50.63	51.63	64.63	51.13	48.75
3565.41	49.63	50.00	64.24	51.00	49.88
3553.45	49.75	50.13	64.00	52.38	51.13
3567.42	50.38	49.88	64.24	53.88	52.13
3539.47	50.13	50.13	63.38	53.63	51.50
3560.99	49.25	50.24	63.75	54.13	51.75
3561.27	50.75	50.13	63.25	54.75	51.75
3552.05	52.75	50.50	62.88	55.00	51.38
3548.97	53.13	49.50	63.00	55.38	51.63
3560.43	55.00	50.50	62.50	58.63	51.50
3576.08	54.25	51.00	63.00	59.88	52.50
3572.53	54.25	52.38	63.38	60.63	52.50
3583.35	53.25	51.38	63.24	61.25	52.88
3569.09	53.75	52.13	62.50	60.00	52.13
3569.65	53.75	51.50	62.38	60.50	53.38
3579.15	53.00	51.63	60.75	61.13	54.50
3586.98	52.63	53.13	60.88	60.25	54.13
3604.86	53.25	52.38	59.63	60.38	54.63
3612.13	53.75	52.75	58.25	60.25	54.75
3615.48	53.75	51.88	58.63	60.00	54.88
3605.98	53.63	52.38	58.00	60.88	54.25
3638.96	53.88	53.25	59.38	61.25	54.75
3652.09	53.00	55.50	60.38	62.00	54.63

13. Although it does not happen *every* summer, many years there is a brief stock market rally somewhere around the early or middle part of the summer. From July 22 to August 25, 1993, there was such a rally when the Dow Jones Industrials rose almost 127 points. However, the Dow lost most of this gain by September 21, 1993. Then the Dow gained all the points back by November 17, 1993. Such variations are fun to track and, for an investor, can be a source of profit (or loss). In this exercise we will use the statistics you have learned so far to do a little analysis of the information in Table 3–13.

   (a) Use a calculator with sample mean and sample standard deviation keys to verify the following information using Table 3–13.

	DJIA	Sears	Delta Air	AT&T	Kodak	McDonald's
$\bar{x}$	3576.62	52.31	51.48	62.15	57.23	52.35
s	30.38	1.80	1.37	2.03	3.97	1.96

(b) For the DJIA and the five stocks, compute the coefficient of variation. Use the coefficient of variation as a measure of *market activity,* and rank order the DJIA and the five stocks from most active to least active. Explain why a high coefficient of variation does not mean the stock went *up* in value. (*Hint:* AT&T as well as most high-tech stocks did not do well in the summer of 1993.) The DJIA had the smallest coefficient of variation (less than 1%). Explain why you expect this to happen. (*Hint:* The DJIA is an index based on a composite of *thirty* of the largest and most stable stocks, while the other coefficients of variation are for only *one* stock.)

(c) Use the information from part a and Chebyshev's theorem to compute endpoints *A* and *B* for an interval centered on the mean such that at least 88.9% of the DJIA closings will fall in the interval *A* to *B*.

Many stock brokers refer to a *support* and *resistance* for the trading range of a stock. A *support* is a value the broker is confident the stock will not sink below. A *resistance* is a value the broker is confident the stock will not rise above. As time goes along, supports and/or resistances are eventually broken because of rallies or declines. Therefore, new supports and resistances are calculated for each situation. There are many different ways to compute supports and resistances, and Chebyshev's theorem is one way. Explain why the number *A* you computed in part c could be thought of as a support and the number *B* could be thought of as a resistance (at the 88.9% level). On August 25, 1993, the DJIA closed at 3652.09. Is this close to the (resistance) *B* value at the top of your *A* to *B* interval? The DJIA had a significant (but temporary) decline after August 25. Explain why Chebyshev's theorem might lead you to suspect this could happen.

(d) Use the information from part a and Chebyshev's theorem to compute an interval *A* to *B* such that at least 88.9% of the Delta Air closing values will fall in the interval *A* to *B*. Explain why *A* could be considered a support and *B* a resistance for a trading range of Delta Air. On August 25, 1993, Delta Air closed at $55.50. How does this compare to the resistance? Do you think the rally in Delta Air stock might be (temporarily) over? Explain. *Note:* After August 25, Delta Air did have a significant decline. However, the stock later broke the resistance (*B* that you computed) and entered a new trading range.

(e) Use the information of part a and compute supports and resistances (at the 88.9% level) for Kodak, Sears, AT&T, and McDonald's.

14. In some reports, the mean and coefficient of variation are given. For instance, in *Statistical Abstract of the United States, 1993,* one report gives the average number of physician visits by males per year. The average reported is 4.8, and the reported coefficient of variation is 3.5. Use this information to determine the standard deviation of the number of visits to physicians made by males.

15. For the next 2 weeks, record how long it takes you to go from your residence (or job) to your first class. Record the values to the nearest minute. Compute the range, mean, sample standard deviation, and coefficient of variation. Use Chebyshev's theorem to compute an interval in which at least 88.9% of the travel times fall. Were there any unusual data values in your data set? How would you explain them?

Section 3.3   Mean and Standard Deviation of Grouped Data

Approximating $\bar{x}$ and s from Grouped Data

If you have a great many data, it can be quite tedious to compute the mean and standard deviation. Even if you have a calculator, you must punch in the data. In many cases a close approximation to the mean and standard deviation is all that is needed, and it is not difficult to approximate these two values from a frequency distribution.

The basic plan is as follows:

1. Make a frequency table corresponding to the histogram.
2. Compute the midpoint for each class and call it x.
3. Count the number of entries in each class and denote the number by f.
4. Add the number of entries from each class together to find the total number of entries n in the sample distribution.

Treat each entry of a class as though it falls on the midpoint (x) of that class. Then the midpoint times the number of entries in a class (xf) represents the sum of the observations in the class. The formulas for the mean and standard deviation are as follows:

Sample mean for a frequency distribution:

$$\bar{x} = \frac{\Sigma xf}{n} \qquad (5)$$

where x is the midpoint of a class,
   f is the number of entries in that class,
   n is the total number of entries in the distribution,
   the summation Σ is over all classes in the distribution.

Sample standard deviation for a frequency distribution:

$$s = \sqrt{\frac{\Sigma(x - \bar{x})^2 f}{n - 1}} \qquad (6)$$

where x is the midpoint of a class,
   f is the number of entries in that class,
   n is the total number of entries in the distribution,
   the summation Σ is over all classes in the distribution.

Example 8

The manager of Pantry Queen Supermarket wants to hire one more checkout clerk. To justify his request to the regional manager, the manager chose a random sample of 50 customers and timed how long each stood in line before a clerk could begin checking the customer out. The written request contained the histogram in Figure 3–6. Approximate the mean and standard deviation of the distribution.

Solution: First, make a table with all the columns necessary to compute the mean and standard deviation (see Table 3–14). (Columns V, VI, and VII are filled in after the mean is computed.)

$n = 50$

Table 3–14 Time in Minutes Before Checkout Begins

I	II	III	IV	V	VI	VII
	Freq.	Midpoint				
Class	f	x	xf	$x - \bar{x}$	$(x - \bar{x})^2$	$(x - \bar{x})^2 f$
0–2	4	1	4	−9.2	84.64	338.56
3–5	3	4	12	−6.2	38.44	115.32
6–8	8	7	56	−3.2	10.24	81.92
9–11	15	10	150	−0.2	0.04	0.60
12–14	13	13	169	2.8	7.84	101.92
15–17	5	16	80	5.8	33.64	168.20
18–20	2	19	38	8.8	77.44	154.88
	$\Sigma f = 50$		$\Sigma xf = 509$			$\Sigma(x - \bar{x})^2 f = 961.40$

$$\bar{x} = \frac{509}{50} = 10.2$$

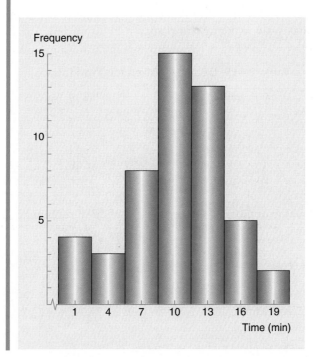

Frequency

Time (min)

Figure 3–6
Time in Minutes Before
Checkout Begins

Use the first four columns to find the mean. The value of n is found by summing Column II.

$$n = \Sigma f = 50$$

The mean is

$$\bar{x} = \frac{\Sigma x f}{n} = \frac{509}{50} \qquad \text{(from the sum of Column IV)}$$

$$= 10.2 \text{ min}$$

Once you have the value of the mean, you can complete Columns V, VI, and VII. (They have already been completed for our convenience.)

$$s = \sqrt{\frac{\Sigma(x - \bar{x})^2 f}{n - 1}}$$

$$= \sqrt{\frac{\text{sum of Column VII}}{(\text{sum of Column II}) - 1}}$$

$$= \sqrt{\frac{961.40}{50 - 1}}$$

$$= \sqrt{19.62}$$

$$= 4.43$$

GUIDED EXERCISE 9

The Marathon Walk for World Peace has a 25-mile route. A random sample of participants walked the distances shown in Table 3–15.

Table 3–15 Distance Walked for World Peace

Distance (miles)	Number of Walkers
1–5	14
6–10	9
11–15	11
16–20	10
21–25	6

(a) What is the value of n (the number of walkers in the sample)?

(a) Add the column giving the number of walkers.

$$n = 50$$

(b) Complete Table 3–16, and compute the mean.

(b) See Table 3–17.

$$\bar{x} = \frac{\Sigma x f}{n} = \frac{575}{50} = 11.5$$

Table 3–16

Class	f (Freq.)	x (Midpoint)	xf
1–5	14	3	42
6–10	9	8	____
11–15	11	____	____
16–20	10	____	____
21–25	6	____	____
	$\Sigma f = 50$		$\Sigma xf =$ ____

Table 3–17 Completion of Table 3–16

Class	f (Freq.)	x (Midpoint)	xf
1–5	14	3	42
6–10	9	8	72
11–15	11	13	143
16–20	10	18	180
21–25	6	23	138
			$\Sigma xf = 575$

(c) Complete Table 3–18.

Table 3–18 Continuation of Table 3–16

$x - \bar{x}$	$(x - \bar{x})^2$	$(x - \bar{x})^2 f$
−8.50	72.25	1011.50
−3.50	12.25	110.25
1.50	2.25	24.75
6.50	42.25	422.50
11.50	____	____

Which column do you sum to compute the standard deviation? Sum that column and find the standard deviation.

(c) The last row of Table 3–18 should read

11.50   132.25   793.50

We sum the $(x - \bar{x})^2 f$ column. That sum is 2362.50.

$$s = \sqrt{\frac{\Sigma(x - \bar{x})^2 f}{n - 1}} = \sqrt{\frac{2362.50}{49}} \approx \sqrt{48.21}$$

$$\approx 6.94$$

Finding $\bar{x}$ and s with Repeated Data

In the case where our data are not grouped but there are several repeated data values, we can use the techniques of grouped data to find the mean and standard deviation fairly quickly. In such cases, we do not need to find a midpoint of a class interval since each class consists of a single data value.

Example 9

A random sample of 60 college football players gave the following information (Table 3–19) about recovery time from shoulder injuries, where

x = number of weeks for recovery

f = number of injured players

Table 3–19 Recovery Times from Shoulder Injuries

Recovery Time x	1	2	3	4	5	6	7	8
Frequency f	5	8	12	19	7	4	3	2

Find the sample mean and then find the sample standard deviation of recovery times.

Solution: We again use a table to organize the data and make computations easier.

Table 3–20 Recovery Times

x	f	xf	$x - \bar{x}$	$(x - \bar{x})^2$	$(x - \bar{x})^2 f$
1	5	5	−2.82	7.95	39.76
2	8	16	−1.82	3.31	26.50
3	12	36	−0.82	0.67	8.07
4	19	76	0.18	0.03	0.62
5	7	35	1.18	1.39	9.75
6	4	24	2.18	4.75	19.01
7	3	21	3.18	10.11	30.34
8	2	16	4.18	17.47	34.94
	$\Sigma f = 60$	$\Sigma xf = 229$			$\Sigma(x - \bar{x})^2 f = 168.99$

We first find the sample mean $\bar{x}$:

$$\bar{x} = \frac{\Sigma xf}{\Sigma f} = \frac{229}{60} \approx 3.82$$

Then we use the value of $\bar{x}$ to compute the entries for the last three columns of the table. To compute the sample standard deviation we note that

$$n = \Sigma f = 60$$

$$s = \sqrt{\frac{\Sigma(x - \bar{x})^2 f}{n - 1}} \approx \sqrt{\frac{168.99}{59}} \approx \sqrt{2.96} \approx 1.69$$

The values we get for $\bar{x}$ and s are exactly (within rounding error) the same as those we would have obtained if we had listed each of the 60 data values separately and computed $\bar{x}$ and s.

Weighted Average

Sometimes we wish to average numbers, but we want to assign more importance or weight to some of the numbers. For instance, suppose your professor tells you that your grade will be based on a midterm and a final exam, each of which has 100 possible points. However, the final exam will be worth 60% of the grade and the midterm only 40%. How could you determine your average score to reflect these different weights? The average you need is the *weighted average*.

If we view the weight of a measurement as a "frequency," then we discover that the formula for the mean of a frequency distribution gives us the weighted average.

$$\text{Weighted average} = \frac{\Sigma xw}{\Sigma w}$$

where w is the weight of the data value x.

Example 10

Suppose your midterm test score is 83 and your final exam score is 95. Using the weights of 40% for the midterm and 60% for the final exam, compute the weighted average of your scores. If the minimum average for an A is 90, will you earn an A?

Solution: By the formula, we multiply each score by its weight and add the results together. Then we divide by the sum of all the weights. Converting the percentages to decimal notation, we get

$$\text{Weighted average} = \frac{83(0.40) + 95(0.60)}{0.40 + 0.60}$$

$$= \frac{33.2 + 57}{1} = 90.2$$

Your average is high enough to earn an A.

In the following exercise we see that the sum of the weights need not always be 1.

GUIDED EXERCISE 10

In an investment portfolio, stocks are rated on a scale of 1 to 10 for dividend earning, security, and capital growth potential. On the scale, 1 equals very poor and 10 equals excellent. In one investment strategy favoring security, the dividend rating is given a weight of 2, the security a weight of 5, and the capital growth potential is given a weight of 3.

(a) Stock A has the ratings shown in Table 3–21. Complete the table and find the weighted average rating of the stock.

(a) $\Sigma w = 10$

The last column has entries 14, 40, and 12, and the sum $\Sigma xw = 66$.

$$\text{Weighted average} = \frac{\Sigma xw}{\Sigma w}$$

$$= \frac{66}{10}$$

$$= 6.6$$

Table 3–21 Stock A Rating

	Rating x	Weight w	xw
Dividend	7	2	_____
Security	8	5	_____
Growth	4	3	_____
	$\Sigma w =$ _____	$\Sigma xw =$ _____	

(b) Stock B is also being considered for the portfolio. It has the ratings shown in Table 3–22. Complete the table and find the weighted average for stock B. How does stock B compare to stock A for this particular investment portfolio?

Table 3–22 Stock B Rating

	Rating x	Weight w	xw
Dividend	2	2	_____
Security	7	5	_____
Growth	10	3	_____
	$\Sigma w =$ _____	$\Sigma xw =$ _____	

(b) $\Sigma w = 10$
The last column has entries 4, 35, and 30, and the sum $\Sigma xw = 69$.

$$\text{Weighted average} = \frac{\Sigma xw}{\Sigma w}$$

$$= \frac{69}{10}$$

$$= 6.9$$

Stock B has a slightly higher weighted average than stock A. For the weights assigned to this investment strategy, stock B will be the better stock. However, if the weights were changed for a different investment portfolio, stock A might have the higher average and be the better choice.

Calculator Note With some scientific calculators, in a statistics mode, you can enter data values as well as respective frequencies. Graphing calculators utilize data lists in which data values can be entered in one list, while respective frequencies can be entered in another list. Then the calculators will compute the mean and standard deviation of the data set. In most instances, the frequency needs to be a counting number. In the case where weights for a weighted average have a positive integer value, the calculators described can give you the weighted average directly.

Section 3.3 Problems

1. In the United States, life expectancy of a male child born between 1979 and 1981 varies by state (including the District of Columbia). Information given in the *Statistical Abstract of the United States, 1989*, 109th edition, shows the life expectancies range from 64.55 to 74.08 years. In the following table, life expectancies are grouped by years.

Life expectancy for men, x (in years)	64–67	68–71	72–75
Number of states, f	1	38	12

(a) Estimate the mean life expectancy in years for all the states.
(b) Estimate the sample standard deviation of life expectancy in years.

2. The life expectancy of a female child born between 1979 and 1981 also varies by state (including the District of Columbia) from 73.70 to 80.33 years. In the following table, life expectancies are grouped by years.

Life expectancy for women, x (in years)	73–75	76–78	79–81
Number of states, f	1	36	14

(a) Estimate the mean life expectancy in years for all the states.
(b) Estimate the sample standard deviation of life expectancy in years.

3. For both men and women, the lowest life expectancy occurs in the District of Columbia. That is the only entry in each of the first classes of problems 1 and 2. Remove that entry and recalculate an estimate for the mean and sample standard deviation of life expectancies
(a) for men.
(b) for women.

4. The Bureau of Land Management (BLM) did a study of the water table near Custer, Wyoming, in the month of June. Based on data from the BLM, a random sample of 20 water wells showed the distance from the ground to the water level (in feet) is

Distance from ground to water level (ft), x	12–14	15–17	18–20	21–23	24–26
Number of wells, f	1	3	8	2	6

Using the midpoints of the depth intervals, estimate (a) the mean depth, (b) the standard deviation, and (c) the coefficient of variation.

5. Based on data from *USA Today* (April 28, 1992), the age distribution and frequency of people doing volunteer work is shown for a random sample of 530 volunteers.

Age	14–17	18–24	25–44	45–64	65–80
Number of volunteers	122	80	159	106	63

Using the midpoints of the age groups, estimate (a) the mean age of the volunteers, (b) the standard deviation of the ages of the volunteers, and (c) the coefficient of variation.

6. Based on data from *USA Today* (October 28, 1992), the ages of a random sample of 300 adults who shop by catalogue are

Age	18–24	25–34	35–44	45–54	55–64	65–80
Number	78	75	48	33	33	33

Estimate the mean age of the adults who shop by catalogue. Estimate the standard deviation of the age of the shoppers and the coefficient of variation.

7. Based on data from *USA Today* (January 15, 1993), the prices of a random sample of 200 new cars are distributed as follows:

Price ($1000)	7–10.4	10.5–13.4	13.5–17.4	17.5–21.4	21.5–25.4	25.5–50
Number of cars	22	42	60	38	16	22

From these data, estimate the mean price of a new car and the standard deviation and coefficient of variation of the price.

8. Based on data from the United States Census Bureau, a histogram of the earnings in thousands of dollars for a random sample of 1000 men at least 15 years old is shown in Figure 3–7. The histogram in Figure 3–8 shows the earnings in thousands of dollars for a random sample of 1000 women who are at least 15 years old (1993 data).
   (a) Estimate the mean earnings, standard deviation, and coefficient of variation for men.
   (b) Estimate the mean earnings, standard deviation, and coefficient of variation for women.

9. Alexander Borbely is a professor at the University of Zurich Medical School, where he is director of the sleep laboratory. The histogram in Figure 3–9 is based on information in his book *Secrets of Sleep*. The histogram displays results from a random sample of 200 subjects. Estimate the mean hours of sleep, standard deviation of hours of sleep, and coefficient of variation.

Figure 3–7 Earnings for Men (in $1000)

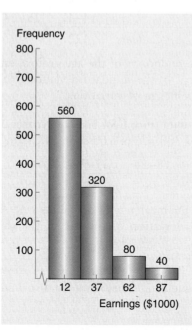
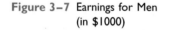

Figure 3–8 Earnings for Women (in $1000)

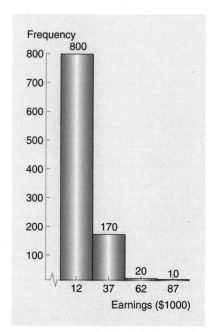
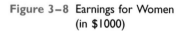

Figure 3–9 Hours of Sleep Each Day (24-Hour Period)

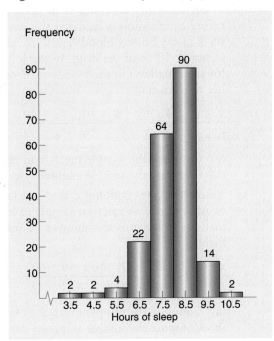

10. The president of the alumni association at Muddybanks College presented the following tabulation of alumni contributions that have been received so far this year:

$ amount	50	100	150	200	500	1000
Number of alumni making this contribution	710	350	92	51	12	16

Find (a) the mean and (b) the sample standard deviation for the contributions.

11. How long do deer live? In Mesa Verde National Park, deer are not hunted, so the life span of deer in a national park might give a reasonable estimate for the natural life span of deer. The following data are from *The Mule Deer of Mesa Verde National Park*, by G. W. Mieran and J. L. Schmidt, published by the Mesa Verde Museum Association (1981)

Age in years	1	2	3	4	5	6	7	8	9	10
Number of Deer	3	7	6	5	4	2	0	1	2	1

(a) Use the methods of grouped data to compute the mean and sample standard deviation of the ages.

(b) Enter the 31 ages individually in a calculator and compute the mean and sample standard deviation of the ages. Are your results the same as in part a? Explain why the grouped-data method should give the same results.

12. An illegal pain-killing drug is sometimes given to race horses in an effort to get them to run faster than normal. A veterinarian working for the racing commission is studying this drug to determine how long the drug stays in the horse's bloodstream. A random sample of horses were given a shot of 10 cc of the drug. In the following table, x is the time in hours for the drug level in the bloodstream to go back to zero and f is the number of horses.

x	2	4	6	8	10	12	14	16
f	1	3	8	11	9	6	4	2

(a) Compute the sample mean $\bar{x}$ of recovery times for this drug.
(b) Compute the sample standard deviation s of recovery times.

13. Allied Air Lines is doing a study of late arrival times for the New York to Atlanta run. A random sample of late flights gave the following information, where x is the number of minutes late and f is the number of flights.

x	10	20	30	40	50	60	70	80	90
f	15	19	10	7	3	2	2	1	1

(a) Compute the sample mean $\bar{x}$ of late arrival times.
(b) Compute the sample standard deviation s of late arrival times.

14. A wildlife research team observed a random sample of 45 Alaskan wolf dens and counted the number of wolf pups per den. The following is a frequency tabulation of the data:

Number of pups	0	1	2	3	4	5	6
Number of dens with this many pups	5	3	6	7	9	8	7

Find (a) the mean number of pups per den $\bar{x}$ and (b) the sample standard deviation s.

15. In your biology class your final grade is based on several things: a lab score, scores on two major tests, and your score on the final exam. There are 100 points available for each score. However, the lab score is worth 25% of your total grade, each major test is worth 22.5%, and the final exam is worth 30%. Compute the weighted average for the following scores: 92 on the lab, 81 on the first major test, 93 on the second major test, and 85 on the final exam.

16. Suppose the weighting for the activities in your biology class changed so that the lab score was still worth 25%, but each of the two major tests also were worth 25%, and the final was worth only 25%. Compute the weighted average for the same set of scores as those that are given in problem 15: Use 92 on lab, 81 on the first major test, 93 on the second major test, and 85 on the final exam. Is the weighted average different from that in problem 15? Since the weights are all the same, did you really need to

use a weighted average, or could you simply have taken the mean of the four scores?

17. At General Hospital nurses are given performance evaluations to determine eligibility for merit pay raises. The supervisor rates them on a scale of 1 to 10 (10 being the highest rating) for several activities: promptness, record keeping, appearance, and bedside manner with patients. Then an average is determined by giving a weight of 2 for promptness, 3 for record keeping, 1 for appearance, and 4 for bedside manner with patients. What is the average rating for a nurse with ratings of 9 for promptness, 7 for record keeping, 6 for appearance, and 10 for bedside manner?

18. The alumni club of Jefferson College gives a $10,000 award to the most outstanding athlete each year. Since competitive sports include football, basketball, baseball, swimming, and tennis, the rating scale is a way of comparing athletes who participate in any of the sports. Each candidate is rated on a scale of 1 to 10 (with 10 being the best) for individual performance, win–loss record of team, grade point average, and sportsmanship. The ratings are then averaged using a weight of 5 for individual performance, 2 for win–loss record of team, 1 for grade point average, and 3 for sportsmanship.
    (a) One athlete had the following ratings: 9 for individual performance, 7 for team record, 6 for grade point average, 8 for sportsmanship. Compute the weighted average of the ratings.
    (b) Another athlete had ratings of 8 for individual performance, 9 for team record, 5 for grade point average, and 9 for sportsmanship. Compute the weighted average of these ratings. Which athlete had the higher average rating?

19. Brunswick Corporation gave the following information about weights and sales of bowling balls.

Weight (lb)	6–8	10–12	13–15	16–17
Sales	15%	39%	27%	19%

Estimate the weighted average of the weight (in pounds) of the bowling balls sold. *Hint:* The weights of the bowling balls are the data values, while the percentages represent the weights in the weighted average formula.

20. An Attitude Research Specialist poll (*USA Today,* May 4, 1992) of more than 2000 college students reported the study time outside the classroom per week to be

Study time (hours)	2–5	6–10	11 or more
Students	26%	40%	34%

To compute a weighted average for study time, we need an upper limit on the 11 or more class.

(a) Use 15 hours as the upper limit for the 11 or more class to make the last class from 11 to 15 hours. Compute the weighted mean of the study times.

(b) Use 20 hours as the upper limit for the 11 or more class to make the last class from 11 to 20 hours. Compute the weighted mean of the study times.

(c) Compare the results of parts a and b and comment on the difference you find.

(d) Keep track of your own outside of class study time for a week. How does your study time compare with the averages of parts a and b?

Section 3.4   Percentiles and Box-and-Whisker Plots

Percentiles

We've seen measures of central tendency and spread for a set of data. The arithmetic mean $\bar{x}$ and the standard deviation s will be very useful to us in later work. However, because they each utilize every data value, they can be heavily influenced by one or two extreme data values. In cases where our data distributions are heavily skewed or even bimodal, we often get a better summary of the distribution by utilizing relative position of data rather than exact values.

Recall that the median is an average computed by using relative position of the data. If we are told that 81 is the median score on a biology test, we know that after the data have been ordered, 50% of the data fall at or below the median value of 81. The median is an example of a percentile; in fact it is the 50th percentile. The general definition of the Pth percentile follows.

> **For whole numbers** P (where $1 \leq P \leq 99$) the Pth *percentile* of a distribution is a value such that $P\%$ of the data fall at or below it.

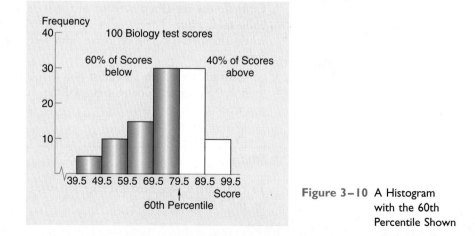

Figure 3–10 A Histogram with the 60th Percentile Shown

In Figure 3–10 we see the 60th percentile marked on a histogram. We see that 60% of the data lie below the mark and 40% lie above it.

GUIDED EXERCISE 11

You took the English achievement test to obtain college credit in freshman English by examination.

(a) If your score was in the 89th percentile, what percentage of scores are at or below yours?

(b) If the scores ranged from 1 to 100 and your raw score is 95, does this necessarily mean that your score is at the 95th percentile?

(a) The percentile means that 89% of the scores were at or below yours.

(b) No, the percentile gives an indication of relative position of the scores. The determination of your percentile has to do with the number of scores at or below yours. If everyone did very well and only 80% of the scores fell at or below yours, you would be at the 80th percentile even though you got 95 out of 100 points on the exam.

There are 99 percentiles, and in an ideal situation, the 99 percentiles divide the data set into 100 equal parts. (See Figure 3–11.)

However, if the number of data elements is not exactly divisible by 100, the percentiles will not divide the data into equal parts.

There are several widely used conventions for finding percentiles. They lead to slightly different values for different situations, but these values are close together. For all conventions, the data are first *ranked* or ordered from smallest to largest. A natural way to find the Pth percentile is to then find a value so that $P\%$ of the data fall at or below it. This will not always be possible, so we take the nearest value satisfying the criterion. It is at this point that there are a variety of processes to determine the exact value of the percentile.

We will not be very concerned about exact procedures for evaluating percentiles in general. However, *quartiles* are special percentiles used so frequently that we want to adopt a specific procedure for their computation.

Quartiles

Quartiles are those percentiles which divide the data into fourths. The *first quartile* Q_1 is the 25th percentile, the *second quartile* Q_2 is the median, and the *third quartile* Q_3 is the 75th percentile. (See Figure 3–12.)

Figure 3–11 Percentiles

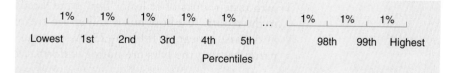

Figure 3–12 Quartiles

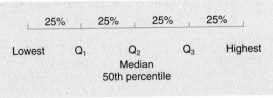

Again, there are many conventions used for computing quartiles, but the following one utilizes the median and is widely adopted.

Procedure to Compute Quartiles

1. Rank the data from smallest to largest.
2. Find the median. This is the 2nd quartile.
3. The first quartile Q_1 is then the median of the lower half of the data; that is, it is the median of the data falling *below* Q_2 (and not including Q_2).
4. The third quartile Q_3 is the median of the upper half of the data; that is, it is the median of the data falling *above* Q_2 (and not including Q_2).

In short, all we do to find the quartiles is to find three medians.

Interquartile Range

The median, or second quartile, is a popular measure of the center utilizing relative position. A useful measure of data spread utilizing relative position is the *interquartile range (IQR)*. It is simply the difference between the third and first quartiles.

$$\text{Interquartile range} = Q_3 - Q_1$$

The interquartile range tells us the spread of the middle half of the data. Now let's look at an example to see how to compute all these quantities.

Example 11

In a hurry? On the run? Hungry as well? How about an ice cream bar as a snack? Ice cream bars are popular among all age groups. *Consumer Reports* did a study of ice cream bars in their August 1989 issue. Twenty-seven bars with taste ratings of at least "fair" were listed, and cost per bar was included in the report. Just how much will an ice cream bar cost? The data, expressed in dollars, appear in Table 3–23. As you can see, the cost varies quite a bit, partly because the bars are not of uniform size.

Table 3–23 Cost of Ice Cream Bars (in dollars)

0.99	1.07	1.00	0.50	0.37	1.03	1.07	1.07
0.97	0.63	0.33	0.50	0.97	1.08	0.47	0.84
1.23	0.25	0.50	0.40	0.33	0.35	0.17	0.38
0.20	0.18	0.16					

(a) Find the quartiles.

Solution: We first order the data from smallest to largest.

Table 3–24 Ranked Cost of Ice Cream Bars (in dollars)

0.16	0.17	0.18	0.20	0.25	0.33	0.33	0.35
0.37	0.38	0.40	0.47	0.50	0.50	0.50	0.63
0.84	0.97	0.97	0.99	1.00	1.03	1.07	1.07
1.07	1.08	1.23					

Next, we find the median. Since the number of data values is 27, there are an odd number of data, and the median is simply the center or 14th value. The value is shown boxed in Table 3–24.

$$\text{Median} = Q_2 = 0.50$$

There are 13 values below the median, and Q_1 is the median of these values. It is the middle or 7th value and is shaded in Table 3–24.

$$\text{First quartile} = Q_1 = 0.33$$

There are also 13 values above Q_2. The median of these is the 7th value from the right end. This value is also shaded in Table 3–24.

$$\text{Third quartile} = Q_3 = 1.00$$

(b) Find the interquartile range.

Solution:

$$IQR = Q_3 - Q_1$$
$$= 1.00 - 0.33$$
$$= 0.67$$

This means that the middle half of the data has a cost spread of 67¢.

When data sets are small, we can easily find the median position. When the sets are larger, it is more convenient to use a formula to find the *position* or *rank* of the median value.

For n pieces of data,

$$\text{Median rank} = \frac{n + 1}{2}$$

If the rank is a whole number, the median is the value in that position. If the rank ends in .5, we take the mean of the data values in the adjacent positions to find the median.

GUIDED EXERCISE 12

Many people consider the number of calories in an ice cream bar as important, if not more important than the cost. The *Consumer Reports* article also included the calorie count of the rated ice cream bars (Table 3–25). There were 22 vanilla-flavored bars rated. Again, the bars varied in size, and some of the smaller bars had fewer calories. The calorie counts for the vanilla bars follow.

Table 3–25 Calories in Vanilla-Flavored Ice Cream Bars

342	377	319	353	295	234	294	286	377
182	310	439	111	201	182	197	209	147
190	151	131	151					

(a) Our first step is to rank the data. Do so.

(a)

Table 3–26 Ranked Data

111	131	147	151	151	182
182	190	197	201	209	234
286	294	295	310	319	342
353	377	377	439		

(b) There are 22 data values. Find the median rank, and then compute the median.

(b) $\text{Median rank} = \dfrac{22 + 1}{2} = 11.5$

This tells us to average the 11th and 12th data values shaded in Table 3–26.

$$\text{Median} = \frac{209 + 234}{2} = 221.5$$

(c) How many values are below the median position? Find Q_1.

(c) Since the median lies halfway between the 11th and 12th values, there are 11 values below the median. Q_1 is the median of these values and falls in the 6th position. $Q_1 = 182$.

(d) There are the same number of data above as below the median. Use this fact to find Q_3.

(d) Q_3 is the median of the upper half of the data. Since there are 11 values in the upper portion, count over 6 values from the right end.

$$Q_3 = 319$$

(e) Find the interquartile range and comment on its meaning.

(e) IQR $= Q_3 - Q_1$

$$= 319 - 182$$

$$= 137$$

The middle portion of the data has a spread of 137 calories.

Box-and-Whisker Plots

The quartiles together with the low and high data values give us a very useful *five-number summary* of the data and its spread.

Five-Number Summary

Lowest value, Q_1, median, Q_3, highest value

We will use these five numbers to create a graphic sketch of the data called a *box-and-whisker plot*. Box-and-whisker plots provide another useful technique for describing data from exploratory data analysis (EDA).

To Make a Box-and-Whisker Plot

1. Draw a vertical scale to include the lowest and highest data values.
2. To the right of the scale draw a box from Q_1 to Q_3.
3. Include a solid line through the box at the median level.
4. Draw solid lines, called *whiskers*, from Q_1 to the lowest value and from Q_3 to the highest value.

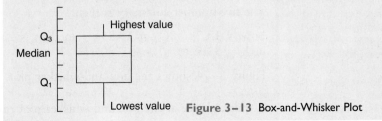

Figure 3-13 Box-and-Whisker Plot

The next example demonstrates the process of making a box-and-whisker plot.

Example 12　Renata College is a small college offering baccalaureate degrees in liberal arts and business. The Development Office (fund raising) did a salary survey of alumni who graduated 2 years ago and have jobs. Sixteen alumni responded to the survey the first week. Table 3–27 shows their annual salaries (in thousands of dollars). Make a box-and-whisker plot.

Table 3–27 Annual Salaries (in thousands of dollars)

28.5	29.5	22.0	20.5	26.8	19.2	13.7	24.1
18.3	17.9	23.6	27.0	33.5	24.6	23.8	26.1

Solution: We rank the data.

Table 3–28 Annual Salaries Ranked

13.7	17.9	18.3	19.2	20.5	22.0	23.6	23.8
24.1	24.6	26.1	26.8	27.0	28.5	29.5	33.5

Since there are 16 data values, we see that

$$\text{Median rank} = (16 + 1)/2 = 8.5$$

The median is the mean of the 8th and 9th values.

$$\text{Median} = (23.8 + 24.1)/2 = 23.95$$

Since there are eight values below the median,

$$\text{Quartile rank} = (8 + 1)/2 = 4.5$$

Q_1 is the mean of the 4th and 5th values.

$$Q_1 = (19.2 + 20.5)/2 = 19.85$$

Q_3 is the mean of the 4th and 5th values from the *high* end.

$$Q_3 = (26.8 + 27)/2 = 26.90$$

The five-number summary is then

Low = 13.7　　　$Q_1 = 19.85$　　　median = 23.95　　　$Q_3 = 26.90$
high = 33.5

Figure 3–14 shows the box-and-whisker plot.

A quick glance at the box-and-whisker plot reveals the following:

(a) The box tells us where the middle half of the data lies, so 50% of the

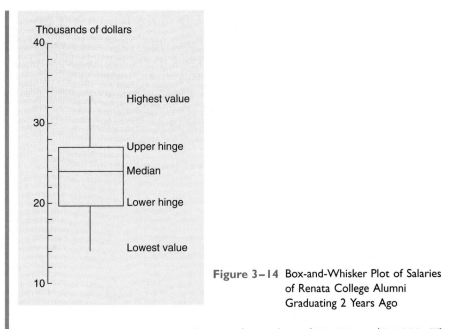

Figure 3–14 Box-and-Whisker Plot of Salaries of Renata College Alumni Graduating 2 Years Ago

salaries lie in the box part and range from about $20,000 to $27,000. The length of the box equals the interquartile range.

(b) The median is about $24,000 and is slightly closer to the top of the box.

(c) The whiskers are about the same length, which says that the range from Q_1 and Q_3 to corresponding extreme values is about the same.

 Calculator Note Box-and-whisker plots are so useful that some graphing calculators such as the TI-82 produce them. On the TI-82, the quartiles Q_1 and Q_3 are calculated as we calculate them in this text. Once the box plot is graphed on the TI-82, the trace key gives the values for minX, Q1, Med (for median), Q3, and maxX (see Figure 3–15).

Figure 3–15 Box Plot on the TI-82 for Data of Table 3–26 Annual Salaries (Window settings: X from 10 to 35, Y from 0 to 10)

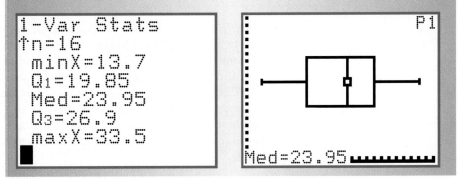

GUIDED EXERCISE 13

The Renata College Development Office also sent a salary survey to alumni who graduated 5 years ago. Again, questions about annual salary were asked. The responses received the first week are summarized in the box-and-whisker plot for Figure 3–16. The plot for the alumni graduating 2 years ago is repeated for comparison.

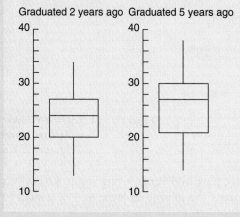

Figure 3–16 Box-and-Whisker Plots for Alumni Salaries (in thousands of dollars)

(a) From Figure 3–16, estimate the median and the extreme values of salaries of alumni graduating five years ago. What is the location of the middle half of the salaries?

(a) The median seems to be $27,000. The extremes are $14,000 and $38,000. The middle half of the data is enclosed by the box with low side at $21,000 and high side at $30,000.

(b) Compare the two box plots and make comments about the salaries of alumni graduating two and five years ago.

(b) The salaries of the alumni graduating 5 years ago have a larger spread but begin slightly higher and extend to levels about $5000 above those graduating 2 years ago. The middle half of the data is also more spread out with higher boundaries and a higher median.

- *Comment:* In exploratory data analysis, *hinges* rather than quartiles are used to create the box. Hinges are computed in a manner similar to the way we compute quartiles. However, in the case of an odd number of data, we include the median itself in both the lower and upper halves of the data (see *Applications, Basics, and Computing of Exploratory Data Analysis,* by Paul Velleman and David Hoaglin, Duxbury Press). This has the effect of shrinking the box and moving the ends of the box slightly toward the median. For an even number of data, the quartiles as we computed them equal the hinges.

- *Comment:* Sometimes, especially in a computer printout of a box-and-whisker plot, the box will be horizontal. Since boxes can be difficult for some printers to draw, endpoints of the box may be shown instead of the entire box.

We have developed the skeletal box-and-whisker plot. Other variations may include *fences,* which are marks placed on either side of the box to represent various portions of the data. Values that lie outside the fences are called *outliers.* These values seem to stand by themselves, away from most of the data. They might be exceptional values and deserve closer study. Or, they may be the result of data entry error. For a more complete discussion of outliers and variations of box plots, see *Applications, Basics, and Computing of Exploratory Data Analysis,* by Velleman and Hoaglin.

Section 3.4 Problems

1. Angela took a general aptitude test and scored in the 82nd percentile for aptitude in accounting. What percentage of the scores were at or below her score? What percentage were above?

2. One standard for admission to Redfield College is that the student must rank in the upper quartile of his or her graduating high school class. What is the minimal percentile rank of a successful applicant?

3. The town of Butler, Nebraska, decided to give a teacher competency exam and defined the passing scores to be those in the 70th percentile or higher. The raw test scores ranged from 0 to 100. Was a raw score of 82 necessarily a passing score? Explain.

4. Clayton and Timothy took different sections of Introduction to Economics. Each section had a different final exam. Timothy scored 83 out of 100 and had a percentile rank in his class of 72. Clayton scored 85 out of 100 but his percentile rank in his class was 70. Who performed better with respect to the rest of the students in the class: Clayton or Timothy? Explain your answer.

5. Medical Group Management Association provided the *New York Times* with data on incomes for medical doctors (1992) in group practice by specialty. The specialty with the highest annual income is cardiovascular surgeons. The 1992 median income was $574,769, and the 90th percentile was $887,057.
   (a) What percentage of the cardiovascular surgeons made more than $574,769?
   (b) What percentage made $887,057 or more?
   (c) What percentage made between $574,765 and $887,057?

6. Medical Group Management Association data show that the median 1992 income for anesthesiologists in group practice was $253,511, while the 90th percentile was $378,261.
   (a) What percentage of the anesthesiologists made less than $253,511?

(b) What percentage of the anesthesiologists made less than $378,261?

(c) What percentage made between $253,522 and $378,261?

7. The following data are percentage increases in annual salary for faculty at the professor rank at Oregon colleges and universities. Source: *Academe: Bulletin of the American Association of University Professors, March/April, 1993.*

5.8	6.4	6.4	10.2	6.0	6.2	6.0	6.1
6.1	1.3	7.2	6.7	10.1	6.4	4.0	

(a) Rank the data.

(b) Compute the five-number summary and the interquartile range.

(c) Make a box-and-whisker plot.

8. The following data are percentage increases in annual salary for faculty at the professor rank at Colorado colleges and universities. Source: *Academe: Bulletin of the American Association of University Professors, March/April, 1993.*

3.0	6.0	7.0	3.5	5.2	2.6	5.8
2.0	1.6	4.8	2.5	2.9	2.8	

(a) Rank the data.

(b) Compute the five-number summary and the interquartile range.

(c) Make a box-and-whisker plot.

(d) Compare this box-and-whisker plot with that in Problem 7. Comment on the differences. Be sure to discuss the locations of the medians, the location of the middle half of the data banks, and the distance from Q_1 and Q_3 to the respective extreme values.

9. At Center Hospital there is some concern about the high turnover of nurses. A survey was done to determine how long (in months) nurses had been in their current positions. The responses of 20 nurses were (in months):

23	2	5	14	25	36	27	42	12	8
7	23	29	26	28	11	20	31	8	36

(a) Rank the data.

(b) Make a box-and-whisker plot of the data.

(c) Find the interquartile range.

10. Another survey was done at Center Hospital to determine how long (in months) clerical staff had been in their current positions. The responses of 20 clerical staff members were (in months):

25	22	7	24	26	31	18	14	17	20
31	42	6	25	22	3	29	32	15	72

(a) Rank the data.

(b) Make a box-and-whisker plot.

(c) Find the interquartile range.

(d) Compare this plot to the one in Problem 9. Discuss the location of the medians, the location of the middle half of the data banks, and the distance from Q_1 and Q_3 to the extreme values.

11. The following data are the number of males and females with the rank of professor at colleges and universities in Hawaii. Source: *Academe: Bulletin of the American Association of University Professors*, March/April, 1993.

Male:	13	23	11	7	34
	6	369	40	6	3
Female:	6	8	5	2	20
	4	58	3	2	9

For each group, do the following:
(a) Rank the data.
(b) Compute the five-number summary and the interquartile range.
(c) Make a box-and-whisker plot.
(d) Compare these box-and-whisker plots and comment on the differences.

12. The following data are the average costs (in dollars) of a single-lens reflex camera for models rated in *Consumer Reports* in December of 1993:

800	650	300	430	560	470	640	830
400	280	800	410	360	600	310	370

(a) Rank the data.
(b) Compute the five-number summary and the interquartile range.
(c) Make a box-and-whisker plot.

13. Many travelers make airline reservations and then do not show up for their scheduled flights. Air Connect Airlines took a random sample of 40 flights and recorded the number of "no-shows" who were using discount fares. The results were

3	5	2	5	1	4	0	7	8	10
12	7	5	0	2	7	5	8	6	12
6	10	18	16	21	9	10	3	9	7
9	10	15	8	4	6	5	7	9	9

(a) Rank the data.
(b) Make a box-and-whisker plot.
(c) Find the interquartile range.

14. Air Connect decided to require discount fares to be paid in advance and a fee to be charged for last-minute (less than 24 hours) cancellations or "no-shows." When this policy was in effect, another random sample of 40 flights was selected and the number of "no-shows" who were using discount fares was recorded. The results were

1	7	6	2	3	2	1	0	3	9
3	1	5	0	7	2	6	3	3	5

| 2 | 9 | 11 | 3 | 6 | 2 | 0 | 4 | 7 | 8 |
| 12 | 0 | 3 | 7 | 6 | 2 | 1 | 1 | 2 | 4 |

(a) Rank the data.

(b) Make a box-and-whisker plot.

(c) Find the interquartile range.

(d) Compare this plot with the one in Problem 13. Discuss the location of the medians, the location of the middle half of the data banks, and the distance from Q_1 and Q_3 to the extreme values.

15. The following data are the annual automobile insurance premiums for preferred suburban and rural customers in Michigan for insurance companies rated by *Consumer Reports* in August of 1992:

Suburban premiums:	2528	2360	2588	2726	3806
	2216	2647	2715	1944	2635
Rural premiums:	1933	1701	2175	2202	2670
	2216	2122	1813	1994	2059

For each group, do the following:

(a) Rank the data.

(b) Compute the five-number summary and the interquartile range.

(c) Make a box-and-whisker plot.

(d) Compare your box-and-whisker plots. Comment on the differences.

16. Box-and-whisker plots for the weekly percentage change in the closing prices of Coca-Cola stock, McDonald's stock, and Disney stock (May to November 1993, *Historical Quotes, Dow Jones News Retrieval Service*) are shown in Figure 3–17. Compare the plots. Answer each of the following questions, and explain each answer.

(a) Which stock has a percentage change distribution that is most symmetrical?

(b) Which stock has a percentage change distribution that is most spread?

(c) Which stock was most volatile during the period from May to November?

(d) Which stock had a median percentage change that was negative? Which stock had more weekly declines than weekly increases?

(e) If you were a conservative investor interested in purchasing one of these stocks but you wanted the one that had percentage declines that were smallest, which would you select? How do the sizes of the percentage increases in this stock compare with those of the other two?

(f) If you were an investor willing to take risks and you wanted a stock with high growth, which of these stocks would you select? Which one had the highest percentage increases? How do the percentage decreases of this stock compare with those of the other two?

17. *Consumer Reports* (August 1992) rated automobile insurance companies and gave annual premiums for top-rated companies in several states.

Figure 3–17 Weekly Percentage Change in Closing Price
(May–November 1993)

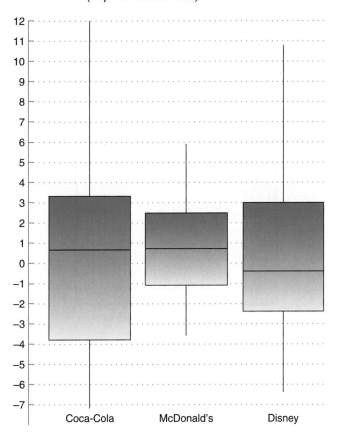

Figure 3–18 shows box plots for annual premiums for urban customers (married couple with one 17-year-old son) in three states. The box plots in Figure 3–18 are all drawn on the same scale on a TI-82 calculator.
(a) Which state has the lowest premium? the highest?

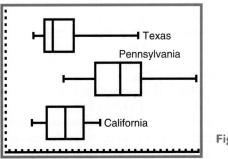

Figure 3–18 Insurance Premium
(Annual, Urban)

Figure 3–19 Five-Number Summaries for Insurance Premiums

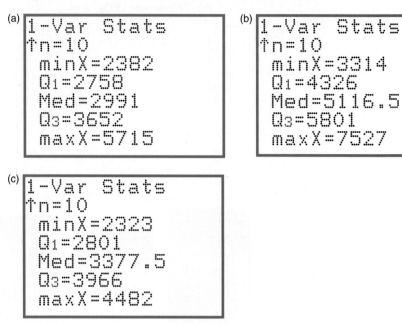

(a)
```
1-Var Stats
↑n=10
 minX=2382
 Q1=2758
 Med=2991
 Q3=3652
 maxX=5715
```

(b)
```
1-Var Stats
↑n=10
 minX=3314
 Q1=4326
 Med=5116.5
 Q3=5801
 maxX=7527
```

(c)
```
1-Var Stats
↑n=10
 minX=2323
 Q1=2801
 Med=3377.5
 Q3=3966
 maxX=4482
```

(b) Which state has the highest median premium?

(c) Which state has the smallest range of premiums? the smallest interquartile range?

(d) Figure 3–19 gives the five-number summaries generated on the TI-82 for the box plots of Figure 3–18. Match the five-number summaries to the appropriate box plot.

 18. The *Statistical Abstract of the United States, 1992* gave the following data about average disposable personal income per capita by state in thousands of dollars for 1991:

15.1	18.7	15.1	19.4	16.0	22.0	18.6	21.9	16.6	15.4
14.8	17.9	15.9	15.4	15.9	14.9	15.3	14.2	14.8	15.5
15.8	16.7	18.5	20.2	17.0	12.4	14.3	13.2	14.7	16.3
13.3	14.3	13.4	11.5	12.9	13.3	13.0	15.2	14.1	13.5
14.7	16.6	13.0	14.2	12.5	16.4	17.0	15.0	17.7	18.2

(a) Rank the data.

(b) Compute the five-number summary and the interquartile range.

(c) Make a box-and-whisker plot.

(d) Comment on the distribution of disposable personal income. How much spread is there from the median to each extreme? How might this distribution be used in the design of marketing strategies and pricing for car sales, home sales, or vacation packages.

19. Some data sets include values so high or so low they seem to stand apart from the rest of the data. These data are called *outliers*. Outliers may be from data collection errors, data entry errors, or simply valid but unusual data values. Regardless of the reason, it is important to identify outliers in the data set and examine the outliers carefully to determine if they are in error. One way to detect outliers is to use a box-and-whisker plot. Data values that fall beyond the limits

    Lower Limit: $Q_1 - 1.5 \times (IQR)$
    Upper Limit: $Q_3 + 1.5 \times (IQR)$

    where IQR is the interquartile range are suspected outliers. In the computer software package Minitab, values beyond these limits are plotted with asterisks (*).

    Students from a statistics class were asked to record their heights in inches. The heights were (as recorded)

65	72	68	64	60	55	73	71
52	63	61	74	69	67	74	50
4	75	67	62	66	80	64	65

    (a) Make a box-and-whisker plot of the data.
    (b) Find the value of the interquartile range (IQR).
    (c) Multiply the IQR by 1.5 and find the lower and upper limits.
    (d) Are there any data values below the lower limit? above the upper limit? List any suspected outliers. What might be some explanations for the outliers?

Summary

In order to characterize numerical data, we use both averages and variation. An average is an attempt to summarize the data into just one number. We studied several important averages: the mode, the median, the mean, and weighted averages. We also looked at trimmed means, which are more resistant to the effects of extreme values. However, an average alone can be misleading; we really need another statistical cross-reference. The measure of data spread, or variation, satisfies the purpose. The variations that we looked at most carefully were the range, the variance, the standard deviation, and the interquartile range. Chebyshev's theorem enables us to estimate the data spread. The coefficient of variation lets us compare relative spread from different data sets. A box-and-whisker plot gives a good visual impression of the range of the data and the location of the middle half of the data.

In later work the average we will use most is the mean; the measure of variation we will use most is the standard deviation. Because the mean and standard deviation are so important, we learned how to estimate these values from data already organized in a frequency distribution.

Important Words and Symbols

	Section		Section
Average	3.1	Population standard	
Mode	3.1	deviation, σ	3.2
Median	3.1	Coefficient of variation	3.2
Mean, $\bar{x}$	3.1	Chebyshev's Theorem	
Trimmed mean	3.1	Mean of grouped data	3.3
Summation symbol, Σ	3.1	Standard deviation of	
Resistant measure	3.1	grouped data	3.3
Variation	3.2	Weighted average	3.4
Range	3.2	Percentile	3.4
Sample variance, s^2	3.2	Quartile	3.4
Sample standard deviation,		Interquartile range	3.4
s	3.2	Median rank	3.4
Sum of the squares, SS_x	3.2	Whisker	3.4
Square of the Sum $(\Sigma x)^2$	3.2	Box-and-whisker plot	
Population size, N	3.2	Outlier	3.4
Population mean, μ	3.2		

Chapter Review Problems

1. In Colorado, a driver's license expires on the driver's birthday every four years. A driver is not permitted to renew the license except during the 90 days prior to and including the driver's birthday during the year in which the license expires. A random sample of 100 renewals showed the number of days before expiration that a license was renewed. The data are grouped such that x represents the days before expiration of license and f represents the frequency.

x	0–29	30–59	60–89
f	65	25	10

   (a) Estimate the sample mean $\bar{x}$ of the days before expiration that a renewal is made.
   (b) Estimate the sample standard deviation s.

2. A random sample of medical malpractice claims that had to be paid last year showed the following amounts (in millions of dollars):

3.2	1.4	0.7	0.2	0.5	2.1
0.8	1.7	1.6	0.5	0.6	0.2

   (a) Make a box-and-whisker plot for these data.
   (b) Compute the sample mean and median. Which is larger?
   (c) Compute the range, sample standard deviation, and coefficient of variation.

3. Laser printers are becoming more and more popular. *PC Magazine* (vol. 8, no. 19) rated 34 laser printers. The list prices (in hundreds of dollars) follow:

125	29	45	57	30	20	19	45
20	22	45	40	80	43	15	27
20	55	24	70	16	65	80	130
45	25	45	15	115	30	63	195
75	170						

(a) Make a box-and-whisker plot of the data. Find the interquartile range.

(b) Make a frequency table using three classes. Then estimate the mean and sample standard deviation.

(c) If you have a statistical calculator or computer, use it to find the actual sample mean and sample standard deviation.

4. Professor Cramer determines a final grade based on attendance, two papers, three major tests, and a final exam. Each of these activities has a total of 100 possible points. However, the activities carry different weights. Attendance is worth 5%, each paper is worth 8%, each test is worth 15%, and the final is worth 34%.

(a) What is the average for a student with 92 on attendance, 73 on the first paper, 81 on the second paper, 85 on test 1, 87 on test 2, 83 on test 3, and 90 on the final exam?

(b) Compute the average for a student with the above scores on the papers, tests, and final exam, but with a score of only 20 on attendance.

5. An elevator is loaded with 16 people and is at its load limit of 2500 lb. What is the mean weight of these people?

6. "Radon: The Problem No One Wants to Face" is the title of an article appearing in *Consumer Reports* (October 1989). Radon is a gas emitted from the ground that can collect in houses and buildings. At certain levels it can cause lung cancer. Radon concentrations are measured in picocuries per liter (pCi/L). A radon level of 4 pCi/L is considered "acceptable." Radon levels in a house vary from week to week. In one house, a sample of 8 weeks had the following readings for radon level (in pCi/L):

1.9	2.8	5.7	4.2	1.9	8.6	3.9	7.2

(a) Find the mean, median, and mode.

(b) Find the sample standard deviation, coefficient of variation and the range.

7. The following table shows the periods of time a sample of 66 Pitkin County prisoners had to wait in jail prior to the beginning of their trials.

Number of months, x	0	1	2	3	4	5	6	7	8
Number of prisoners, f	20	17	9	5	0	6	3	4	2

(a) Find the mean number of months waited.
(b) Find the sample standard deviation of the waiting times.

8. Radar was used to check speeds on a random sample of 20 cars in rush-hour traffic on an Atlanta expressway at 7:30 A.M. with the following results (in miles per hour):

50	60	48	60	56	55	60	58	50	45
55	40	45	66	50	60	55	38	55	60

(a) Make a box-and-whisker plot of the data. Find the interquartile range.
(b) Find the mean, median, and mode.
(c) Comment on the statement: "On the average, cars do not exceed the speed limit (55) during the early morning rush hour." Which average is being referred to in this statement? For which averages is this statement *not* true?

9. The following data are from the *Historical Statistics of the United States; Economic Report of the President.* The data give U.S. rate of inflation, as a percent, for the years 1970 to 1989.

5.9	4.3	3.3	6.2	11.0	9.1	5.8	6.5	7.7	11.3
13.5	10.4	6.1	3.2	4.3	3.6	1.9	4.0	4.4	4.6

(a) Use a calculator with mean and standard deviation keys to verify that the mean inflation rate was 6.36%, with sample standard deviation 3.17% for this 20-year period.
(b) Use Chebyshev's theorem to find an interval of inflation rates centered about the mean in which you would expect at least 50% of the years to fall. (*Hint:* Solve $1 - \dfrac{1}{k^2} = 0.50$ to obtain $k = \sqrt{2}$.)
(c) Use Chebyshev's theorem to find an interval of inflation rates centered about the mean in which you would expect at least 75% of the years to fall.

10. The circumferences (distance around) of 94 blue spruce trees selected at random in Roosevelt National Forest were measured. The results to the nearest inch were grouped in Table 3–29. Using the midpoints of the tree circumference classes, find the mean and standard deviation.

Table 3–29 Circumference of Blue Spruce Trees

Circumference (in.)	Number of Trees
10–24	6
25–39	20
40–54	52
55–69	16

11. The following set of numbers consists of the ages (rounded to the nearest year) of 10 people selected at random who were convicted of armed robbery last year in Brooks County, Mississippi:

    19   24   26   23   19   27   46   52   27   27

    (a) Find the mean, median, and mode.
    (b) Find the range and sample standard deviation.

12. The number of tourists visiting Silver City, Colorado, each day during the first week of July last year were:

    310   418   512   452   365   570   432

    (a) Find the mean and median.
    (b) Is there a mode?
    (c) Find the range and population standard deviation.

13. (a) Is it possible that the range and standard deviation can be equal? If your answer is yes, give an example of a data set where they are equal.
    (b) Is it possible that the mean, median and mode can all be equal? Is it possible they can all be different? If your answer is yes to either question, give an example to illustrate your answer.

14. A racing car manufacturer makes two models, the Zapper and Zonker, which are alike in every respect except body design and styling. To determine if the body design of the Zapper has less wind resistance, both cars are tested at the Indianapolis Speedway. The following table gives lap times in minutes on the 2.5-mile track:

Zapper	1.0	0.9	1.0	0.8	0.9	1.0	0.9	1.0
Zonker	1.3	1.2	1.0	0.9	1.1	0.9	1.4	1.3

    (a) Find the mean lap time $\bar{x}$ for both the Zapper and the Zonker.
    (b) Find the sample standard deviation s for both.
    (c) Which model had better average lap times? Was its performance consistently better? How is this reflected in the standard deviation of lap times?

15. A performance evaluation for new sales representatives at Office Automation Incorporated involves several ratings done on a scale of 1 to 10, with 10 the highest rating. The activities rated include new contacts, successful contacts, total contacts, dollar volume of sales, and reports. Then an overall rating is determined by using a weighted average. The weights are 2 for new contacts, 3 for successful contacts, 3 for total contacts, 5 for dollar value of sales, and 3 for reports. What would the overall rating be for a sales representative with ratings of 5 for new contacts, 8 for successful contacts, 7 for total contacts, 9 for dollar volume of sales, and 7 for reports?

DATA HIGHLIGHTS

1. *The Story of Old Faithful* is a short book written by George Marler and published by the Yellowstone Association. Chapter 7 of this interesting book talks about the effect of the 1959 earthquake on eruption intervals for Old Faithful Geyser. Dr. John Rinehart (a senior research scientist with the National Oceanic and Atmospheric Administration) has done extensive studies of the eruption intervals before and after the 1959 earthquake. Examine Figure 3–20. Notice the general shape. Is the graph more or less symmetrical? Does it have a single mode frequency? The mean interval between eruptions has remained steady at about 65 minutes for the past 100 years. Therefore, the 1959 earthquake did not significantly change the mean, but it did change the distribution of eruption intervals. Examine Figure 3–21. Would you say there are really two frequency modes? One shorter and the other longer? Explain. The overall mean is about the same for both graphs, but one graph has a much larger standard deviation (for eruption intervals) than the other. Do no calculations, just look at both graphs, and then explain which graph has the smaller and which has the larger standard deviation. Which distribution will have the larger coefficient of variation? In everyday terms, what would this mean if you were actually at Yellowstone waiting to see the next eruption of Old Faithful? Explain your answer.

2. The age distribution of the 400 wealthiest people in the United States is shown in Figure 3–22 (*USA Today*, October 5, 1992). Use class midpoints

Figure 3–20 Typical Behavior of Old Faithful Geyser Before 1959 Quake

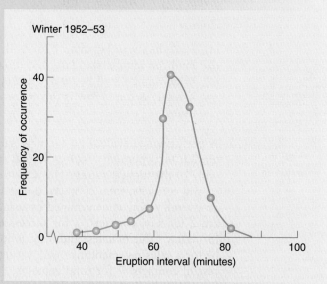

Figure 3–21 Typical Behavior of Old Faithful Geyser
After 1959 Quake

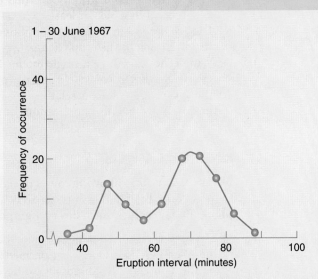

Figure 3–22 Ages of the 400 Wealthiest People
(October 5, 1992)

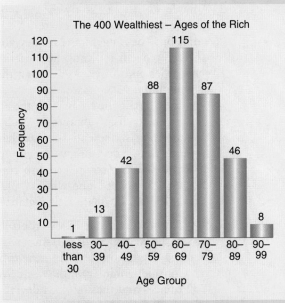

Source: Copyright 1992, USA TODAY. Reprinted with
permission.

and the provided frequencies to estimate the mean and standard deviation of this frequency distribution. Then use Chebyshev's theorem to find an age interval in which at least 75% of the wealthiest people will be found. Did we need to make any assumptions about the age distributions of these people? Look at the graph again. Would you say the shape is more or less symmetrical? Is there a single mode? Recall our study of relative frequencies in Section 2.2. Write a brief explanation of how you could convert the given figure into a relative-frequency histogram. In your discussion include some possible applications of such a relative-frequency histogram.

LINKING CONCEPTS

Discuss each of the following topics in class or review the topics on your own. Then write a brief but complete essay in which you summarize the main points. Please include formulas and graphs as appropriate.

1. An average is an attempt to summarize a collection of data into just *one* number. Discuss how the mean, median, and mode all represent averages in this context. Also discuss the differences among these averages. Why is the mean a balance point? Why is the median a midway point? Why is the mode the most common data point? List three areas of daily life where you think either the mean, median, or mode would be the best choice to describe an "average."

2. Why do we need to study the variation of a collection of data? Why isn't the average by itself adequate? We have studied three ways to measure variation. The range, standard deviation, and to a large extent, a box-and-whisker plot all indicate the variation within a data collection. Discuss similarities and differences among these ways to measure data variation. Why would it seem reasonable to pair the median with a box-and-whisker plot and to pair the mean with the standard deviation? What are the advantages and disadvantages of each method of describing data spread? Comment on statements such as the following: (a) The range is easy to compute, but it doesn't give much information, (b) although the standard deviation is more complicated to compute, it has some significant applications, (c) the box-and-whisker plot is fairly easy to construct, and it gives a lot of information at a glance.

3. Why is the coefficient of variation important? What do we mean when we say the coefficient of variation has no units? What advantage can there be in having no units? Why is *relative size* important?

   Consider robin eggs; the mean weight of a collection of robin eggs is 0.72 ounces and the standard deviation is 0.12 ounces. Now consider elephants; the mean weight of elephants in the zoo is 6.42 tons, with a standard deviation 1.07 tons. The units of measurement are different and there is a great deal of difference between the size of an elephant and a robin's egg. Yet the coefficient of variation is about the same for both. Comment on this from the viewpoint of the size of the standard deviation relative to the mean.

4. What is Chebyshev's theorem? Suppose you have a friend who knows very little about statistics. Write a paragraph or two in which you describe Chebyshev's theorem for your friend. Keep the discussion as simple as possible, but be sure to get the main ideas across to your friend. Suppose he or she asks "what is this stuff good for" and suppose you respond (a little sarcastically) that Chebyshev's theorem applies to everything from butterflies to the orbits of the planets! Would you be correct? Explain.

5. Have each student count the amount of loose change (not paper money) brought to class today. Use a calculator with mean and standard deviation buttons to compute the mean and standard deviation for the class. (Perhaps the professor can enter the data in the calculator while the students tell him or her the numbers.)

   (a) Compute the endpoints of the interval $\bar{x} - 2s$ to $\bar{x} + 2s$. Have each student raise a hand if the amount of loose change that was counted falls in this interval. Explain why you expect about 75% or more of the class to raise their hands.

   (b) Compute the endpoints of the interval $\bar{x} - \sqrt{2}s$ to $\bar{x} + \sqrt{2}s$. Repeat part a for this interval. Explain why you expect about 50% or more of the class to raise their hands.

   (c) Suppose we take the point of view that our statistics class is a sample of the entire student body. What percentage of the entire student body do you expect will have from $\bar{x} - 3s$ to $\bar{x} + 3s$ cents in loose change. Is your answer a lower estimate for the actual percentage? Explain.

   (d) Write a paragraph or two in which you discuss how in part c we have used inferential statistics to estimate the population (i.e., student body) distribution of loose change using a sample (i.e., our statistics class) from that population.

Using Technology

The problems in this section may be done using statistical computer software or calculators with statistical functions. Displays and suggestions are given for Minitab (Release 9), the TI-82 graphing calculator, and ComputerStat.

Descriptive Statistics—Ungrouped Data

Statistical software packages and graphing calculators all provide descriptive statistics such as mean, median, and standard deviation for data. Most statistical software and graphing calculators will order the data for you so that you can find the mode. In some cases the quartiles values Q_1 and Q_3 are also given.

Minitab

In Minitab, you enter the data in a column and then enter the DESCRIBE command. The commands

```
MTB > SET C1
DATA> (enter your data)
DATA> END
MTB > DESCRIBE C1
MTB > SORT C1 put in C2
MTB > PRINT C2
MTB > BOXPLOT C1
```

allow you to enter your data in column 1, and then Minitab provides the sample mean, median, 5% trimmed mean, sample standard deviation, standard error of the mean (see Chapter 6), the minimum, maximum, Q_1 and Q_3 for the data in column C1. The SORT command sorts the data of column C1 and puts the sorted list in column C2. When you print C2, you can scan the data to find the mode. Finally the BOXPLOT command draws a box plot for the data in C1.

Note: Minitab uses a slightly different method to compute Q_1 and Q_3 than that shown in this text, so that the values for Q_1 and Q_3 shown in Minitab will be slightly different from those you compute or those shown on the TI-82.

There are also commands available to find the sample mean, sample standard deviation, median, minimum, and maximum of data entered in rows. See a manual for these commands.

TI-82

Enter the data in a list such as L1. Then, in the STAT menu select the CALC option. Select 1-Var Stats. At the 1-Var Stats prompt, type L1. The following screens show you output from a typical data set (Problem 19 of Section 3.4).

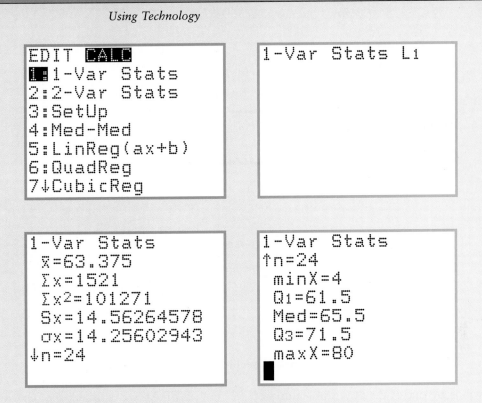

```
EDIT CALC
1:1-Var Stats
2:2-Var Stats
3:SetUp
4:Med-Med
5:LinReg(ax+b)
6:QuadReg
7↓CubicReg
```

```
1-Var Stats L1
```

```
1-Var Stats
 x̄=63.375
 Σx=1521
 Σx²=101271
 Sx=14.56264578
 σx=14.25602943
↓n=24
```

```
1-Var Stats
↑n=24
 minX=4
 Q1=61.5
 Med=65.5
 Q3=71.5
 maxX=80
▮
```

The TI-82 also produces a box plot. Press STAT PLOT and select box plot. Then set the WINDOW with Xmin = minimum data value and Xmax = maximum data value. The following displays use the same data as summarized in the previous displays.

```
STAT PLOTS
1:Plot1...
   On ▥ L1
2:Plot2...
   Off ▥ L2
3:Plot3...
   Off ⬢ L1 L2 ▪
4↓PlotsOff
```

```
WINDOW FORMAT
 Xmin=4
 Xmax=80
 Xscl=3
 Ymin=⁻5
 Ymax=20
 Yscl=1
```

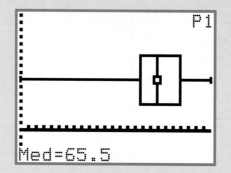

ComputerStat

In ComputerStat follow the instructions on the screen to enter your data. Then under the Descriptive Statistics menu, select Averages and Variation for Ungrouped Data.

Application I

Using the software or calculator available to you, do the following.

1. Trade winds are one of the beautiful features of island life in Hawaii. The following data represent total air movement in miles each day over a weather station in Hawaii as determined by a continuous anemometer recorder. The period of observation is January 1 to February 15, 1971.

26	14	18	14	113	50	13	22
27	57	28	50	72	52	105	138
16	33	18	16	32	26	11	16
17	14	57	100	35	20	21	34
18	13	18	28	21	13	25	19
11	19	22	19	15	20		

Source: United States Department of Commerce, National Oceanic and Atmospheric Administration, Environmental Data Service. *Climatological Data, Annual Summary, Hawaii,* vol. 67, no. 13. Asheville: National Climatic Center, 1971, 11, 24.

(a) Enter the data.

(b) Use the computer to find the sample mean, median, and (if it exists) mode.

(c) Use the computer to find the range, sample variance, and sample standard deviation.

(d) As a topic in Exploratory Data Analysis (EDA) we studied the box-and-whisker plot. Use the five-number summary provided by the computer to make a box-and-whisker plot of total air movement over the weather station.

(e) There are four exceptionally high data values: 113, 105, 138, and 100. The strong winds of January 5 (113 reading) brought in a cold front that dropped snow on Haleakala National Park (at the 8000 ft elevation). The residents were so excited that they drove up to see the snow and caused such a massive traffic jam that the Park Service had to close the road. The winds of January 15 and 16 (readings 105 and 138) brought in a storm that created more damaging funnel clouds than any other storm to that date in the recorded history of Hawaii. The strong winds of January 28 (reading 100) accompanied a storm with funnel clouds that did much damage. Eliminate these values (i.e., 100, 105, 113, 138) from the data bank and redo parts (a), (b), (c), (d). Compare your results with those previously obtained. Which average is most affected? What happens to the standard deviation? How do the two box-and-whisker plots compare?

Descriptive Statistics — Grouped Data

ComputerStat has a program specifically written to handle grouped data. In Minitab, you need to write your own Minitab program. On the TI-82, you need to find midpoints first, and then the calculator will process the grouped data.

Minitab

First find the midpoints of the data classes. Enter these in column C1 and the corresponding frequencies in C2. Then create a program using the formulas given in the section to compute the mean and standard deviations of the grouped data. The following program will print the mean and standard deviation of grouped data.

```
MTB > #  enter midpoints in C1
MTB > #  enter frequencies in C2
MTB > SUM C2 put in K1
MTB > Let C3 = C1*C2
MTB > SUM C3 put in K2
MTB > NAME K3 = 'MEAN'
MTB > LET K3 = K2/K1
MTB > LET C4 = (C1 — K3)**2*C2
MTB > SUM C4 put in K4
MTB > LET K5 = SQRT(K4/(K1 — 1))
MTB > NAME K5 = 'STDEV'
MTB > PRINT K3, K5
```

TI-82

Enter midpoints in list L1 and frequencies in list L2. Then choose SetUp...under CALC. The Xlist should be L1 and the Freq should be L2. Then select 1-Var Stats for L1,L2. The final screen will give you the mean and standard deviation for the grouped data.

Select →

```
EDIT  CALC
1:1-Var Stats
2:2-Var Stats
3:SetUp
4:Med-Med
5:LinReg(ax+b)
6:QuadReg
7↓CubicReg
```

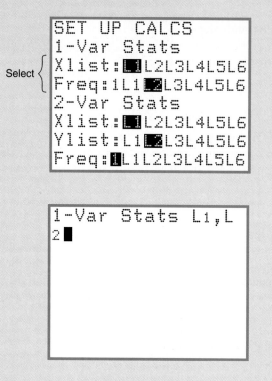

Select {

```
SET UP CALCS
1-Var Stats
Xlist:█1L2L3L4L5L6
Freq:1L1█2L3L4L5L6
2-Var Stats
Xlist:█1L2L3L4L5L6
Ylist:L1█2L3L4L5L6
Freq:█L1L2L3L4L5L6
```

```
1-Var Stats L1,L
2█
```

ComputerStat

Under the Descriptive Menu, select Grouped Data. Enter data as instructed.

Application 2

Using the software or calculator available to you, do the following.

1. Sometimes natural beauty takes a form that is very austere. The summit of Longs Peak in Colorado (elevation 14,256 ft) is very beautiful, and in winter very austere. In the following data, x = hourly peak gusts in miles per hour of winter wind on the summit of Longs Peak and f = frequency of occurrence for a sample period of 1518 observation hours.

   (a) Using the class limits, compute each class midpoint. (*Hint:* Compute the first class midpoint. To get the others, just keep adding 10 to the previous class midpoint.)

   (b) Enter the class midpoints and class frequencies into the computer.

   (c) Use the computer to find the approximate sample mean, sample variance, and sample standard deviation of hourly peak gusts of winter wind on the summit of Longs Peak.

Hourly Peak Gust mph	Total Hours of Occurrence Number
0–9	141
10–19	217
20–29	376
30–39	290
40–49	195
50–59	143
60–69	61
70–79	37
80–89	21
90–99	11
100–109	12
110–119	3
120–129	5
130–139	3
140–149	3

(In addition to the values shown in the table, there were three incidences where the wind gusts exceeded 150 mph.)

Source: Glidden, D. E. *Winter Wind Studies in Rocky Mountain National Park.* Estes Park, Colo.: Rocky Mountain Nature Association, 1982, 23.

Computer Displays

How much can you expect to pay for a compact disc player? It depends on the quality and features you want. However, shopping around for the best price might also make a difference. *Consumer Digest* (December, 1989) gives list and "best" prices on a variety of models of compact disc players. Several computer displays are shown that summarize the data for a random sample of 25 models. For each model we used the "list" price in the list price display and the corresponding "best" price in the best price displays. Use the computer displays to compare the "list" and "best" prices.

In Minitab, the STDEV is the sample standard deviation. The Minitab procedure to compute quartiles Q1 and Q3 is slightly different from that described in Section 3.4 of this chapter.

ComputerStat Display:
"List" Price Summary for 25 CD Players

```
SAMPLE MODE = 300
SAMPLE MEAN = 392.4
SAMPLE VARIANCE = 41770.25
SAMPLE STANDARD DEVIATION = 204.377
SAMPLE COEFFICIENT OF VARIATION = 5.
SAMPLE RANGE = 729
FIVE NUMBER SUMMARY FOR BOX-AND-WHI
LOW VALUE = 170
FIRST QUARTILE VALUE = 249.5
MEDIAN VALUE = 300
THIRD QUARTILE VALUE = 450
HIGH VALUE = 899
```

Minitab Display:
"Best" Price Summary for 25 CD Players

```
MTB > describe c2
```

	N	MEAN	MEDIAN	TRMEAN	STDEV	SEMEAN
C2	25	351.1	270.0	336.4	190.5	38.1

	MIN	MAX	Q1	Q3
C2	170.0	899.0	220.0	410.0

Minitab 9.0 has two levels of graphics, character and professional. The following displays show box plots in each mode:

Character Display

Figure 3–23 Minitab 9.0 Display of Box-and-Whisker Plot for "Best Price"

```
MTB > GStd.
MTB > BoxPlot C2.


                   -------------
          ----I  +     I----------        *    *    *
                   -------------
          ----+---------+---------+---------+---------+---------+--C2
            150       300       450       600       750       900
```

Professional Graphics Display

Figure 3–24 Minitab 9.0 Display of Box-and-Whisker
Plot for "Best Price"

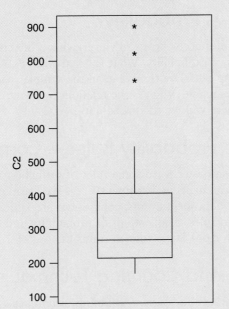

Section 4.1

What Is Probability?

Probabilities occur practically everywhere. In this section we study basic concepts of probability. What is a statistical experiment? What is a sample space, and what are the events in the sample space? How are probability assignments made? What is the relationship between probability and statistics? Where will we use probability?

Section 4.2

Some Probability Rules—Compound Events

In this section we learn some rules of probability that are valid in all probability assignments and sample spaces. We learn about mutually exclusive events, independent events, conditional probability, addition rules, and multiplication rules. Applications of probability and compound events are important for our later work in statistics.

Section 4.3

Trees and Counting Techniques

Tree diagrams and general counting techniques are useful in the construction of probability sample spaces. If a statistical experiment involves several stages, then the multiplication rule for counting, permutations, and combinations can be important tools in determining the probability of each outcome of the experiment.

Section 4.4

Introduction to Random Variables and Probability Distributions

We discuss discrete and continuous random variables. Then we examine discrete probability distributions in more detail. The expected value and standard deviation for discrete probability distributions are calculated.

CHAPTER FOUR

*Pierre-Simon Laplace
(1749–1827)*

This renowned French astronomer and mathematician wrote *The Analytical Theory of Probability*.

Elementary Probability Theory

We see that the theory of probabilities is at bottom only common sense reduced to calculation; it makes us appreciate with exactitude what reasonable minds feel by a sort of instinct, often without being able to account for it.

Pierre Simon Laplace

This is how the great mathematician Laplace described the theory of mathematical probability. The discovery of the mathematical theory of probability was shared by two Frenchmen: Blaise Pascal and Pierre Fermat. These seventeenth-century scholars were attracted to the subject by the inquiries of the Chevalier de Méré, a gentleman gambler.

Although the first applications of probability were to games of chance and gambling, today the subject seems to pervade almost every aspect of modern life. Everything from the orbits of spacecraft to the social behavior of woodchucks is described in terms of probabilities.

Focus Problem ▶ How Often Do Lie Detectors Lie?

James Burke is an educator who is known for his interesting science-related radio and television shows aired by the British Broadcasting Corporation. His book *Chances: Risk and Odds in Everyday Life* (Virginia Books, London, 1991) contains a great wealth of fascinating information about probabilities. The following quote is from Professor Burke's book:

If I take a polygraph test and lie, what is the risk I will be detected? According to some studies there's about a 72 percent chance you will be caught by the machine.

What is the risk that if I take a polygraph test it will incorrectly say that I lied? At least 1 in 15 will be thus falsely accused.

Both these statements contain conditional probabilities, which we will study in Section 4.2. Information from that section will allow us to answer the following questions:

Suppose a person answers 10% of a long battery of questions with lies. Assume that the remaining 90% of the questions are answered truthfully.

1. Estimate the percentage of answers the polygraph will *wrongly* indicate as lies.

2. Estimate the percentage of answers the polygraph will *correctly* indicate as lies.

If the polygraph indicated that 30% of the questions were answered as lies, what would you estimate for the *actual* percentage of questions the person answered as lies?

Section 4.1   What Is Probability?

Basic Concepts

We encounter statements in terms of probability all the time. An excited sports announcer claims that Sheila has a 90% chance of breaking the world record in the upcoming 100-yard dash. Henry figures that if he guesses on a true–false question, the probability of getting it right is 1/2. The Right to Health Lobby claims the probability is 0.40 of getting an erroneous report from a medical lab in one low-cost health center. They are consequently lobbying for a federal agency to license and monitor all medical laboratories.

When we use probability in a statement, we're using a *number between 0 and 1* to indicate the likelihood of an event. We'll use the notation $P(A)$ (read, *P of A*) to denote the probability of event A. The closer to 1 the probability assignment is, the more likely the event is to occur. If the event A is certain to occur, then $P(A)$ should be 1.

It is important to know what probability statements mean and how to compute or assign probabilities to events because probability is the language of inferential statistics. For instance, suppose a college counselor claims that 70% of first-year students receive counseling to help plan their schedules. Because of the high percentage of students needing help, he is requesting that an additional counselor be hired. You want to test the counselor's claim. In doing so, you pick a random sample of 30 first-year students and find that only three of them got help from a counselor. Can you challenge the counselor's claim on the basis of this random sample in which only 10% of the students got counselor help with their schedules? To answer this question, we need to find the *probability* of picking a random sample of first-year students in which only 10% got counselor help. This is the kind of question we will consider in hypothesis testing (Chapter 9).

In the meantime, we need to learn how to find probabilities or assign them to events. There are three major methods. One is *intuition*. The sports announcer probably used Sheila's performances in past track events and his own confidence in her running ability as a basis for his prediction that she has a

Relative Frequency

90% chance of breaking the world record. In other words, the announcer feels that the probability is 0.90 that Sheila will break the world record.

The Right to Health Lobby used another method to arrive at their probability statement. They took the *relative frequency* with which erroneous lab reports occurred. From a random sample of $n = 100$, they found $f = 40$ erroneous lab reports. From this they computed the relative frequency of erroneous lab reports via formula (1).

Probability Formula for Relative Frequency

$$\text{Probability of an event} = \text{relative frequency} = \frac{f}{n} \qquad (1)$$

where f is the frequency of an event,
n is the sample size.

In the case of the lab reports, we have

$$\text{Relative frequency} = \frac{f}{n} = \frac{40}{100} = 0.40$$

The relative frequency of erroneous lab reports was used as the *probability* of erroneous reports.

The technique of using the relative frequency of an event as the probability of that event is a common way of assigning probabilities and will be used a great deal in later chapters. The underlying assumption we make is that if events occurred a certain percentage of times in the past, they will occur about the same percentage of times in the future. In fact, this can be strengthened to a very general statement called the *law of large numbers*.

Law of Large Numbers

Law of Large Numbers

In the long run, as the sample size increases and increases, the relative frequencies of outcomes get closer and closer to the theoretical (or actual) probability value.

The law of large numbers is the reason such businesses as health insurance, automobile insurance, and gambling casinos can exist and make a profit. In Central City, Colorado, there are many casinos with many slot machines. The winnings of a gambler on a single play or even a few plays are uncertain (small sample size). This is one of the reasons gambling is exciting. However, on tens of thousands of plays, the theoretical or actual probability of winning favors the casino. That's why the casino and its owners regard gambling as a business. The house is guaranteed a profit in the long run.

Equally Likely Events

Henry used the third method of assigning probabilities when he determined the probability of correctly guessing the answer to a true–false question. Essentially, he used the probability formula for *equally likely outcomes.*

> **Probability Formula When Outcomes Are Equally Likely**
>
> $$\text{Probability of an event} = \frac{\text{number of outcomes favorable to event}}{\text{total number of outcomes}} \qquad (2)$$

In Henry's case, there are two possible outcomes. A test answer will be either correct or wrong. Since he is guessing, we assume that the outcomes are equally likely, and only one is "favorable" to being correct. So, by Formula (2),

$$P(\text{correct answer}) = \frac{\text{no. of favorable outcomes}}{\text{total no. of outcomes}} = \frac{1}{2}$$

We've seen three ways to assign probabilities: intuition, relative frequency, and, when outcomes are equally likely, a formula. Which do we use? Most of the time it depends on the information that is at hand or that can be feasibly obtained. Our choice of methods also depends on the particular problem. In Guided Exercise 1 you will see three different situations, and you will decide which way to assign the probabilities. *Remember, probabilities are numbers between 0 and 1, so don't assign probabilities outside this range.*

GUIDED EXERCISE 1

Assign a probability to the indicated event on the basis of the information provided. Indicate the technique you use: intuition, relative frequency, or the formula for equally likely outcomes.

(a) The director of the Readlot College Health Center wishes to open an eye clinic. To justify the expense of such a clinic, the director reports the probability that a student selected at random from the college roster needs corrective lenses. He took a random sample of 500 students to compute this probability and found that 375 of them needed corrective lenses. What is the probability that a Readlot College student selected at random needs corrective lenses?

(a) In this case we are given a sample size of 500, and we are told 375 of these students need glasses. It is appropriate to use a relative frequency for the desired probability:

$$P(\text{student needs glasses}) = \frac{f}{n} = \frac{375}{500} = 0.75$$

(b) The Friends of the Library host a fund-raising barbecue. George is on the cleanup committee. There are four members on this committee, and they draw lots to see who will clean the

(b) There are four people on the committee, and each is equally likely to be drawn. It is appropriate to use the formula for equally likely events. George can be drawn in only one way,

grills. Assuming that each member is equally likely to be drawn, what is the probability George will be assigned the grill cleaning job?

so there is only one outcome favorable to that event.

$$P(\text{George}) = \frac{\text{no. of favorable outcomes}}{\text{total no. of outcomes}} = \frac{1}{4} = 0.25$$

(c) Joanna photographs whales for Sea Life Adventure Films. On her next expedition, she is to film blue whales feeding. Her boss asks her what she thinks the probability of success will be for this particular assignment. She gives an answer based on her knowledge of the habits of blue whales and the region she is to visit. She is almost certain she will be successful. What specific number do you suppose she gave for the probability of success, and how do you suppose she arrived at it?

(c) Since Joanna is almost certain of success, she should make the probability close to 1. We would say $P(\text{success})$ is above 0.90 but less than 1. We think the probability assignment was based on intuition.

No matter how we compute probabilities, it is useful to know what outcomes are possible in a given setting. For instance, if you are going to decide the probability that Hardscrabble will win the Kentucky Derby, you need to know which other horses will be running.

Sample Space

A *statistical experiment* (or simply an experiment) can be thought of as any activity that results in a definite outcome. Usually the outcome is in the form of a description, count, or measurement. For example, tossing a coin can be thought of as an experiment. There are only two possible outcomes: heads or tails. The set of all possible outcomes of an experiment is the *sample space*. If you toss a coin, the sample space for that experiment consists of the two outcomes (heads or tails).

It is especially convenient to know the sample space in the case where all outcomes are equally likely because then we can compute probabilities of various events by using Formula (2).

$$P(\text{event } A) = \frac{\text{no. of outcomes favorable to } A}{\text{total no. of outcomes}} \qquad (2)$$

To use this formula, we need to know the sample space so that we can determine which outcomes are favorable to the event in question as well as the total number of outcomes.

Example 1

Human eye color is controlled by a single pair of genes (one from the father and one from the mother) called a *genotype*. Brown eye color, B, is dominant over blue eye color, ℓ. Therefore, in the genotype Bℓ, consisting of one brown gene B and one blue gene ℓ, the brown gene dominates. A person with a Bℓ genotype has brown eyes.

If both parents are brown-eyed and have genotype Bℓ, what is the probability that their child will have blue eyes? What is the probability the child will have brown eyes?

Solution: To answer these questions we need to look at the sample space of all possible eye color genotypes for the child. They are given in Table 4–1.

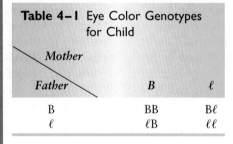

Table 4–1 Eye Color Genotypes for Child

	Mother	
Father	B	ℓ
B	BB	Bℓ
ℓ	ℓB	$\ell\ell$

The four possible genotypes for the child are equally likely, so we can use Formula (2) to compute probabilities. Blue eyes can occur only with the $\ell\ell$ genotype, so there is only one outcome favorable to blue eyes. By Formula (2),

$$P(\text{blue eyes}) = \frac{\text{no. of favorable outcomes}}{\text{total no. of outcomes}} = \frac{1}{4}$$

Brown eyes occur with the three remaining genotypes: BB, Bℓ, and ℓB. By Formula (2),

$$P(\text{brown eyes}) = \frac{\text{no. of favorable outcomes}}{\text{total no. of outcomes}} = \frac{3}{4}$$

GUIDED EXERCISE 2

Professor Gutierrez is making up a final exam for a course in literature of the Southwest. He wants the last three questions to be of the true–false type. In order to guarantee that the answers do not follow his favorite pattern, he lists all possible true–false combinations for three questions on slips of paper and then picks one at random from a hat.

(a) Finish listing the outcomes in the given sample space.

TTT FTT
TTF FTF
TFT _____
TFF _____

(a) The missing outcomes are FFT and FFF.

(b) What is the probability that all three items will be false? Use the formula

$$P(\text{all F}) = \frac{\text{no. of favorable outcomes}}{\text{total no. of outcomes}}$$

(b) There is only one outcome, FFF, favorable to all false, so

$$P(\text{all F}) = \frac{1}{8}$$

(c) What is the probability that exactly two items will be true?

(c) There are three outcomes that have exactly two true items: TTF, TFT, and FTT. Thus,

$$P(\text{two T}) = \frac{\text{no. of favorable outcomes}}{\text{total no. of outcomes}} = \frac{3}{8}$$

Complement of an Event

There is one more important point about probability assignments. The sum of all the probabilities assigned to outcomes in a sample space must be 1. This makes sense. If you think the probability is 0.65 that you will win a tennis match, you assume the probability is 0.35 that your opponent will win. This fact is particularly useful, for if the probability that an event occurs is denoted by p and the probability that it *does not* occur is denoted by q, we have

$p + q = 1$ since the sum of the probabilities of the outcomes must be 1,

or

$$q = 1 - p \tag{3}$$

For an event A, the event *not A* is called the *complement of A**. To compute the probability of the complement of A, we use Formula (3) and find

$$P(\textit{not A}) = 1 - P(A)$$

Example 2

The probability that a college student without a flu shot will get the flu is 0.45. What is the probability that a college student will *not* get the flu if the student has not had the flu shot?
Solution: In this case, we have

$$P(\text{will get flu}) = p = 0.45$$

$$P(\text{will } not \text{ get flu}) = q = 1 - p = 1 - 0.45 = 0.55$$

GUIDED EXERCISE 3

A veterinarian tells you that if you breed two cream-colored guinea pigs, the probability that an offspring will be pure white is 0.25. What is the probability that it will not be pure white?

(a) $P(\text{pure white}) + P(not \text{ pure white}) = $ _____

(b) $P(not \text{ pure white}) = $ _____

(a) 1

(b) $1 - 0.25$, or 0.75

---

*The complement of event A is often symbolized by the compact notation A^c or $\bar{A}$. However, in this text we will continue to use the more expanded description *not A* to refer to the complement of A. That is, *not A* refers to all the outcomes of the sample space that are not favorable to event A. (For Bayes's theorem in Appendix I we use A^c for the complement of A.

The important facts about probabilities we have seen in this section are

1. The probability of an event A is denoted by $P(A)$.
2. The probability of any event is a number between 0 and 1. The closer to 1 the probability is, the more likely the event is.
3. The sum of the probabilities of outcomes in a sample space is 1.
4. Probabilities can be assigned by using three methods: intuition, relative frequencies, or the formula for equally likely outcomes.
5. The probability that an event occurs plus the probability that the same event does not occur is 1.

Probability Related to Statistics

We conclude this section with a few comments on the nature of statistics versus probability. Although statistics and probability are closely related fields of mathematics, they are nevertheless separate fields. It can be said that probability is the medium through which statistical work is done. In fact, if it were not for probability theory, inferential statistics would not be possible.

Put very briefly, probability is the field of study that makes statements about what will occur when samples are drawn from a *known population*. Statistics is the field of study that describes how samples are to be obtained and how inferences are to be made *about unknown populations*.

A simple but effective illustration of the difference between these two subjects can be made by considering how we treat the contents of two boxes:

- Box I contains three green balls, five red balls, and four white balls.
- Box II contains a collection of colored balls, but the exact number and colors of the balls is unknown.

The study of probability would investigate Box I, where we already know the contents of the box. Typical probability questions would be

1. If one ball is drawn from Box I, what is the probability that the ball is green?
2. If three balls are drawn from Box I, what is the probability that one is white and two are red?
3. If four balls are drawn from Box I, what is the probability that none is red?

Box I

Probability

Given: 3 green balls, 5 red balls, 4 white balls

Box II

Statistics

Exact number and colors of balls are unknown

The study of statistics would investigate Box II, where we do not know the exact contents of the box. Typical work in statistics would ask us to draw a random sample of balls from Box II and, based on the sample results, make a conjecture about the colors and numbers of the population of balls in Box II.

In another sense, probability and statistics are like flip sides of the same coin. On the probability side, you know the overall description of the population (contents of Box I). The central problem is to compute the likelihood that a specific outcome will happen. On the statistics side, you only know the results of a sample drawn from Box II. The central problem is to describe the sample (descriptive statistic) and to draw conclusions about the population of Box II based on the sample results (inferential statistics).

In statistical work, the inferences we draw about an unknown population are not claimed to be absolutely correct. Since the population remains unknown (in a theoretical sense), we must accept a "best guess" for our conclusions and act using the most probable answer rather than absolute certainty.

Probability is the topic of this chapter. However, we will not study probability just for its own sake. Probability is a wonderful field of mathematics, but we will study mainly the ideas from probability that are needed for a proper understanding of statistics. We will move quickly from general facts and terminology about probability to counting techniques and a brief discussion about random variables and their probability distributions.

Even though we have only a brief introduction to probability, we will be able to answer questions raised in situations such as the following:

- Commercial salmon fishing is very important in Alaska. Since the salmon are sold by weight, it is useful to know the average weight of a freshly caught salmon. How large a sample of freshly caught salmon is needed if we want to be 95% sure the mean weight of the sample is within plus or minus 1 ounce of the mean weight of all catchable salmon in Alaskan waters? For the answer to this type question, see Example 6 in Section 8.4, in which we discuss probability as applied to sample size.

- Retail sales account for about two-thirds of all the money flow in the United States economy. For their first job after graduation, many college graduates are either in sales or in charge of a sales team. Whether you are a salesperson or in charge of a sales team, *sales quotas* are important. Suppose you are a bond broker and your job is to sell a particular bond issue by phone. History shows that the probability is about 20% that any one phone call will result in a bond sale. Your sales supervisor claims that you should make at least nine sales each day. How many phone calls should you make if you want to be 99% sure of getting your nine sales? For the answer to this type of question, see Section 5.3, in which we discuss probabilities and quota problems.

- Many practical situations call on us to choose between two competing statements. *Consumer Reports* (November 1991) did a study on the maintenance records of two competing brands of cellular phones. Each brand claims to have the lowest maintenance costs. Is one brand actually better than the other? If there is an apparent difference, is the difference statistically significant at, say, a 1% level (of risk)? For answers to these kinds of questions, see Section 9.7, in which we discuss tests for differences.

All the listed examples require some use of probability. This is why we encourage you to study this chapter carefully. Your time in doing so will be well spent.

Section 4.1 Problems

1. In your own words, carefully answer the question: What is probability? List three methods of assigning probabilities.

2. List examples of where probability might be applied in business, medicine, social science, and natural science. Why do you think probability will be useful in the study of statistics?

3. Which of the following numbers cannot be the probability of some event?
   (a) 0.71 (b) 4.1 (c) $\frac{1}{8}$ (d) −0.5
   (e) 0.5 (f) 0 (g) 1 (h) 150%

4. (a) Explain why −0.41 cannot be the probability of some event.
   (b) Explain why 1.21 cannot be the probability of some event.
   (c) Explain why 120% cannot be the probability of some event.
   (d) Can the number 0.56 be the probability of an event? Explain.

5. Laser treatments are used in a variety of medical situations. The *New England Journal of Medicine* (Feb. 16, 1989) reported on an experiment utilizing a laser to remove port wine–colored birthmarks. In the experiment, the laser treatment was used on 35 children (3 months to 14 years of age). For 33 of the children the birthmarks disappeared. From these data, estimate the probability of successful removal of this type of birthmark by laser treatment.

6. Isabel Briggs Myers was a pioneer in the study of personality types. The personality types are broadly defined according to four main preferences. Do married couples choose similar or different personality types in their mates? The following data give an indication (Source: I. B. Myers and M. H. McCaulley, *A Guide to the Development and Use of the Myers-Briggs Type Indicators*, p. 71).

Similarities and Differences in a Random Sample of 375 Married Couples	
Number of Similar Preferences	Number of Married Couples
All four	34
Three	131
Two	124
One	71
None	15

Suppose that a married couple is selected at random.
(a) Use the data to estimate the probability that they will have 0, 1, 2, 3, or 4 personality preferences in common.
(b) Do the probabilities add up to 1? Why should they? What is the sample space in this problem?

7. How do you find out about a job? The national Center for Career Strategies, Inc., has data on information sources that have led to actual jobs. Data adapted from a report in *USA Today* (August 31, 1989) show sources for 1000 jobs selected at random:

Source	Number of Jobs Obtained from Source
Mass mailing	50
Help-wanted ads	140
Executive search firms	110
Networking	700

(a) Use these data to estimate the probability that a job selected at random would have the listed source.
(b) Do these possibilities add up to 1? Should they? Why? Note that we are assuming that each job had only one of the listed sources.

8. Do couples get engaged or not? If they are engaged, how long did they date before becoming engaged? A poll of 1000 couples conducted by Bruskin and Goldring Research for Korbel Champagne Cellars gave the following information (*USA Today,* July 6, 1992):

Length of Dating Time Before Engagement	
Time	No. of Couples
Never engaged	200
Less than 1 year	240
1 to 2 years	210
More than 2 years	350

(a) Use the data to estimate the probability that a dating couple chosen at random is not engaged, dated less than 1 year before getting engaged, dated 1 to 2 years before getting engaged, or dated more than 2 years before getting engaged.
(b) Do the probabilities of part a add up to 1? Why should they? What is the sample space in this problem?

9. When do creative people get their *best* ideas? *USA Today* (January 3, 1990) did a survey of 966 inventors (who hold U.S. patents) and obtained the following information:

Time of Day When Best Ideas Occur	
Time	No. of Inventors
6 A.M.–12 noon	290
12 noon–6 P.M.	135
6 P.M.–12 midnight	319
12 midnight–6 A.M.	222

(a) Assuming that the time interval includes the left limit and all the times up to but not including the right limit, estimate the probability that an inventor has a best idea from 6 A.M. to 12 noon, from 12 noon to 6 P.M., from 6 P.M. to 12 midnight, from 12 midnight to 6 A.M.

(b) Do the probabilities of part a add up to 1? Why should they? What is the sample space in this problem?

10. *Four-eyes:* a term referring to people who wear corrective eyeglasses or contact lenses. How likely is it that a person selected at random is a *four-eyes*? This question is answered by James Burke in his book *Chances: Risk and Odds in Every Day Life.* About 56% of the general population wears corrective eyeglasses, while 3.6% wears contact lenses. (Assume no one wears both at the same time.)

(a) Consider the events: wear corrective eyeglasses, wear contact lenses, wear neither. Can we use these events to form a sample space? What is the probability of each event? Do these probabilities add up to 1?

(b) What is the probability that a person selected at random does *not* wear corrective eyeglasses? What is the probability that a person selected at random does *not* wear contact lenses?

(c) Consider the event: person does not wear any eye correction. Is this event the complement of any event in the sample space? Use the complement relationship to find the probability that a person selected at random does *not* wear any eye correction.

11. "Oh, leave me alone!" How do people want to be treated when they have the flu? A Sterling Health poll of 1000 people gave the following information (*USA Today,* October 8, 1993):

Want to be ...	No. of People
Left alone	770
Waited on hand and foot	160
Treated differently	70

(a) Consider the events: want to be left alone, want to be waited on hand and foot, want to be treated differently. Do these events form a sample space for the way people who have the flu wish to be treated? Use relative frequencies to assign probabilities to these events. Do the probabilities add up to 1? Why should they?

(b) Find the probability of the event do *not* want to be left alone. Find the probability of the event do *not* want to be waited on hand and foot.

12. A botanist has developed a new hybrid cotton plant that can withstand insects better than other cotton plants. However, there is some concern about the germination of seeds from the new plant. To estimate the probability that a seed from the new plant will germinate, a random sample of 3000 seeds were planted in warm, moist soil. Of these seeds, 2430 germinated.

(a) How would you estimate the probability that a seed will germinate? What is your estimate?

(b) How would you estimate the probability that a seed will *not* germinate? What is your estimate?

(c) Either a seed germinates, or it does not. What is the sample space in this problem? Do the probabilities assigned to the sample space add up to 1? Should they add up to 1? Explain.

(d) Are the outcomes in the sample space of part c equally likely?

13. (a) If you roll a single die and count the number of dots on top, what is the sample space of all possible outcomes? Are the outcomes equally likely?

(b) Assign probabilities to the outcomes of the sample space of part a. Do the probabilities add up to 1? Should they add up to 1? Explain.

(c) What is the probability of getting a number less than 5 on a single throw?

(d) What is the probability of getting 5 or 6 on a single throw?

14. John runs a computer software store. Yesterday he counted 127 people who walked by his store, 58 of whom came into the store. Of the 58, only 25 bought something in the store.

(a) Estimate the probability that a person who walks by the store will enter the store.

(b) Estimate the probability that a person who walks into the store will buy something.

(c) Estimate the probability that a person who walks by the store will come in *and* buy something.

(d) Estimate the probability that a person who comes into the store will buy nothing.

Section 4.2   Some Probability Rules—Compound Events

Probability of A and B

You roll two dice. What is the probability that you will get a 5 on each die? You draw two cards from a well-shuffled, standard deck without replacing the first card before drawing the second. What is the probability that they will both be aces?

It seems that these two problems are nearly alike. They are alike in the sense that in each case you are to find the probability of two events occurring *together*. In the first problem you are to find

$$P(5 \text{ on 1st die } and \text{ 5 on 2nd die})$$

In the second you want

$$P(\text{ace on 1st card } and \text{ ace on 2nd card})$$

Independent Events

The two problems differ in one important aspect, however. In the dice problem, the outcome of a 5 on the first die does not have any effect on the probability of getting a 5 on the second die. Because of this, the events are *independent*. In general, two events are independent if the occurrence or non-occurrence of one does not change the probability that the other will occur.

In the card problem, the probability of an ace on the first card is 4/52, since there are 52 cards in the deck and 4 of them are aces. If you get an ace on the first card, then the probability of an ace on the second is changed to 3/51, because one ace has already been drawn and only 51 cards remain in the deck. Therefore, the two events in the card-draw problem are *not* independent. They are, in fact, *dependent*, since the outcome of the first draw changes the probability of getting an ace on the second card.

Why does the *independence* or *dependence* of two events matter? The type of events determines the way we compute the probability of the two events happening together. If two events A and B are *independent*, then we use Formula (4) to compute the probability of the event A and B:

> For independent events,
>
> $$P(A \text{ and } B) = P(A) \cdot P(B)$$ (4)

If the events are *dependent*, then we must take into account the changes in the probability of one event caused by the occurrence of the other event. The notation $P(A, \text{ given } B)$ denotes the probability that event A will occur, *given* that event B has occurred. This is called a *conditional probability*. We read $P(A, \text{ given } B)$ as "probability of A given B." If A and B are dependent events, then $P(A) \neq P(A, \text{ given } B)$ because the occurrence of event B has changed the probability that event A will occur. A standard notation for $P(A, \text{ given } B)$ is $P(A \mid B)$. However, we will use the more expanded notation $P(A, \text{ given } B)$ to remind you that we assume that event B has already occurred. In Appendix I, where Bayes's theorem is discussed, we will revert to the more standard notation $P(A \mid B)$. We use either Formula (5) or Formula (6) to compute the probability of A *and* B when the events A and B are dependent.

> For dependent events,
>
> $$P(A \text{ and } B) = P(A) \cdot P(B, \text{ given that } A \text{ has occurred})$$ (5)
>
> $$P(A \text{ and } B) = P(B) \cdot P(A, \text{ given that } B \text{ has occurred})$$ (6)

We will use either Formula (5) or Formula (6) according to the information available.

Formulas (4), (5), and (6) constitute the *multiplication rules* of probability. They help us compute the probability of events happening together when the sample space is too large for convenient reference or when it is not completely known.

Let's use the multiplication rules to complete the dice and card problems. We'll compare the results with those obtained by using the sample space directly.

Example 3　Suppose you are going to throw two fair dice. What is the probability of getting a 5 on each die?

Solution Using the Multiplication Rule: The two events are independent, so we should use Formula (4). $P(5$ on 1st die *and* 5 on 2nd die$) = P(5$ on 1st$)$ $\cdot P(5$ on 2nd$)$. To finish the problem, we need only compute the probability of getting a 5 when we throw one die.

There are six faces on a die, and on a fair die each is equally likely to come up when you throw the die. Only one face has five dots, so by Formula (2) for equally likely outcomes,

$$P(5 \text{ on die}) = \frac{1}{6}$$

Now we can complete the calculation.

$$P(5 \text{ on 1st die } \textit{and } 5 \text{ on 2nd die}) = P(5 \text{ on 1st}) \cdot P(5 \text{ on 2nd})$$

$$= \frac{1}{6} \cdot \frac{1}{6}$$

$$= \frac{1}{36}$$

Solution Using Sample Space: The first task is to write down the sample space. Each die has six equally likely outcomes, and each outcome of the second die can be paired with each of the first. The sample space is shown in Figure 4–1. The total number of outcomes is 36, and only one is favorable to a 5 on the first die *and* a 5 on the second. The 36 outcomes are equally likely, so by Formula (2) for equally likely outcomes,

$$P(5 \text{ on 1st } \textit{and } 5 \text{ on 2nd}) = \frac{1}{36}$$

The two methods yield the same result. The multiplication rule was easier to use because we did not need to look at all 36 outcomes in the sample space for tossing two dice.

Figure 4–1 Sample Space for Two Dice

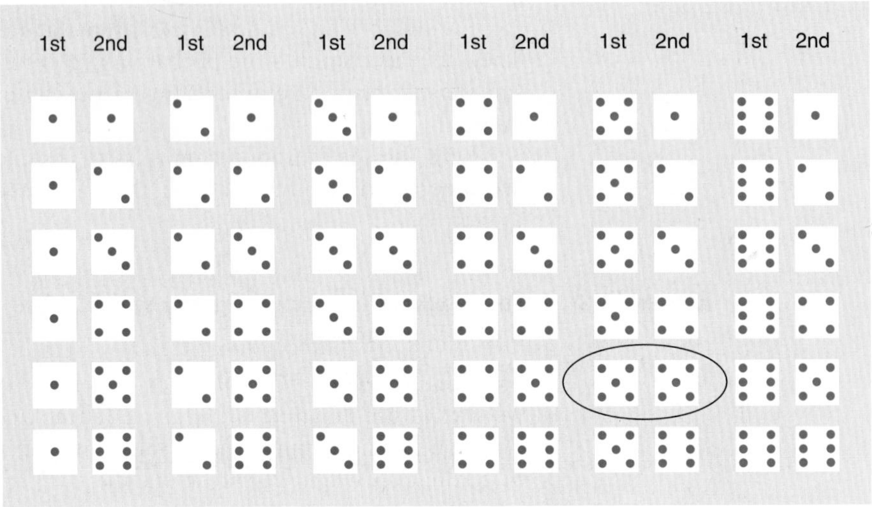

Example 4 | Compute the probability of drawing two aces from a well-shuffled deck of 52 cards if the first card is not replaced before the second card is drawn.

Multiplication Rule Method: These events are *dependent*. The probability of an ace on the first card is 4/52, but on the second card the probability of an ace is only 3/51 if an ace was drawn for the first card. An ace on the first draw changes the probability for an ace on the second draw. By the multiplication rule for dependent events,

$$P(\text{ace on 1st } and \text{ ace on 2nd}) = P(\text{ace on 1st}) \cdot P(\text{ace on 2nd, } given \text{ ace on 1st})$$

$$= \frac{4}{52} \cdot \frac{3}{51} = \frac{12}{2652} = 0.0045$$

Sample Space Method: We won't actually look at the sample space because each of the 51 possible outcomes for the second card must be paired with each of the 52 possible outcomes for the first card. This gives us a total of 2652 outcomes in the sample space! We'll just think about the sample space and try to list all the outcomes favorable to the event of aces on both cards. The 12 favorable outcomes are shown in Figure 4–2. By the formula for equally likely outcomes,

$$P(\text{ace on 1st card } and \text{ ace on 2nd card}) = \frac{12}{2652} = 0.0045$$

Again, the two methods agree.

Figure 4–2 Outcomes Favorable to Drawing Two Aces

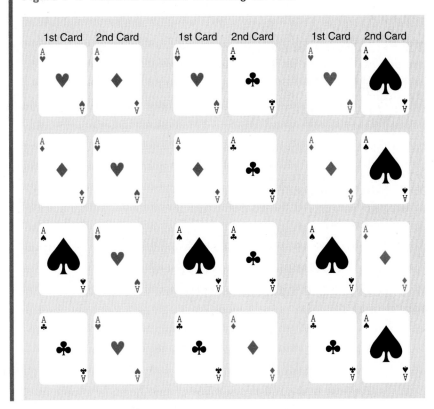

The multiplication rules apply whenever we wish to determine the probability of two events happening *together*. To indicate together, we use *and* between the events. But before you use a multiplication rule to compute the probability of *A and B,* you must determine if *A* and *B* are independent or dependent events. Let's practice using the multiplication rule.

GUIDED EXERCISE 4

A quality-control procedure for testing Ready-Flash flash bulbs consists of drawing two bulbs at random from each lot of 100 without replacing the first bulb before drawing the second. If both are defective, the entire lot is rejected. Find the probability that both bulbs are defective if the lot contains 10 defective flash bulbs. Since we are drawing the bulbs at random, assume that each bulb in the lot has an equal chance of being drawn.

(a) What is the probability of getting a defective bulb on the first draw?

(a) The sample space consists of all 100 bulbs. Since each is equally likely to be drawn and there are 10 defective ones,

$$P(\text{defective bulb}) = \frac{10}{100} = \frac{1}{10}$$

(b) The first bulb drawn is not replaced, so there are only 99 bulbs for the second draw. What is the probability of getting a defective bulb on the second draw if the first bulb was defective?

(b) If the first bulb is defective, then there are only 9 defective bulbs left among the 99 remaining bulbs in the lot.

$P(\text{defective bulb on 2nd draw, }$ *given* $\text{ defective bulb on 1st}) = \frac{9}{99} = \frac{1}{11}$

(c) Are the probabilities computed in parts a and b different? Does drawing a defective bulb on the first draw change the probability of getting a defective bulb on the second draw? Are the events dependent?

(c) The answer to all these questions is yes.

(d) Use the formula for dependent events,

$P(A \text{ and } B) = P(A) \cdot P(B, \text{ given } A \text{ has occurred})$

to compute $P(\text{1st bulb defective } and \text{ 2nd bulb defective})$.

(d) $P(\text{1st defective } and \text{ 2nd defective}) = \frac{1}{10} \cdot \frac{1}{11}$

$$= \frac{1}{110}$$

$$= 0.009$$

GUIDED EXERCISE 5

Andrew is 55, and the probability that he will be alive in 10 years is 0.72. Ellen is 35, and the probability that she will be alive in 10 years is 0.92. Assuming that the life span of one will have no effect on the life span of the other, what is the probability they will both be alive in 10 years?

(a) Are these events dependent or independent?

(a) Since the life span of one does not affect the life span of the other, the events are independent.

(b) Use the appropriate multiplication rule to find

$P(\text{Andrew alive in 10 years } and \text{ Ellen alive in 10 years})$

(b) We use the rule for independent events:

$$P(A \text{ and } B) = P(A) \cdot P(B)$$

$P(\text{Andrew alive } and \text{ Ellen alive})$

$= P(\text{Andrew alive}) \cdot P(\text{Ellen alive})$

$= (0.72)(0.92) = 0.66$

One of the multiplication rules can be used any time we are trying to find the probability of two events happening *together*. Pictorially, we are looking for the probability of the shaded region in Figure 4–3.

Probability of A or B

Another way to combine events is to consider the possibility of one event *or* another occurring. For instance, if a sports car saleswoman gets an extra bonus if she sells a convertible or a car with leather upholstery, she is inter-

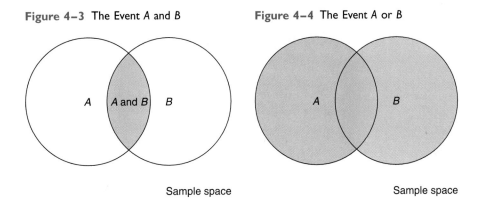

Figure 4–3 The Event A and B

Sample space

Figure 4–4 The Event A or B

Sample space

ested in the probability that you will buy a car that is a convertible *or* has leather upholstery. Of course, if you bought a convertible with leather upholstery, that would be fine, too. Pictorially, the shaded portion of Figure 4–4 represents the outcomes satisfying the *or* condition. Notice that the condition *A or B* is satisfied by any one of the following conditions:

1. Any outcome of *A* occurs.
2. Any outcome of *B* occurs.
3. Any outcome in *A* and *B* occurs.

It is important to distinguish between the *or* combinations and the *and* combinations because we apply different rules to compute their probabilities.

GUIDED EXERCISE 6

Indicate how each of the following pairs of events are combined. Use either the *and* combination or the *or* combination.

(a) Satisfying the humanities requirement by taking a course in the history of Japan or by taking a course in classical literature

(a) Use the *or* combination.

(b) Buying new tires and aligning the tires

(b) Use the *and* combination.

(c) Getting an A not only in psychology but also in biology

(c) Use the *and* combination.

(d) Having at least one of these pets: cat, dog, bird, rabbit

(d) Use the *or* combination.

Once you decide that you are to find the probability of an *or* combination rather than an *and* combination, what formula do you use? Again, it depends on the situation. If you want to compute the probability of drawing either a jack or a king on a single draw from a well-shuffled deck of cards, the formula is simple:

$$P(\text{jack } or \text{ king}) = P(\text{jack}) + P(\text{king}) = \frac{4}{52} + \frac{4}{52} = \frac{8}{52} = \frac{2}{13}$$

since there are 4 jacks and 4 kings in a deck of 52 cards.

If you want to compute the probability of drawing a king or a diamond on a single draw, the formula is a bit more complicated. We have to take the overlap of the two events into account so that we do not count the outcomes twice. We can see the overlap of the two events in Figure 4–5.

$$P(\text{king}) = \frac{4}{52} \qquad P(\text{diamond}) = \frac{13}{52} \qquad P(\text{king } and \text{ diamond}) = \frac{1}{52}$$

If we simply add $P(\text{king})$ and $P(\text{diamond})$, we're including $P(\text{king } and \text{ diamond})$ twice in the sum. To compensate for this double summing, we simply subtract $P(\text{king } and \text{ diamond})$ from the sum. Therefore,

$$P(\text{king } or \text{ diamond}) = P(\text{king}) + P(\text{diamond}) - P(\text{king } and \text{ diamond})$$

$$= \frac{4}{52} + \frac{13}{52} - \frac{1}{52}$$

$$= \frac{16}{52} = \frac{4}{13}$$

Figure 4–5 Drawing a King or a Diamond from a Standard Deck

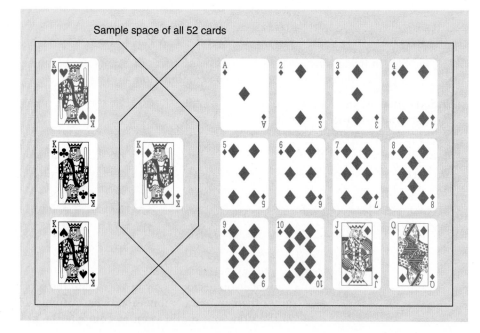

Sample space of all 52 cards

Mutually Exclusive Events

We say the events A and B are *mutually exclusive* if they cannot occur together. This means that A and B have no outcomes in common or, put another way, that $P(A \text{ and } B) = 0$. Formula (7) is the addition rule for *mutually exclusive* events A and B.

> For *mutually exclusive* events A and B,
>
> $$P(A \text{ or } B) = P(A) + P(B)$$

(7)

If the events are not mutually exclusive, we must use the more general Formula (8), which is the general addition rule for any events A and B.

> For any events A and B,
>
> $$P(A \text{ or } B) = P(A) + P(B) - P(A \text{ and } B)$$

(8)

You may ask: Which formula should we use? The answer is: Use Formula (7) only if you know that A and B are mutually exclusive (i.e., cannot occur together); if you do not know whether A and B are mutually exclusive, then use Formula (8). Formula (8) is valid either way. Notice that when A and B are mutually exclusive, then $P(A \text{ and } B) = 0$, so Formula (8) reduces to Formula (7).

GUIDED EXERCISE 7

The Cost Less Clothing Store carries seconds in slacks. If you buy a pair of slacks in your regular waist size without trying them on, the probability the waist will be too tight is 0.30 and the probability it will be too loose is 0.10.

(a) Are the events too tight or too loose mutually exclusive?

(a) The waist cannot be both too tight and too loose at the same time, so the events are mutually exclusive.

(b) If you choose a pair of slacks at random in your regular waist size, what is the probability that the waist will be too tight *or* too loose?

(b) Since the events are mutually exclusive,

$P(\text{too tight } or \text{ too loose})$
$= P(\text{too tight}) + P(\text{too loose})$
$= 0.30 + 0.10$
$= 0.40$

GUIDED EXERCISE 8

Professor Jackson is in charge of a program to prepare people for a high school equivalency exam. Records show that 80% of the students need work in math, 70% need work in English, and 55% need work in both areas.

(a) Are the events need math and need English mutually exclusive?

(a) These events are not mutually exclusive, since some students need both. In fact.

$$P(\text{need math } and \text{ need English}) = 0.55$$

(b) Use the appropriate formula to compute the probability that a student selected at random needs math *or* needs English.

(b) Since the events are not mutually exclusive, we use Formula (8):

$$\begin{aligned} P(&\text{need math } or \text{ need English}) \\ &= P(\text{need math}) + P(\text{need English}) \\ &\qquad - P(\text{need math } and \text{ English}) \\ &= 0.80 + 0.70 - 0.55 \\ &= 0.95 \end{aligned}$$

Combination of Several Events

The addition rule for mutually exclusive events can be extended so that it applies to the situation in which we have more than two events that are each mutually exclusive to all the other events.

Example 5

Laura is playing Monopoly. On her next move she needs to throw a sum bigger than 8 on the two dice in order to land on her own property and pass Go. What is the probability that Laura will roll a sum bigger than 8?

Solution: When two dice are thrown, the largest sum that can come up is 12. Consequently, the only sums larger than 8 are 9, 10, 11, and 12. These outcomes are mutually exclusive, since only one of these sums can possibly occur on one throw of the dice. The probability of throwing more than 8 is the same as

$$P(9 \text{ or } 10 \text{ or } 11 \text{ or } 12)$$

Since the events are mutually exclusive,

$$\begin{aligned} P(9 \text{ or } 10 \text{ or } 11 \text{ or } 12) &= P(9) + P(10) + P(11) + P(12) \\ &= \frac{4}{36} + \frac{3}{36} + \frac{2}{36} + \frac{1}{36} \\ &= \frac{10}{36} = \frac{5}{18} \end{aligned}$$

To get the specific values of $P(9)$, $P(10)$, $P(11)$, and $P(12)$, we used the sample space for throwing two dice (see Figure 4–1). There are 36 equally likely outcomes—for example, those favorable to 9 are 6,3; 3,6; 5,4; and 4,5. So $P(9) = 4/36$. The other values can be computed in a similar way.

The multiplication rule for independent events also extends to more than two independent events. If you toss a fair coin, then roll a fair die, and finally draw a card from a standard deck of bridge cards, the three events are independent. To compute the probability of the outcome heads on the coin *and* five on the die *and* an ace for the card, we use the extended multiplication rule for independent events together with the facts

$$P(\text{head}) = \frac{1}{2} \qquad P(5) = \frac{1}{6} \qquad P(\text{ace}) = \frac{4}{52} = \frac{1}{13}$$

Then

$$P(\text{head } and \text{ five } and \text{ ace}) = \frac{1}{2} \cdot \frac{1}{6} \cdot \frac{1}{13}$$

$$= \frac{1}{156}$$

Further Examples

Most of us have been asked to participate in a survey. Schools, retail stores, churches, and government offices all conduct surveys. There are many types of surveys, and it is not our intention to give a general discussion of this topic. Let us study a very popular method called the *simple tally survey*. Such a survey consists of a collection of column and row questions. These questions are appropriate to the information you want and are designed to cover the *entire* population of interest. In addition, the questions should be designed so that we can partition the sample space of responses into distinct (that is, mutually exclusive) sectors.

If the survey includes responses from a reasonable large random sample, then the results should be representative of your population. In this case we can estimate simple probabilities, conditional probabilities, and the probabilities of some combinations of events directly from the results of the survey.

Example 6 At Hopewell Electronics, all 140 employees were asked about their political affiliation. The employees were grouped by type of work, as executives or production workers. The results with row and column totals are shown in Table 4–2.

Table 4–2 Employee Type and Political Affiliation

Type of Employee	Political Affiliation			Row Total
	D Democrat	R Republican	I Independent	
E Executive	5	34	9	48
PW Production Worker	63	21	8	92
Column total	68	55	17	140 Grand total

Suppose an employee is selected at random from the 140 Hopewell employees. Let us use the following notation to represent different events of choosing: E = executive; PW = production worker; D = Democrat; R = Republican; I = Independent.

(a) Compute $P(D)$ and $P(E)$.

    Solution: To find these probabilities, we look at the *entire* sample space.

$$P(D) = \frac{\text{no. of Democrats}}{\text{no. of employees}} = \frac{68}{140} = 0.486$$

$$P(E) = \frac{\text{no. of executives}}{\text{no. of employees}} = \frac{48}{140} = 0.343$$

(b) Compute $P(D, \text{ given } E)$.

    Solution: For the conditional probability, we *restrict* our attention to the portion of the sample space satisfying the condition of being an executive.

$$P(D, \text{ given } E) = \frac{\text{no. of executives who are Democrats}}{\text{no. of executives}} = \frac{5}{48} = 0.104$$

(c) Are the events D and E independent?

    Solution: One way to determine if the events D and E are independent is to see if $P(D) = P(D, \text{ given } E)$ [or equivalently, if $P(E) = P(E, \text{ given } D)$]. Since $P(D) = 0.486$ and $P(D, \text{ given } E) = 0.104$, we see that $P(D) \neq P(D, \text{ given } E)$. This means that the events D and E are *not* independent. The probability of event D "depends on" whether or not event E has occurred.

(d) Compute $P(D \text{ and } E)$.

    Solution: This probability is not conditional, so we must look at the entire sample space.

$$P(D \text{ and } E) = \frac{\text{no. of executives who are Democrats}}{\text{total no. of employees}} = \frac{5}{140} = 0.036$$

Let's recompute this probability using the rules of probability for dependent events.

$$P(D \text{ and } E) = P(E) \cdot P(D, \text{ given } E) = \frac{48}{140} \cdot \frac{5}{48} = \frac{5}{140} = 0.036$$

The results using the rules are consistent with those using the sample space.

(e) Compute $P(D \text{ or } E)$.

    Solution: From part (d) we know that the events Democrat or executive are not mutually exclusive, because $P(D \text{ and } E) \neq 0$. Therefore,

$$P(D \text{ or } E) = P(D) + P(E) - P(D \text{ and } E)$$
$$= \frac{68}{140} + \frac{48}{140} - \frac{5}{140} = \frac{111}{140} = 0.793$$

GUIDED EXERCISE 9

Using Table 4–2, let's consider other probabilities regarding the type of employees at Hopewell and their political affiliation. This time let's consider the production worker and the affiliation of Independent. Suppose an employee is selected at random from the group of 140.

(a) Compute $P(I)$ and $P(PW)$.

(a)
$$P(I) = \frac{\text{no. of independents}}{\text{total no. of employees}}$$
$$= \frac{17}{140} = 0.121$$

$$P(PW) = \frac{\text{no. of production workers}}{\text{total no. of employees}}$$
$$= \frac{92}{140} = 0.657$$

(b) Compute $P(I, \text{given } PW)$. This is a conditional probability. Be sure to restrict your attention to production workers since that is the condition given.

(b)
$$P(I, \text{given } PW) = \frac{\text{no. of independent production workers}}{\text{no. of production workers}}$$
$$= \frac{8}{92} = 0.087$$

(c) Compute $P(I \text{ and } PW)$. In this case look at the entire sample space and at the number of employees who are both Independent and in production.

(c)
$$P(I \text{ and } PW) = \frac{\text{no. of independent production workers}}{\text{total no. of employees}}$$
$$= \frac{8}{140} = 0.057$$

(d) Use the multiplication rule for dependent events to calculate $P(I \text{ and } PW)$. Is the result the same as that of part c?

(d) By the multiplication rule,
$$P(I \text{ and } PW) = P(PW) \cdot P(I, \text{given } PW)$$
$$= \frac{92}{140} \cdot \frac{8}{92} = \frac{8}{140} = 0.057$$

The results are the same.

(e) Compute $P(I \text{ or } PW)$. Are the events mutually exclusive?

(e) Since the events are not mutually exclusive,
$$P(I \text{ or } PW) = P(I) + P(PW) - P(I \text{ and } PW)$$
$$= \frac{17}{140} + \frac{92}{140} - \frac{8}{140}$$
$$= \frac{101}{140} = 0.721$$

In this section we have studied some important rules that are valid in all probability spaces. The rules and definitions of probability are not only interesting, but they also have extensive *applications* in our everyday lives. If you are inclined to continue your study of probability a little farther, we recommend *Bayes's theorem* in Appendix I. The Reverend Thomas Bayes (1702–1761) was an English mathematician who discovered an important relation for conditional probabilities.

Section 4.2 Problems

In Problems 1–12 use the appropriate addition or multiplication rules. When possible, verify results by considering the sample space.

1. M&M plain candies come in a variety of colors. According to the manufacturer, M&M/Mars, the color distribution is

Color	Orange	Green	Red	Yellow	Brown	Tan
Percent	15%	10%	20%	20%	30%	5%

Suppose you have a large bag of plain M&M candies and you reach in and take one candy at random. Find
   (a) *P*(orange candy *or* tan candy. Are these outcomes mutually exclusive? Why?
   (b) *P*(yellow candy *or* red candy). Are these outcomes mutually exclusive? Why?
   (c) *P*(*not* brown candy).

2. Consider an urn containing 10 balls, all identical except for color. There are 4 red balls, 2 blue balls, 3 yellow balls, and 1 green ball. You draw one ball out at random from the urn. Find
   (a) *P*(red ball *or* green ball). Are these outcomes mutually exclusive? Why?
   (b) *P*(blue ball *or* yellow ball). Are these outcomes mutually exclusive? Why?
   (c) *P*(*not* red ball).

3. Consider a standard deck of 52 playing cards. (A standard deck contains four suits: hearts, diamonds, clubs, spades. In each suit there are 13 cards: those numbered 2 through 10, one jack, one queen, one king, and one ace. The hearts and diamonds are red cards, while the clubs and spades are black.) You draw one card at random. Find
   (a) *P*(ace *or* heart). Are these outcomes mutually exclusive? Why?
   (b) *P*(heart *or* red card). Are these outcomes mutually exclusive? Why?
   (c) *P*(2 *or* 10). Are these outcomes mutually exclusive? Why?
   (d) *P*(*not* a diamond).

4. In the 100th Congress of the United States, the age distribution of the senators (as reported in *Statistical Abstract of the United States, 1989,* 109th ed. was

Age	Under 40	40–49	50–59	60–69	70–79	80 & Over
Number of Senators	5	30	36	22	5	2

Frequency Dist (handwritten annotation)

For a senator selected at random from the 100th Congress, find the probability that the senator is the specified age.
(a) P(senator under 40 years old)
(b) P(senator in 40s *or* 50s)
(c) P(senator at least 60 years old)
(d) P(senator under 50 years of age)

5. You roll two fair dice: a green one and a red one.
(a) Are the outcomes on the dice independent?
(b) Find P(5 on green die *and* 3 on red die).
(c) Find P(3 on green die *and* 5 on red die).
(d) Find P((5 on green die *and* 3 on red die) *or* (3 on green die *and* 5 on red die)).

6. You roll two fair dice: a green one and a red one.
(a) Are the outcomes on the dice independent?
(b) Find P(1 on green die *and* 2 on red die).
(c) Find P(2 on green die *and* 1 on red die).
(d) Find P((1 on green die *and* 2 on red die) *or* (2 on green die *and* 1 on red die)).

7. Two fair dice are rolled: a green one and a red one.
(a) What is the probability of getting a sum of 6?
(b) What is the probability of getting a sum of 4?
(c) What is the probability of getting a sum of 6 *or* 4? Are these outcomes mutually exclusive?

8. Two fair dice are rolled: a green one and a red one.
(a) What is the probability of getting a sum of 7?
(b) What is the probability of getting a sum of 11?
(c) What is the probability of getting a sum of 7 *or* 11? Are these outcomes mutually exclusive?

9. You draw two cards from a standard deck of 52 cards without replacing the first one before drawing the second.
(a) Are the outcomes on the two cards independent? Why?
(b) Find P(ace on 1st card *and* king on 2nd).
(c) Find P(king on 1st card *and* ace on 2nd card).
(d) Find the probability of drawing an ace and a king in either order.

10. You draw two cards from a standard deck of 52 cards without replacing the first one before drawing the second.
(a) Are the outcomes on the two cards independent? Why?
(b) Find P(3 on 1st card *and* 10 on 2nd).
(c) Find P(10 on 1st card *and* 3 on 2nd).
(d) Find the probability of drawing a 10 and a 3 in either order.

11. You draw two cards from a standard deck of 52 cards, but before you draw the second card, you put the first one back and reshuffle the deck.
(a) Are the outcomes on the two cards independent? Why?
(b) Find P(ace on 1st card *and* king on 2nd).

(c) Find P(king on 1st card *and* ace on 2nd).

(d) Find the probability of drawing an ace and a king in either order.

12. You draw two cards from a standard deck of 52 cards, but before you draw the second card, you put the first one back and reshuffle the deck.

(a) Are the outcomes on the two cards independent? Why?

(b) Find P(3 on 1st card *and* 10 on 2nd).

(c) Find P(10 on 1st card *and* 3 on 2nd).

(d) Find the probability of drawing a 10 and a 3 in either order.

 13. *USA Today* (June 24, 1993) gave the following information about ages of children receiving toys. The percentages represent all toys sold.

Age (years)	Percentage of Toys
2 and under	15%
3–5	22%
6–9	27%
10–12	14%
13 and over	22%

What is the probability that a toy is purchased for someone

(a) 6 years or older?

(b) 12 years or younger?

(c) between 6 and 12 years old?

(d) between 3 and 9 years old?

A child between 10 and 12 years old looks at this probability distribution and asks, "Why are people more likely to buy toys for kids older than me (13 and over) than for kids in my age group (10–12)?" How would you respond?

 14. Based on data from the *Statistical Abstract of the United States* (112th ed.), only about 14% of senior citizens (65 years or older) get the flu each year. However, about 24% of the people under 65 years old get the flu each year. In the general population, there are 12.5% senior citizens (65 years or older).

(a) What is the probability that a person selected at random from the general population is a senior citizen who will get the flu this year?

(b) What is the probability that a person selected at random from the general population is a person under age 65 who will get the flu this year?

(c) Answer parts a and b for a community that has 95% senior citizens.

(d) Answer parts a and b for a community that has 50% senior citizens.

15. In this problem you are asked to solve part of the Chapter 4 Focus Problem (found on page 185). In his book *Chances: Risk and Odds in Every Day Life*, James Burke says that there is a 72% chance a polygraph test

(lie detector test) will catch a person who is in fact lying. Furthermore, there is approximately a 7% chance that the polygraph will falsely accuse someone of lying.

(a) Suppose that a person answers 90% of a long battery of questions truthfully. What percentage of the story will the polygraph *wrongly* indicate is a lie?

(b) Suppose that a person answers 10% of a long battery of questions with lies. What percentage of the story will the polygraph *correctly* indicate is a lie?

(c) Repeat parts a and b if 50% of the questions are answered truthfully and 50% are answered with lies.

(d) Repeat parts a and b if 15% of the questions are answered truthfully and the rest are answered with lies.

16. This problem continues the Chapter 4 Focus Problem. The solution involves applying several basic probability rules and a little algebra to solve an equation.

(a) If the polygraph (of Problem 15) said 30% of the questions were answered with lies, what would you estimate for the actual percentage of lies in the story? *Hint:* Let *B* = event detector indicates a lie. We are given *P*(*B*) = 0.30. Let *A* = event person is lying, so *not A* = event person is not lying. Then

$$P(B) = P(A \text{ and } B) + P(not\ A \text{ and } B)$$
$$P(B) = P(A)P(B, \text{ given } A) + P(not\ A)P(B, \text{ given not } A)$$

Replacing *P*(*not A*) by 1 − *P*(*A*) gives

$$P(B) = P(A)P(B, \text{ given } A) + [1 - P(A)]P(B, \text{ given not } A)$$

Substitute known values for *P*(*B*), *P*(*B, given A*), and *P*(*B, given not A*) into the last equation and solve for *P*(*A*).

(b) If the polygraph (of Problem 15) said 70% of questions were answered with lies, what would you estimate for the actual percentage of lies in the story?

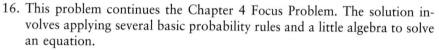

17. In the book *Chances: Risk and Odds in Every Day Life,* James Burke says that 56% of the general population wears eyeglasses, while only 3.6% wears contacts. He also says that of those who do wear glasses, 55.4% are women and 44.6% are men. Of those who wear contacts, 63.1% are women and 36.9% are men. Assume that no one wears both glasses and contacts. For the next person you encounter at random, what is the probability that this person is

(a) a woman wearing glasses?

(b) a man wearing glasses?

(c) a woman wearing contacts?

(d) a man wearing contacts?

(e) none of the above?

18. Gasoline-powered automobiles are a major source of pollution. Alternative fuels such as ethanol or methanol lower some of the hydrocarbon emissions. However, building cars that run on alternative fuels will cost more. A survey in *USA Today* (November 7, 1989) reported how much a person selected at random would be willing to pay for the option of using alternative fuels. As reported, 27.5% of the respondents would not be willing to pay anything, 9.6% would be willing to pay less than $200, 13.5% would be willing to pay from $200 to $599, 2.1% would be willing to pay from $600 to $999, 26.2% would be willing to pay $1000 or more, and 21.1% don't know. Based on this survey, if we picked an adult at random, find the probability that this person would be willing to pay $600 or more for the option of using alternative fuels. What is the probability the person would be willing to pay no more than $199?

19. The following is based on information from the *Statistical Abstract of the United States, 1992*. In this table, the columns are years in which students graduated from college with a bachelor's degree. The rows are high school grade average for these students. In 1976, therefore, a random sample of 577 new college graduates showed that 419 had a high school grade average of A, 123 had a high school grade average of B, and so on.

| High School Grade Average | College Graduate by Year | | | |
	1976	1980	1986	Row Total
A	419	593	607	1619
B	123	249	280	652
C	24	61	77	162
D	11	36	45	92
Column total	577	939	1009	2525

Suppose that a college graduate is selected at random from the pool of 1976, 1980, and 1986 graduates. Let us use the following notation for events:

1976 = event a student graduated from college in 1976

A = event a student had a high school grade average of A

The other events are defined in a similar way.

(a) Compute $P(A)$, $P(B)$, $P(C)$, and $P(D)$. Explain the meaning of these numbers. Is a college graduate more likely to have had a higher grade average in high school?

(b) Compute $P(1976)$, $P(1980)$, and $P(1986)$. Explain the meaning of these numbers. Is a college graduate more likely to be a recent (1986) graduate?

(c) Compute $P(1976, given$ A$)$, $P(1980, given$ A$)$, and $P(1986, given$ A$)$. Explain the meaning of these numbers.

(d) Compute $P(1976, given$ D$)$, $P(1980, given$ D$)$, and $P(1986, given$ D$)$. Explain the meaning of these numbers, and compare your answers to those in part c.

(e) Compute $P($C$, given$ 1976$)$, $P($C$, given$ 1980$)$, and $P($C$, given$ 1986$)$. Explain the meaning of these numbers.

(f) Compute $P($A or B$)$. Are these events mutually exclusive?

(g) Compute $P($B and 1976$)$, $P($B and 1980$)$, and $P($B and 1986$)$. Are more students graduating each year? Could this account for the increasing probabilities?

(h) Compute $P($B or 1976$)$. Are these events mutually exclusive? Compute $P($C or 1980$)$. Are these events mutually exclusive?

20. The following is based on information taken from *World Almanac, 1993.* In this table, the columns are popular vote (rounded to nearest thousand) received by the 1992 presidential candidates: Clinton, Bush, and Perot. The rows are six New England states. Therefore, a random sample of 674 voters in Maine showed that 262 voted for Clinton, and so on.

State	Clinton	Bush	Perot	Row Total
Maine (ME)	262	207	205	674
New Hampshire (NH)	207	200	120	527
Vermont (VT)	126	86	62	274
Massachusetts (MA)	1315	804	630	2749
Rhode Island (RI)	199	122	95	416
Connecticut (CT)	681	575	348	1604
Column total	2790	1994	1460	6244

Suppose that a voter is drawn at random from one of the six New England states. Let VT = event this person is from Vermont, and let Clinton = event this person voted for Clinton. Other events are defined in a similar way. Compute each of the following probabilities, and explain the meaning of the numbers you obtain.

(a) $P($Clinton$)$, $P($Bush$)$, and $P(not$ Perot$)$

(b) $P($Clinton$, given$ NH$)$, $P($Bush$, given$ NH$)$, and $P($Perot$, given$ NH$)$

(c) $P($Clinton$, given$ MA$)$, $P($Bush$, given$ MA$)$, and $P($Perot$, given$ MA$)$

(d) $P($NH$)$, $P($NH$, given$ Clinton$)$, $P($NH$, given$ Bush$)$, and $P($NH$, given$ Perot$)$

(e) $P($Clinton or Bush$)$, $P($Clinton or Perot$)$, and $P($Bush or Perot$)$

(f) $P($Clinton and MA$)$, $P($Bush and CT$)$, and $P($Perot and ME$)$

(g) $P($Clinton or MA$)$, $P($Bush or CT$)$, and $P($Perot or ME$)$. *Hint:* Are these events mutually exclusive? See part f.

21. A new grading policy has been proposed by the dean of the College of Education for all education majors. All faculty and students in education were asked to give their opinion about the new grading policy. The results are shown below.

		Opinion		
	Favor	*Neutral*	*Oppose*	*Row Total*
Students	353	75	191	619
Faculty	11	5	18	34
Column total	364	80	209	653

Suppose that someone is selected at random from the College of Education (either student or faculty). Let us use the following notation for events: S = student, F = faculty, Fa = favor, N = neutral, O = oppose. In this notation, P(O, given S) represents the probability that the person selected opposes the new grading policy, given that the person is a student.
(a) Compute P(Fa), P(Fa, given F), and P(Fa, given S).
(b) Compute P(F and Fa).
(c) Are the events F = faculty and Fa = favor policy independent? Explain.
(d) Compute P(S, given O) and P(S, given N).
(e) Compute P(S and Fa) and P(S and O).
(f) Compute P(S) and P(S, given Fa). Are the events S = student and Fa = favor policy independent? Explain.
(g) Compute P(Fa or O). Are these events mutually exclusive?

22. In a sales effectiveness seminar, a group of sales representatives tried two approaches to selling a customer a new automobile: the aggressive approach and the passive approach. From 1160 customers, the following record was kept:

	Sales Result		
	Sale	*No Sale*	*Row Total*
Aggressive	270	310	580
Passive	416	164	580
Column total	686	474	1160

Suppose that a customer is selected at random from the 1160 participating customers. Let us use the following notation for events: A = aggressive

approach, *Pa* = passive approach, *S* = sale, *N* = no sale. So *P(A)* is the probability that an aggressive approach was used, and so on.
(a) Compute *P(S)*, *P(S, given A)*, and *P(S, given Pa)*.
(b) Are the events *S* = sale and *Pa* = passive approach independent? Explain.
(c) Compute *P(A and S)* and *P(Pa and S)*.
(d) Compute *P(N)* and *P(N, given A)*.
(e) Are the events *N* = no sale and *A* = aggressive approach independent? Explain.
(f) Compute *P(A or S)*.

23. The following table shows how 558 people applying for a credit card were classified according to home ownership and length of time in present job.

	Length of Time in Present Job		
	Less than 2 Years	*2 or More Years*	*Row Total*
Owner	73	194	267
Renter	210	81	291
Column total	283	275	558

Suppose that a person is chosen at random from the 558 applicants. Let *O* = event this person owns home, *R* = event this person rents, *L* = event this person has had present job less than 2 years, and *M* = event this person has had present job 2 years or more.
(a) Compute *P(O)*, *P(O, given L)*, and *P(O, given M)*.
(b) Compute *P(O and M)* and *P(O or M)*.
(c) Compute *P(R)*, *P(R, given L)*, and *P(R, given M)*.
(d) Compute *P(R and L)* and *P(R or L)*.
(e) Are the events *O* = own home and *M* = present job 2 or more years independent? Explain. Are the events mutually exclusive? Explain.

24. In a small, rural community in West Virginia, those adults seeking work or having work were classified as follows:

	Employment Status		
	Unemployed	*Employed*	*Row Total*
Men	206	412	618
Women	386	305	691
Column total	592	717	1309

Suppose that a person is chosen at random from those seeking work or having work. Let M = event this person is a man, W = event this person is a woman, U = event this person is unemployed, and E = event this person is employed.

(a) Compute P(U), P(U, given M), and P(U, given W).
(b) Compute P(E), P(E, given M), and P(E, given W).
(c) Compute P(M), P(M, given E), and P(M, given U).
(d) Compute P(W), P(W, given E), and P(W, given U).
(e) Compute P(M and E) and P(W or U).
(f) Are the events W = woman and U = unemployed mutually exclusive? Explain.
(g) Are the events M = man and E = employed independent? Explain.

25. Brookridge College did a survey of former students who were incoming freshmen 8 years ago. Of these former students, some graduated from college and some dropped out and did not graduate. Using national averages, the college established a salary cutoff point for upper middle income. From the surveys they were able to determine present salaries of the former students participating in the survey. The classification for those holding jobs today is shown below.

	Salary Level		
	Below Upper Middle Income	*At or Above Upper Middle Income*	*Row Total*
College graduate	105	406	511
College dropout	351	291	642
Column total	456	697	1153

Suppose that a former student is drawn at random from the people classified above. Let G = event this person graduated, D = event this person dropped out of college, B = event salary is below upper middle income, and A = event salary is at or above upper middle income.

(a) Compute P(A), P(A, given G), and P(A, given D).
(b) Compute P(B), P(B, given G), and P(B, given D).
(c) Compute P(G), P(G, given A), and P(G, given B).
(d) Compute P(D), P(D, given A), and P(D, given B).
(e) Compute P(G and A) and P(D or B).
(f) Are the events A = above upper middle income salary and G = graduated from college independent? Explain.
(g) Are the events B = below upper middle income salary and D = dropped out of college mutually exclusive? Explain.

26. At Litchfield College of Nursing, 85% of incoming freshmen nursing students are female and 15% are male. Recent records indicate that 70% of the entering female students will graduate with a BSN degree, while 90% of the male students will obtain a BSN degree. If an incoming freshman nursing student is selected at random, find
    (a) *P*(student will graduate, *given* student is female).
    (b) *P*(student will graduate *and* student is female).
    (c) *P*(student will graduate, *given* student is male).
    (d) *P*(student will graduate *and* student is male).
    (e) *P*(student will graduate). Note that those who will graduate are either males who will graduate or females who will graduate.
    (f) The events described by the phrases "will graduate *and* is female" and "will graduate, *given* female" seem to be describing the same students. Why are the probabilities *P*(will graduate *and* is female) and *P*(will graduate, *given* female) different?

27. Wing Foot is a shoe franchise commonly found in shopping centers across the United States. Wing Foot knows that their stores will not show a profit unless they gross over $93,000 per year. Let *A* be the event that a new Wing Foot store grosses over $93,000 its first year. Let *B* be the event that a store grosses over $93,000 its second year. Wing Foot has an administrative policy of closing a new store if it does not show a profit in *either* of the first 2 years. The accounting office at Wing Foot provided the following information: 65% of *all* Wing Foot stores show a profit the first year; 71% of *all* Wing Foot stores show a profit the second year (this includes stores that did not show a profit in the first year); however, 87% of Wing Foot stores that showed a profit the first year also showed a profit the second year. Compute the following:
    (a) *P*(*A*)
    (b) *P*(*B*)
    (c) *P*(*B, given A*)
    (d) *P*(*A and B*)
    (e) *P*(*A or B*)
    (f) What is the probability that a new Wing Foot store will not be closed after 2 years? What is the probability that a new Wing Foot store will be closed after 2 years?

28. Cut-Rate Sam's Appliance Store has received a shipment of 12 toasters. Sam does not know that 8 are defective.
    (a) Pete is the first person to buy one of these toasters. What is the probability it is defective?
    (b) Iris comes in after Pete and buys a toaster. What is the probability that her toaster is defective if Pete's was defective? If Pete's was not defective?
    (c) What is the probability that both Pete's and Iris's toasters are defective?

29. AnyState Insurance Company issues new contracts to their automobile insurance customers every 36 months. The AnyState accounting office found that 8% of all their new contract customers made an automobile accident claim during the first contract. During the second contract, about 8% of the customers again made automobile accident claims. However, 23% of the customers who made accident claims during the first contract also made accident claims during the second contract. Let A be the event that a customer makes an automobile accident claim during the first contract, and let B be the event that a customer makes a claim during the second contract. Compute the following:
    (a) $P(A)$
    (b) $P(B)$
    (c) $P(B, \text{given } A)$
    (d) $P(A \text{ and } B)$
    (e) $P(A \text{ or } B)$
    (f) What is the probability that a customer makes it through both contract periods without making an auto accident claim?

30. The Eastmore Program is a special program to help alcoholics. In the Eastmore Program, an alcoholic lives at home but undergoes a two-phase treatment plan. Phase I is an intensive group-therapy program lasting 10 weeks. Phase II is a long-term counseling program lasting 1 year. Eastmore Programs are located in most major cities, and past data gave the following information, based on percentages of success and failure collected over a long period of time: the probability that a client will have a relapse in phase I is 0.27; the probability that a client will have a relapse in phase II is 0.23. However, if a client did not have a relapse in phase I, then the probability that this client will not have a relapse in phase II is 0.95. If a client did have a relapse in phase I, then the probability that this client will have a relapse in phase II is 0.70. Let A be the event that a client has a relapse in phase I and B be the event that a client has a relapse in phase II. Let C be the event that a client has no relapse in phase I and D be the event that a client has no relapse in phase II. Compute the following:
    (a) $P(A)$, $P(B)$, $P(C)$, and $P(D)$
    (b) $P(B, \text{given } A)$ and $P(D, \text{given } C)$
    (c) $P(A \text{ and } B)$ and $P(C \text{ and } D)$
    (d) $P(A \text{ or } B)$
    (e) What is the probability that a client will go through both phase I and phase II without a relapse?
    (f) What is the probability that a client will have a relapse in both phase I and phase II?
    (g) What is the probability that a client will have a relapse in either phase I or phase II?

31. The state medical school has discovered a new test for tuberculosis. (If the test indicates a person has tuberculosis, the test is positive.) Experimen-

tation has shown that the probability of a positive test is 0.82, given a person has tuberculosis. The probability is 0.09 that the test registers positive, given the person does not have tuberculosis. Assume that in the general population the probability that a person has tuberculosis is 0.04. What is the probability that a person chosen at random will

(a) have tuberculosis and a positive test?
(b) not have tuberculosis?
(c) not have tuberculosis and have a positive test?

Section 4.3   Trees and Counting Techniques

When outcomes are equally likely, we compute the probability of an event by using the formula

$$P(A) = \frac{\text{number of outcomes favorable to the event } A}{\text{number of outcomes in the sample space}}$$

The probability formula requires that we be able to determine the number of outcomes in the sample space. In the problems we have done in previous sections, this task has not been difficult because the number of outcomes was small or the sample space consisted of fairly straightforward events. The tools we present in this section will help you count the number of possible outcomes in larger sample spaces or those formed by more complicated events.

Tree Diagrams

A *tree diagram* helps us display the outcomes of an experiment consisting of a series of activities. The total number of outcomes corresponds to the total number of final branches in the tree. Perhaps the best way to learn to make a tree diagram is to see one. In the next example we will see a tree diagram and analyze its parts.

Example 7

Jacqueline is in the nursing program and is required to take a course in psychology and one in anatomy and physiology (*A* and *P*) next semester. She also wants to take Spanish II. If there are four sections of psychology, two of *A* and *P*, and three of Spanish, how many different class schedules can Jacqueline choose from? (Assume that the times of the sections do not conflict with each other.) Figure 4–6 shows a tree diagram for Jacqueline's possible schedules.
Solution: Let's study the tree diagram and see how it shows Jacqueline's schedule choices. There are four branches from Start. These branches indicate the four possible choices for psychology sections. No matter which section of psychology Jacqueline chooses, she can choose from the two available *A* and *P* sections. Therefore, we have two branches leading from *each* psychology branch. Finally, after the psychology and *A* and *P* sections are selected, there are three choices for Spanish II. That is why there are three branches from *each A* and *P* section.

The tree ends with a total of 24 branches. This number of end branches tells us the number of possible schedules. The outcomes themselves can be

Figure 4–6 Tree Diagram for Selecting Class Schedules

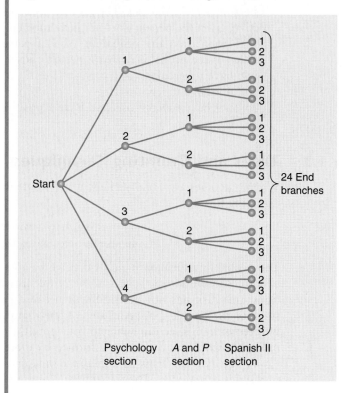

listed from the tree by following each series of branches from Start to the end. For instance, the top branch from Start generates the schedules shown in Table 4–3.

Table 4–3 Schedules Utilizing Section 1 of Psychology

Psychology Section	A and P Section	Spanish II Section
1	1	1
1	1	2
1	1	3
1	2	1
1	2	2
1	2	3

Following the second branch from Start, we see all the possible schedules utilizing Section 2 of psychology (see Table 4–4). The other 12 schedules can be listed in a similar manner.

Table 4–4 Schedules Utilizing Section 2 of Psychology

Psychology Section	A and P Section	Spanish II Section
2	1	1
2	1	2
2	1	3
2	2	1
2	2	2
2	2	3

We draw a tree diagram in stages, indicating the possible outcomes for the first event, second event, and so forth. The next exercise will lead you through the process.

GUIDED EXERCISE 10

Louis plays three tennis matches. Use a tree diagram to list the possible win and loss sequences Louis can experience for the set of three matches.

(a) On the first match Louis can win or lose. From Start, indicate these two branches.

(a) **Figure 4–7** W = Win, L = Lose

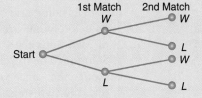

(b) Regardless of whether Louis wins or loses the first match, he plays the second and can again win or lose. Attach branches representing these two outcomes to *each* of the first match results.

(b) **Figure 4–8** W = Win, L = Lose

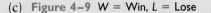

(c) Louis may win or lose the third match. Attach branches representing these two outcomes to *each* of the second match results.

(c) **Figure 4–9** W = Win, L = Lose

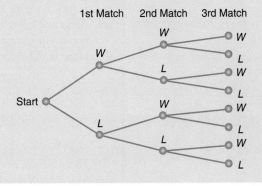

(d) How many possible win–lose sequences are there for the three matches?

(e) Complete this list of win–lose sequences.

1st	2nd	3rd
W	W	W
W	W	L
W	L	W
W	L	L
—	—	—
—	—	—
—	—	—
—	—	—

(d) Since there are eight branches at the end, there are eight sequences.

(e) The last four sequences all involve a loss on Match 1.

1st	2nd	3rd
L	W	W
L	W	L
L	L	W
L	L	L

Tree diagrams help us display the outcomes of an experiment involving several stages. If we label each branch of the tree with an appropriate probability, we can use the tree diagram to help us compute probabilities of an outcome displayed on the tree. One of the easiest ways to illustrate this feature of tree diagrams is to use an experiment of drawing balls out of an urn. We do this in the next example.

Example 8

Suppose there are five balls in an urn. They are identical except in color. Three of the balls are red and two are blue. You are instructed to draw out one ball, note its color, and set it aside. Then you are to draw out another ball and note its color. What are the outcomes of the experiment? What is the probability of each outcome?

Solution: The tree diagram in Figure 4–10 will help us answer these questions. Notice that since you did not replace the first ball before drawing the second one, the two stages of the experiment are dependent. The probability associated with the color of the second ball depends on the color of the first ball. For instance, on the top branches, the color of the first ball drawn is red, so we compute the probabilities of the colors on the second ball accordingly. The tree diagram helps us organize the probabilities.

From the diagram, we see that there are four possible outcomes to the experiment. They are

$$RR = \text{red on 1st } and \text{ red on 2nd}$$
$$RB = \text{red on 1st } and \text{ blue on 2nd}$$
$$BR = \text{blue on 1st } and \text{ red on 2nd}$$
$$BB = \text{blue on 1st } and \text{ blue on 2nd}$$

To compute the probability of each outcome, we will use the multiplication rule for dependent events. As we follow the branches for each outcome, we will find the necessary probabilities.

Figure 4–10 Tree Diagram for Urn Experiment

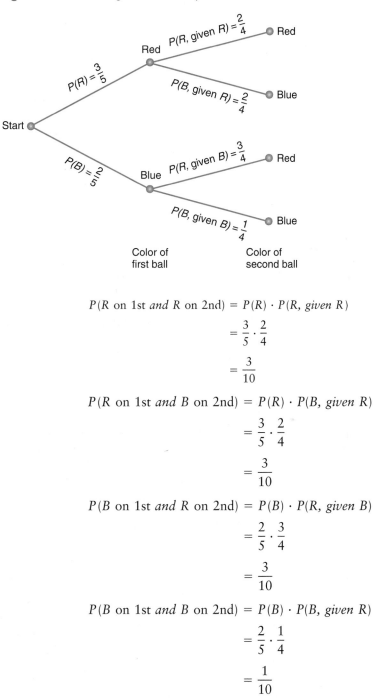

Color of first ball

Color of second ball

$$P(R \text{ on 1st } and \ R \text{ on 2nd}) = P(R) \cdot P(R, \text{ given } R)$$

$$= \frac{3}{5} \cdot \frac{2}{4}$$

$$= \frac{3}{10}$$

$$P(R \text{ on 1st } and \ B \text{ on 2nd}) = P(R) \cdot P(B, \text{ given } R)$$

$$= \frac{3}{5} \cdot \frac{2}{4}$$

$$= \frac{3}{10}$$

$$P(B \text{ on 1st } and \ R \text{ on 2nd}) = P(B) \cdot P(R, \text{ given } B)$$

$$= \frac{2}{5} \cdot \frac{3}{4}$$

$$= \frac{3}{10}$$

$$P(B \text{ on 1st } and \ B \text{ on 2nd}) = P(B) \cdot P(B, \text{ given } R)$$

$$= \frac{2}{5} \cdot \frac{1}{4}$$

$$= \frac{1}{10}$$

Notice that the probabilities of the outcomes in the sample space add to 1, as they should.

GUIDED EXERCISE 11

Repeat the urn experiment with the five balls, three of which are red and two of which are blue. This time *replace* the first ball before drawing the second.

(a) Draw a tree diagram for the outcomes of this experiment. Show the probabilities of each stage on the appropriate branch. (*Hint:* Are the stages dependent or independent?)

(a) **Figure 4–11** Tree Diagram for Urn Experiment (With Replacement)

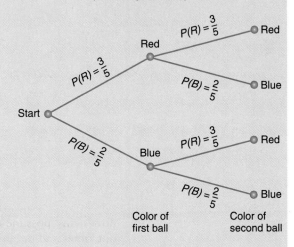

Color of first ball   Color of second ball

(b) List the four possible outcomes of the experiment (i.e., list the sample space).

(b) Red on 1st *and* red on 2nd
Red on 1st *and* blue on 2nd
Blue on 1st *and* red on 2nd
Blue on 1st *and* blue on 2nd

(c) Use the multiplication rule for independent events and the probabilities shown on your tree to compute the probability of each outcome.

(c) $P(\text{1st } R \text{ and 2nd } R) = P(R) \cdot P(R)$

$$= \frac{3}{5} \cdot \frac{3}{5}$$

$$= \frac{9}{25}$$

$P(\text{1st } R \text{ and 2nd } B) = P(R) \cdot P(B)$

$$= \frac{3}{5} \cdot \frac{2}{5}$$

$$= \frac{6}{25}$$

$P(\text{1st } B \text{ and 2nd } R) = P(B) \cdot P(R)$

$$= \frac{2}{5} \cdot \frac{3}{5}$$

$$= \frac{6}{25}$$

$$P(\text{1st } B \text{ and 2nd } B) = P(B) \cdot P(B)$$

$$= \frac{2}{5} \cdot \frac{2}{5}$$

$$= \frac{4}{25}$$

(d) Do the probabilities of the outcomes in the sample space add up to 1?

(d) Yes, as they should.

(e) Compare the tree diagram of this exercise with that of the previous example in which the first ball was not replaced before the second was drawn. Are the outcomes the same? Are the probabilities of the corresponding outcomes the same?

(e) The outcomes are the same: *RR, RB, BR,* and *BB*. However, because one experiment did not permit replacement of the first ball before the second was drawn and the other experiment required replacement, the corresponding probabilities of the second stages of the experiment are different. The corresponding probabilities of the final outcomes are also different.

Multiplication Rule of Counting

When an outcome is composed of a series of events, tree diagrams tell us how many possible outcomes there are. They also help us list the individual outcomes and organize the probabilities associated with each stage of the outcomes. However, if we are only interested in the number of outcomes created by a series of events, the multiplication rule will give us the total number of outcomes more directly. We state the multiplication rule for an outcome composed of a series of two events.

Multiplication Rule of Counting

If there are n possible outcomes for event E_1 and m possible outcomes for event E_2, then there are a total of $n \times m$ or nm possible outcomes for the series of events E_1 followed by E_2.

The rule extends to outcomes created by a series of three, four, or more events. We simply multiply the number of outcomes possible for each step in the series of events to get the total number of outcomes for the series.

Example 9 | The Night Hawk is the new car model produced by Limited Motors, Inc. It comes with a choice of two body styles, three interior package options, and four different colors, as well as the choice of automatic or standard transmission. Select-an-Auto Car Dealership wants to carry one of each of the different types of Night Hawks. How many cars are required?
Solution: There are four items to select. We take the product of the number of choices for each item.

$$\begin{pmatrix} \text{no. of body} \\ \text{styles} \end{pmatrix} \begin{pmatrix} \text{no. of} \\ \text{interiors} \end{pmatrix} \begin{pmatrix} \text{no. of} \\ \text{colors} \end{pmatrix} \begin{pmatrix} \text{no. of transmission} \\ \text{types} \end{pmatrix}$$

$$(2)(3)(4)(2) = 48$$

Select-an-Auto must stock 48 cars in order to have one of each possible type.

GUIDED EXERCISE 12

The Old Sage Inn offers a special dinner menu each night. There are two appetizers to choose from, three main courses, and four desserts. A customer can select one item from each category. How many different meals can be ordered from the special dinner menu?

(a) Each special dinner consists of three items. List the item and the number of choices per item.

(a) Appetizer—2; main course—3; dessert—4

(b) To find the number of different dinners composed of the three items, multiply the number of choices per item together.

(b) $(2)(3)(4) = 24$
There are 24 different dinners that can be ordered from the special dinner menu.

Sometimes when we consider n items, we need to know the number of different ordered *arrangements* of the n items that are possible. The multiplication rules can help us find the number of possible ordered arrangements. Let's consider the classic example of determining the number of different ways in which eight people can be seated at a dinner table. For the first chair, there are eight choices. For the second chair, there are seven choices, since one person is already seated. For the third chair, there are six choices, since two people are already seated. By the time we get to the last chair, there is only one person left for that seat. We can view each arrangement as an outcome of a series of eight events. Event 1 is *fill the first chair*, event 2 is *fill the second chair*, and so forth. The multiplication rule will tell us the number of different outcomes.

Choices for	1st	2nd	3rd	4th	5th	6th	7th	8th	Chair position
	↓	↓	↓	↓	↓	↓	↓	↓	
	(8)	(7)	(6)	(5)	(4)	(3)	(2)	(1)	= 40,320

In all, there are 40,320 different seating arrangements for eight people. It is no wonder that it takes a little time to seat guests at a dinner table!

Factorial Notation   The multiplication pattern shown above is not unusual. In fact, it is an example of the multiplication indicated by the factorial notation 8!.

! is read *factorial*

8! is read *8 factorial*

$8! = 8 \cdot 7 \cdot 6 \cdot 5 \cdot 4 \cdot 3 \cdot 2 \cdot 1$

In general, $n!$ indicates the product of n with each of the positive counting numbers less than n. By special definition $0! = 1$.

Factorial Notation

For a counting number n,

$$n! = n(n-1)(n-2)\cdots 1$$
$$0! = 1$$
$$1! = 1$$

GUIDED EXERCISE 13

(a) Evaluate $3!$.

(a) $3! = 3 \cdot 2 \cdot 1 = 6$

(b) How many different ways can three objects be arranged in order? How many choices do you have for the first position? for the second position? for the third position?

(b) We have three choices for the first position, two for the second position, and one for the third position. By the multiplication rule, we have

$$(3)(2)(1) = 3! = 6 \text{ arrangements}$$

(c) Verify step b with a three-stage tree diagram.

(c) **Figure 4–12　Three Choices**

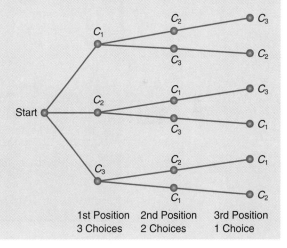

1st Position	2nd Position	3rd Position
3 Choices	2 Choices	1 Choice

Permutations

We have considered the number of ordered arrangements of n objects taken as an entire group. Specifically, we considered a dinner party for eight and found the number of ordered seating arrangements for all eight people. However, suppose you have an open house and have only five chairs. How many ways can five of the eight people seat themselves in the chairs? The formula we use to compute this number is called the *permutation formula*. We will simply state the formula and show you how to use it.

Counting Rule for Permutations

The number of ways to *arrange in order* n distinct objects, taking them r at a time, is

$$P_{n,r} = \frac{n!}{(n-r)!} \tag{9}$$

where n and r are whole numbers and $n \geq r$.

Example 10

Let's compute the number of ordered seating arrangements we have for eight people in five chairs.

Solution: In this case we are considering a total of $n = 8$ different people, and we wish to arrange $r = 5$ of these people. Substituting into Formula (9), we have

$$P_{n,r} = \frac{n!}{(n-r)!}$$

$$P_{8,5} = \frac{8!}{(8-5)!}$$

$$= \frac{8!}{3!}$$

$$= \frac{40{,}320}{6}$$

$$= 6720$$

Calculator Note Most scientific calculators have a factorial key often designated x! or n!. On TI graphing calculators, the factorial operation ! is found in the MATH menu under the PRB (for probability) option. If you have the ! function available on your calculator, use it to calculate 8! and 3! directly, and divide the result. Many of these same calculators have the permutation

Figure 4–13 TI-82 Display of ! and $P_{r,s}$

```
8!
                    40320
3!
                        6
8 nPr 5
                6720
```

function built in, often labeled nPr. Again, on the TI graphing calculators, you find the permutation operation nPr within the MATH menu under PRB. You can, of course, use the permutation function directly with the numbers 8 and 5 and obtain the result 6720. In addition to the nPr operation, these calculators also have the combinations operation discussed after the next exercise. The label for the combinations operations is usually nCr. Figure 4–13 shows these calculations on a TI-82 screen.

GUIDED EXERCISE 14

The board of directors of Belford Community Hospital has 12 members. Three officers—president, vice president, and treasurer—must be elected from the members. How many different possible slates of officers are there? We will view a slate of officers as a list of three people with one person for president listed first, one person for vice president listed second, and one person for treasurer listed third. For instance, if Mr. Acosta, Ms. Hill, and Mr. Smith wish to be on a slate together, there are several different slates possible, depending on which one will run for president, which for vice president, and which for treasurer. Not only are we asking for the number of different groups of three names for a slate, we are also concerned about order, since it makes a difference which name is listed in which position.

(a) What is the size of the group from which the slates of officers will be selected? This is the value of n.

(a) $n = 12$

(b) How many people will be selected for each slate of officers? This is the value of r.

(b) $r = 3$

(c) Each slate of officers is composed of three candidates. Different slates occur as we arrange the three candidates in the positions of president, vice president, and treasurer. For this reason, we need to consider the number of *permutations* of twelve items arranged in groups of three. Compute $P_{n,r}$.

(c)
$$P_{n,r} = \frac{n!}{(n-r)!}$$

$$P_{12,3} = \frac{12!}{(12-3)!} = \frac{12!}{9!} = \frac{479,001,600}{362,880}$$

$$= 1,320$$

There are 1320 different possible slates of officers. An alternative is to use your calculator directly to compute $P_{12,3}$.

Combinations

In each of our previous counting formulas, we have taken the *order* of the objects or people into account. But what if order is not important? For instance, suppose we need to choose three members from the 12-member board of directors of Belford Community Hospital to go to a convention. We are interested in *different groupings* of 12 people so that each group contains 3 people. The order is of no concern, since all 3 will go to the convention. In other words, we need to consider the number of different *combinations* of 12 people taken 3 at a time. Our next formula will help us compute this number of different combinations.

Counting Rule for Combinations

The number of *combinations* of n objects taken r at a time is

$$C_{n,r} = \frac{n!}{r!(n-r)!} \tag{10}$$

where n and r are whole numbers and $n \geqslant r$. Other commonly used notations for combinations include $_nC_r$ and $\binom{n}{r}$.

Notice the difference between the concepts of permutations and combinations. When we consider permutations, we are considering groupings *and order*. When we consider combinations, we are considering only the number of different groupings. For combinations, order within the groupings is not considered. As a result, the number of combinations of n objects taken r at a time is generally smaller than the number of permutations of the same n objects taken r at a time. In fact, the combinations formula is simply the permutations formula with the number of permutations of each distinct group divided out. In the formula for combinations, notice the factor of $r!$ in the denominator.

Now let's look at an example in which we compute the number of *combinations* of twelve people taken three at a time.

Example 11 Three members from the group of 12 on the board of directors at Belford Community Hospital will be selected to go to a convention with all expenses paid. How many different groups of three are there?

Solution: In this case we are interested in *combinations* rather than permutations of 12 people taken 3 at a time. Using Formula (10), we get

$$C_{n,r} = \frac{n!}{r!(n-r)!} \quad \text{or} \quad C_{12,3} = \frac{12!}{3!(12-3)!} = \frac{12!}{3!9!}$$

$$= \frac{479,001,600}{(6)(362,880)} = 220$$

There are 220 different possible groups of 3 to go to the convention.

Another way to get the solution is to use your calculator to evaluate $C_{12,3}$ directly. Since order is not considered, this number is much smaller than the number of different slates of three officers we computed in Guided Exercise 14.

We have different formulas for permutations and combinations of n objects taken r at a time. How do you decide which one to use? Always ask yourself if order in the groups of r objects is relevant. If it is, use $P_{n,r}$. If order is not relevant, use $C_{n,r}$.

GUIDED EXERCISE 15

In your political science class you are given a list of 10 books. You are to select 4 to read during the semester. How many different *combinations* of 4 books are available from the list of 10?

(a) Is the order in which you read the books relevant to the task of selecting the books?

(a) No.

(b) Do we use the number of permutations or combinations of 10 books taken 4 at a time?

(b) Since consideration of order in which the books are selected is not relevant, we compute the number of *combinations* of 10 books taken 4 at a time.

(c) How many books are available from which to select? How many must you read? What is the value of n? of r?

(c) There are 10 books among which you must select 4 to read. $n = 10$ and $r = 4$.

(d) Compute $C_{10,4}$ to determine the number of different groups of 4 books from the list of 10.

(d)

$$C_{n,r} = \frac{n!}{r!(n-r)!}$$

$$C_{10,4} = \frac{10!}{4!(10-4)!}$$

$$= \frac{10!}{4!6!}$$

$$= \frac{3,628,800}{(24)(720)}$$

$$= 210$$

There are 210 different groups of 4 books to select from the list of 10. An alternate method of solution is to use the $_nC_r$ key on your calculator.

We have introduced you to three counting formulas: the multiplication rule, the permutations rule, and the combinations rule. There are other rules that apply when the objects are not distinct. Many counting problems are easy to state and fairly difficult to solve. Some have you combine several counting rules. However, the problems for this section are all straightforward. Some ask you to use your counting abilities to compute probabilities.

Section 4.3 Problems

1. (a) Draw a tree diagram to display all the possible head–tail sequences that can occur when you flip a coin three times.
   (b) How many sequences contain exactly two heads?
   (c) *Probability extension:* Assuming the sequences are all equally likely, what is the probability that you will get exactly two heads when you toss a coin three times?

2. (a) Draw a tree diagram to display all the possible outcomes that can occur when you flip a coin and then toss a die.
   (b) How many outcomes contain a head and a number greater than four?
   (c) *Probability extension:* Assuming the outcomes displayed in the tree diagram are all equally likely, what is the probability that you will get a head *and* a number greater than four when you flip a coin and toss a die?

3. There are six balls in an urn. They are identical except for color. Two are red, three are blue, and one is yellow. You are to draw a ball from the urn, note its color, and set it aside. Then you are to draw another ball from the urn and note its color.
   (a) Make a tree diagram to show all possible outcomes of the experiment. Label the probability associated with each stage of the experiment on the appropriate branch.
   (b) *Probability extension:* Compute the probability for each outcome of the experiment.

4. Repeat the experiment described in Problem 3. However, replace the first ball before you draw the second one.
   (a) Make a tree diagram to show all possible outcomes of the experiment. Label the probability associated with each stage of the experiment on the appropriate branch.
   (b) *Probability extension:* Compute the probability for each outcome of the experiment.

5. Consider three true–false questions. There are two possible outcomes for each question: true or false.
   (a) Draw a tree diagram showing all possible sequences of responses for the three questions. Does your tree diagram look similar to the one in Problem 1? Why would you expect this result?
   (b) *Probability extension:* Only one sequence will contain all three correct answers. Assuming you are guessing and all of the sequences are equally likely to occur when you guess, what is the probability of getting all three questions correct?

6. (a) Make a tree diagram to show all the possible sequences of answers for three multiple-choice questions, each with four possible responses.
   (b) *Probability extension:* Assuming that you are guessing the answers so that all outcomes listed in the tree are equally likely, what is the probability that you will guess the one sequence that contains all three correct answers?

7. Four wires (red, green, blue, and yellow) need to be attached to a circuit board. A robotic device will attach the wires. The wires can be attached in any order, and the production manager wishes to determine which order would be fastest for the robot to use. Use the multiplication rule of counting to determine the number of all the possible sequences of assembly that must be tested. (*Hint:* There are four choices for the first wire, three for the second, two for the third, and only one for the fourth.)

8. A sales representative must visit four cities: Omaha, Dallas, Wichita, and Oklahoma City. There are direct air connections between each of the cities. Use the multiplication rule of counting to determine the number of different choices the sales representative has for the order in which to visit the cities. How is this problem similar to Problem 7?

9. You have two decks of cards (52 cards per deck), and you draw one card from each deck.
   (a) Use the multiplication rule of counting to determine the number of pairs of cards possible.
   (b) There are four kings in each deck. How many pairs of kings are possible?
   (c) *Probability extension:* Assuming all pairs are equally likely to be drawn, what is the probability of drawing two kings?

10. You toss a pair of dice.
    (a) Use the multiplication rule of counting to determine the number of possible pairs of outcomes. (Recall that there are six possible outcomes for each die.)
    (b) There are three even numbers on each die. How many outcomes are possible with even numbers appearing on each die?
    (c) *Probability extension:* What is the probability that both dice will show an even number?

11. Barbara is a research biologist for Green Carpet Lawns. She is studying the effects of fertilizer type, temperature at time of application, and water treatment after application. She has four fertilizer types, three temperature zones, and three water treatments to test. Use the multiplication rule of counting to determine the number of different lawn plots she needs to have in order to test each fertilizer type, temperature range, and water treatment configuration.

12. The Deli Special lunch offers a choice of three different sandwiches, four kinds of salads, and five different desserts. Use the multiplication rule of

Figure 4–16 When Smokers
            Begin Puffing*

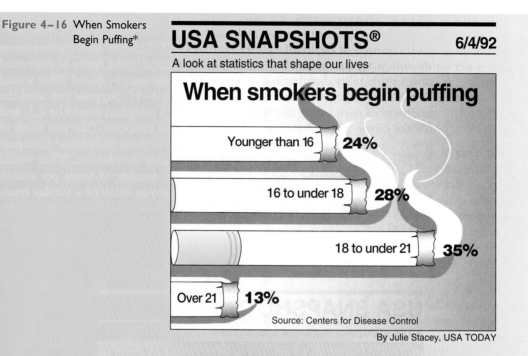

USA SNAPSHOTS®   6/4/92

A look at statistics that shape our lives

When smokers begin puffing

Younger than 16   **24%**

16 to under 18   **28%**

18 to under 21   **35%**

Over 21   **13%**

Source: Centers for Disease Control

By Julie Stacey, USA TODAY

Figure 4–17 How Much Time
            We Spend Reading
            the Sunday Paper*

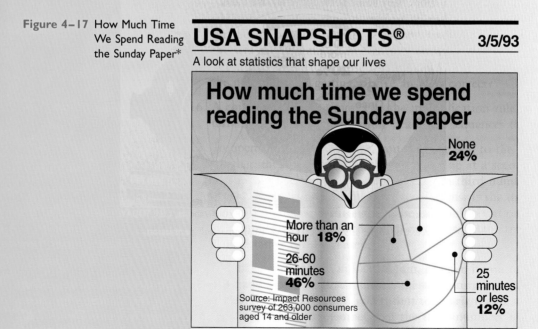

USA SNAPSHOTS®   3/5/93

A look at statistics that shape our lives

How much time we spend reading the Sunday paper

None **24%**

More than an hour **18%**

26-60 minutes **46%**

25 minutes or less **12%**

Source: Impact Resources survey of 263,000 consumers aged 14 and older

By Marty Baumann, USA TODAY

*Source: Copyright 1992, USA TODAY. Copyright 1993, USA TODAY. Reprinted with permission.

LINKING CONCEPTS 4

Discuss each of the following topics in class or review the topics on your own. Then write a brief but complete essay in which you summarize the main points. Please include formulas and graphs as appropriate.

1. Discuss the following concepts and give examples from everyday life where you encounter each concept.

   (a) Sample space.
   (b) Probability assignment to a sample space. In your discussion be sure to include answers to the following questions.
       (i) Is there more than one valid way to assign probabilities to a sample space? Explain and give an example.
       (ii) How can probabilities be estimated by relative frequencies? How could probabilities be computed if events are equally likely?

2. Discuss the concepts of mutually exclusive events and independent events. List several examples of each type of event from everyday life.

   (a) If A and B are mutually exclusive events, does it follow that A and B *cannot* be independent events? Give an example to demonstrate your answer. (*Hint:* Discuss an election where only one person can win the election. Let A be the event that party A's candidate wins, let B be the event that party B's candidate wins. Does the outcome of one event determine the outcome of the other event? Are A and B mutually exclusive events?)
   (b) Discuss conditions under which $P(A \text{ and } B) = P(A) \cdot P(B)$ is true. Under what conditions is this not true?
   (c) Discuss conditions under which $P(A \text{ or } B) = P(A) + P(B)$ is true. Under what conditions is this not true?

3. What is a random variable? What is the difference between a discrete random variable and a continuous random variable? Consider discrete probability distributions. What does the graph of a discrete probability distribution look like? Would it be correct to say that the mean of the distribution is the balance point, and the standard deviation is a description of the spread of the distribution? In the next chapter we will study an important discrete probability distribution and then in Chapter 6 and later chapters, we will see examples of continuous probability distributions. In all cases the concepts of the mean and standard deviation of the probability distributions will be important.

4. Although we learn a good deal about probability in this course, the main emphasis is on statistics. Write a few paragraphs in which you talk about the distinction between probability and statistics. In what types of problems would probability be the main tool? In what types of problems would statistics be the main tool? Give some examples of both types of problems. What kind of outcome or conclusions do we expect from each type problem?

Using Technology

The problems in this section may be done using statistical computer software or calculators with statistical functions. Displays and suggestions are given for Minitab (Release 9), the TI-82 graphing calculator, and ComputerStat.

Expected Value and Standard Deviation of a Discrete Probability Distribution

Minitab

Minitab has a number of built-in probability distributions. You also can enter a discrete probability distribution and draw random samples from such a distribution. However, there are no direct commands available to compute the expected value and standard deviation for general discrete probability distributions. But we can find the mean and standard deviation of discrete probability distributions by utilizing the programming capacity in Minitab and our knowledge of the formulas for mean and standard deviation. A brief Minitab program that will calculate these parameters follows.

```
MTB > NOTE THIS PROGRAM WILL MAKE A DISCRETE PROBABILITY DISTRIBUTION
MTB > NOTE AND COMPUTE THE MEAN AND STANDARD DEVIATION
MTB > NOTE ENTER X VALUES IN COLUMN 1 AND FREQUENCIES IN COLUMN 2
MTB > NAME C1 = 'X' C2 = 'FREQ' C3 = 'P(X)' C6 = 'MEAN' C7 = 'ST. DEV'
MTB > SUM C2, PUT IN K1
MTB > LET C3 = C2/K1
MTB > LET C4 = C1*C3
MTB > SUM C4, PUT IN K2
MTB > LET C5 = (C1 — K2)**2*C3
MTB > LET K4 = SQRT(SUM(C5))
MTB > LET C6(1) = K2
MTB > LET C7(1) = K4
MTB > PRINT C1 C2 C3 C6 C7
```

TI-82

The TI-82 does not permit fractional values for frequencies. Consequently, we cannot use the STAT mode to find the mean and standard deviation of a discrete probability distribution. As with Minitab, it is possible to write a program utilizing formulas given in Section 4.4 to do the necessary calculations.

ComputerStat

Since ComputerStat was specifically designed to go with this text, there is a program that gives expected values and standard deviations of discrete probability distributions. Under the Probability Distributions menu, select the program Expected Value and Standard Deviation of a Probability Distribution. Follow the instructions on the screen.

Applications

1. During the seventh anniversary year of the Colorado Lottery one of the games was called Lucky 7's. To play Lucky 7's, all you need to do is purchase a Lucky 7's lottery ticket ($1), and scratch the ticket to expose 9 numbers. You win if there are a suitable number of 7's in appropriate places. The advertised odds of winning are based on a total of 10,080,000 tickets sold. For Lucky 7's, the following information was given:

Value of Prize (in dollars)	Number of Winners Possible
0	7,499,184
1 (free lottery ticket)	1,552,320
2	927,360
7	40,320
17	40,320
27	20,160
700	252
7,000	84

Source: Adapted from information given for the game Lucky 7's, 1990. Colorado Lottery, Pueblo, Colorado.

(a) Use the preceding information to calculate the probability of winning 0, 2, 7, 17, 27, 700, or 7000 dollars or a $1 lottery ticket.
(b) Compute the expected value and standard deviation of this probability distribution.
(c) Proceeds from the Colorado State Lottery benefit state parks and recreation areas. Look at your answer to part (b). When you buy a Colorado State Lottery ticket, what are your expected winnings? How much have you effectively contributed to state parks and recreation? (Remember, each ticket costs $1.)

2. For those marriages that ended in divorce, the following information was given about the length of the marriage.

Length of Marriage to Nearest Year or Span of Years	Percentage
0	4.4
1	8.1
2	9.0
3	9.2
4	8.4
5	7.2
6	6.2
7	5.7
8	4.7
9	4.1
10–14	13.5
15–19	8.0
20–24	5.4
25–29	3.3
30–34	2.8

(*Note:* The last class is really open-ended: 30 or more years. However, in order to process the data, we need a right endpoint, so we will treat all years over 34 as 34.)

Source: Copyright ©1983 by Andrew Hacker. Reprinted from U/S: A Statistical Portrait of the American People, by Andrew Hacker. Reprinted by permission of the Author's agent, Robin Straus Agency, Inc.

The information with midpoints of class intervals (where necessary) gives a probability distribution that a marriage ending in divorce will last 0, 1, 2, 3, 4, 5, 6, 7, 8, 9, 12, 17, 22, 27, or 32 years. Find the expected value and standard deviation of this probability distribution.

Binomial Experiments

Some problems are characterized by the feature that there are exactly *two* possible outcomes of interest. In this section we will discuss *binomial experiments*. What *is* a binomial experiment? What *is not* a binomial experiment? What are the *key features* of a binomial experiment? Where do binomial experiments occur in everyday life, and why are they important?

The Binomial Distribution

In this section we learn how to compute binomial probabilities using the formula

$$P(r) = C_{n,r} p^r q^{n-r}$$

First, we examine in detail a special case for only $n = 3$ trials. Then we extend our results to the general formula. For convenience sake, we also learn how to use a binomial distribution table as found in Appendix II for selected values of n and p. The section concludes with several applications.

Additional Properties of the Binomial Distribution

In this section we graph binomial probability distributions. Then we study the expected value $\mu = np$ and the standard deviation $\sigma = \sqrt{npq}$ of binomial distributions. The section concludes with several examples of a type of problem known as a *quota problem*. Such problems occur in many areas of everyday life.

The Geometric and Poisson Probability Distributions

The geometric and Poisson distributions are related in different ways to the binomial distribution. If you have time to study only one distribution in this chapter, then many people would consider the binomial distribution to be the most important. However, all three distributions taken together cover a large variety of everyday real-world problems. If you choose to study this section, your time and effort will be rewarded by a wide range of interesting applications. Another related distribution is the hypergeometric distribution. A discussion of this distribution can be found in Appendix I.

Voltaire
(1694—1778)

One of France's greatest writers, Voltaire explored philosophical and moral issues throughout much of his writing.

The Binomial Probability Distribution and Related Topics

He who has heard the same thing told by 12,000 eye-witnesses has only 12,000 probabilities, which are equal to one strong probability, which is far from certainty.

Voltaire

When it is not in our power to determine what is true, we ought to follow what is most probable.

Descartes

It is important to realize that statistics and probability do not deal in the realm of certainty. If there is any realm of human knowledge where genuine certainty exists, you may be sure that our statistical methods are not needed there. In most human endeavors and in almost all the natural world around us, the element of chance happenings cannot be avoided. When we cannot expect something with true certainty, we must rely on probability to be our guide. In this and the next chapter we will study some of the most important probability distributions of mathematical statistics. Their influence will be felt throughout our entire study of statistics.

Focus Problem ▶ Personality Types

Isabel Briggs Myers was a pioneer in the study of personality types. Her work has been used successfully in counseling, educational, and industrial settings. In the book *A Guide to the Development and Use of the Myers-Briggs Type Indicators,* by Myers and McCaully, it was reported that based on a very large sample (2282 professors), approximately 45% of all university professors are extroverted.

Suppose you have classes with six different professors.

1. What is the probability that all six are extroverts?
2. What is the probability that none of your professors is an extrovert?
3. What is the probability that at least two of your professors are extroverts?
4. In a group of six professors selected at random, what is the *expected number* of extroverts? What is the *standard deviation* of the distribution?
5. Suppose you were assigned to write an article for the student newspaper and you were given a quota (by the editor) of interviewing at least three extroverted professors. How many professors would you interview to be at least 90% sure of filling the quota?

- *Comment:* Both extroverted and introverted professors can be excellent teachers.

Section 5.1   Binomial Experiments

On a TV quiz show each contestant has a try at the wheel of fortune. The wheel of fortune is a roulette wheel with 36 slots, one of which is gold. If the ball lands in the gold slot, the contestant wins $50,000. No other slot pays. What is the probability that the quiz show will have to pay the fortune to three contestants out of 100?

Features of a
Binomial Experiment

In this problem the contestant and the quiz show sponsors are concerned about only two outcomes from the wheel of fortune: The ball lands on the gold, or the ball does not land on the gold. This problem is typical of an entire class of problems that are characterized by the feature that there are exactly two possible outcomes (for each trial) of interest. These problems are called *binomial experiments,* or *Bernoulli experiments,* after Jacob Bernoulli who studied them extensively in the late 1600s.

A *binomial experiment* must have these features:

1. There are a fixed number of trials. We denote this number by the letter n.
2. The n trials are independent and repeated under identical conditions.
3. Each trial has only two outcomes: success, denoted by S, and failure, denoted by F.
4. For each individual trial, the probability of success is the same. We denote the probability of success by p and that of failure by q. Since each trial results in either success or failure, $p + q = 1$ and $q = 1 - p$.
5. The central problem of a binomial experiment is to find the probability of r successes out of n trials.

Example 1 Let's see how the wheel of fortune problem meets the criteria of a binomial experiment. We'll take the criteria one at a time.

1. Each of the 100 contestants has a trial at the wheel, so there are $n = 100$ trials in this problem.

2. Assuming that the wheel is fair, the trials are independent, since the result of one spin of the wheel has no effect on the results of other spins.

3. We are interested in only two outcomes on each spin of the wheel: The ball either lands on the gold, or it does not. Let's call landing on the gold *success* (S) and not landing on the gold *failure* (F). In general, the assignment of the terms *success* and *failure* to outcomes does not imply good or bad results. These terms are assigned simply for the user's convenience.

4. On each trial the probability p of success (landing on the gold) is 1/36, since there are 36 slots and only one of them is gold. Consequently, the probability of failure is

$$q = 1 - p = 1 - \frac{1}{36} = \frac{35}{36}$$

on each trial.

5. We want to know the probability of 3 successes out of 100 trials, so r = 3 in this example. It turns out that the probability the quiz show will have to pay the fortune to 3 contestants out of 100 is about 0.23. In the next section we'll see how this probability was computed.

GUIDED EXERCISE 1

The registrar of a college noted that for many years the withdrawal rate from an introductory chemistry course has been 35% each term. If 80 students register for the course, what is the probability that 55 will complete it?

This is a binomial experiment. Let's see how it fits each of the specifications.

(a) Each of the 80 students enrolled in the course can make the decision to withdraw or complete the course. The decision of each student can be thought of as a trial. How many trials are there? $n = $ _____?

(a) There are 80 trials, so $n = 80$.

(b) In this problem we will assume that the decision one student makes about withdrawing from the course does not affect the decision of any other student. Under this assumption, are the trials independent?

(b) Yes.

(c) A trial consists of a student deciding to withdraw or complete the chemistry course. How many possible outcomes are there to each trial?

(c) Two: the decision to withdraw or the decision to complete the course.

(d) Let's call completing the course success. Then, withdrawing is failure. The probability of failure for each trial is $q = 0.35$. Use the fact that $q = 1 - p$ to find p, the probability of success for each trial.

(d) Since $q = 0.35$ and $q = 1 - p$, p must equal 0.65.

(e) In this problem we want to know the probability of $r =$ _____ successes out of $n =$ _____ trials.

(e) $r = 55$; $n = 80$.

A binomial experiment must satisfy all the criteria. One criterion that is fairly easy to check is whether each trial has exactly two possible outcomes (see Guided Exercise 2).

GUIDED EXERCISE 2

We want to determine if the following experiment is binomial:
  A random sample of 30 men between the ages of 20 and 35 is taken from the population of Teliville. Each man is asked to name his favorite TV program.

(a) The response of each of the 30 men is a trial, so there are $n =$ _____ trials.

(a) $n = 30$

(b) How many outcomes are possible on each trial? Can this be a binomial experiment?

(b) There are many possible outcomes—as many as there are programs on TV in Teliville. This *cannot* be a binomial experiment, since each trial has more than two possible outcomes.

Independence Criterion

Independence is another criterion the binomial trials must satisfy. In other words, the outcome of one trial cannot affect the outcome of any other trial. Example 2 illustrates a case in which the condition of independence is violated.

Example 2 The intramural committee of a college consists of four women and six men. To select a chairperson and recorder, they put all the members' names in a hat and draw two names without replacing the first name drawn. The first name drawn will be chairperson, and the second will be recorder. What is the probability that both offices will be held by women? Analyze this problem to see if it is a binomial experiment.

Solution: Each draw is a trial, so there are two trials. The outcome under consideration is whether the name drawn is that of a woman or not. We'll define success to be that a woman's name is drawn.

These trials are not independent because the outcome of the first trial affects the probability of success on the second trial. The probability of a woman on the first draw is 4/10. Since the name of the first draw is not replaced, the probability of a woman on the second draw is 3/9 if a woman was selected on the first draw and 4/9 if a man was chosen on the first draw. In either case, the probability of success on the second trial has been affected by the outcome of the first trial.

Since the trials are not independent, the problem is not a binomial experiment.

Anytime we make selections from a population *without replacement, we do not have independent trials.* However, replacement is often not practical. If the number of trials is quite small with respect to the population, we *almost* have independent trials, and we can say the situation is *closely approximated* by a binomial experiment. For instance, suppose we select 20 tuition bills at random from a collection of 10,000 bills issued at one college and observe if the bill is in error or not. If 600 of the 10,000 bills are in error, then the probability that the first one selected is in error is 600/10,000, or 0.0600. If the first is in error, then the probability that the second is in error is 599/9999, or 0.0599. Even if the first 19 bills selected are in error, the probability that the 20th is also in error is 581/9981, or 0.0582. All these probabilities round to 0.06, and we can say that the independence condition is approximately satisfied.

GUIDED EXERCISE 3

Let's analyze the following binomial experiment to determine p, q, n, and r:

According to the *Textbook of Medical Physiology*, 5th edition, by Arthur Guyton, 9% of the population has blood type B. Suppose we choose 18 people at random from the population and test the blood type of each. What is the probability that 3 of these people have blood type B? (*Note:* Independence is approximated because 18 people is an extremely small sample with respect to the entire population.)

(a) In this experiment we are observing whether or not a person has type B blood. We will say we have a success if the person has type B blood. What is failure?

(a) Failure occurs if a person does not have type B blood.

(b) The probability of success is 0.09, since 9% of the population has type B blood. What is the probability of failure, q?

(b) The probability of failure is

$$q = 1 - p$$
$$= 1 - 0.09 = 0.91$$

(c) In this experiment there are $n = $ _____ trials.

(d) We wish to compute the probability of 3 successes out of 18 trials. In this case $r = $ _____.

(c) In this experiment $n = 18$.

(d) In this case $r = 3$.

In the next section we will see how to compute the probability of r successes out of n trials when we have a binomial experiment.

Section 5.1 Problems

In this section we are interested primarily in the criteria for a binomial experiment. In section 5.2 we will learn how to compute the actual binomial probabilities.

Which of the following are binomial experiments? For those which are binomial experiments,

(a) What makes up a *trial?*

(b) What is a *success?* a *failure?*

(c) What are the values of n, p, q, and r or the range of values for r?

For those which are not binomial experiments, what is it that keeps them from being so?

1. At Community Hospital, the nursing staff is large enough so that 80% of the time a nurse can respond to a room call within 3 minutes. Last night there were 73 room calls. We wish to find the probability nurses responded to 62 of them within 3 minutes.

2. A travel agent has four different packages which he claims are very popular. He claims that 99% of all customers enjoy the Hawaii package, 95% enjoy the Europe package, 96% enjoy the Alaska package, and 97% enjoy the New York package. Last month he sold 51 packages. We wish to find the probability that his clients enjoyed 43 of them.

3. *Harper's Index* states that 10% of all adult residents in Washington, D.C., are lawyers. For a random sample of 15 adult Washington, D.C., residents, we want to find the probability that 3 are lawyers.

4. A new over-the counter medication is advertised as reducing blood pressure for 99% of those who use it. A random sample of 100 people with high blood pressure took the medication. We wish to find the probability that 8 will have reduced blood pressure.

5. A survey of top executives at 100 of the nation's largest corporations reported in *USA Today* (October 19, 1989) showed that 33% of them felt that Japanese was the most important language for a successful business career during the next 20 years. Spanish was the language recommendation by 44% of the executives. Other languages were recommended by 23% of the executives. Suppose 20 of these executives formed an advisory council for the Business Division at Lakeview College. We wish to find the probability that 15 of them would recommend the same foreign language.

6. Based on information from the *Denver Post,* it is estimated that 70% of all cars on the Valley Highway are going faster than the speed limit. Radar was used to observe the speeds of 22 cars selected at random on the highway. However, when 11 of the cars were observed, a police car was in plain view of the drivers. When the other 11 cars were observed, no police car was in sight. We wish to find the probability that of the 22 cars observed, 12 were going over the speed limit.

7. Six firefighters volunteer for weekend duty so that they can have Thanksgiving Day off. However, the Chief says that only two are needed that weekend. To decide who works the weekend duty instead of Thanksgiving Day, they take turns drawing straws. Four straws are of one length and two are shorter. The straws are not replaced after being drawn. The firefighters who draw the short straws get to work on the weekend instead of on Thanksgiving Day. We wish to find the probability that firefighters George and Carol are selected for weekend duty.

8. *Chances: Risk and Odds in Everyday Life,* by James Burke, claims that 71% of all single men would welcome a woman taking the initiative in asking for a date. A random sample of 20 single men was asked if they would welcome a woman taking the initiative in asking for a date. We want to compute the probability that at least 18 of the men will say yes. *Hint:* What range of r values will be used?

9. State Farm Insurance Company (Mountain States Office) reports that 36% of all automobile property damage claims are made by single males under 25 years of age. In Denver, a random sample of 619 automobile damage claims is under study. We want to estimate the probability that between 45 and 50 (including 45 and 50) of these claims are made by single males under 25 years of age. *Hint:* What range of r values will be used?

10. *Harper's Index* states that 50% of all federal prison inmates are serving time for drug dealing. A random sample of 125 files for prisoners in state, local, and federal prisons was obtained. We want to compute the probability that at least 55 of these files indicate that the prisoner is serving time for drug dealing.

11. Based on information from *U.S.A. Today* (December 20, 1993), 70% of all people over 35 years of age prefer a Christmas vacation in a warm, sunny climate. A random sample of 42 college students was asked where they would prefer to spend their Christmas vacation. We want to estimate the probability that 30 would prefer a warm, sunny climate.

12. A national study at Michigan State University (published in part by *U.S.A. Today,* December 10, 1993) showed that approximately 79% of all 18-year-olds go on dates. In a random sample of 37 people who are 18-year-olds, we want to estimate the probability that 29 or more go on dates.

13. *Harper's Index* reports that nationally only 14% of all home burglaries are solved (i.e., burglars caught and convicted). For a random sample of

300 home burglaries, we want to estimate the probability that 40 or fewer will be solved.

14. James Burke, in his books *Chances: Risk and Odds in Everyday Life,* states that only 6% of all people worth over $1 million inherited their wealth. In a random sample of 250 people, we want to estimate the probability there are at least 12 people who inherited over $1 million.

15. An investor claims that there is a 73% chance that a bull market will begin if the volume of stocks traded on the New York Stock Exchange remains over 200 million shares per day for 3 weeks. Otherwise, the probability is only 20% that a bull market will occur. We wish to find the probability that in a 5-year period, nine bull markets will begin.

16. Steve and Kathy guide climbing parties up Longs Peak. They say that when the weather is good, the probability of reaching the summit (without having to turn around for some reason) is 0.80, but when the weather is not so good, the probability is 0.50. Next summer Steve and Kathy have 20 guided climbs scheduled. We wish to find the probability that they will make it to the summit 14 times.

Section 5.2   The Binomial Distribution

The central problem of a binomial experiment is to find the probability of r successes out of n trials. In this section we'll see how to find these probabilities.

A Model with Three Trials

Suppose you are taking a timed final exam. You have three multiple-choice questions left to do. Each question has four suggested answers, and only one of the answers is correct. You have only 5 seconds left to do these three questions, so you decide to mark answers on the answer sheet without even reading the questions. Assuming that your answers are randomly selected, what is the probability that you get zero, one, two, or all three questions correct?

This is a binomial experiment. Each of the questions can be thought of as a trial, so there are $n = 3$ trials. The possible outcomes on each trial are success S, indicating a correct response, or failure F, meaning a wrong answer. The trials are independent, since the outcome of any one trial does not affect the outcome of the others.

What is the probability of success on any question? Since you are guessing and there are four answers from which to select, the probability of a correct answer is 0.25. The probability q of a wrong answer is then 0.75. In short, we have a binomial experiment with $n = 3$, $p = 0.25$, and $q = 0.75$.

Now what are the possible outcomes in terms of success or failure for these three trials? Let's use the notation *SSF* to mean success on the first question, success on the second, and failure on the third. There are eight possible combinations of *S*'s and *F*'s. They are

SSS   SSF   SFS   FSS   SFF   FSF   FFS   FFF

Table 5–1 Outcomes for a Binomial Experiment with $n = 3$ Trials

Outcome	Probability of Outcome				r (No. of Successes)
SSS	$P(SSS) = P(S)P(S)P(S)$	$= p^3$	$= (0.25)^3$	$= 0.016$	3
SSF	$P(SSF) = P(S)P(S)P(F)$	$= p^2q$	$= (0.25)^2(0.75)$	$= 0.047$	2
SFS	$P(SFS) = P(S)P(F)P(S)$	$= p^2q$	$= (0.25)^2(0.75)$	$= 0.047$	2
FSS	$P(FSS) = P(F)P(S)P(S)$	$= p^2q$	$= (0.25)^2(0.75)$	$= 0.047$	2
SFF	$P(SFF) = P(S)P(F)P(F)$	$= pq^2$	$= (0.25)(0.75)^2$	$= 0.141$	1
FSF	$P(FSF) = P(F)P(S)P(F)$	$= pq^2$	$= (0.25)(0.75)^2$	$= 0.141$	1
FFS	$P(FFS) = P(F)P(F)P(S)$	$= pq^2$	$= (0.25)(0.75)^2$	$= 0.141$	1
FFF	$P(FFF) = P(F)P(F)P(F)$	$= q^3$	$= (0.75)^3$	$= 0.422$	0

To compute the probability of each outcome, we can use the multiplication law because the trials are independent. For instance, the probability of success on the first two questions and failure on the last is

$$P(SSF) = P(S) \cdot P(S) \cdot P(F) = p \cdot p \cdot q = p^2q = (0.25)^2(0.75) = 0.047$$

In a similar fashion, we can compute the probability of each of the eight outcomes. These are shown in Table 5–1, along with the number of successes r associated with each trial.

Now we can compute the probability of r successes out of three trials for $r = 0, 1, 2,$ or 3. Let's compute $P(1)$. The notation $P(1)$ stands for the probability of one success. For three trials, there are three different outcomes that show exactly one success. They are the outcomes *SFF, FSF,* and *FFS*. So

$$P(1) = P(SFF \text{ or } FSF \text{ or } FFS) = P(SFF) + P(FSF) + P(FFS)$$
$$= pq^2 + pq^2 + pq^2$$
$$= 3pq^2$$
$$= 3(0.25)(0.75)^2$$
$$= 0.422$$

In the same way we can find $P(0)$, $P(2)$, and $P(3)$. These values are shown in Table 5–2.

Table 5–2 $P(r)$ for $n = 3$ Trials, $p = 0.25$

r (No. of Successes)	$P(r)$ (Probability of r Successes in 3 Trials)		$P(r)$ for $p = 0.25$
0	$P(0) = P(FFF)$	$= q^3$	0.422
1	$P(1) = P(SFF) + P(FSF) + P(FFS)$	$= 3pq^2$	0.422
2	$P(2) = P(SSF) + P(SFS) + P(FSS)$	$= 3p^2q$	0.141
3	$P(3) = P(SSS)$	$= p^3$	0.016

We have done quite a bit of work to determine your chances of $r = 0, 1, 2,$ or 3 successes on three multiple-choice questions if you are just guessing. And now we see that there is only a small chance (about 0.016) that you will get them all correct.

The model we constructed in Table 5–2 to compute the probability of r successes out of three trials can be used for any binomial experiment with $n = 3$ trials. Simply change the values of p and q to fit the experiment. In Guided Exercise 4 we will use this model again.

GUIDED EXERCISE 4

Maria is doing a study on the issue of the quarter system versus the semester system. To obtain faculty input, she mails out questionnaires to the faculty. The probability that a faculty member returns the completed questionnaire is 0.65. Three faculty members chosen at random from the foreign language department are sent questionnaires. Compute the probability that *exactly two* completed questionnaires are returned and the probability that *all three* are returned. We'll do these computations in steps.

(a) In this problem what are the values of n, p, q?

    (a) $n = 3$, $p = 0.65$, $q = 1 - 0.65 = 0.35$

(b) The probability that exactly two questionnaires will be returned is P (_____). In this case $r =$ _____ . By Table 5–2,

$$P(2) = 3p^2q \text{ for } n = 3 \text{ trials}$$

Use this formula to compute $P(2)$.

    (b) We want $P(2)$, so $r = 2$:

$$P(2) = 3(0.65)^2(0.35) = 0.444$$

(c) Use the appropriate formula from Table 5–2 to compute the probability that all three questionnaires will be returned.

    (c) $P(3) = p^3 = (0.65)^3 = 0.275$

General Formula for Binomial Probability Distribution

Table 5–2 can only be used as a model for computing the probability of r successes out of *three* trials. How can we compute the probability of 7 successes out of 10 trials? We can develop a table for $n = 10$, but this would be a tremendous task because there are 1024 possible combinations of successes and failures on 10 trials. Fortunately, mathematicians have given us a direct formula to compute the probability of r successes for any number of trials.

Formula for the Binomial Probability Distribution:

$$P(r) = C_{n,r}p^rq^{n-r}$$

where $C_{n,r} = (n!)/(r!(n - r)!)$ is the *binomial coefficient*. Values of $C_{n,r}$ for various values of n and r can be found in Table 3 of Appendix II.

Those of you who studied the section on counting techniques (Section 4.3) will recognize the symbol $C_{n,r}$ as the symbol used for the number of combinations of n objects taken r at a time. For those who did not study Section 4.3, a brief description of the meaning of the symbol $C_{n,r}$ follows. Examples and exercises will show you how to do the calculations necessary to compute $C_{n,r}$.

In the meantime, let's look more carefully at the formula itself. There are two main parts. The expression $p^r q^{n-r}$ is the probability of getting one outcome with r successes and $n - r$ failures. The binomial coefficient $C_{n,r}$ counts the number of outcomes that have r successes and $n - r$ failures. For instance, in the case of $n = 3$ trials, we saw in Table 5–1 that the probability of getting an outcome with one success and two failures was pq^2. This is the value of $p^r q^{n-r}$ when $r = 1$ and $n = 3$. We also observed that there were three outcomes with one success and two failures so $C_{3,1}$ is 3.

Table of Appendix II gives the values of the binomial coefficient $C_{n,r}$ for selected values of n and r. However, you can compute $C_{n,r}$ directly from a formula. This formula is optional. You may skip it and go on to examples where we use the binomial probability distribution to compute $P(r)$.

Table for $C_{n,r}$ (margin note)

Optional

The formula for the computation of the binomial coefficient $C_{n,r}$ is

$$C_{n,r} = \frac{n!}{r!(n-r)!}$$

where $n!$ (read, *n factorial*) is the product of n with all the counting numbers less than n. $0!$ is defined to be 1.

Example:

$$C_{5,3} = \frac{5!}{3!(5-3)!} = \frac{5!}{3!(2!)} = \frac{5 \cdot \overset{2}{\cancel{4}} \cdot \cancel{3} \cdot \cancel{2} \cdot \cancel{1}}{\cancel{3} \cdot \cancel{2} \cdot \cancel{1}(\cancel{2} \cdot \cancel{1})} = 10$$

This means that there are 10 ways to list three successes and two failures when we have five trials.

Note: Some calculators have a factorial key, usually indicated by !. But if yours does not, you can compute a factorial by doing the necessary multiplications. It is a good idea to cancel as much as possible (as shown in the example) before doing the multiplications. Otherwise, you can easily generate numbers too large for the calculator display. Table 2 of Appendix II has values for 1 factorial through 20 factorial.

Now let's take a look at an application of the binomial distribution formula in Example 3.

Example 3　Video games are popular, and Nintendo is one of the most popular. In fact, their market researchers claim that in the near future 22% of U.S. households will have the Nintendo videogame system. Based on this projection, what is the probability that for a random sample of 12 households, exactly 5 will have Nintendo?

Solution: (a) This is a binomial experiment with 12 trials. If we assign success to having Nintendo in a household, the probability of success is 0.22. We are interested in the probability of 5 successes. We have

$$n = 12 \quad p = 0.22 \quad q = 0.78 \quad r = 5$$

By the formula,

$$P(5) = C_{12,5}(0.22)^5(0.78)^{12\,-\,5}$$

$$= 792(0.22)^5(0.78)^7 \qquad \text{Use Table 3 (Appendix II) or a calculator}$$

$$\approx 792(0.0005)(0.1757) \qquad \text{Use a calculator}$$

$$\approx 0.07$$

There is a 7% chance that *exactly* 5 of the 12 households will have Nintendo.

(b) Many calculators have a built-in combinations function. On the TI-82, you can find the combinations function under the math menu. It is designated nCr. To compute $P(5)$ for $n = 12$, $p = 0.22$, $q = 0.78$, and $r = 5$ directly, enter the value of n, call the nCr function, enter the value of r, and then multiply the result by the appropriate powers of 0.22 and 0.78. Figure 5–1 displays the screen for computing $P(5)$. Notice the use of the ^ symbol for powers.

Figure 5–1 TI-82 Display

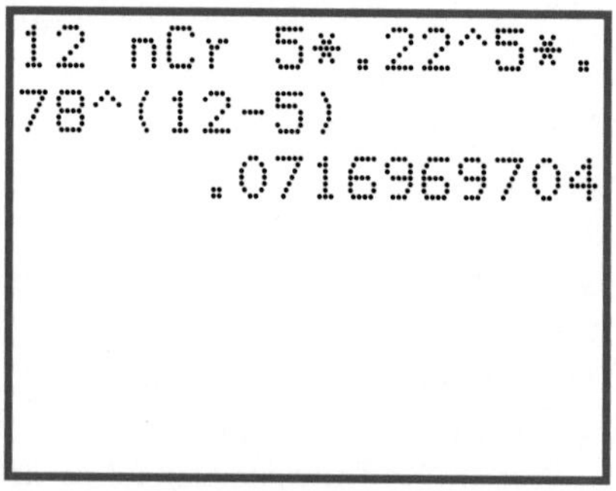

```
12 nCr 5*.22^5*.
78^(12-5)
        .0716969704
```

Table for *P(r)*

In many cases we will be interested in the probability of a range of successes rather than in the probability of an exact number of successes. For instance, we might wish to compute the probability that *at least* 5 of the 12 households will have Nintendo. In such a case we need to use the addition rule for mutually exclusive events.

$$P(at\ least\ 5\ \text{successes}) = P(r \geqslant 5)$$
$$= P(r = 5\ or\ 6\ or\ 7\ or\ 8\ or\ 9\ or\ 10\ or\ 11\ or\ 12)$$
$$= P(5) + P(6) + P(7) + P(8) + P(9) + P(10)$$
$$+ P(11) + P(12)$$

It would be quite a task to compute all the required probabilities by using the formula. Table 4 of Appendix II gives values for $P(r)$ for selected p and values of n through 20. To use the table, find the section labeled with your value of n. Then find the entry in the column headed by your value of p and the row labeled by the r value of interest.

Table 4 of Appendix II has only a limited selection of values for p. In fact, for Example 3 the probability of success, $p = 0.22$, is not available in the table. However, for other problems in this text you will find the specified value of p. The next example demonstrates the use of Table 4 (Appendix II) to find binomial probabilities.

Example 4

A biologist is studying a new hybrid tomato. It is known that the seeds of this hybrid tomato have probability 0.70 of germinating. The biologist plants 10 seeds.

(a) What is the probability that *exactly* 8 seeds will germinate?
   Solution: This is a binomial experiment with $n = 10$ trials. Each seed planted represents an independent trial. We'll say germination is success, so the probability for success on each trial is 0.70.

$$n = 10 \qquad p = 0.70 \qquad q = 0.30 \qquad r = 8$$

We wish to find $P(8)$, the probability of exactly eight successes.
   In Table 4, Appendix II, find the section with $n = 10$. Then find the entry in the column headed by $p = 0.70$ and the row headed by the r value 8. This entry is 0.233.

$$P(8) = 0.233$$

(b) What is the probability that *at least* 8 seeds will germinate?
   Solution: In this case we are interested in the probability of 8 or more seeds germinating. This means we are to compute $P(r \geqslant 8)$. Since the events are mutually exclusive, we can use the addition rule

$$P(r \geqslant 8) = P(r = 8\ or\ r = 9\ or\ r = 10) = P(8) + P(9) + P(10)$$

We already know the value of $P(8)$. We need to find $P(9)$ and $P(10)$.
   Use the same part of the table but find the entries in the row headed by the r value 9 and then the r value 10. Be sure to use the column headed by the value of p, 0.70.

$$P(9) = 0.121 \quad \text{and} \quad P(10) = 0.028$$

Now we have all the parts necessary to compute $P(r \geq 8)$.

$$P(r \geq 8) = P(8) + P(9) + P(10)$$
$$= 0.233 + 0.121 + 0.028$$
$$= 0.382$$

In Guided Exercise 5 you'll practice using the formula for $P(r)$ in one part and then use Table 4 (Appendix II) for $P(r)$ values in the second part.

GUIDED EXERCISE 5

A rarely performed and somewhat risky eye operation is known to be successful in restoring the eyesight of 30% of the patients who undergo the operation. A team of surgeons has developed a new technique for this operation that has been successful for four of six operations. Does it seem likely that the new technique is much better than the old? We'll use the binomial probability distribution to answer this question. We'll compute the probability of at least four successes in six trials for the old technique.

(a) Each operation is a binomial trial. In this case, $n =$ _____ , $p =$ _____ , $q =$ _____ , $r =$ _____ .

(a) $n = 6$, $p = 0.30$, $q = 1 - 0.30 = 0.70$, $r = 4$

(b) Use your values of n, p, and q, as well as Table 3 of Appendix II to compute $P(4)$ from the formula:

$$P(r) = C_{n,r}p^{r}q^{n-r}$$

(b) $P(4) = C_{6,4}(0.30)^4(0.70)^2$
$= 15(0.0081)(0.490)$
$= 0.060$

(c) Compute the probability of *at least* four successes out of the six trials.

$$P(r \geq 4) = P(r = 4 \text{ or } r = 5 \text{ or } r = 6)$$
$$= P(4) + P(5) + P(6)$$

Use Table 4 of Appendix II to find values of $P(4)$, $P(5)$, and $P(6)$. Then use these values to compute $P(r \geq 4)$.

(c) To find $P(4)$, $P(5)$, and $P(6)$ in Table 4, we look in the section labeled $n = 6$. Then we find the column headed by $p = 0.30$. To find $P(4)$, we use the row labeled $r = 4$. For the values of $P(5)$ and $P(6)$, use the same column but change the row headers to $r = 5$ and $r = 6$, respectively.

$$P(r \geq 4) = P(4) + P(5) + P(6)$$
$$= 0.060 + 0.010 + 0.001$$
$$= 0.071$$

(d) Under the older operation technique, the probability that at least four patients out of six regain their eyesight is _____ . Does it seem that the new technique is better than the old? Would you encourage the surgeon team to do more work on the new technique?

(d) It seems the new technique is better than the old, since, by pure chance, the probability of four or more successes out of six trials is only 0.071 for the old technique. This means one of the following two things may be happening:

(i) The new method is no better than the old method, and our surgeons have encountered a rare event (probability 0.071), or

(ii) The new method is in fact better. We think it is worth encouraging the surgeons to do more work on the new technique.

Section 5.2 Problems

In each of the following problems, the binomial distribution will be used. Please answer the following questions and then complete the problem.

(a) What makes up a trial? What is a success? What is a failure?

(b) What are the values of n, p, and q?

1. A fair quarter is flipped three times. For each of the following probabilities, use the formula for the binomial distribution and a calculator to compute the requested probability. Next, look up the probability in Table 4 of Appendix II and compare the table result with the computed result.

   (a) Find the probability of getting exactly three heads.

   (b) Find the probability of getting exactly two heads.

   (c) Find the probability of getting two or more heads.

   (d) Find the probability of getting exactly three tails.

2. Richard has just been given a 10-question multiple-choice quiz in his history class. Each question has 5 answers, of which only one is correct. Since Richard has not attended class recently, he doesn't know any of the answers. Assuming that Richard guesses on all 10 questions, find the indicated probabilities.

   (a) What is the probability that he will answer all questions correctly?

   (b) What is the probability that he will answer all questions incorrectly?

   (c) What is the probability that he will answer at least one of the questions correctly? Compute this probability two ways. First, use the rule for mutually exclusive events and the probabilities shown in Table 4 of Appendix II. Then use the fact that $P(r \geq 1) = 1 - P(r = 0)$. Compare the two results. Should they be equal? Are they equal? If not, how do you account for the difference?

   (d) What is the probability that Richard will answer at least half the questions correctly?

3. The percentage of American men who say they would marry the same woman if they had it to do all over again is 80%. The percentage of American women who say they would marry the same man again is 50% (*Harper's Index*, 1991).

   (a) What is the probability that in a group of 10 married men, at least 7 will claim that they would marry the same woman again? What is the probability that less than half will say this?

   (b) What is the probability that in a group of 10 married women, at least 7 will claim they would marry the same man again? What is the probability that less than half will say this?

4. A new parking lot on campus would require the destruction of several dozen very large spruce trees that are too large to dig up and replant. The student newspaper stated that 70% of the student body opposes the new parking lot. A random sample of 20 students was asked about the proposed new parking lot. Assuming that the student newspaper is correct, find the probability that
   (a) All 20 students oppose the new lot.
   (b) At least 15 oppose the new lot.
   (c) No more than 10 oppose the new lot.
   (d) From 10 to 15 oppose the new lot (including 10 and 15).

5. Approximately 90% of the trout that are caught with a fly and released will live to be caught by another angler (*Rocky Mountain Streamside*, a publication of *Trout Unlimited*).
   (a) Suppose you catch and release eight trout. What is the probability that six or more live? What is the probability that they all live. What is the probability that no more than one dies?
   (b) Suppose you catch and release 15 trout. What is the probability that 12 or more live? What is the probability that they all live? What is the probability that no more than 2 die?

6. A research team at Cornell University conducted a study showing that approximately 10% of all businessmen who wear ties wear them so tight that they actually reduce blood flow to the brain, diminishing cerebral functions (*Chances: Risk and Odds in Everyday Life*, by James Burke). At a board meeting of 20 businessmen, all of whom wear ties, what is the probability that
   (a) At least one tie is too tight.
   (b) More than two ties are too tight.
   (c) None are too tight.
   (d) At least 18 are *not* too tight.

7. *Consumer Reports* (August 1993) states that approximately 70% of all people who buy eyeglasses from a private doctor's office were highly satisfied, whereas only 50% of those who received eyeglasses from Sears Optical were highly satisfied.
   (a) For a group of six patients at a private doctor's office, what is the probability that all six will be highly satisfied? What is the probability that more than half will be highly satisfied? What is the probability that less than two will be highly satisfied?
   (b) Answer the questions of part a for six customers at Sear's Optical.

8. *Consumer Reports* (June 1993) indicates that about 10% of all push-type power lawn mowers needed major repairs within 5 years of purchase. However, for tractor-type riding lawn mowers, about 25% needed major repairs.
   (a) Suppose you own a hardware store and you sell nine push-type power lawn mowers on a given day. What is the probability that two or more

will need major repairs within 5 years? What is the probability that none will need major repairs?

(b) Suppose you sell four tractor-type riding lawn mowers. What is the probability that at least one will need major repairs within 5 years? What is the probability that all four will need major repairs?

9. After examining daily receipts over the past year, it was found that the Blue Parrot Italian Restaurant has been grossing over $2200 a day for about 85% of its business days. Using this as a reasonably accurate measure, find the probability that the Blue Parrot will gross over $2200

(a) At least 5 days in the next 7 business days.
(b) At least 5 days in the next 10 business days.
(c) Less than 3 days in the next 5 business days.
(d) Less than 7 days in the next 10 business days.
(e) Less than 3 days in the next 7 business days. If this actually happened, might it shake your confidence in the statement $p = 0.85$? Might you suspect that p is less than 0.85? Explain.

10. Trevor is interested in purchasing the local hardware/sporting goods store in the small town of Dove Creek, Montana. After examining accounting records for the past several years, he found that the store has been grossing over $450 per day about 60% of the business days it is open. Estimate the probability the store will gross over $450

(a) At least 3 out of 5 business days.
(b) At least 6 out of 10 business days.
(c) Less than 5 out of 10 business days.
(d) Less than 6 out of the next 20 business days. If this actually happened, might it shake a person's confidence in the statement $p = 0.60$? Might it make a person suspect that p is less than 0.60? Explain.
(e) More than 17 out of the next 20 business days. If this actually happened, might a person suspect that p is greater than 0.60? Explain.

11. Alzheimer's disease is a progressive, irreversible disorder, and at this time the cause and cure are unknown. However, researchers at the University of Minnesota developed a "brief, efficient and accurate means of predicting Alzheimer's" in persons (from 65 to 85 years of age). The test takes about 10 minutes and requires the patient to try and recall 10 words after using each word twice in sentences. According to the report in the *Archives of Neurology* journal (February 1989), the test results are accurate 95% of the time. If the test is administered to a random sample of 16 people (from 65 to 85 years old), what is the probability the test results are accurate for

(a) At least 15 of the people?
(b) No more than 12 of the people?
(c) Fewer than 10 of the people?
(d) From 10 to 16 (including 10 and 16) of the people?

12. The Tasty Bean Coffee Company claims that its coffee is so good that you can distinguish it from any other coffee. Five different brands of coffee

(one of them Tasty Bean) are set before tasters who are to pick the one that tastes the best. Suppose there is really no difference in the way any of these coffees taste; however, each of four tasters picks one coffee anyway (not knowing which is which, because the coffee is in identical cups). What is the probability that

(a) All four tasters choose Tasty Bean?

(b) None of them chooses Tasty Bean?

(c) At least three choose Tasty Bean?

13. Approximately 75% of all marketing personnel are extroverts, whereas about 60% of all computer programmers are introverts (*A Guide to the Development and Use of the Meyers-Briggs Type Indicator,* by Meyers and McCaulley, 1990)

    (a) At a meeting of 15 marketing personnel, what is the probability that 10 or more are extroverts? What is the probability that 5 or more are extroverts? What is the probability that all are extroverts?

    (b) In a group of 5 computer programmers, what is the probability that none are introverts? What is the probability that 3 or more are introverts? What is the probability that all are introverts?

14. The *Denver Post* (January 30, 1990) made the statement that about 5% of all items checked by scanners in grocery stores and variety stores are given the wrong price. If this is the case, what is the probability that in scanning different items,

    (a) None of the items scanned out of 8 is wrongly priced?

    (b) At least 1 item scanned out of 12 is wrongly priced?

    (c) More than 2 items out of 16 are wrongly priced?

    (d) More than 5 items out of 16 are wrongly priced. If this actually happened, would it tend to shake your confidence in the statement $p = 0.05$? Would you begin to suspect that p is greater than 0.05? Explain.

15. Approximately 85% of all the U.S. chief executive officers (CEOs) have a college degree (*Chances: Risk and Odds in Everyday Life,* by James Burke).

    (a) In a group of three CEOs, what is the probability that none has a college degree? That more than one have a college degree?

    (b) In a group of seven CEOs, what is the probability that three or more have college degrees? What is the probability that all have college degrees?

16. The following is based on information taken from *The Wolf in the Southwest: The Making of an Endangered Species,* edited by David Brown, University of Arizona Press, 1988. Before 1918, approximately 55% of the wolves in the New Mexico and Arizona region were male, and 45% were female. However, cattle ranchers in this area have made a determined effort to exterminate wolves. From 1918 to the present, approximately 70% of wolves in this region are male and 30% are female. Many wolves are known to live in a group or extended family of wolves.

    (a) Before 1918, in an extended family of 12 wolves, what is the probability that 6 or more were male? What is the probability that 6 or more were female? What is the probability that less than 4 were female?

(b) Answer part a for the period from 1918 to the present.

17. Based on information from the reference in Problem 16, it was found that approximately 75% of all active wolf dens contain five or more pups. In a study of six active wolf dens, what is the probability that
    (a) Less than half the wolf dens have five or more pups?
    (b) Four or more of the dens have five or more pups?
    (c) All the dens have five or more pups?
    (d) None of the wolf dens has 5 or more pups? If this actually happened, might it make you suspect that p is less than 0.75 in the region where the study occurred? Explain.

18. The following is based on information from *Prehistoric New Mexico,* by Stuart and Gauthier, University of New Mexico Press, 1988. In extended family groups of prehistoric people who lived in what is now the Southwest United States, about 25% were hunters and 75% were people who did not for some reason participate in hunting. An ancient archaeological site consists of an isolated cliff dwelling. The site indicates that 15 people lived in this dwelling as an extended family. What is the probability that
    (a) Three or more were hunters?
    (b) More than five were hunters?
    (c) Ten or more were not hunters?
    (d) Five or more were not hunters?
    (e) More than 10 were hunters? If reliable archaeological data indicated that this actually happened, might you suspect that p is greater than 0.25 for this extended family? Explain.

19. The following is based on information from *Bandelier Archaeological Excavation Project: Summer 1989 Excavations at Burnt Mesa Pueblo,* edited by Kohler, Washington State University, 1990. At an archaeological site in Bandelier National Monument, approximately 15% of the chipped stone tools are made from Jemez obsidian, and 55% are made from basalt.
    (a) If 11 chipped stone tools are discovered, what is the probability that at least 3 will be made from Jemez obsidian?
    (b) If 5 chipped stone tools are discovered, what is the probability that at least 2 will be made from basalt.
    (c) If 10 chipped stone tools are discovered, what is the probability that at least 4 are neither Jemez obsidian nor basalt?

20. *USA Today* (December 30, 1993) indicated that approximately 60% of all registered voters voted in the Clinton/Bush/Perot presidential election. At a social gathering there are 16 registered voters who are discussing the election. What is the probability that
    (a) None of them voted?
    (b) Half or more voted?

Figure 5–2 Graph of the Binomial Distribution for
n = 6 and p = 0.7

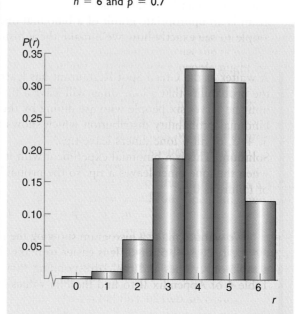

GUIDED EXERCISE 6

Jim enjoys playing basketball. He figures that he makes about 50% of the field goals he attempts during a game. Make a histogram showing the probability that Jim will make 0, 1, 2, 3, 4, 5, or 6 shots out of six attempted field goals.

(a) This is a binomial experiment with $n =$ _____ trials. In this situation we'll say success occurs when Jim makes an attempted field goal. What is the value of p?

(a) In this example $n = 6$ and $p = 0.5$.

(b) Use Table 4 of Appendix II to complete Table 5–4 of $P(r)$ values for $n = 6$ and $p = 0.5$.

(b)

Table 5–4

r	P(r)
0	0.016
1	0.094
2	0.234
3	_____
4	_____
5	_____
6	_____

Table 5–5 Completion of Table 5–4

r	P(r)
.	.
.	.
.	.
3	0.312
4	0.234
5	0.094
6	0.016

(c) Use the values of $P(r)$ given in Table 5–5 to complete the histogram in Figure 5–3.

Figure 5–3 Graph of Binomial Distribution for $n = 6$ and $p = 0.5$

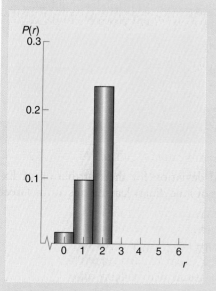

Figure 5–4 Completion of Figure 5–3

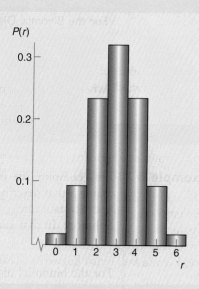

(d) The area of the bar over $r = 2$ is 0.234. What is the area of the bar over $r = 4$? How does the probability that Jim makes two field goals out of six compare with the probability that he makes four field goals out of six?

(d) The area of the bar over $r = 4$ is also 0.234. Jim is as likely to make two out of six field goals as he is to make four out of six.

In Example 5 and Guided Exercise 6 we see the graphs of two binomial distributions associated with $n = 6$ trials. The two graphs are different because the probability of success p is different in the two cases. In Example 5, $p = 0.7$ and the graph is skewed to the left—that is, the left tail is longer. In Guided Exercise 6, p is equal to 0.5 and the graph is symmetrical—that is, if we fold it in half, the two halves coincide exactly. Whenever *p equals 0.5, the graph of the binomial distribution will be symmetrical no matter how many trials we have.* In Chapter 7 we will see that if the number of trials n is quite large, the binomial distribution is almost symmetrical even when p is not close to 0.5.

Mean and Standard Deviation of Binomial Probability Distributions

Two other features that help describe the graph of any distribution are the balance point of the distribution and the spread of the distribution about that balance point. The *balance point* is the mean μ of the distribution, and the *measure of spread* that is most commonly used is the standard deviation σ. The mean μ is the *expected value* of the number of successes.

the number n of cells necessary to ensure that (choose the correct statement)

(i) $P(r \geq 3) = 0.97$ or

(ii) $P(r \leq 3) = 0.97$

(b) We need to find a value for n so that

$$P(r \geq 3) = 0.97$$

Let's try $n = 4$. Then $r \geq 3$ means $r = 3$ or 4 so

$$P(r \geq 3) = P(3) + P(4)$$

Use Table 4 with $n = 4$ and $p = 0.85$ to find values of $P(3)$ and $P(4)$. Then compute $P(r \geq 3)$ for $n = 4$. Will $n = 4$ guarantee that $P(r \geq 3)$ is at least 0.97? (Table 4 is in Appendix II.)

(c) Now try $n = 5$ cells. For $n = 5$,

$$P(r \geq 3) = P(3) + P(4) + P(5)$$

since r can be 3, 4, or 5. Are $n = 5$ cells adequate? [Be sure to find new values of $P(3)$ and $P(4)$ since we now have $n = 5$.]

(b) $P(3) = 0.368$
$P(4) = 0.522$
$P(r \geq 3) = 0.368 + 0.522 = 0.890$

Thus $n = 4$ is *not* sufficient to be 97% sure that at least three cells will work. For $n = 4$, the probability that at least three will work is only 0.890.

(c) $P(r \geq 3) = P(3) + P(4) + P(5)$
$= 0.138 + 0.392 + 0.444$
$= 0.974$

Thus $n = 5$ cells are required if we want to be 97% sure that there will be at least three working cells.

In part I and part II we got different values for n. Why? In part I we had $n = 4$ and $\mu = 3.4$. This means that if we put up lots of satellites with four cells, we can expect that an *average* of 3.4 cells will be working per satellite. But for $n = 4$ cells there is only a probability of 0.89 that at least three cells will work in any one satellite. In part II we are trying to find the number of cells necessary so that the probability is 0.97 that at least three will work in any *one* satellite. If we use $n = 5$ cells, then we can satisfy this requirement.

Quota Problems

Quotas occur in many aspects of everyday life. The manager of a sales team gives every member of the team a weekly sales quota. In some districts, police have a monthly quota for the number of traffic tickets issued. Nonprofit organizations have recruitment quotas for donations or new volunteers. The basic ideas used to compute quotas also can be used in medical science (how frequently should checkups occur), quality control (how many production flaws should be expected), or risk management (how many bad loans should a bank expect in a certain investment group). Such problems come from many different sources, but they all have one thing in common: They are solved using the binomial probability distribution.

Example 7 is a quota problem. Junk bonds are sometimes controversial. In some cases junk bonds have been the salvation of a basically good company that has had a run of bad luck. From another point of view, junk bonds are not much more than a gambler's effort to make money by shady ethics.

The book *Liar's Poker,* by Michael Lewis, is an exciting and sometimes humorous description of his career as a Wall Street bond broker. Most bond brokers, including Mr. Lewis, are ethical people. However, the book does contain an interesting discussion of Michael Milken and shady ethics. In the book, Mr. Lewis says, "If it was a good deal, the brokers kept it for themselves; if it was a bad deal, they'd try to sell it to their customers." In Example 7 we use some binomial probabilities for a brief explanation of what Mr. Lewis's book is talking about.

Example 7 | Junk bonds can be profitable as well as risky. Why are investors willing to consider junk bonds? Suppose you can buy junk bonds at a tremendous discount. You try to choose "good" companies with a "good" product. The company should have done well but for some reason did not. Suppose you only consider companies with a 35% estimated risk of default, and your financial investment goal requires four bonds to be "good" bonds in the sense that they will not default before a certain date. Remember, junk bonds that do not default are usually very profitable because they carry a very high rate of return. The other bonds in your investment group can default (or not) without harming your investment plan. Suppose you want to be 95% certain of meeting your goal (quota) of at least four good bonds. How many junk bond issues should you buy to meet this goal?

Solution: Since the probability of default is 35%, the probability of a "good" bond is 65%. Let success S represent a good bond. Let n be the number of bonds purchased, and let r be the number of good bonds in this group. We want

$$P(r \geq 4) \geq 0.95$$

This is equivalent to

$$1 - P(0) - P(1) - P(2) - P(3) \geq 0.95$$

Since the probability of success is $p = P(S) = 0.65$, we only need to look in the binomial table under $p = 0.65$ and different values of n to find the *smallest value* of n that will satisfy the preceding relation. Table 4 in Appendix II shows that if $n = 10$ when $p = 0.65$, then

$$1 - P(0) - P(1) - P(2) - P(3) = 1 - 0 - 0 - 0.004 - 0.021$$
$$= 0.975$$

The probability 0.975 satisfies the condition of being greater than or equal to 0.95. We see that 10 is the smallest value of n for which the condition

$$P(r \geq 4) \geq 0.95$$

is satisfied. Under the given conditions (a good discount on price, no more than 35% chance of default, and a fundamentally good company), you can be 95% sure of meeting your investment goal with $n = 10$ (carefully selected) junk bond issues.

In this example we see that by carefully selecting junk bonds, there is a high probability of getting some good bonds that will produce a real profit. What do you do with the other bonds that aren't so good? Perhaps the quote from *Liar's Poker* will suggest what is sometimes attempted.

Section 5.3 Problems

1. Consider a binomial distribution with $n = 5$ trials. Use the probabilities given in Table 4 in Appendix II to make histograms showing the probability of $r = 0, 1, 2, 3, 4, 5$ successes for each of the following. Comment on the skewness of each distribution.
   (a) The probability of success is $p = 0.50$.
   (b) The probability of success is $p = 0.25$.
   (c) The probability of success is $p = 0.75$.
   (d) What is the relationship between the distributions shown in parts b and c?
   (e) If the probability of success is $p = 0.73$, do you expect the distribution to be skewed to the right or to the left? Why?

2. Figure 5–5 shows histograms of several binomial distributions with $n = 6$ trials. Match the given probability of success with the best graph.
   (a) $p = 0.30$ goes with graph _____ .
   (b) $p = 0.50$ goes with graph _____ .
   (c) $p = 0.65$ goes with graph _____ .
   (d) $p = 0.90$ goes with graph _____ .
   (e) In general, when the probability of success p is close to 0.5, would you say that the graph is more symmetrical or more skewed? In general, when the probability of success p is close to 1, would you say that the graph is skewed to the right or to the left? What about when p is close to 0?

3. National studies indicate that 45% of all senior citizens (those over 65 years of age) have high blood pressure. At a nursing station in a medical clinic 12 senior citizens have just completed a routine physical exam.
   (a) Let r represent the number of senior citizens who have high blood pressure. Make a histogram showing the probability of r for $r = 0$ through 12.
   (b) Find the mean μ of this probability distribution. What is the expected number of these senior citizens who have high blood pressure?
   (c) Find the standard deviation σ of the probability distribution.

4. The quality control inspector of a production plant will reject a batch of syringes if two or more defectives are found in a random sample of eight syringes taken from the batch. Suppose the batch contains 1% defective syringes.

Figure 5–5 Binomial Probability Distributions with $n = 6$ (generated on the TI-82 calculator)

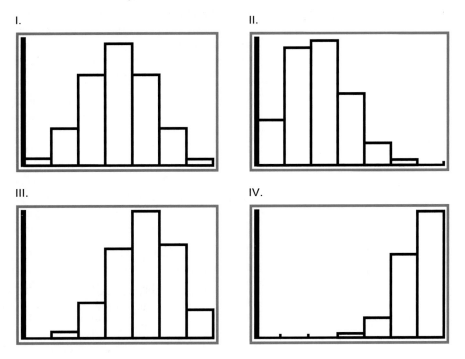

(a) Make a histogram showing the probability of $r = 0, 1, 2, 3, 4, 5, 6, 7, 8$ defective syringes in a random sample of eight syringes.

(b) Find μ. What is the expected number of defective syringes the inspector will find?

(c) What is the probability that the batch will be accepted?

(d) Find σ.

 5. Old Friends Information Service is a California Company that is in the business of finding addresses of long lost friends. Old Friends claims to have a 70% success rate (*Wall Street Journal*, January 3, 1994). Suppose you have the names of six friends for whom you have no addresses and decide to use Old Friends to track them.

(a) Make a histogram showing the probability of $r = 0$ to 6 friends for whom an address will be found.

(b) Find the mean and standard deviation of this probability distribution. What is the expected number of friends for whom addresses will be found?

(c) How many names would you have to submit to be 97% sure that at least two addresses will be found?

 6. The Mountain States Office of State Farm Insurance Company reports that approximately 85% of all automobile damage liability claims were

made by people under 25 years of age. A random sample of five auto-mobile insurance liability claims is under study.

(a) Make a histogram showing the probability that $r = 0$ to 5 claims are made by people under 25 years of age.

(b) Find the mean and standard deviation of this probability distribution. For samples of size 5, what is the expected number of claims made by people under 25 years of age?

7. *USA Today* (July 7, 1992) reported that about 20% of all people in the United States are illiterate. Suppose you take seven people at random off a city street.

(a) Make a histogram showing the probability distribution of the number of illiterate people out of the seven people in the sample.

(b) Find the mean and standard deviation of this probability distribution. Find the expected number of people in this sample who are illiterate.

(c) How many people would you need to interview to be 98% sure that at least seven of these people can read and write (are not illiterate)?

8. The *New York Times* (January 5, 1994) reported that approximately 65% of all cars sold in the United States are made by the big three auto makers (Chrysler, Ford, General Motors). For a group of 12 cars selected at random on the highway,

(a) Make a histogram of the probability distribution of the number of cars in this sample that are made by the big three auto makers.

(b) Find the mean and standard deviation of this probability distribution. Find the expected number of cars in this sample that are made by the big three auto makers.

(c) How many cars would you need to observe on the highway to be 95% sure that at least 5 were made by the big three auto makers?

(d) How many cars would you need to observe on the highway to be 99% sure that at least 2 were *not* made by the big three auto makers?

9. The *Wall Street Journal* (December 28, 1993) reported that approximately 25% of the people who are told a product is *improved* will believe that it is in fact improved. The remaining 75% believe that this is just hype (the same old thing with no real improvement). Suppose a marketing study consisted of a random sample of eight people who are given a sales talk about a new, *improved* product.

(a) Make a histogram showing the probability that $r = 0$ to 8 people believe the product is in fact improved.

(b) Compute the mean and standard deviation of this probability distribution.

(c) How many people are needed in the marketing study to be 99% sure that at least one person believes the product to be improved?

10. The National Forest Service uses satellites with infrared sensors to detect forest fires in remote wilderness areas. The satellites are very sensitive and do find all the hot spots. However, the satellites register geothermal hot

spots, cloud cover, manmade bonfires, etc., as well as hot spots caused by forest fires. Over a period of years, the Forest Service has decided that only 85% of the hot spots reported by the satellite are forest fires. The usual procedure is to send out a reconnaissance plane to check on what the satellite has detected. Let us say that the satellite was successful if it reports a hot spot that is a forest fire.

Recently, the satellite reported nine hot spots in the remote Seward Peninsula of Alaska.

(a) Find the probability $P(r)$ of r successes for r ranging from 0 to 9.

(b) Make a histogram for the probability distribution of part a.

(c) Based on the satellite information, what is the expected number μ of real forest fires on the Seward Peninsula?

(d) What is the standard deviation σ?

(e) How many hot spots must the satellite report to be 99.9% sure of at least one real forest fire?

11. Vince is a computer software salesman who has a history of making a successful sales call 40% of the time. If Vince has a sales quota of at least five sales this week, how many sales calls must he make to be 95% sure of meeting the quota?

12. June solicits contributions for charity by phone. She has a history of being successful at getting a donor on 55% of her calls. If June has a quota to get at least four donors each day, how many calls must she make to be 96.4% sure of meeting the quota?

13. In the summer of 1990, archaeological excavation at Burnt Mesa Pueblo showed that about 10% of the flaked stone objects were finished arrow points (*Bandelier Archaeological Excavation Project: Summer 1990 Excavations at Burnt Mesa Pueblo*, edited by Kohler, Washington State University, 1992). How many flaked stone objects need to be found to be 90% sure that at least one is a finished arrow point? (*Hint:* Use a calculator.)

14. Over a long period of time it has been observed that Vicky has probability 0.7 of hitting a target with a single rifle shot. Suppose Vicky fires five shots at the target.

(a) Make a histogram showing the probability of r successes (hits) when $r = 0$ to 5.

(b) Find the mean μ of this probability distribution. How many hits is Vicky expected to make?

(c) Find the standard deviation σ of this probability distribution.

(d) How many shots should Vicky fire to be 99.9% sure of hitting the target with at least three shots?

15. *USA Today* (June 2, 1993) reports that about 80% of all prison inmates become repeat offenders. Alice is a social worker whose job is to counsel people released from prison. Let us say success means a person does not become a repeat offender. Alice has been given a group of four parolees.

Example 8

An automobile assembly plant produces sheet metal door panels. Each panel moves on an assemblyline. As the panel passes a robot, a mechanical arm will perform spot welding at different locations. Each location has a magnetic dot painted where the weld is to be made. The robot is programmed to locate the magnetic dot and perform the weld. However, experience shows that on each trial the robot is only 85% successful at locating the dot. If it cannot locate the magnetic dot, it is programmed to *try again*. The robot will keep trying until it finds the dot (and does the weld) or the door panel passes out of the robot's reach.

(a) What is the probability that the robot's first success will be on attempts $n = 1, 2$, or 3?
Solution: Since the robot will keep trying until it is successful, the geometric distribution is appropriate. In this case, success S means that the robot finds the correct location. The probability of success is $p = P(S) = 0.85$. The probabilities are

n	$P(n) = p(1 - p)^{n-1} = 0.85(0.15)^{n-1}$
1	$0.85(0.15)^0 = 0.85$
2	$0.85(0.15)^1 = 0.1275$
3	$0.85(0.15)^2 = 0.0191$

(b) The assemblyline moves so fast that the robot only has a maximum of three chances before the door panel is out of reach. What is the probability that the robot will be successful before the door panel is out of reach?
Solution: Since $n = 1$ or 2 or 3 are mutually exclusive, then

$$P(n = 1 \text{ or } 2 \text{ or } 3) = P(1) + P(2) + P(3)$$
$$= 0.85 + 0.1275 + 0.0191$$
$$= 0.9966$$

This means that the weld should be correctly located about 99.7% of the time.

(c) What is the probability that the robot will not be able to locate the correct spot within three tries? If 10,000 panels are made, what is the expected number of defectives? Comment on the meaning of this answer in the context of "forecasting failure" and the "limits of design."
Solution: The probability that the robot will correctly locate the weld is 0.9966 from part b. Therefore, the probability that it cannot do so (after three unsuccessful tries) is $1 - 0.9966 = 0.0034$. If we made 10,000 panels, we would expect (forecast) $(10,000)(0.0034) = 34$ defectives. We could reduce this by inspecting *every* door, but such a solution is most likely too costly. If a defective weld of this type is not considered too dangerous, we can accept an expected 34 failures out of 10,000 panels due to the limits of our production design—that is, the speed of the assemblyline and the accuracy of the robot. If this is not acceptable, a new (perhaps more costly) design is needed.

Poisson Probability Distribution

If we examine the binomial distribution as the number of trials n gets larger and larger while the probability of success p gets smaller and smaller, we obtain the *Poisson distribution*. Siméon Denis Poisson (1781–1840) was a French mathematician who studied probabilities of rare events that occur infrequently in space, time, volume, and so forth. The Poisson distribution applies to accident rates, arrival times, defect rates, the incidents of bacteria in the air, smoke alarms, and many other areas of everyday life.

As with the binomial distribution, we assume only two outcomes: A particular event occurs (success) or does not occur (failure) during the specified time period or space. The events need to be independent so that one success does not change the probability of another success during the specified interval. We are interested in computing the probability of r successes in the given time period, space, volume, or specified interval.

Poisson Distribution

Let λ (Greek letter lambda) be the mean number of successes over time, volume, area, and so forth. Let r be the number of successes ($r = 0, 1, 2, 3, \ldots$) in a corresponding interval of time, volume, area, and so forth. Then the probability of r successes in the interval is

$$P(r) = \frac{e^{-\lambda}\lambda^r}{r!}$$

where e is called *Euler's constant* and is approximately equal to 2.7183

There are many applications of the Poisson distribution. For example, if we take the point of view that waiting time can be subdivided into many small intervals, then the actual arrival (of whatever we are waiting for) during any one of the very short intervals could be thought of as an infrequent (or rare) event. This means that the Poisson distribution can be used as a mathematical model to describe the probability of arrivals such as cars to a gas station, planes at an airport, calls to a fire station, births of babies, and even fish arriving on a fisherman's line.

Example 9

Pyramid Lake is located in Nevada on the Paiute Indian Reservation. The lake is described as a lovely jewel in a beautiful desert setting. In addition to its natural beauty, the lake contains some of the world's largest cutthroat trout. Eight- to ten-pound trout are not uncommon and 12- to 15-pound trophies are taken each season. The Paiute Nation uses highly trained fish biologists to study and maintain this famous fishery. In one of their publications, *Creel Chronicle* (Vol. 3, No. 2, Nov.–Dec. 1992), the following information was given about the November catch for boat fishermen.

Total fish per hour = 0.667

Suppose that you decide to fish Pyramid Lake for 7 hours during the month of November.

(a) Use the information provided by the fishery biologist in *Creel Chronicle* to find a probability distribution for *r* the number of fish (of all sizes) you catch in a period of 7 hours.
Solution: For fish of all sizes, the mean success rate *per hour* is 0.667

$$\lambda = 0.667/1 \text{ hour}$$

Since we want to study a *7-hour interval,* we use a little arithmetic to adjust λ to 7 hours. That is, we adjust λ so that it represents the average number of fish expected in a 7-hour period.

$$\lambda = \frac{0.667}{1 \text{ hour}} \cdot \left(\frac{7}{7}\right) = \frac{4.669}{7 \text{ hours}}$$

For convenience, let us use the rounded value $\lambda = 4.7$ for a 7-hour period. Since *r* is the number of successes (fish caught) in the corresponding 7-hour period and $\lambda = 4.7$ for this period, we use the Poisson distribution to get

$$P(r) = \frac{e^{-\lambda}\lambda^r}{r!} = \frac{e^{-4.7}(4.7)^r}{r!}$$

Recall that $e = 2.7183 \ldots$ is Euler's constant. Most calculators have e^x, y^x, and n! keys (see your calculator manual), so the Poisson distribution is not hard to compute.

(b) What is the probability that in 7 hours you will get 0, 1, 2, or 3 fish of any size?
Solution: Using the result of part a, we get

$$P(0) = \frac{e^{-4.7}(4.7)^0}{0!} = 0.0091 \approx 0.01$$

$$P(1) = \frac{e^{-4.7}(4.7)^1}{1!} = 0.0427 \approx 0.04$$

$$P(2) = \frac{e^{-4.7}(4.7)^2}{2!} = 0.1005 \approx 0.10$$

$$P(3) = \frac{e^{-4.7}(4.7)^3}{3!} = 0.1574 \approx 0.16$$

The probabilities of getting 0, 1, 2, or 3 fish are about 1%, 4%, 10%, and 16% respectively.

(c) What is the probability that you will get 4 or more fish in the 7-hour fishing period?
Solution: The sample space of all *r* values is $r = 0, 1, 2, 3, 4, 5, \ldots$ and so on. The probability in the entire sample space is 1, and these events are mutually exclusive. Therefore,

$$1 = P(0) + P(1) + P(2) + P(3) + P(4) + P(5) + \cdots$$

So

$$P(r \geq 4) = P(4) + P(5) + \cdots = 1 - P(0) - P(1) - P(2) - P(3)$$
$$= 1 - 0.01 - 0.04 - 0.10 - 0.16$$
$$= 0.69$$

There is about a 69% chance that you will catch 4 or more fish in a 7-hour period.

Use of Tables

Table 5 in Appendix II is a table of the Poisson probability distribution for selected values of λ and the number of successes r. Table 5–6 is an excerpt from that table.

To find the value of $P(r = 2)$ when $\lambda = 0.25$, look in the column headed by 0.25 and the row headed by 2.

Table 5–6 Excerpt from Appendix II, Table 5, "Poisson Probability Distribution"

				λ		
r	0.05	0.10	0.15	0.20	0.25	0.30
0	0.9512	0.9048	0.8607	0.8187	0.7788	0.7408
1	0.0476	0.0905	0.1291	0.1637	0.1947	0.2222
2	0.0012	0.0045	0.0097	0.0164	0.0243	0.0333
3	0.0000	0.0002	0.0005	0.0011	0.0020	0.0033
4	0.0000	0.0000	0.0000	0.0001	0.0001	0.0003
5	0.0000	0.0000	0.0000	0.0000	0.0000	0.0000

Calculator Note Before calculators were so readily available, tables of values for the Poisson distribution were given for various values of λ and r. However, the tables are limited to specific values of λ and r. Calculators make the computation of $P(r)$ for any values of λ and r very straightforward. You need a scientific or graphing calculator. Look in your manual for the location of the e^x, $x!$, and x^y or y^x keys. On some calculators you use the ^ key for exponents. On graphing calculators, the factorial key ! is often included in a math menu. Again, see your calculator manual. (See also Figure 5–6.)

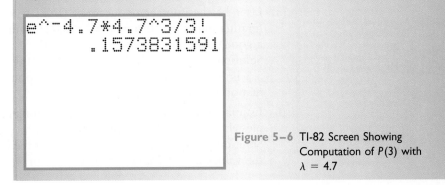

```
e^-4.7*4.7^3/3!
         .1573831591
```

Figure 5–6 TI-82 Screen Showing Computation of $P(3)$ with $\lambda = 4.7$

Poisson Approximation to the Binomial Probability Distribution

In the preceding examples we have seen how the Poisson distribution can be used over intervals of time, space, area, and so on. However, the Poisson distribution also can be used as a probability distribution for "rare" events. In the binomial distribution, if the number of trials n is large while the probability p of success is quite small, we call the event (success) a "rare" event. Put another way, it can be shown that for most practical purposes, the Poisson distribution will be a very good approximation to the binomial distribution provided that the number of trials n is larger than or equal to 100 and $\lambda = np$ is less than 10. As n gets larger and p gets smaller, the approximation becomes better and better.

Consider the binomial distribution with

$$n = \text{number of trials}$$

$$r = \text{number of successes}$$

$$p = \text{probability of success on each trial}$$

If $n \geq 100$ and $np < 10$, then r has a binomial distribution that is approximated by a Poisson distribution with $\lambda = np$.

Example 10 Isabel Briggs Myers was a pioneer in the study of personality types. Today the Myers-Briggs Type Indicator is used in many career counseling programs as well as in many industrial settings where people must work closely together as a team. The 16 personality types are discussed in detail in the book, *A Guide to the Development and Use of the Myers-Briggs Type Indicators,* by Myers and McCaulley. Each personality type has its own special contribution in any group activity. One of the more "rare" types is INFJ (introverted, intuitive, feeling, judgmental), which occurs in only about 2.1% of the population. Suppose that a high school graduating class has 167 students, and suppose that we call success the event that a student is of personality type INFJ.

(a) Let r be the number of successes (INFJ students) in the $n = 167$ trials (graduating class). If $p = P(S) = 0.021$, will the Poisson distribution be a good approximation to the binomial?
Solution: Since $n = 167$ is greater than 100 and $\lambda = np = 167(0.021) \approx 3.5$ is less than 10, the Poisson distribution should be a good approximation to the binomial.

(b) Estimate the probability that this graduating class has 0, 1, 2, 3, or 4 people who have the INFJ personality type.
Solution: Since Table 5 (Appendix II) for the Poisson distribution includes the values $\lambda = 3.5$ and $r = 0, 1, 2, 3,$ or 4, we may simply look up the

values for $P(r)$, $r = 0, 1, 2, 3, 4$:

$$P(r = 0) = 0.0302 \qquad P(r = 1) = 0.1057$$
$$P(r = 2) = 0.1850 \qquad P(r = 3) = 0.2158$$
$$P(r = 4) = 0.1888$$

Since the outcomes $r = 0, 1, 2, 3,$ or 4 successes are mutually exclusive, we can compute the probability of 4 or fewer INFJ types by the addition rule for mutually exclusive events:

$$P(r \leq 4) = P(0) + P(1) + P(2) + P(3) + P(4)$$
$$= 0.0302 + 0.1057 + 0.1850 + 0.2158 + 0.1888$$
$$= 0.7255$$

The probability that the graduating class will have 4 or fewer INFJ personality types is about 0.73.

(c) Estimate the probability that this class has 5 or more INFJ personality types.

Solution: Because the outcomes of a binomial experiment are all mutually exclusive, we have

$$P(r \leq 4) + P(r \geq 5) = 1$$

or $$P(r \geq 5) = 1 - P(r \leq 4) = 1 - 0.7255 = 0.2745$$

The probability is approximately 0.27 that there will be 5 or more INFJ personality types in the graduating class.

Summary

In this section we have studied two discrete probability distributions. The Poisson distribution gives us the probability of r successes. The Poisson distribution also can be used to approximate the binomial distribution when $n \geq 100$ and $np < 10$. The geometric distribution gives us the probability that our first success will occur on the nth trial. In the next guided exercise we will see situations in which each of these distributions applies.

GUIDED EXERCISE 9

For each problem, first identify the type of probability distribution needed to solve the problem: Geometric or Poisson. Then solve the problem.

(i) Denver, Colorado is prone to severe hail storms. Insurance agents claim that a home owner in Denver can expect to replace his or her roof (due to hail damage) once every 10 years. What is the probability that in 12 years a homeowner in Denver will need to replace the roof twice because of hail?

(ii) A telephone network substation will keep trying to connect a long-distance call to a trunk line until the 4th attempt has been made. After the

3. Anthropological studies at Casa del Rito indicate that approximately 5% of all pot shards at the excavation site are from the traditional type of pot known as *Socorro black on white* (*Bandelier Archaeological Excavation Project: Summer 1990 Excavations at Burnt Mesa Pueblo and Casa del Rito,* edited by Kohler, Washington State University Department of Anthropology, 1992). Let $n = 1, 2, 3, \ldots$ represent the number of pot shards that must be discovered (and examined) until the *first* Socorro black on white is found.
   (a) Write out a formula for the probability distribution of the random variable n.
   (b) What is the probability that the first Socorro black on white pot shard is found on trial $n = 5$.
   (c) What is the probability that the first Socorro black on white pot shard is found on trial $n = 10$.
   (d) What is the probability that more than three pot shards have to be examined before finding the first Socorro black on white?

4. On the leeward side of the island of Oahu in the small village of Nanakuli, about 80% of the residents are of Hawaiian ancestry (*The Honolulu Advertiser,* December 26, 1993). Let $n = 1, 2, 3, \ldots$ represent the number of people you must meet until you encounter the *first* person of Hawaiian ancestry in the village of Nanakuli.
   (a) Write out a formula for the probability distribution of the random variable n.
   (b) Compute the probability that $n = 1$, $n = 2$, $n = 3$
   (c) Compute the probability that $n \geqslant 4$.
   (d) In Waikiki it is estimated that about 4% of the residents are of Hawaiian ancestry. Repeat parts a, b, and c for Waikiki.

5. Approximately 71% of all modern college students claim that the main reason they are attending college is to make more money after graduation. In 1967, approximately 83% of all college students claimed that they were attending college primarily to develop a meaningful philosophy of life (*Chances: Risk and Odds in Everyday Life,* by James Burke). Let $n = 1, 2, 3, \ldots$ represent the *first* person who is a college student selected at random whom you encounter who says he or she is in college primarily to make more money after graduation.
   (a) Write out a formula for the probability distribution of the random variable n.
   (b) Find the probability that $n = 1$, $n = 2$, $n \geqslant 3$.
   (c) Repeat parts a and b when n represents the *first* person who was a college student in 1967 selected at random who claimed the primary reason for attending college was to develop a meaningful philosophy of life.

6. Approximately 3.6% of all (untreated) Jonathan apples had bitter pit in a study conducted by the botanists Ratkowsky and Martin (*Australian*

Journal of Agricultural Research, Vol. 25, pp. 783–790, 1974). (Bitter pit is a disease of apples resulting in a soggy core, which can be caused either by overwatering the apple tree or by a calcium deficiency in the soil.) Let n be a random variable that represents the first Jonathan apple chosen at random that has bitter pit.
(a) Write out a formula for the probability distribution of the random variable n.
(b) Find the probability that $n = 3$, $n = 5$, $n = 12$.
(c) Find the probability that $n \geq 5$.

7. At Fontaine Lake Camp on Lake Athabasca in northern Canada, history shows that about 30% of the guests catch lake trout over 20 pounds on a 4-day fishing trip (reference: Athabasca Fishing Lodges, Saskatoon, Canada). Let n be a random variable that represents the *first* trip to Fontaine Lake Camp on which a guest catches a lake trout over 20 pounds.
    (a) Write out a formula for the probability distribution of the random variable n.
    (b) Find the probability that a guest catches a lake trout weighing at least 20 pounds for the *first* time on trip number 3.
    (c) Find the probability that it takes more than three trips for a guest to catch a lake trout weighing at least 20 pounds.

8. At Burnt Mesa Pueblo in one of the archaeological excavation sites, the artifact density (number of prehistoric artifacts per 10 liters of sediment) was 1.5 (see reference in Problem 3). Suppose you are going to dig up and examine 50 liters of sediment at this site. Let $r = 0, 1, 2, 3, \ldots$ be a random variable that represents the number of prehistoric artifacts found in your 50 liters of sediment.
    (a) Explain why the Poisson distribution would be a good choice for the probability distribution of r. What is λ? Write out the formula for the probability distribution of the random variable r.
    (b) Compute the probability that in your 50 liters of sediment you will find two prehistoric artifacts; that you will find three artifacts; that you will find four artifacts.
    (c) Find the probability that you will find three or more artifacts in the 50 liters of sediment.
    (d) Find the probability you will find less than three prehistoric artifacts in the 50 liters of sediment.

9. In his doctoral thesis, L. A. Beckel (University of Minnesota, 1982) studied the social behavior of river otters during the mating season. An important role in the bonding process of river otters is social grooming. After extensive observations, Dr. Beckel found that one group of river otters under study had a frequency of grooming of approximately 1.7 for each 10 minutes. Suppose that you are observing river otters for 30 minutes. Let $r = 0, 1, 2, \ldots$ be a random variable that represents the number of times (in a 30-minute interval) that one otter grooms another.

15. Jim is a real estate agent who sells large commercial buildings. Because his commission is so large on a single sale, he does not need to sell many buildings to make a good living. History shows that Jim has a record of selling an average of eight large commercial buildings in 275 days.
    (a) Explain why a Poisson probability distribution would be a good choice for r = number of buildings sold in a given time interval.
    (b) In a 60-day period, what is the probability that Jim will make no sales? one sale? two or more sales?
    (c) In a 90-day period, what is the probability that Jim will make no sales? two sales? three or more sales?

16. *The Honolulu Advertizer* (June 6, 1993) stated that in Honolulu there was an average of 661 burglaries per 100,000 households in that year. In the Kohola Drive neighborhood there are 316 homes. Let r = number of these homes that will be burglarized in a year.
    (a) Explain why the Poisson approximation to the binomial would be a good choice for the random variable r. What is n? What is p? What is λ to the nearest tenth?
    (b) What is the probability that there will be no burglaries this year in the Kohola Drive neighborhood?
    (c) What is the probability that there will be no more than one burglary in the Kohola Drive neighborhood?
    (d) What is the probability there will be two or more burglaries in the Kohola Drive neighborhood?

17. *Harper's Index* (1991) reported that the number of (Orange County, California) convicted drunk drivers whose sentence included a tour of the morgue was 569, out of which only 1 became a repeat offender.
    (a) Suppose that out of 1000 newly convicted drunk drivers, all were required to take a tour of the morgue. Let us assume that the probability of a repeat offender is still $p = 1/569$. Explain why the Poisson approximation to the binomial would be a good choice for r = number of repeat offenders out of 1000 convicted drunk drivers who toured the morgue. What is λ to the nearest tenth?
    (b) What is the probability that $r = 0$?
    (c) What is the probability that $r > 1$?
    (d) What is the probability that $r > 2$?
    (e) What is the probability that $r > 3$?

18. *USA Today* (February 8, 1990) reported that for all airlines, the number of lost bags was

    May: 6.02 per 1000 passengers
    December: 12.78 per 1000 passengers

    Note: A passenger could lose more than one bag.

    (a) Let r = number of bags lost per 1000 passengers in May. Explain why the Poisson distribution would be a good choice for the random variable r. What is λ to the nearest tenth?

(b) In the month of May, what is the probability that out of 1000 passengers, no bags are lost? 3 or more bags are lost? 6 or more bags are lost?

(c) In the month of December, what is the probability that out of 1000 passengers, no bags are lost? 6 or more bags are lost? 12 or more bags are lost? (Round λ to the nearest whole number.)

19. *Chances: Risk and Odds in Everyday Life,* by James Burke, reports that the probability that a police officer will be killed in the line of duty is 0.5% (or less).

(a) In a police precinct with 175 officers, let r = number of police officers killed in the line of duty. Explain why the Poisson approximation to the binomial would be a good choice for the random variable r. What is n? What is p? What is λ to the nearest tenth?

(b) What is the probability that no officer in this precinct will be killed in the line of duty?

(c) What is the probability one or more officers in this precinct will be killed in the line of duty?

(d) What is the probability that two or more officers in this precinct will be killed in the line of duty?

20. *Chances: Risk and Odds in Everyday Life,* by James Burke, reports that only 2% of all local franchises are business failures. In a Colorado Springs shopping complex, there are 137 franchises (restaurants, auto shops, print shops, convenience stores, hair salons, and so on).

(a) Let r be the number of these franchises that are business failures. Explain why a Poisson approximation to the binomial would be appropriate for the random variable r. What is n? What is p? What is λ (round to the nearest tenth)?

(b) What is the probability that none of the franchises will be a business failure?

(c) What is the probability that two or more of the franchises will be business failures?

(d) What is the probability that four or more franchises will be business failures?

21. (a) For $n = 100$, $p = 0.02$, and $r = 2$, compute $P(r)$ using the formula for the binomial distribution and your calculator:

$$P(r) = C_{n,r}p^r(1 - p)^{n - r}$$

(b) For $n = 100$, $p = 0.02$, and $r = 2$, estimate $P(r)$ using the Poisson approximation to the binomial.

(c) Compare the results of parts a and b. Does it appear that the Poisson distribution with $\lambda = np$ provides a good approximation for $P(r = 2)$?

(d) Repeat parts a to c for $r = 3$.

6. The three engines of a jet airliner are arranged to operate independently. The probability of an in-flight engine failure is 0.05 for each single engine. Let r represent the number of engines that fail during a flight.

   (a) Make a histogram of the probability distribution of r.
   (b) What is the probability that no failures occur? What is the probability that more than one failure occurs?
   (c) What is the expected value and standard deviation of the r probability distribution?

7. It is estimated that 75% of a grapefruit crop is good; the other 25% have rotten centers which cannot be detected unless the grapefruit are cut open. The grapefruit are sold in sacks of 10. Let r be the number of good grapefruit in a sack.

   (a) Make a histogram of the probability distribution of r.
   (b) What is the probability of getting no more than one bad grapefruit in a sack? What is the probability of getting at least one good grapefruit in a sack?
   (c) What is the expected number of good grapefruit in a sack?
   (d) What is the standard deviation of the r probability distribution?

8. Camp Wee-O-Wee has found that about 8% of young campers get poison ivy each season. If 273 children are registered for the summer season, about how many can be expected to get poison ivy?

9. A survey has found that about 17% of all M.D.s in the United States have changed their specialty at least once. In a city with 600 M.D.s, what is the expected number who have changed specialties?

10. The Orchard Café has found that about 5% of the parties who make reservations don't show up. If 82 party reservations have been made, how many can be expected to show up? Find the standard deviation of this distribution.

11. The We Care Lawn Service has found that about one out of five people will respond favorably to a certain telephone sales pitch. Suppose 15 people are called. Let r be the number who respond favorably.

    (a) Make a histogram for the r probability distribution.
    (b) What is the expected number of people who will respond favorably? Find the standard deviation of the r distribution.
    (c) What is the probability that at least three respond favorably? What is the probability that exactly three respond favorably?

12. The dropout rate at Rock High is 17%. If 1500 students have enrolled, how many can be expected to drop out?

13. Jack Rabbit Car Wax has developed two new car waxes: Flopsie and Mopsie. To determine if consumers really prefer one over the other, both waxes were applied to the same car (Flopsie on the right side and Mopsie

on the left). A random sample of 20 car owners were asked which side of the car had the best polish job. If there is actually no difference in consumer preference (i.e., 50% prefer Flopsie), what is the probability that at most 5 car owners state a preference for Flopsie?

14. When David drives from Columbus to Cincinnati, the probability is 0.75 that at any given time he is going faster than the speed limit. If there are four radar traps between Columbus and Cincinnati, what is the probability David will be caught at least once (assume independence)?

15. Ten thousand thumbtacks were dropped on a table, and 6500 landed with the point up. If 500 tacks are dropped, how many would you expect to land point up?

16. There are three true–false questions on a psychology test. Rita is out of time and just guesses, so the probability of a correct answer is 0.50.

   (a) Draw a histogram showing the probability of $r = 0, 1, 2, 3$ correct answers for the three questions.
   (b) What is the expected number of correct answers?
   (c) Find the standard deviation of the r distribution.

17. A person with a cough is a *persona non grata* on airplanes, elevators, or at the theater. In theaters especially, the irritation level rises with each muffled explosion. According to Dr. Brian Carlin, a Pittsburgh pulmonologist, in any large audience you'll hear about 11 coughs per minute (*USA Today,* October 4, 1993).

   (a) Let r = number of coughs in a given time interval. Explain why the Poisson distribution would be a good choice for the probability distribution of r.
   (b) Find the probability of 3 or fewer coughs (in a large auditorium) in a 1-minute period.
   (c) Find the probability of at least 3 coughs (in a large auditorium) in a 30-second period.

18. Flying over the western states with mountainous terrain in a small aircraft is 40% riskier than flying over similar distances in flatter portions of the nation according to a General Accounting Office study completed in response to a congressional request. The accident rate for small aircraft in the 11 mountainous western states is 2.4 per 100,000 flight operations (*Denver Post,* January 11, 1994).

   (a) Let r = number of accidents for a given number of operations. Explain why the Poisson distribution would be a good choice for the probability distribution of r.
   (b) Find the probability of no accidents in 100,000 flight operations.
   (c) Find the probability of at least 4 accidents in 200,000 flight operations.

19. Records over the past year show that 1 out of 350 loans made by Mammon Bank have defaulted. Find the probability that 2 or more out of 300

loans will default. *Hint:* Is it appropriate to use the Poisson approximation to the binomial distribution?

20. In the Colorado Lottery, the probability of winning the grand prize with one ticket is about 1/5,000,000 (1 in 5 million). Suppose you join a pool that buys 500,000 tickets (at a cost of $1 per ticket). What is the probability that *none* of the tickets purchased by the pool will be a grand prize winner? What is the probability that one will be? *Hint:* Is it appropriate to use the Poisson approximation to the binomial?

21. An experiment consists of tossing a coin a specified number of times and recording the outcomes.

  (a) What is the probability that the *first* head will occur on the second trial? Does this probability change if we toss the coin three times? What if we toss the coin four times? What probability distribution model do we use to compute these probabilities?

  (b) What is the probability that the *first* head will occur on the 4th trial? after the 4th trial?

22. Cathy is planning to take the Certified Public Accountant Examination (CPA exam). Records kept by the college of business from which she graduated indicate that 83% of the students who have graduated pass the CPA exam. Assume that the exam is changed each time it is given. Let $n = 1$, 2, 3, . . . represent the number of times a person takes the CPA exam until the *first* pass. (Assume the trials are independent).

  (a) What is the probability that Cathy passes the CPA exam on the first try?

  (b) What is the probability that Cathy passes the CPA exam on the second or third try?

DATA HIGHLIGHTS

1. Examine Figure 5–7, "Time to Develop" (*USA Today,* December 9, 1992). Let us assume that the information is representative of the general population of camera owners.

  (a) Out of a group of 10 camera owners, what is the probability that 5 or more of the owners have had the film in their camera for 2 weeks or less?

  (b) Out of a group of 10 camera owners, what is the probability that at least one doesn't know how long the film has been in the camera? *Hint:* Use the formula for the binomial distribution.

  (c) Out of a group of 10 camera owners, what is the expected number that leave film in the camera from 1 to 3 months? What is the standard deviation?

  (d) What is the probability that the 5th camera owner you ask is the first who did not know how long the film had been in the camera? *Hint:* Use geometric distribution.

Figure 5–7 Time to Develop (December 9, 1992)

USA SNAPSHOTS®

A look at statistics that shape our lives

Time to develop
How long film stays in people's cameras:

2 weeks or less **40%**

2-4 weeks **19%**

1-3 months **19%**

3 months to a year **12%**

3% More than a year

Don't know **7%**

Source: Fuji Photo Film U.S.A. Inc. random survey of 1,010 adults

By Nick Galifianakis, USA TODAY

Source: Copyright 1992, USA TODAY. Reprinted with permission.

Figure 5–8 Weighty Matters (December 13, 1989)

USA SNAPSHOTS®

A look at statistics that shape our lives

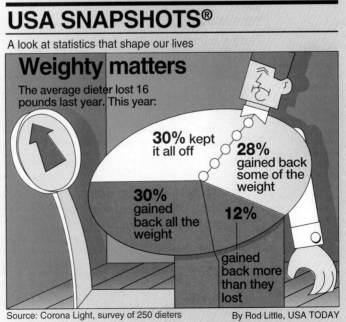

Weighty matters
The average dieter lost 16 pounds last year. This year:

30% kept it all off

28% gained back some of the weight

30% gained back all the weight

12% gained back more than they lost

Source: Corona Light, survey of 250 dieters

By Rod Little, USA TODAY

Source: Copyright 1989, USA TODAY. Reprinted with permission.

Figure 5–9 Baggage Handling (December 16, 1992)

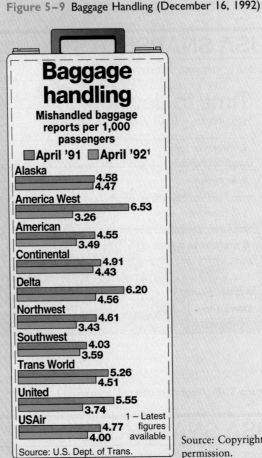

Baggage handling

Mishandled baggage reports per 1,000 passengers

■ April '91   ■ April '92¹

Airline	April '91	April '92¹
Alaska	4.58	4.47
America West	6.53	3.26
American	4.55	3.49
Continental	4.91	4.43
Delta	6.20	4.56
Northwest	4.61	3.43
Southwest	4.03	3.59
Trans World	5.26	4.51
United	5.55	3.74
USAir	4.77	4.00

1 – Latest figures available

Source: U.S. Dept. of Trans.
By Julie Stacey, USA TODAY

Source: Copyright 1992, USA TODAY. Reprinted with permission.

2. Examine Figure 5–8 on page 313, "Weighty Matters" (*USA Today*, December 13, 1989). Let us assume that the information is representative of the general population of dieters.

   (a) How many dieters would you need to interview to be 95% sure of finding at least one who has kept off all the weight he or she lost?

   (b) How many dieters would you need to interview to be 95% sure of finding at least three who have kept off all the weight they lost?

   (c) What is the probability that the third dieter you interview will be the first to have gained back more than he or she lost? *Hint:* Use the geometric distribution.

3. Examine Figure 5–9, "Baggage Handling" (*USA Today*, June 16, 1992).

   (a) Suppose that 329 passengers just got off a commercial flight. Explain why the Poisson distribution would be a good choice for the random variable r, where r = number of lost bags per 329 passengers.

(b) For the April 1991 data for America West, what is λ, the expected number of lost bags for our 329 passengers. What is the probability of no lost bags? What is the probability of at least one lost bag? What is the probability of at least two lost bags?
(c) Repeat part b for the April 1992 data for America West. Do you notice any differences in your answers compared with those for part b? Explain.

LINKING CONCEPTS

Discuss each of the following topics in class or review the topics on your own. Then write a brief but complete essay in which you summarize the main points. Please include formulas and graphs as appropriate.

1. Discuss what we mean by a binomial experiment. As you can see, a binomial process or binomial experiment involves a lot of assumptions! For example, all the trials are supposed to be independent and repeated under identical conditions. Is this always true? Can we always be completely certain the probability of success does not change from one trial to the next? In the real world there is almost nothing we can be absolutely sure about, so the *theoretical* assumptions of the binomial probability distribution often will not be completely satisfied. Does that mean we cannot use the binomial distribution to solve practical problems? Looking at this chapter, the answer that appears is that we can indeed use the binomial distribution even if all the assumptions are not *exactly* met. We find in practice that the conclusions are sufficiently accurate for our intended application. List three applications of the binomial distribution for which you think, although some of the assumptions are not exactly met, there is adequate reason to apply the binomial distribution anyhow.

2. Why do we need to learn the formula for the binomial probability distribution? Using the formula repeatedly can be very tedious. To cut down on tedious calculations most people will use a binomial table such as found in Appendix II of this book.
(a) However, there are many applications where a table in the back of *any* book is not adequate. For instance, compute

$$P(r = 3) \quad \text{where } n = 5 \text{ and } p = 0.735$$

Do you find the result in the table? Do the calculation by using the formula. List some other situations in which a table might not be adequate to solve a particular binomial distribution problem.
(b) The formula itself also has limitations. For instance, consider the difficulty of computing

$$P(r \geq 285) \quad \text{where } n = 500 \text{ and } p = 0.6$$

What are some of the difficulties you run into? Consider the calculation of $P(r = 285)$. You will be raising 0.6 and 0.4 to very high powers; this will give you very, very small numbers. Then you need to compute $C_{500,285}$, which is a very, very large number. When combining extremely large and extremely small numbers in the same calculation most accuracy is lost unless you carry a huge number of significant digits. If this isn't tedious enough, then consider the steps that you need in order to compute

$$P(r \geq 285) = P(r = 285) + P(r = 286) + \cdots + P(r = 500)$$

Does it seem clear that we need a better way to compute $P(r \geq 285)$? In Chapter 7 you will find a much better way to compute binomial probabilities when the number of trials is large.

3. In Chapter 3 we learned about means and standard deviations. In Chapter 4 we learned that probability distributions can also have a mean and standard deviation. Discuss what is meant by the expected value and standard deviation of a binomial distribution. How does this relate back to the material we learned in Chapters 3 and 4?

4. In Chapter 2 we looked at the shapes of distributions. Review the concepts of skewness and symmetry; then categorize the following distributions as to skewness or symmetry:
   (a) A binomial distribution with $n = 11$ trials and $p = 0.50$
   (b) A binomial distribution with $n = 11$ trials and $p = 0.10$
   (c) A binomial distribution with $n = 11$ trials and $p = 0.90$

In general, does it seem true that binomial probability distributions in which the probability of success is close to 0 are skewed right, whereas those with probability of success close to 1 are skewed left?

Using Technology

The problems in this section may be done using either statistical computer software or calculators that have statistical functions. Displays and suggestions are given for Minitab (Release 9), the TI-82 graphing calculator, and ComputerStat.

Binomial Distributions

Although tables of binomial probabilities can be found in most libraries, such tables are often inadequate. Either the value of p (the probability of success on a trial) you are looking for is not in the table, or the value of n (the number of trials) you are looking for is too large for the table. In Chapter 7 we will study the normal approximation to the binomial. This approximation is a great help in many practical applications. Even so, we sometimes use the formula for the binomial probability distribution on a computer or graphing calculator to compute the probability we want.

Minitab

In Minitab the commands

```
MTB > PDF;
SUB > BINOMIAL N = 6 P = .27.
```

generate the probabilities for 0 to 6 successes for a binomial distribution with $n = 6$ trials and probability of success on a single trial $p = 0.27$. You can change the values of N and P to fit your application. Using the command CDF in place of PDF will generate cumulative probabilities.

TI-82

On the TI-82 you will need to use the formula to evaluate binomial probabilities. This calculator has a TABLE feature that displays a table of values. For example, to generate the values of a binomial probability distribution with number of trials $n = 6$ and probability of success on a single trial $p = 0.27$, use the steps that are shown on page 318.

(a) First set up the table with the TblSet key.
Choose TblMin = 0

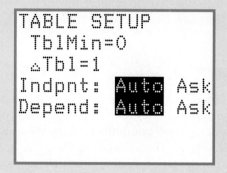

```
TABLE SETUP
 TblMin=0
 △Tbl=1
Indpnt: Auto  Ask
Depend: Auto  Ask
```

(b) Press the Y= key and enter the binomial formula as a function, using x in place of r.

```
Y1■6 nCr X*(.27)
^X*(.73)^(6-X)
Y2=
Y3=
Y4=
Y5=
Y6=
Y7=
```

(c) Press the TABLE key. The values in the Y1 column are the probabilities for r = 0 through r = 6 successes.

```
 X    | Y1
 0    | .15133
 1    | .33584
 2    | .31053
 3    | .15314
 4    | .04248
 5    | .00628
 6    | 3.9E-4
X=0
```

Making appropriate changes in the values of n and p will generate values for other binomial distributions.

ComputerStat

Under the Probability Distributions menu, select Binomial Coefficients and Probability Distributions. This program prompts you to enter the number of trials and the probability of success on a single trial. Then it prints the probabilities and cumulative probabilities for $R = 0$ to N successes. A program option shows the graph of the distribution.

Applications

The following percentages were obtained over many years of observation by the U.S. Weather Bureau. All data listed are for the month of December.

Location	Long-Term Mean % of Clear Days in Dec.
Juneau, Alaska	18%
Seattle, Washington	24%
Hilo, Hawaii	36%
Honolulu, Hawaii	60%
Las Vegas, Nevada	75%
Phoenix, Arizona	77%

Adapted from *Local Climatological Data,* U.S. Weather Bureau publication, "Normals, Means, and Extremes" Table.

In the locations listed, the month of December is a relatively stable month with respect to weather. Since weather patterns from one day to the next are more or less the same, it is reasonable to use a binomial probability model.

1. Let r be the number of clear days in December. Since December has 31 days, $0 \le r \le 31$. Using appropriate computer software or calculators available to you, find the probability $P(r)$ for each of the listed locations when $r = 0, 1, 2, \ldots, 31$.

2. For each location what is the expected value of the probability distribution? What is the standard deviation?

You may find that using cumulative probabilities and appropriate subtraction of probabilities will make the solution of Problems 3 to 7 easier than adding probabilities.

3. Estimate the probability that Juneau will have at most 7 clear days in December.

4. Estimate the probability that Seattle will have from 5 to 10 (including 5 and 10) clear days in December.

5. Estimate the probability that Hilo will have at least 12 clear days in December.

6. Estimate the probability that Phoenix will have 20 or more clear days in December.

7. Estimate the probability that Las Vegas will have from 20 to 25 (including 20 and 25) clear days in December.

TI-82 Display

The TI-82 will give the general shape of a binomial distribution. Enter the number of successes in one list and the corresponding probabilities in another list. Since the histogram requires whole numbers for frequencies, simply "clear" the decimals in the probabilities. The following screens show the process used to obtain the histogram of a binomial distribution with $n = 6$ trials and probability of success $p = 0.37$.

L1 = number of successes
L2 = probability with decimal cleared

Select the Histogram plot

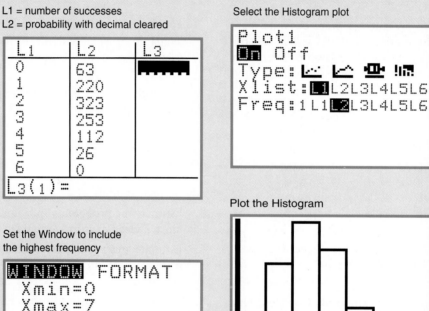

Set the Window to include the highest frequency

Plot the Histogram

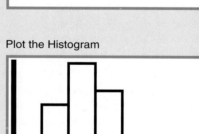

Computer Displays

Most statistical software packages will generate binomial probability distributions. The user may specify the number of successes and the probability of success on a single trial. In many packages there is an option to obtain a cumulative distribution as well.

Minitab Display: Binomial Distribution and Cumulative Distribution for Number of Trials = 6 and Probability of Success = 0.27

```
MTB>PDF;
SUBC>BINOMIAL N = 6, P = 0.27.

    BINOMIAL WITH N = 6 P = 0.270000
     K        P(X = K)
     0         0.1513
     1         0.3358
     2         0.3105
     3         0.1531
     4         0.0425
     5         0.0063
     6         0.0004
MTB>CDF;
SUBC>BINOMIAL N = 6, P = 0.27.

    BINOMIAL WITH N = 6 P = 0.270000
     K P(X LESS OR = K)
     0            0.1513
     1            0.4872
     2            0.7977
     3            0.9508
     4            0.9933
     5            0.9996
     6            1.0000
```

Minitab Display: Poisson Distribution and Cumulative Distribution for Lambda = 3.8

```
MTB > pdf;
SUBC> poisson lambda = 3.8.
     K              P( X = K)

   0.00               0.0224
   1.00               0.0850
   2.00               0.1615
   3.00               0.2046
   4.00               0.1944
   5.00               0.1477
   6.00               0.0936
   7.00               0.0508
   8.00               0.0241
   9.00               0.0102
  10.00               0.0039
  11.00               0.0013
  12.00               0.0004
  13.00               0.0001
  14.00               0.0000


MTB > cdf;
SUBC> poisson lambda = 3.8.
     K   P( X Less OR = K)

   0.00               0.0224
   1.00               0.1074
   2.00               0.2689
   3.00               0.4735
   4.00               0.6678
   5.00               0.8156
   6.00               0.9091
   7.00               0.9599
   8.00               0.9840
   9.00               0.9942
  10.00               0.9981
  11.00               0.9994
  12.00               0.9998
  13.00               1.0000
  14.00               1.0000
```

ComputerStat Display: Binomial Distribution for Number of Trials = 6 and Probability of Success = 0.37

```
         BINOMIAL TABLE FOR N = 6 TRIALS WITH PROBABILITY OF
                  SUCCESS ON A SINGLE TRIAL P = .37

SUCCESSES(R)     BINOMIAL COEFF.(C)          P(R)        P(0< = X< = R)
     0               1                    .0625235         .0625235
     1               6                    .2203209         .2828444
     2              15                    .3234871         .6063315
     3              20                    .2533127         .8596441
     4              15                    .1115782         .9712223
     5               6                   2.621202E-02       .9974343
     6               1                   2.565727E-03       1


       EXPECTED VALUE = 2.22 STANDARD DEVIATION = 1.182624
```

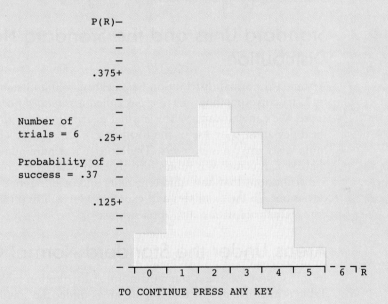

```
            P(R)—
                —
                —
                —
          .375+
                —
                —
Number of       —
trials = 6  .25+
                —
Probability of  —
success = .37   —
                —
          .125+
                —
                —
                —
                —
                 ‾0‾ 1‾ 2‾ 3‾ 4‾ 5‾ 6 ‾R
          TO CONTINUE PRESS ANY KEY
```

Graphs of Normal Probability Distributions

In this section we study the general shape of graphs of normal curves. Of special interest is the location of μ, the population mean, and how the shape is changed by σ, the population standard deviation. If we can assume that our distribution (of sample values) is more or less symmetrical and bell-shaped (which is the case for a normal distribution), then the *empirical rule* can be used to give more definite results than Chebyshev's theorem. Control charts are another application of normal (or approximately normal) distributions. Control charts are used extensively in medical science, industrial production, and financial work.

Standard Units and the Standard Normal Distribution

A standard normal distribution has mean $\mu = 0$ and standard deviation $\sigma = 1$. Its corresponding variable z is called a *standard normal variable,* or z *score.* We can standardize any normal distribution x with mean μ and standard deviation σ by use of the formula $z = (x - \mu)/\sigma$. The way this formula is set up, z has no *units.* Therefore, z is a pure number. This means that we can compare z values directly even when they come from (normal) x distributions that have different units and/or different means and standard deviations. In the examples and exercises you will find that z scores are a convenient tool with many applications.

Areas Under the Standard Normal Curve

In this section we use a standard normal distribution table (see front flap or Table 6 in Appendix II) to compute areas under the standard normal curve. Such areas are in fact probabilities that z values will fall in given intervals.

Areas Under Any Normal Curve

We use the formula $z = (x - \mu)/\sigma$ to convert a normal distribution of x values into corresponding z values. Then we use the methods of Section 6.3 to compute probabilities that x values (and corresponding z values) are in given intervals. Finally, we compute inverse normal probabilities. That is, given a certain probability in a left or right tail of a standard normal distribution, we find the z value corresponding to this given probability. Inverse normal probabilities have a number of applications, especially in guarantee problems and some types of insurance problems.

Normal Distributions

Heinrich Rudolf Hertz
(1857–1894)

This German physicist was largely responsible for doing pioneering work in electromagnetic theory.

One cannot escape the feeling that these mathematical formulas have an independent existence and an intelligence of their own, that they are wiser than we are, wiser even than their discoverers, that we get more out of them than was originally put into them.

Heinrich Hertz

How can it be that mathematics, a product of human thought independent of experience, is so admirably adapted to the objects of reality?

Albert Einstein

Heinrich Hertz was a pioneer in the study of radio waves. His work and the later work of Maxwell and Marconi led the way to modern radio, television, and radar. Albert Einstein is world renowned for his great discoveries in relativity and quantum mechanics. Everyone who has worked in both mathematics and real-world applications cannot help but marvel how the "pure thought" of the mathematical sciences can predict and explain events in other realms. In this chapter we will study the single most important type of probability distribution in all of mathematical statistics: the normal distribution. Why is the normal distribution so important? Two of the reasons are that it applies to a wide variety of situations and other distributions tend to become normal under certain conditions.

Focus Problem ▶ Attendance at Exhibition Shows

For many years Denver, as well as most other cities, have hosted large exhibition shows in big auditoriums. These shows include house and gardening shows, fishing and hunting shows, car shows, boat shows, Native American powwows, and so on. Information provided by Denver show sponsors indicates that most shows have an average attendance of about 8000 people per day with an estimated standard deviation of about 500 people. Suppose that the daily attendance figures follow a normal distribution.

1. What is the probability that the daily attendance will be less than 7200 people?

325

2. What is the probability that the daily attendance will be more than 8900 people?

3. What is the probability that the daily attendance will be between 7200 and 8900 people?

Most exhibition shows open in the morning and close in the late evening. A study of Saturday arrival times showed that the average arrival time was 3 hours and 48 minutes after the doors open and the standard deviation was estimated at about 52 minutes. Suppose that the arrival times follow a normal distribution.

4. At what time after the doors open will 90% of the people who are coming to the Saturday show have arrived?

5. At what time after the doors open will only 15% of the people who are coming to the Saturday show have arrived?

6. Do you think the probability distribution of arrival times for Friday might be different from the distribution of arrival times for Saturday? Explain.

Section 6.1   Graphs of Normal Probability Distributions

One of the most important examples of a continuous probability distribution is the *normal distribution*. This distribution was studied by the French mathematician Abraham de Moivre (1667–1754) and later by the German mathematician Carl Friedrich Gauss (1777–1855), whose work is so important that the normal distribution is sometimes called *Gaussian*. The work of these mathematicians provided a foundation upon which much of the theory of statistical inference is based.

Applications of a normal probability distribution are so numerous that some mathematicians refer to it as "a veritable Boy Scout knife of statistics." However, before we can apply it, we must examine some of the properties of a normal distribution.

A rather complicated formula, presented in advanced statistics books, defines a normal distribution in terms of μ and σ, the mean standard deviation of the population distribution. It is only through this formula that we can verify if a distribution is normal. However, we can look at the graph of a normal distribution and get a good pictorial idea of some of the essential features of any normal distribution.

Normal Curve

The graph of a normal distribution is called a *normal curve*. It possesses a shape very much like the cross section of a pile of dry sand. Because of its shape, blacksmiths would sometimes use a pile of dry sand in the construction of a mold for a bell. Thus the normal curve is also called a *bell-shaped curve* (see Figure 6–1).

We see that a general normal curve is smooth and symmetrical about the vertical line over the mean μ. Notice that the highest point of the curve occurs over μ. If the distribution were graphed on a piece of sheet metal, cut out,

Figure 6–1 A Normal Curve

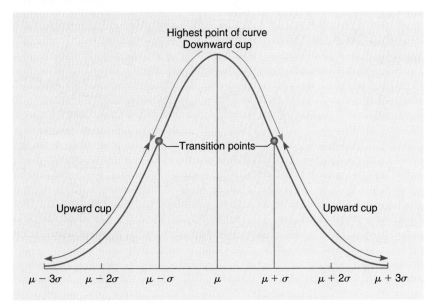

and placed on a knife edge, the balance point would be at μ. We also see that the curve tends to level out and approach the horizontal (x axis) like a glider making a landing. However, in mathematical theory, such a glider would never quite finish its landing because a normal curve never touches the horizontal axis.

The parameter σ controls the spread of the curve. The curve is quite close to the horizontal axis at $\mu + 3\sigma$ and $\mu - 3\sigma$. Thus, if the standard deviation σ is large, the curve will be more spread out; if it is small, the curve will be more peaked. Figure 6–1 shows the normal curve cupped downward for an interval on either side of the mean μ. Then it begins to cup upward as we go to the lower part of the bell. The exact places where the transition between the upward and downward cupping occur are above the points $\mu + \sigma$ and $\mu - \sigma$.

Let's summarize the important properties of a normal curve.

1. The curve is "bell-shaped" with the highest point over the mean μ.

2. It is symmetrical about a vertical line through μ.

3. The curve approaches the horizontal axis but never touches or crosses it.

4. The transition points between cupping upward and downward occur at $\mu + \sigma$ and $\mu - \sigma$.

GUIDED EXERCISE 1

Each of the curves in Figure 6–2 fails to be a normal curve. Give reasons why these curves are not normal curves.

Figure 6–2

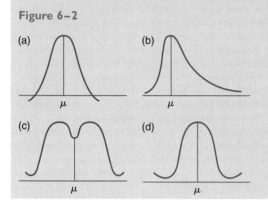

(a) A normal curve gets closer and closer to the horizontal axis, but it never touches it or crosses it.

(b) A normal curve must be symmetrical. This curve is not.

(c) A normal curve is bell-shaped with one peak. Because this curve has two peaks, it is not normal.

(d) The tails of a normal curve must get closer and closer to the x axis. In this curve the tails are going away from the x axis.

GUIDED EXERCISE 2

The points A, B, and C are indicated on the normal curve in Figure 6–3. One of these points is μ, one is $\mu + \sigma$, and one $\mu - 2\sigma$.

(a) Which point corresponds to the mean? What is the value of μ?

(b) Which point corresponds to $\mu + \sigma$? Use the values of $\mu + \sigma$ and μ to compute σ.

(c) Which point corresponds to $\mu - 2\sigma$?

(a) The mean μ is under the peak of the normal curve. The point B corresponds to the mean, so $\mu = 10$.

(b) The point C where the curve changes from cupped down to cupped up is one standard deviation σ from the mean. The point C is $\mu + \sigma$. Since $\mu + \sigma = 12$ and $\mu = 10$, $\sigma = 2$.

(c) Since $\mu = 10$ and $\sigma = 2$ we see that

$$\mu - 2\sigma = 10 - 2(2) = 6$$

Point A corresponds to $\mu - 2\sigma$.

Figure 6–3 A Normal Curve

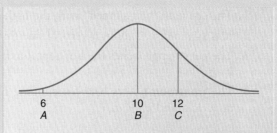

Figure 6-4 Examples of Normal Curves

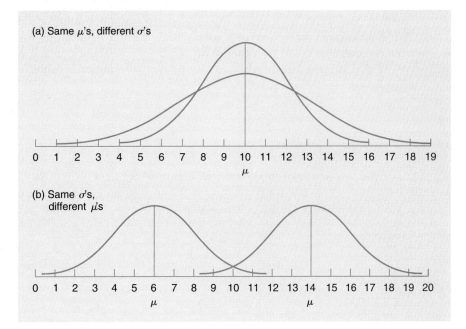

(a) Same μ's, different σ's

0 1 2 3 4 5 6 7 8 9 10 11 12 13 14 15 16 17 18 19
μ

(b) Same σ's, different μ's

0 1 2 3 4 5 6 7 8 9 10 11 12 13 14 15 16 17 18 19 20
μ μ

The parameters which control the shape of a normal curve are the mean μ and the standard deviation σ. When both μ and σ are specified, a specific normal curve is determined. In brief, μ locates the balance point and σ determines the extent of the spread. Figure 6-4 shows some normal curves for different μ's and σ's.

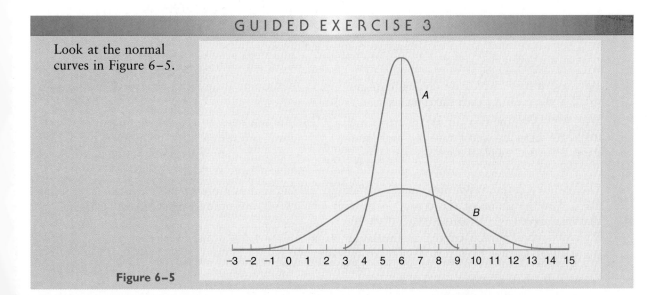

GUIDED EXERCISE 3

Look at the normal curves in Figure 6-5.

A

B

-3 -2 -1 0 1 2 3 4 5 6 7 8 9 10 11 12 13 14 15

Figure 6-5

(a) Do these distributions have the same mean? If so, what is it?

(b) One of the curves corresponds to a normal distribution with $\sigma = 3$ and the other to one with $\sigma = 1$. Which curve has which σ?

(a) The means are the same, since both graphs have the high point over 6. $\mu = 6$.

(b) Curve A has $\sigma = 1$, and curve B has $\sigma = 3$. (Since curve B is more spread out, it has the larger σ value.)

GUIDED EXERCISE 4

Look at the normal curves in Figure 6–6.

Figure 6–6

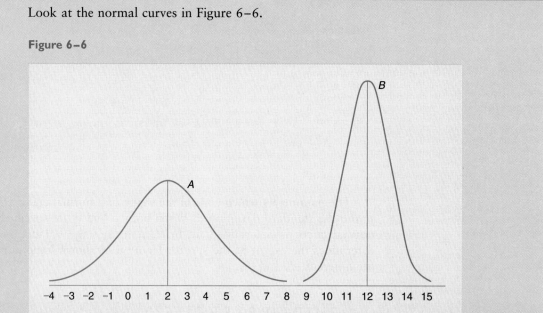

(a) Do these distributions have the same mean? What is the mean of each distribution?

(b) Is it true that of the two curves, the curve with the larger mean also must have the larger standard deviation? Explain your answer.

(c) The standard deviations of these curves are not given, but the shape of the curves indicates that one curve has a larger standard deviation than the other. Which curve has the larger standard deviation?

(a) No. Curve A has $\mu = 2$; curve B has $\mu = 12$.

(b) It is not true. In general, the mean and standard deviations have no influence on each other. So a curve with a large mean need not have a large standard deviation.

(c) Curve A is more spread out than curve B, so curve A has the larger standard deviation.

Empirical Rule

The total area under any normal curve studied in this book will *always* be 1. The graph of the normal distribution is important because the portion of the *area* under the curve above a given interval represents the *probability* that a measurement will lie in that interval.

In Section 3.2 we studied Chebyshev's theorem. This theorem gives us information about the *smallest* proportion of data that lies within 2, 3, or *k* standard deviations of the mean. This result applies to *any* distribution. However, for normal distributions, we can get a much more precise result, which is given by the *empirical rule*.

Empirical Rule

For a distribution that is symmetrical and bell-shaped (in particular, for a normal distribution):

Approximately 68% of the data values will lie within one standard deviation on each side of the mean.

Approximately 95% of the data values will lie within two standard deviations on each side of the mean.

Approximately 99.7% (or almost all) of the data values will be within three standard deviations on each side of the mean.

The preceding statement is called the *empirical rule* because, for symmetrical, bell-shaped distributions, the given percentages are observed in practice. Furthermore, for the normal distribution, the empirical rule is a direct consequence of the very nature of the distribution (see Figure 6-7). Notice that

Figure 6–7 Area Under a Normal Curve

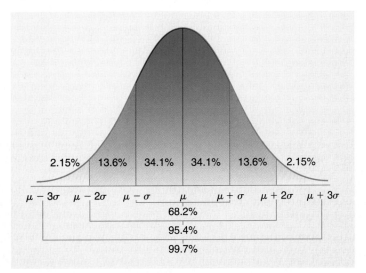

the empirical rule is a stronger statement than Chebyshev's theorem in that it gives *definite percentages,* not just lower limits. Of course, the empirical rule only applies to normal or symmetrical, bell-shaped distributions, whereas Chebyshev's theorem applies to all distributions.

Example 1

The playing life of a Sunshine radio is normally distributed with mean $\mu = 600$ hours and standard deviation $\sigma = 100$ hours. What is the probability that a radio selected at random will last from 600 to 700 hours?

Solution: The probability that the playing time will be between 600 and 700 hours is equal to the percentage of the total area under the curve that is shaded in Figure 6–8. Since $\mu = 600$ and $\mu + \sigma = 600 + 100 = 700$, we see that the shaded area is simply the area between μ and $\mu + \sigma$. The area from μ to $\mu + \sigma$ is 34.1% of the total area. This tells us that the probability a Sunshine radio will last between 600 and 700 playing hours is 0.341.

Figure 6–8 Distribution of Playing Times

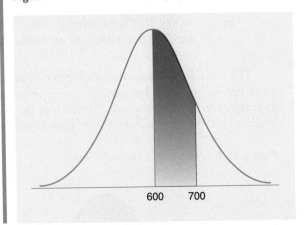

600	700

GUIDED EXERCISE 5

The yearly wheat yield per acre on a particular farm is normally distributed with mean $\mu = 35$ bushels and standard deviation $\sigma = 8$ bushels.

(a) Shade the area under the curve in Figure 6–9 that represents the probability that an acre will yield between 19 and 35 bushels.

(a) See Figure 6–10.

(b) Is the area the same as the area between $\mu - 2\sigma$ and μ?

(b) Yes, since $\mu = 35$ and $\mu - 2\sigma = 35 - 2(8) = 19$.

Figure 6-9

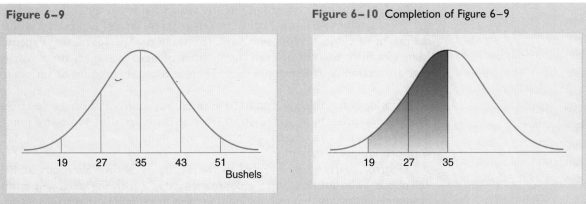

Bushels

Figure 6-10 Completion of Figure 6-9

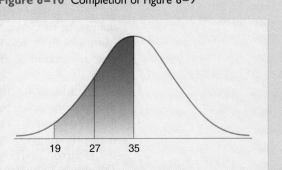

(c) Use Figure 6-7 to find the percentage of area over the interval between 19 and 35.

(d) What is the probability that the yield will be between 19 and 35 bushels per acre?

(c) The area between the values $\mu - 2\sigma$ and μ is 47.7% of the total area.

(d) It is 47.7% of the total area, which is 1. Therefore, the probability is 0.477 that the yield will be between 19 and 35 bushels.

Example 1 and Guided Exercise 5 both involve intervals beginning with one number and ending with another from among the following:

$$\mu - 3\sigma \qquad \mu - 2\sigma \qquad \mu - \sigma \qquad \mu \qquad \mu + \sigma \qquad \mu + 2\sigma \qquad \mu + 3\sigma$$

The following facts are used for these problems:

1. About 68.2% of the area under a normal curve falls in the interval between $\mu + \sigma$ and $\mu - \sigma$.
2. About 95.4% of the area falls between $\mu + 2\sigma$ and $\mu - 2\sigma$.
3. About 99.7% of the area falls between $\mu + 3\sigma$ and $\mu - 3\sigma$.

These intervals and percentages are important to remember because they serve as rough guides to normal distributions.

However, to find the probability that a measurement lies in an interval such as that between $\mu + 0.4\sigma$ and $\mu + 0.7\sigma$, we need more machinery. This machinery is developed in the next section. In Sections 6.3 and 6.4 we see how to find the probability that a measurement from a normal distribution lies in *any* specified interval.

Control Charts

If we are examining data over a period of equally spaced time intervals or in some sequential order, then *control charts* are especially useful. Business managers and people in charge of production processes are aware that there exists an inherent amount of variability in any sequential set of data. For example, the sugar content of bottled drinks taken sequentially off a production line, the extent of clerical errors in a bank from day to day, advertising expenses from month to month, or even the number of new customers from year to year are examples of sequential data. There is a certain amount of variability in each.

A random variable x is said to be in *statistical control* if it can be described by the *same* probability distribution when it is observed at successive points in time. Control charts combine graphic and numerical descriptions of data with probability distributions.

Control charts were invented in the 1920s by Walter Shewhart at Bell Telephone Laboratories. Since a control chart is a *warning device*, it is not absolutely necessary that our assumptions and probability calculations be precisely correct. For example, the x distributions need not follow a normal distribution exactly. Any mound-shaped and more or less symmetrical distribution will be good enough.

How do we make a control chart? A control chart for a variable x is a plot of the observed x values (on the vertical scale) in time sequence order (the horizontal scale represents time). There is a center line at height μ and dashed control limits at $\mu \pm 2\sigma$ and at $\mu \pm 3\sigma$. How do we pick values for μ and σ? In most practical cases, values for μ (population mean) and σ (population standard deviation) are computed from past data for which the process we are studying was known to be *in control*. Methods for choosing the sample size to fit given error tolerances can be found in Chapter 8.

Sometimes values for μ and σ are chosen as *target values*. That is, μ and σ values are chosen as set goals or targets which reflect the production level or service level at which a company hopes to perform. To be realistic, such target assignments for μ and σ should be reasonably close to actual data taken when the process was operating at a satisfactory production level.

In the next example, we will make a control chart. Then we will discuss ways to analyze the control chart to see if a process or service is "in control."

Example 2 | Susan Tamara is director of personnel at the Antlers Lodge in Denali National Park, Alaska. Every summer Ms. Tamara hires many part-time employees from all over the United States. Most of these are college students seeking summer employment. Perhaps the biggest activity for Ms. Tamara's staff is that of "making up" the rooms each day. The lodge has 385 rooms, and from long experience Ms. Tamara has determined that by 3:30 P.M. each day the average number of rooms not made up is $\mu = 19.3$ with standard deviation $\sigma = 4.7$. Even though the lodge has a policy that guest rooms be made up by 3:30 P.M., Ms. Tamara knows that there will always be a few rooms not made up by this time because there is a high personnel turnover and corresponding reassignment of staff to new jobs for which they are in a training period. Every 15 days Ms. Tamara has a general staff meeting. Before the meeting, she examines several control charts for the restaurant, the gift shop, and, of course, housekeeping. For the past 15 days, the housekeeping unit has reported the following number of rooms not ready by 3:30 P.M. (Table 6–1).

Table 6–1 Number of Rooms Not Made Up by 3:30 P.M.

Day	1	2	3	4	5	6	7	8
X = *number of rooms*	11	20	25	23	16	19	8	25
Day		9	10	11	12	13	14	15
X = *number of rooms*		17	20	23	29	18	14	10

Make a control chart for these data.

Before we make a control chart, we need to know a few things about the distribution of rooms that are not made up by 3:30 P.M. Ms. Tamara is aware from long experience that the distribution is symmetrical and bell-shaped. It is approximately normal, with mean $\mu = 19.3$ and standard deviation $\sigma = 4.7$. In addition, this distribution of x values is acceptable to the top administration of the Antlers Lodge.

Solution: A control chart for a variable x is a plot of the observed x values (vertical scale) in time sequence order (the horizontal scale represents time). Place horizontal lines at

The mean $\mu = 19.3$
The control limits $\mu \pm 2\sigma = 19.3 \pm 2(4.7)$ or 9.90 and 28.70
The control limits $\mu \pm 3\sigma = 19.3 \pm 3(4.7)$ or 5.20 and 33.40

Then plot the data from Table 6–1. (See Figure 6–11.)

Figure 6–11 Number of Rooms Not Made Up by 3:30 P.M.

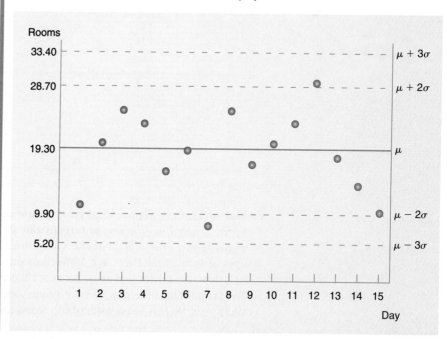

Once we have made a control chart, the main question is the following: As time goes on, is the x variable continuing in this same distribution, or is the distribution of x values changing? If the x distribution is continuing more or less the same, we say it is in *statistical control*. If it is not, we say it is *out of control*.

There are many popular methods used to set off a warning signal that a process is out of control. Remember, a random variable x is said to be *out of control* if successive time measurements of x indicate that it is no longer following the target probability distribution. We will assume that the target distribution is (approximately) normal and has (user-set) target values for μ and σ.

Three of the most popular warning signals are described next:

1. ***Out-of-Control Signal I:*** *One point falls beyond the* 3σ *level.* What is the probability signal I will be a false alarm? By the empirical rule, the probability that a point lies within 3σ of the mean is 0.997. The probability that signal I will give a false alarm is $1 - 0.997 = 0.003$. Remember, a false alarm means that the x distribution is really on the target distribution, and we simply have a very rare (probability of 0.003) event. (See Figure 6–12.)

Figure 6–12 Out-of-Control Signal I: One Point Beyond the 3σ Level

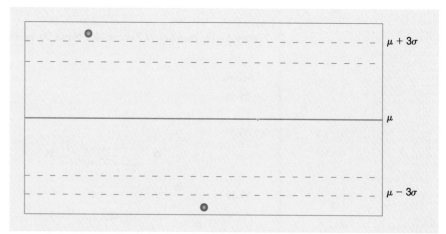

2. ***Out-of-Control Signal II:*** *A run of nine consecutive points on one side of the center line (the line at target value* μ*).* What is the probability that signal II is a false alarm? If the x distribution and the target distribution are the same, then there is a 50% chance that any x values will lie above or below the center line at μ. Because the samples are (time) independent, the probability of a run of nine points on one side of the center line is $(0.5)^9 = 0.002$. If we consider both sides, this probability becomes 0.004.

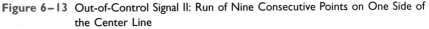

Figure 6–13 Out-of-Control Signal II: Run of Nine Consecutive Points on One Side of
the Center Line

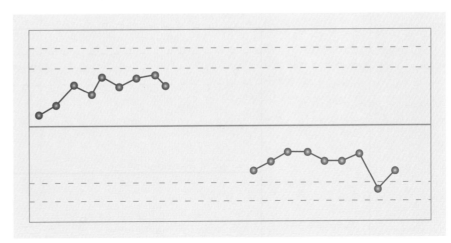

Therefore, the probability that signal II is a false alarm is approximately
0.004. (See Figure 6–13.)

3. ***Out-of-Control Signal III:*** *At least two of three consecutive points lie
   beyond the 2σ level on the same side of the center line.* What is the probability that signal III will produce a false alarm? By the empirical rule, the
   probability that an x value will lie above the 2σ level is about 0.025. If
   we use the binomial probability distribution (with success being the point
   is above 2σ), then the probability of two or more successes out of three
   trials is

$$\frac{3!}{2!1!}(0.025)^2(0.975) + \frac{3!}{3!0!}(0.025)^3 \approx 0.002$$

If we take into account *both* above or below the center line, it follows
that the probability that signal III is a false alarm is about 0.004. (See
Figure 6–14.)

Remember, a control chart is only a warning device, and it is possible to
get a false alarm. A false alarm happens when one (or more) of the out-of-
control signals occurs but the x distribution is really on the target or assigned
distribution. In this case, we simply have a rare event (probability of 0.003 or
0.004). In practice, whenever a control chart indicates that a process is out of
control, it is usually a good precaution to examine what is going on. If the
process is out of control, corrective steps can be taken before things get a lot
worse. Since false alarms are rare, they are a small price to pay if we can avert
what might become real trouble.

Section 6.1 Problems

1. Which, if any, of the curves in Figure 6–18 look(s) like a normal curve? If a curve is not a normal curve, tell why.

Figure 6–18

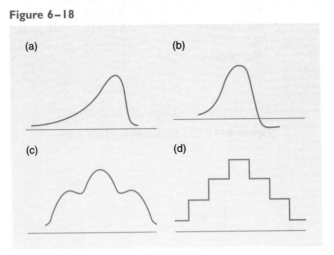

2. Look at the normal curve in Figure 6–19, and find μ, $\mu + \sigma$, and σ.

Figure 6–19

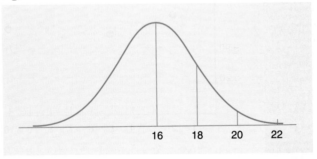

3. Look at the two normal curves in Figures 6–20 and 6–21. Which has the larger standard deviation? What is the mean of the curve in Figure 6–20? What is the mean of the curve in Figure 6–21?

Figure 6–20

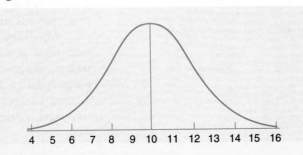

Figure 6–21

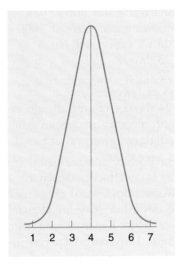

4. Sketch a normal curve
   (a) With mean 15 and standard deviation 2.
   (b) With mean 15 and standard deviation 3.
   (c) With mean 12 and standard deviation 2.
   (d) With mean 12 and standard deviation 3.
   (e) Consider two normal curves. If the first one has a larger mean than the second one, must it have a larger standard deviation than the second one as well?

5. What percentage of the area under the normal curve lies
   (a) To the left of μ?
   (b) Between $\mu - \sigma$ and $\mu + \sigma$?
   (c) Between $\mu - 3\sigma$ and $\mu + 3\sigma$?

6. What percentage of the area under a normal curve lies
   (a) To the right of μ?
   (b) Between $\mu - 2\sigma$ and $\mu + 2\sigma$?
   (c) To the right of $\mu + 3\sigma$?

7. Assuming that the heights of college women are normally distributed, with mean 65 in. and standard deviation 2.5 in. (based on information from *Statistical Abstract of the United States*, 112th edition), answer the following questions. (*Hint:* Use Problem 6 and Figure 6–7.)
   (a) What percentage of women are taller than 65 in.?
   (b) What percentage of women are shorter than 65 in.?
   (c) What percentage of women are between 62.5 in. and 67.5 in.?
   (d) What percentage of women are between 60 in. and 70 in.?

If the number of tickets goes out of control below the mean, the patrol takes some of its forces off of I-70 and puts them in other places where they are very much needed.

Week	1	2	3	4	5	6	7	8	9
No. of tickets	45	33	30	25	32	34	35	30	33

Week	10	11	12	13	14	15	16	17	18
No. of tickets	36	32	30	34	23	25	22	20	15

Week	19	20
No. of tickets	16	23

Make a control chart, and plot the preceding data on the control chart. Identify all out-of-control signals (high or low) that you find in the control chart by type (I, II, or III).

Section 6.2 Standard Units and the Standard Normal Distribution

Normal distributions vary from one another in two main ways: the mean μ may be located anywhere on the x axis, and the bell shape may be more or less spread according to the size of the standard deviation σ. The differences among the normal distributions cause difficulties when we try to compute the area under the curve in a specified interval and, hence, the probability that a measurement will fall in that interval.

It would be a futile task to try to set up a table of areas under the normal curve for each different μ and σ combination. We need a way to standardize the distributions so that we can use *one* table of areas for *all* normal distributions. We achieve this standardization by considering how many standard deviations a measurement lies from the mean. In this way we can compare a value in one normal distribution with a value in another different normal distribution. The next situation shows how this is done.

Suppose that Tina and Jack are in two different sections of the same course. Each section is quite large, and the scores on the midterm exams of each section follow a normal distribution. In Tina's section, the average (mean) was 64 and her score was 74. In Jack's section, the mean was 72 and his score was 82. Both Tina and Jack were pleased that their scores were each 10 points above the average of each respective section. However, the fact that each was 10 points above average does not really tell us how each did *with respect to the other students in the section*. In Figure 6–22 we see the normal distribution of grades for each section.

Tina's 74 was higher than most of the other scores in her section, while Jack's 82 is only an upper middle score in his section. Tina's score is far better with respect to her class than Jack's score with respect to his class.

Standard Score

The preceding situation demonstrates that it is not sufficient to know the difference between a measurement (x value) and the mean of a distribution.

Figure 6–22 Distributions of Midterm Scores

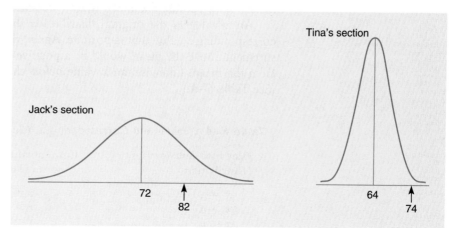

We need also to consider the spread of the curve, or the standard deviation. What we really want to know is the number of standard deviations between a measurement and the mean. This "distance" takes both μ and σ into account.

There is a simple formula that we can use to compute the number z of standard deviations between a measurement x and the mean μ of a normal distribution with standard deviation σ:

$$\begin{pmatrix} \text{Number of standard deviations} \\ \text{between the measurement and} \\ \text{the mean} \end{pmatrix} = \begin{pmatrix} \dfrac{\text{difference between the}}{\text{measurement and the mean}} \\ \dfrac{}{\text{standard deviation}} \end{pmatrix}$$

Written in symbols, this formula is

$$z = \frac{x - \mu}{\sigma}$$

Definition: The *z value* or *z score* tells us the number of standard deviations the original measurement is from the mean. The z value is in *standard units*.

The mean is a special value of a distribution. Let's see what happens when we convert $x = \mu$ to a z value:

$$z = \frac{x - \mu}{\sigma}$$

$$= \frac{\mu - \mu}{\sigma} \qquad \text{for } x = \mu$$

$$= 0$$

The mean of the original distribution is always zero, in standard units. This makes sense because the mean is zero standard variations from itself.

An x value in the original distribution that is *above* the mean μ has a corresponding z value that is *positive*. Again, this makes sense because a measurement above the mean would be a positive number of standard deviations from the mean. Likewise, an x value *below* the mean has a *negative* z value. (See Table 6–4.)

Table 6–4 x Values and Corresponding z Values

x Value in Original Distribution	Corresponding z Value or Standard Unit
$x = \mu$	$z = 0$
$x > \mu$	$z > 0$
$x < \mu$	$z < 0$

Note:

Unless otherwise stated, in the remainder of the book we will take the word *average* to be the arithmetic mean $\bar{x}$.

Example 4

A pizza parlor franchise specifies that the average (mean) amount of cheese on a large pizza should be 8 oz and the standard deviation only 0.5 oz. An inspector picks out a large pizza at random in one of the pizza parlors and finds that it is made with 6.9 oz of cheese. Assume that the amount of cheese on a pizza follows a normal distribution. If the amount of cheese is more than *three* standard deviations below the mean, the parlor will be in danger of losing its franchise. (Remember, in a normal distribution we are unlikely to find measurements more than three standard deviations from the mean, since 99.7% of all measurements fall within three standard deviations of the mean.)

How many standard deviations from the mean is 6.9? Is the pizza parlor in danger of losing its franchise?

Solution: Since we want to know the number of standard deviations from the mean, we want to convert 6.9 to standard z units.

$$z = \frac{x - \mu}{\sigma}$$

$$= \frac{6.9 - 8}{0.5}$$

$$= -2.20$$

Therefore, the amount of cheese on the selected pizza is only 2.20 standard deviations from the mean. Note that the fact that z is negative indicates that the amount of cheese was 2.20 standard deviations *below* the mean. The parlor will not lose its franchise based on this sample.

GUIDED EXERCISE 7

A student has computed that it takes an average (mean) of 17 minutes with a standard deviation of 3 minutes to drive from home, park the car, and walk to an early morning class.

(a) One day it took the student 21 minutes to get to class. How many standard deviations from the average is that? Is the z value positive or negative? Explain why it should be either positive or negative?

(a) The number of standard deviations from the mean is given by the z value:

$$z = \frac{x - \mu}{\sigma} = \frac{21 - 17}{3} = 1.33$$

The z value is positive. We would expect a positive z value, since 21 minutes is *more* than the mean of 17.

(b) Another day it took only 12 minutes for the student to get to class. What is this measurement in standard units? Is the z value positive or negative? Why should it be positive or negative?

(b) The measurement in standard units is

$$z = \frac{x - \mu}{\sigma} = \frac{12 - 17}{3} = -1.67$$

Here the z value is negative, as we should expect, because 12 minutes is less than the mean of 17 minutes.

(c) Another day it took 17 minutes for the student to go from home to class. What is the z value? Why should you expect this answer?

(c) In this case the value is

$$z = \frac{x - \mu}{\sigma} = \frac{17 - 17}{3} = 0.00$$

We expect this result because 17 minutes is the mean, and the z value of the mean is always zero.

Raw Score

We have seen how to convert from x measurements to standard units z. We can easily reverse the process if we know μ and σ for the original distribution. For when we solve

$$z = \frac{x - \mu}{\sigma}$$

for x, we get

$$x = z\sigma + \mu$$

Example 5 In Example 4 we talked about the amount of cheese required by a franchise for a large pizza. Again, the mean amount of cheese required is 8 oz with a standard deviation of 0.5 oz. The parlor can lose its franchise if the amount of cheese on their large pizza is more than three standard deviations below the mean. What is the minimum amount of cheese that can be placed on a large pizza according to the franchise?

Solution: Here we need to convert $z = -3$ to information about x oz of cheese. We use the formula

$$x = z\sigma + \mu$$
$$= -3(0.5) + 8$$
$$= 6.5 \text{ oz}$$

The franchise will not approve a large pizza with less than 6.5 oz of cheese.

In many testing situations we hear the terms *raw score* and *z score*. The raw score is just the score in the original measuring units, and the z score is the score in standard units. Guided Exercise 8 illustrates these different units.

GUIDED EXERCISE 8

Marulla's z score on a college entrance exam is 1.3. If the raw scores have a mean of 480 and a standard deviation of 70 points, what is her raw score?

Here we are given z, σ, and μ. We need to find the raw score x corresponding to the z score 1.3.

$$x = z\sigma + \mu$$
$$= 1.3(70) + 480$$
$$= 571$$

Example 6

A tire manufacturer claims that the average life of its tires is 18,000 miles. The tire life is normally distributed with a standard deviation of 1400 miles. The company will refund two-thirds of the original purchase price if a tire wears out at a mileage two or more standard deviations below the mean. (The company should not have to give too many refunds, since 95.4% of the tires should have a life within $\pm 2\sigma$ of μ.) Translate the condition for a two-thirds cost refund into actual miles on the tire.

Solution: Here we are interested in all z values less than or equal to -2, so $z \leq -2$. We need to translate this condition into a statement about x. The upper bound for z is -2 (see Figure 6–23).

Figure 6–23

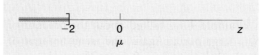

Figure 6–24

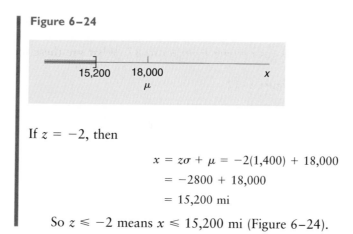

If $z = -2$, then

$$x = z\sigma + \mu = -2(1,400) + 18,000$$
$$= -2800 + 18,000$$
$$= 15,200 \text{ mi}$$

So $z \leq -2$ means $x \leq 15,200$ mi (Figure 6–24).

GUIDED EXERCISE 9

A company called Camp Comfort makes down-filled sleeping bags. The amount of down in an adult sleeping bag has a mean of 32 oz and a standard deviation of 0.9 oz. Quality control specifies that if the down fill in a product is less than or equal to -2.7 standard deviations from the mean, the item must be sold as a second.

(a) Does -2.7 standard deviations less than the mean translate to $z \leq -2.7$?

(a) Yes.

(b) The upper limit is $z = -2.7$. Translate this value into a weight in ounces for down in a sleeping bag.

(b) $x = z\sigma + \mu = -2.7(0.9) + 32$
$= -2.43 + 32 = 29.57$

(c) $z \leq -2.7$ is the same as $x \leq$ _____.

(c) $z \leq -2.7$ is the same as $x \leq 29.57$.

(d) Indicate these values on the number lines in Figure 6–25.

(d) See Figure 6–26.

Figure 6–25

Figure 6–26 Completion of Figure 6–25

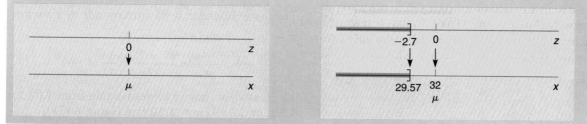

Figure 6–30 The Transformation of a Normal Distribution to the Standard Normal Distribution

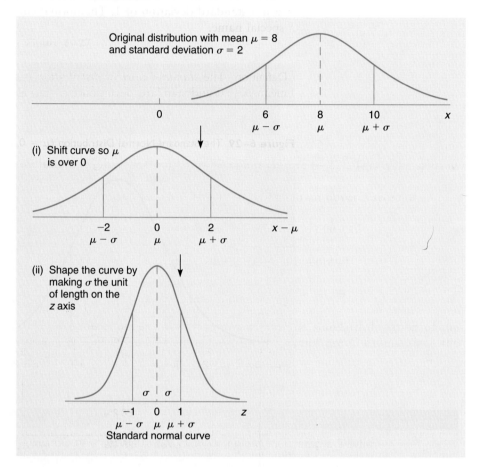

(i) Shift curve so μ is over 0

(ii) Shape the curve by making σ the unit of length on the z axis

Standard normal curve

The resulting standard distribution will always have mean $\mu = 0$ and standard deviation $\sigma = 1$.

Section 6.2 Problems

In these problems assume that all the distributions are *normal*. In all problems in Chapter 6, *average* is always taken to be the arithmetic mean, $\bar{x}$.

1. The college Physical Education Department offered an Advanced First Aid course last semester. The scores on the comprehensive final exam were normally distributed, and the z scores for some of the students are shown below:

Robert, 1.10   Jan, 1.70   Susan, -2.00
Joel, 0.00   John, -0.80 Linda, 1.60

(a) Which of these students scored above the mean?

(b) Which of these students scored on the mean?

(c) Which of these students scored below the mean?

(d) If the mean score was $\mu = 150$ with standard deviation $\sigma = 20$, what was the final exam score for each student? $x = z\sigma + \mu$

2. Scores on teacher evaluations at Freemont State College follow a normal distribution. The standardized scores for members of the Mathematics Department are:

Dr. Lee, 0.30   Dr. Willis, 0.00

Dr. Smith, −1.20   Mr. Lang, 2.30

Ms. Anderson, −0.75   Dr. Barnes, 1.85

(a) Which professors scored above the mean?

(b) Which scored below the mean?

(c) Which scored on the mean?

(d) If the mean score was $\mu = 73$ and the standard deviation was $\sigma = 10$, what was the raw score for each professor?

3. You Drive Car Rental Company keeps careful records of mileage and maintenance for each of its cars. For the fleet of 1-year-old cars, the mileages on the various cars followed a normal distribution with mean 12,750 miles and standard deviation 1540 miles. Find standardized z values for the following mileages of 1-year-old rental cars.

(a) 13,900   (c) 11,475   (e) 14,000

(b) 12,750   (d) 9780   (f) 10,500

4. Air Connect is a commuter airline that serves the East Coast. The time interval from the time the planes begin to load passengers to the time of takeoff has been found to be normally distributed with mean 25 minutes and standard deviation 6 minutes. Find the standardized z values for the following passenger loading times in minutes:

(a) 21   (c) 25   (e) 10

(b) 12   (d) 38   (f) 42

5. Data collected over a period of years shows that the average daily temperature in Honolulu is $\mu = 73°F$ with standard deviation $\sigma = 5°F$ (U.S. Department of Commerce: *Environmental Data Service*). Convert each of the following intervals in °F to an interval of z values.

(a) $53°F < x < 93°F$

(b) $x < 65°F$

(c) $78°F < x$

Convert each of the following intervals of z values to intervals in °F.

(d) $1.75 < z$

(e) $z < -1.90$

(f) $-1.80 < z < 1.65$

6. Fawns between 1 and 5 months old in Mesa Verde National Park have a body weight that is approximately normally distributed with mean $\mu = 27.2$ kilograms and standard deviation $\sigma = 4.3$ kilograms (based on

information from *The Mule Deer of Mesa Verde National Park*, by G. W. Mierau and J. L. Schmidt, Mesa Verde Museum Association, 1981). Let x be the weight of a fawn in kilograms. Convert each of the following x intervals to z intervals.

(a) $x < 30$

(b) $19 < x$

(c) $32 < x < 35$

Convert each of the following z intervals to x intervals.

(d) $-2.17 < z$

(e) $z < 1.28$

(f) $-1.99 < z < 1.44$

(g) If a fawn weighs 14 kilograms, would you say it is an unusually small animal? Explain using z values and Figure 6–29.

(h) If a fawn is unusually large, would you say that the z value for the weight of the fawn will be close to 0, −2 or 3? Explain.

7. The fall deer population in Mesa Verde National Park is approximately normally distributed with mean 4400 deer and standard deviation 620 deer (see the reference in Problem 6). Let x be the random variable that represents the size of the deer population in Mesa Verde National Park in the fall of a given year. Convert each of the following x intervals to z intervals.

(a) $3300 < x$

(b) $x < 5400$

(c) $3500 < x < 5300$

Convert each of the following z intervals to x intervals.

(d) $-1.12 < z < 2.43$

(e) $z < 1.96$

(f) $2.58 < z$

(g) If the fall deer population were 2800 deer, would that be considered an unusually low number? If the fall population were 6300, would that be considered an unusually high population? Explain using z values and Figure 6–29.

8. Intelligence quotient tests scores (IQ scores) have a population mean $\mu = 100$ and population standard deviation $\sigma = 15$ (*World Book Encyclopedia*). Convert each of the following given standard z intervals to $x =$ IQ score intervals.

(a) $0 \leq z \leq 1$

(b) $0 \leq z \leq 0.42$

(c) $-2.04 \leq z \leq 2.07$

(d) $-1.96 \leq z$

(e) $z \leq 2.58$

(f) $z \geq 0.94$

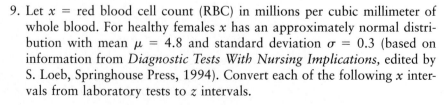

9. Let $x =$ red blood cell count (RBC) in millions per cubic millimeter of whole blood. For healthy females x has an approximately normal distribution with mean $\mu = 4.8$ and standard deviation $\sigma = 0.3$ (based on information from *Diagnostic Tests With Nursing Implications*, edited by S. Loeb, Springhouse Press, 1994). Convert each of the following x intervals from laboratory tests to z intervals.

(a) $4.5 < x$

(b) $x < 4.2$

(c) $4.0 < x < 5.5$

Convert each of the following z intervals to x intervals.

(d) $z < -1.44$

(e) $1.28 < z$

(f) $-2.25 < z < -1.00$

(g) If a female had a red blood cell count of 5.9 or higher, would that be considered unusually high? Explain using z values and Figure 6-29.

10. Let x = white cell count (WBC) per cubic millimeter of whole blood. Then x has a distribution that is approximately normal with mean $\mu = 7500$ and standard deviation $\sigma = 1750$ (see reference in Problem 9). Convert each of the following x intervals to z intervals.

(a) $9000 < x$

(b) $x < 6000$

(c) $3500 < x < 4500$

Convert each of the following z intervals to x intervals.

(d) $z < 1.15$

(e) $2.19 < z$

(f) $0.25 < z < 1.25$

(g) If someone had a white blood cell count of 2500, would that be considered unusually high or low? Explain using z values and Figure 6-29.

11. Let x = hemoglobin count (HC) in grams per 100 millimeters of whole blood. Then x has a distribution that is approximately normal with mean $\mu = 14$ and standard deviation $\sigma = 1$ (see reference in Problem 9). Suppose that you are a nurse or a doctor who has just received a laboratory report analyzing a female patient's blood. Let RBC be the red blood cell count, WBC be white blood cell count, and HC be hemoglobin concentration (for means and standard deviation of RBC and WBC, see Problems 9 and 10). For each of the following patients, convert the laboratory results to z values. Which of the lab reports is unusually high? unusually low? about normal? See Figure 6-29.

(a) Patient A: RBC = 4.75, WBC = 1000, HC = 16

(b) Patient B: RBC = 3.9, WBC = 7050, HC = 12.5

(c) Patient C: RBC = 4.9, WBC = 6920, HC = 17.4

(d) Patient D: RBC = 5.9, WBC = 12,000, HC = 15.8

12. Tree ring dates were used extensively in archaeological studies at Burnt Mesa Pueblo (*Bandelier Archaeological Excavation Project: Summer 1989 Excavations at Burnt Mesa Pueblo*, edited by Kohler, Washington State University Department of Anthropology, 1990). At one site on the mesa, tree ring dates (for many samples) gave a mean date μ_1 = year 1272 with standard deviation $\sigma_1 = 35$ years. At a second, removed site, the tree ring dates gave a mean of μ_2 = year 1122 with standard deviation $\sigma_2 = 40$ years. Assume that both sites had dates that were approximately normally

distributed. In the first area an object was found and dated as $x_1 =$ year 1250. In the second area another object was found and dated as $x_2 =$ year 1234.

(a) Convert both x_1 and x_2 to z values, and locate both these values under the standard normal curve of Figure 6–29.

(b) Which of these two items is the more unusual as an archaeological find in its location?

13. The general manager of a computer software sales company is reviewing the sales record of two sales representatives, Niko and Walter. In Niko's district the long-term mean sales have been $27,520 each month with standard deviation $2450. In Walter's district the long-term mean sales have been $24,170 each month with standard deviation $2670. In both districts the distribution of monthly sales is approximately normal.

 Recently, Niko's sales have been $31,600 each month in his district and Walter's sales have been $30,950 each month in his district.

(a) Walter sold less than Niko in recent months. Does this mean that Walter is not as good a sales representative? Explain.

(b) Convert the recent sales records for both Niko and Walter to standard z values. Locate these z values under a standard normal curve and compare them.

(c) If both Niko and Walter were up for promotion and only one could be promoted, which would you choose? Explain.

14. Professors Adams and Riley are both teaching different sections of the same course, Political Science 201. Harold is in Professor Adams's class, and Mary is in Professor Riley's class. On the midterm exam Harold got 193 points, while Mary got 182 points. The scores of both exams were normally distributed, with Professor Adams's exam having a mean $\mu_1 = 180$ and standard deviation $\sigma_1 = 20$ points. For Professor Riley's exam, the mean was $\mu_2 = 165$ with standard deviation $\sigma_2 = 10$ points. If both professors grade on a normal curve, who did better, Harold or Mary? Explain your answer.

Section 6.3   Areas Under the Standard Normal Curve

In Section 6.2 we saw how we can convert *any* normal distribution to the *standard* normal distribution. We can change any x value to a z value and back again. But what is the advantage of all this work? The advantage is that there are extensive tables that show the area under the standard normal curve for almost any interval along the z axis. The areas are important because they are equal to the *probability* that the measurement of an item selected at random falls in this interval. Thus the *standard* normal distribution can be a tremendously helpful tool.

 For instance, Sunshine Stereo guarantees their cassette decks for a period of 2 years. The company statistician has computed that the cassette deck life is normally distributed with mean 2.3 years and standard deviation 0.4 years. What is the probability that a cassette deck will stop working during the guarantee period?

To answer questions of this type, we convert the given normal distribution to the standard normal distribution. Then we use a table to find the area over the interval in question and, hence, the probability an item selected at random will fall in that interval. Before we can carry out this plan, though, we must practice using Table 6 of Appendix II to find areas under the standard normal curve. Figure 6–31 illustrates areas which correspond to various interval descriptions.

In Section 6.1 we observed that for a normal distribution, about 68.2% of the data falls within one standard deviation of the mean, about 95.4% falls within two standard deviations, and about 99.7% falls within three standard deviations of the mean. For the standard normal curve, the standard deviation equals 1, and the mean is 0. The interval within one standard deviation of the mean is just the interval from -1 to 1. Figure 6–32 shows the standard normal curve and the areas within one, two, and three standard deviations of the mean.

Figure 6–32 shows us how to obtain certain areas under a standard normal curve. How do we find other areas under the standard normal curve? The most convenient way is to use a table. Because of the symmetry of the normal curve, it is possible to obtain all the areas we will need if we have only a table of areas from $z = 0$ to $z =$ some positive number. The following sequence of examples will show how this can be done using Table 6 of Appendix II.

Figure 6–31 Areas Under a Standard Normal Probability Curve

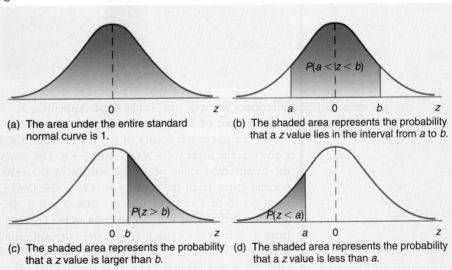

(a) The area under the entire standard normal curve is 1.

(b) The shaded area represents the probability that a z value lies in the interval from a to b. $P(a < z < b)$

(c) The shaded area represents the probability that a z value is larger than b. $P(z > b)$

(d) The shaded area represents the probability that a z value is less than a. $P(z < a)$

(c) Estimate a range of snow pack measurements centered about the mean in which about 95% of the years will fall.

16. The Customer Service Center in a large New York department store has determined that the amount of time spent with a customer about a complaint is normally distributed with mean 9.3 minutes and standard deviation 2.5 minutes. What is the probability that for a randomly chosen customer with a complaint the amount of time spent resolving the complaint will be

(a) Less than 10 minutes?
(b) More than 5 minutes?
(c) Between 8 and 15 minutes?

17. The Fight For Life emergency helicopter service is available for medical emergencies occurring from 15 to 90 miles from the hospital. Emergencies that occur closer to the hospital can be handled effectively by ambulance service. A long-term study of the service shows that the response time from receipt of the dispatch call to arrival at the scene of the emergency is normally distributed with mean 42 minutes and standard deviation 8 minutes. For a randomly received call, what is the probability that the response time will be

(a) Between 30 and 45 minutes?
(b) Less than 30 minutes?
(c) More than 60 minutes?

18. The life of a Sunshine electric coffeepot is normally distributed with mean 4 years and standard deviation 6 months. The manufacturer will replace, free of charge, any Sunshine coffeepot that breaks down under guarantee. If the manufacturer does not want to replace more than 3% of the coffeepots, for how long should the guarantee be made (round to the nearest month)?

DATA HIGHLIGHTS

1. Examine Figure 6–57, "Sports Shoes: Men Spend More" (USA Today, May 4, 1992). The average amount spent by women on sports shoes was $29.44 with (an estimated) standard deviation of $4.25. We assume that the distribution of prices paid is approximately normal.

(a) Use the empirical rule to find a range prices in which 68% of the shoe sales will fall. Also find a 95% and 99.7% price range for sales of women's shoes.
(b) What is the probability that a woman who buys sports shoes will spend less than $20? more than $40? between $20 and $40.
(c) Suppose a sales ad claims that 90% of all women's sports shoes cost more than a certain model. If this is the case, estimate how much that model should cost.

Figure 6–57 Sports Shoes: Men Spend More

By Web Bryant, USA TODAY

Source: Copyright 1992, USA TODAY. Reprinted with permission.

The average amount spent by men on sports shoes was $44.16 with (an estimated) standard deviation of $6.50. Assume that the distribution of prices paid is approximately normal.

(d) Use the empirical rule to find a 68% range of prices paid by men for sports shoes.

(e) What is the probability that a man who buys sports shoes will spend less than $30? more than $60? between $30 and $60?

(f) Suppose that a sales ad claims that 75% of all men's sports shoes cost more than a certain model shoe. Estimate the cost of that model shoe.

How does your own experience relate to these data? Go to a store that sells sport shoes. How do prices compare between the men's model of a shoe and the comparable model for women? Look at the price range for men's sport shoes and the price range for women's sports shoes. Are your observations consistent with the data shown in Figure 6–57? What do you suppose the definition of a sports shoe is? Do you think the shoe should be specifically designed for use in a sports activity? Do you think any canvas or nylon shoe should be categorized as a sports shoe? How might the definition of sport shoe affect the data? Notice that the data in Figure 6–57 show that more pairs of women's sport shoes are sold than men's. List some reasons you think might account for this difference. Would some of these reasons also relate to the lower average price per pair for women's shoes?

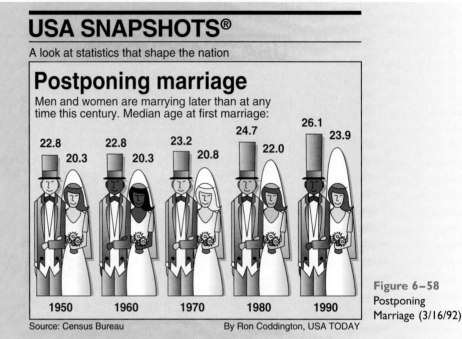

USA SNAPSHOTS®

A look at statistics that shape the nation

Postponing marriage

Men and women are marrying later than at any time this century. Median age at first marriage:

22.8 20.3   22.8 20.3   23.2 20.8   24.7 22.0   26.1 23.9

1950   1960   1970   1980   1990

Source: Census Bureau   By Ron Coddington, USA TODAY

Figure 6–58
Postponing
Marriage (3/16/92)

Source: Copyright 1992, USA TODAY. Reprinted with permission.

2. Examine Figure 6-58 "Postponing Marriage" (*USA Today*, May 16, 1992). Government documents and the Census Bureau show that the age at (first) marriage for U.S. citizens is approximately normally distributed for both men and women. For men the average age is about 26 years, and for women the average is about 24 years. For both sexes the standard deviation is about 2.5 years.

(a) If the distribution is symmetrical and mound-shaped (such as the normal distribution), why would you expect the median, mean, and mode to be equal?

(b) What is the probability that a man is over age 30 at the time of his (first) marriage? What is the probability that he is under age 20? What is the probability that he is between 20 and 30?

(c) What is the probability that a woman is over age 28 at the time of her (first) marriage? What is the probability that she is under age 18? What is the probability that she is between 18 and 28?

(d) At what age are only 10% of eligible bachelors (who have never been married before) left? At what age are only 5% left?

(e) At what age are only 10% of eligible women (who have never been married before) left? At what age are only 5% left?

3. *Fitness Walking* is a book by Sweetgall, Rippe, and Katch (Perigee Books, published by the Putnam Publishing Group). In this book the authors out-

line the "step test" for men and women. A step 8 inches high is used. A person does 24 complete step-ups in 60 seconds. This activity is carried on for 3 minutes. Then, 30 seconds after stopping, the number of heartbeats for the *next* 30 seconds is recorded. A lower heartbeat count indicates a stronger heart.

For men in the age group 20 to 29, the average heartbeat for the step test is 41.5 with standard deviation approximately 3.5. Assume that the step test results have an approximate normal distribution.

(a) Use the empirical rule to compute heartbeat intervals in which 68% of the men (aged 20 to 29) would fall, in which 95% would fall, and in which 99.7% would fall.

(b) Estimate the percentage of men aged 20 to 29 that have a test result below 36.

(c) Estimate the percentage of men aged 20 to 29 that have a test result higher than 49.

(d) Remember, a smaller count for the step test indicates a stronger heart. What test scores would you expect for that 15% of the population of men (aged 20 to 29) with the strongest hearts? What range of scores would you expect for that 15% with the weakest hearts?

LINKING CONCEPTS

Discuss each of the following topics in class or review the topics on your own. Then write a brief but complete essay in which you summarize the main points. Please include formulas and graphs as appropriate.

1. If you look up the word *normal* in a dictionary, you will find it is synonymous with the words *standard* or *usual*. Consider the very wide and general applications of the normal probability distribution. Comment on why good synonyms for *normal probability distribution* might be the *standard probability distribution* or the *usual probability distribution*. List at least three random variables from everyday life for which you think the normal probability distribution could be applicable.

2. Why are standard z values so important? Is it true that z values have no units of measurement? Why would this be desirable for comparing data sets with *different* units of measurement? How can we assess differences in quality or performance by simply comparing z values under a standard normal curve? Examine the formula to compute standard z values. Notice it involves *both* the mean and standard deviation. Recall that in Chapter 3 we commented that the mean of a data collection was not entirely adequate to describe the data; you need the standard deviation as well. Discuss this topic again in the light of what you now know about normal distributions and standard z values.

3. If you look up the word *empirical* in a dictionary, you find it means relying on experiment and observation rather than on theory. Discuss the empirical rule in this context. The empirical rule certainly applies to the normal distribution, but does it also apply to a wide variety of other distributions that are not *exactly* (theoretically) normal? Discuss the terms mound-shaped and symmetrical. Draw several sketches of distributions that are mound-shaped *and* symmetrical. Draw sketches of distributions that are not mound-shaped *or* not symmetrical. To which distributions will the empirical rule apply?

4. Most companies that manufacture a product have a division of quality control or quality assurance. The purpose of the quality control division is to make reasonably certain that the products manufactured are up to company standards. Write a brief essay in which you describe how the statistics you have learned so far could be applied to an industrial application (such as control charts and the Antlers Lodge example).

Using Technology

The problems in this section may be done using statistical computer software or calculators with statistical functions. Displays and suggestions are given for Minitab (Release 9), the TI-82 graphing calculator, and ComputerStat.

Applications

1. The average earnings of a city government employee in October 1990 are given for a sample of 18 cities in the United States (*Statistical Abstract of the United States, 112 ed.*).

City	Average Earnings for October 1990
New York	2,783
Chicago	3,002
Los Angeles	3,488
Philadelphia	2,843
Houston	2,061
Detroit	2,663
Dallas	1,945
San Diego	3,019
Phoenix	2,876
Baltimore	1,910
San Antonio	2,227
Indianapolis	1,910
San Franciso	3,648
Memphis	2,287
Washington, D.C.	2,930
Milwaukee	2,431
San Jose	3,453
Cleveland	2,521

Source: United States Department of Commerce, Bureau of the Census. *Statistical Abstract of the United States.* 112 ed. Washington: GPO, 1992.

(a) To compare the earnings from one city to another, we look at z values. In following Minitab program, the average earnings are entered into column C1. Then z values are computed for each data entry and are stored in column C2.

```
MTB > NAME C1 = 'SALARY'
MTB > NAME C2 = 'ZVALUE'
MTB > MEAN C1 put into K1
   MEAN    =     2666.5
MTB > STDEV C1 put into K2
   ST.DEV. =      547.60
MTB > LET C2 = (C1 - K1)/K2
MTB > PRINT C1 C2
```

ROW	SALARY	ZVALUE
1	2783.00	0.21272
2	3002.00	0.61264
3	3488.00	1.50067
4	2843.00	0.32229
5	2061.00	−1.10576
6	2663.00	−0.00642
7	1945.00	−1.31760
8	3019.00	0.64369
9	2876.00	0.38255
10	1910.00	−1.38151
11	2227.00	−0.80262
12	1910.00	−1.38151
13	3648.00	1.79234
14	2287.00	−0.69305
15	2930.00	0.48116
16	2431.00	−0.43009
17	3453.00	1.43624
18	2521.00	−0.26573

(b) Look at the z values for each salary. Which are above average? Which are below average?

(c) Which salaries are within one standard deviation of the mean?

2. The standard normal probability distribution is very important in all of statistics. In Table 6 of Appendix II we have listed some standard normal probabilities. What if you wanted a more accurate table (that is, one with more significant

digits displayed), with more entries? How could you use a computer to find probabilities in a standard normal table? The complete answer to this question is quite technical and requires mathematics beyond the scope of this text. However, the basic formulas are very accurate and can be used by anyone. These formulas can be found in the following reference:

> Abramowitz and Stegun, *Handbook of Mathematical Functions*. National Bureau of Standards, 1968.

We suggest that interested readers consult this reference.

(a) Determine whether your software or calculator produces areas under the standard normal curve, and then generate a brief table for z values -3.5, -3, -2.5, 2, -1.5, -1, -0.5, 0, 0.5, 1, 1.5, 2, 2.5, 3, 3.5.

The MINITAB program shown below produces such a table. Notice that the table is organized differently from Table 6 in Appendix II because the areas are those to the *left* of a specified z value (see the accompanying figure).

(b) Look at the entries in the Minitab-generated table of areas under the standard normal distribution. Use Table 6 of Appendix II and the techniques shown in this chapter to find the areas to the left of $z = 1.50$, $z = -0.50$, $z = -2.50$, and $z = -3.00$. Compare these results to the results generated by Minitab.

```
MTB >  SET C1
DATA> -3.5:3.5/.5
DATA> END
MTB > NAME C1 'Z'
MTB > NAME C2 'AREA<Z'
MTB > CDF C1 C2;
SUBC> NORMAL MU 0 SIGMA 1.
MTB > PRINT C1 C2
```

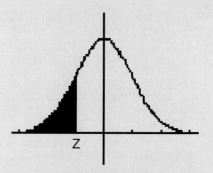

ROW	Z	AREA<Z
1	-3.5	0.000233
2	-3.0	0.001350
3	-2.5	0.006210
4	-2.0	0.022750
5	-1.5	0.066807
6	-1.0	0.158655
7	-0.5	0.308538
8	0.0	0.500000
9	0.5	0.691462
10	1.0	0.841345
11	1.5	0.933193
12	2.0	0.977250
13	2.5	0.993790
14	3.0	0.998650
15	3.5	0.999767

Computer and Calculator Displays

The following displays show you some examples of features relating to the normal distribution which are available through computer software packages and graphing calculators.

TI-82 Display

The formula for the standard normal probability density function is

$$y = \frac{1}{\sqrt{2\pi}}\, e^{\frac{-z^2}{2}}$$

This formula can be entered into the TI-82 calculator to produce a graph of the standard normal distribution. The following windows show some of the steps used to graph the standard normal distribution.

I. Enter the formula

II. Set *x* and *y* values

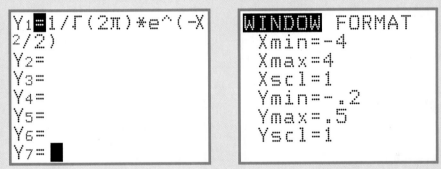

III. Graph

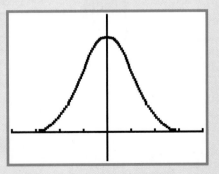

TI-82 Display

Control Chart for Data of Example 2
You can create a control chart on the TI-82 by using the following steps:

1. Enter the observation number in list L1 and the observation itself in L2.
2. Under STAT PLOT, select scatter plot.
3. Using the Y= key, enter Y1 = value of μ, Y2 = value of $\mu + 2\sigma$, Y3 = value of $\mu - 2\sigma$, Y4 = value of $\mu + 3\sigma$, Y5 = value of $\mu - 3\sigma$.
4. Set WINDOW to accommodate the data.
5. Press GRAPH.

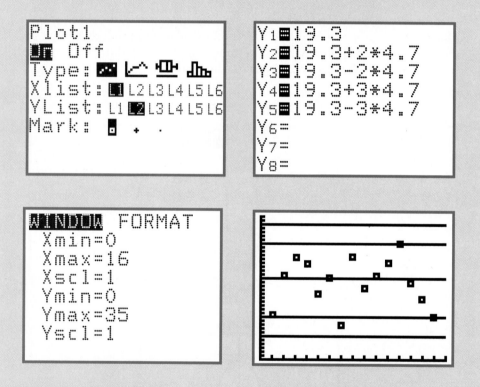

Minitab Display:
Graph of Normal Probability Distribution

```
MTB > set C1
DATA> -3:3/.01
DATA> end
MTB > pdf c1 c2;
SUBC> normal mu = 0 sigma = 0.5.
MTB > Plot C2*C1;
SUBC> Connect.
SubC> Title "Normal Curve, Mu = 0, Sigma = 0.5".
```

Normal Curve, Mu = 0, Sigma = 0.5

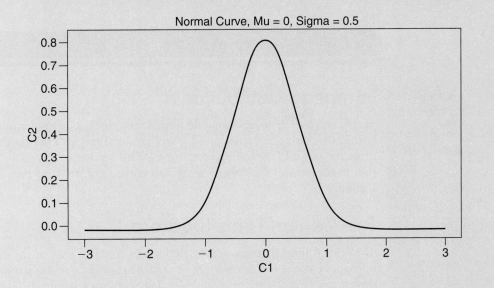

Minitab Display:
Control Chart Data of Example 2

```
MTB > set c1
DATA> 11 20 25 23 16 19 8 25
DATA> 17 20 23 29 18 14 10
DATA> end
MTB > ichart c1;
SUBC> mu 19.3;
SUBC> sigma 4.7;
SUBC> title 'Number of Rooms'.
```

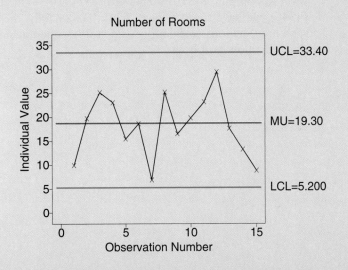

Number of Rooms

CHAPTER OVERVIEW

Section 7.1 | Sampling Distributions

In this section we review some important terminology. Populations, samples, parameters, sample statistic, and sampling distributions are important concepts for our understanding of statistics. This section serves as an introduction to the central limit theorem, which is the main topic of the next section.

Section 7.2 | The Central Limit Theorem

The central limit theorem and related topics contain some of the most important applications of statistics we have seen so far in our study. Not only are these topics interesting in themselves, but much of Chapter 8, "Estimation," and Chapter 9, "Hypothesis Testing" (as well as later material), relies heavily on the central limit theorem. Study this section thoroughly; it is indeed *central* to much of statistics.

Section 7.3 | Normal Approximation to the Binomial Distribution

The binomial distribution of Chapter 5 has many practical applications in everyday life. However, if the number of trials n is large, and if we must compute the probability of r successes for a large number of values of r, then the calculations can be very tedious. For example, if $n = 500$ and we want to compute $P(310 \leq r \leq 340) = P(310) + P(311) + P(312) + \cdots + P(340)$, we have to do a lot of work. Fortunately, there is a way to avoid such long, tedious calculations and still get good accurate results. This section will show you how.

CHAPTER SEVEN

Aldous Huxley
(1894–1963)

This British novelist and critic wrote about the theme of the human being confronted by the modern world.

Introduction to Sampling Distributions

No one *wants* to learn by mistakes, but we cannot learn enough from success to go beyond the state of the art. . . . Such is the nature not only of science and engineering, but of all human endeavors.

Henry Petroski

Experience isn't what happens to you. It's what you make out of what happens to you.

Aldous Huxley

Henry Petroski is a professor of engineering at Duke University, and Aldous Huxley is a well-known modern writer. Both seem to imply that experience, mistakes, information, and life itself are closely related. Life and uncertainty appear to be inseparable. Only those who are no longer living can escape chance happenings. Mistakes are bound to occur. However, not all mistakes are bad. The discovery of penicillin was a "mistake" when mold (penicillin) was accidentally introduced into a bacteria culture by Alexander Fleming in 1928.

Most of the really important decisions in life will involve incomplete information. In one lifetime we simply cannot experience *everything*. Nor should we even want to! This is one reason why *experience by way of sampling* is so important. Statistics can help you have the experiences and yet maintain some control over mistakes. Remember, it is what you make out of experience (sample data) that is of real value.

In this chapter we will study how information from samples relates to information about populations. We cannot be certain that the information from a sample reflects corresponding information about the entire population, but we can describe likely differences. Study this chapter and the following material carefully. We believe that your effort will be rewarded by helping you appreciate the joy and wonder of living in an uncertain universe.

401

Focus Problem ▶ Impulse Buying

The Food Marketing Institute, Progressive Grocer, New Products News, and Point of Purchaser Advertising Institute are organizations that analyze supermarket sales. One of the interesting discoveries was that the average amount of impulse buying in a grocery store was very time-dependent. As reported in the *Denver Post* (September 10, 1989), "when you dilly dally in a store for 10 unplanned minutes, you can kiss nearly $20 good bye." For this reason, it is in the best interest of the supermarket to keep you in the store *longer*. In the *Post* article, it was pointed out that long checkout lines (near end-aisle displays), "samplefest" events of tasting free samples, video kiosks, magazine and book sections, and so on help keep customers in the store longer. On average, a single customer who strays from his or her grocery list can plan on impulse spending of $20 for every 10 minutes wandering about in the supermarket.

Let x represent the dollar amount spent on supermarket impulse buying in a 10-minute (unplanned) shopping interval. Based on the *Post* article, the mean of the x distribution is about $20 and the (estimated) standard deviation is about $7.

(a) Consider a random sample of $n = 100$ customers each of whom has 10 minutes of unplanned shopping time in a supermarket. From the central limit theorem, what can you say about the probability distribution of $\bar{x}$, the *average* amount spent by these customers due to impulse buying? Is the $\bar{x}$ distribution approximately normal? What is the mean and standard deviation of the $\bar{x}$ distribution? Is it necessary to make any assumption about the x distribution? Explain.

(b) What is the probability that $\bar{x}$ is between $18 and $22?

(c) Let us assume that x has a distribution that is approximately normal. What is the probability that x is between $18 and $22?

(d) In question b we used $\bar{x}$, the *average* amount spent, computed for 100 customers. In part (c), we used x, the amount spent by only *one* individual customer. The answers for parts (b) and (c) are very different. Why would you expect this to happen? In this example, $\bar{x}$ is a much more predictable or reliable statistic than x. Consider that almost all marketing strategies and sales pitches are designed for the *average* customer and *not* the *individual* customer. How does the central limit theorem tell us that the average customer is much more predictable than the individual customer?

Section 7.1   Sampling Distributions

Let us begin with some common statistical terms. Most of these have been discussed before, but this is a good time to review them.

From a statistical point of view, a *population* can be thought of as a set of measurements (or counts), either existing or conceptual. We discussed populations at some length in Chapter 1. A *sample* is a subset of measurements from the population. For our purposes, the most important samples are *random samples,* which were discussed in Section 2.1.

Parameter

A *population parameter* is a numerical descriptive measure of a population. Examples of population parameters are the population mean μ, population variance σ^2, population standard deviation σ, and the population proportion of successes p in a binomial distribution.

Statistic

A *statistic* is a numerical descriptive measure of a sample (usually a random sample). Examples of statistics are the sample mean $\bar{x}$, sample variance s^2, sample standard deviation s, and the sample estimate $\hat{p} = r/n$ (read $\hat{p}$ as "p hat") for the proportion of successes in a binomial distribution. Notice that for a given population a specified parameter is a *fixed* quantity, while the statistic might vary depending on which sample has been selected.

Often we do not have access to all the measurements of an entire population, so we must use measurements from a sample instead. In such cases, we will use a statistic (such as $\bar{x}$, s, or $\hat{p}$) to make *inferences* about corresponding population parameters (e.g., μ, σ, or p). The principal types of inferences we will make are

1. To *estimate* the value of a population parameter.

2. To formulate a *decision* about the value of a population parameter.

Sampling Distribution

In order to evaluate the reliability of our inferences, we will need to know the probability distribution for the statistic we are using. Such a probability distribution is called a *sampling distribution*. Perhaps an example will help clarify this discussion.

Example 1

Pinedale, Wisconsin, is a rural community with a children's fishing pond. Posted rules say that all fish under 6 inches must be returned to the pond, only children under 12 years old may fish, and a limit of five fish may be kept per day. Susan is a college student who was hired by the community last summer to make sure the rules were obeyed and to see that the children were safe from accidents. The pond contains only rainbow trout and has been well stocked for many years. Each child has no difficulty catching his or her limit of five trout.

As a project for her biometrics class, Susan kept a record of the lengths (to the nearest inch) of all trout caught last summer. Hundreds of children visited the pond and caught their limit of five trout, so Susan has a lot of data. To make Table 7–1, Susan selected 100 children at random and listed the length of each of the five trout caught by a child in the sample. Then, for each child, she listed the mean length of the five trout that child caught.

Now let us turn our attention to the following question: What is the average (mean) length of a trout taken from the Pinedale children's pond last summer?

Solution: We can get an idea of the average length by looking at the far right column of Table 7–1. But just looking at 100 of the $\bar{x}$ values doesn't tell as much. Let's organize our $\bar{x}$ values into a frequency table. We used a class width of 0.38 to make Table 7–2.

Table 7–1 Length Measurements of Trout Caught by a Random Sample of 100 Children at the Pinedale Children's Pond

Sample	Length (to nearest inch)					$\bar{x} =$ Sample Mean
1	11	10	10	12	11	10.8
2	11	11	9	9	9	9.8
3	12	9	10	11	10	10.4
4	11	10	13	11	8	10.6
5	10	10	13	11	12	11.2
6	12	7	10	9	11	9.8
7	7	10	13	10	10	10.0
8	10	9	9	9	10	9.4
9	10	10	11	12	8	10.2
10	10	11	10	7	9	9.4
11	12	11	11	11	13	11.6
12	10	11	10	12	13	11.2
13	11	10	10	9	11	10.2
14	10	10	13	8	11	10.4
15	9	11	9	10	10	9.8
16	13	9	11	12	10	11.0
17	8	9	7	10	11	9.0
18	12	12	8	12	12	11.2
19	10	8	9	10	10	9.4
20	10	11	10	10	10	10.2
21	11	10	11	9	12	10.6
22	9	12	9	10	9	9.8
23	8	11	10	11	10	10.0
24	9	12	10	9	11	10.2
25	9	9	8	9	10	9.0
26	11	11	12	11	11	11.2
27	10	10	10	11	13	10.8
28	8	7	9	10	8	8.4
29	11	11	8	10	11	10.2
30	8	11	11	9	12	10.2
31	11	9	12	10	10	10.4
32	10	11	10	11	12	10.8
33	12	11	8	8	11	10.0
34	8	10	10	9	10	9.4
35	10	10	10	10	11	10.2
36	10	8	10	11	13	10.4
37	11	10	11	11	10	10.6
38	7	13	9	12	11	10.4
39	11	11	8	11	11	10.4
40	11	10	11	12	9	10.6
41	11	10	9	11	12	10.6
42	11	13	10	12	9	11.0
43	10	9	11	10	11	10.2
44	10	9	11	10	9	9.8
45	12	11	9	11	12	11.0

Sample	Length (to nearest inch)					$\bar{x} =$ Sample Mean
46	13	9	11	8	8	9.8
47	10	11	11	11	10	10.6
48	9	9	10	11	11	10.0
49	10	9	9	10	10	9.6
50	10	10	6	9	10	9.0
51	9	10	12	10	9	10.0
52	7	11	10	11	10	9.8
53	9	11	9	11	12	10.4
54	12	9	8	10	11	10.0
55	8	11	10	9	10	9.6
56	10	10	9	9	13	10.2
57	9	8	10	10	12	9.8
58	10	11	9	8	9	9.4
59	10	8	9	10	12	9.8
60	11	9	9	11	11	10.2
61	11	10	11	10	11	10.6
62	12	10	10	9	11	10.4
63	10	10	9	11	7	9.4
64	11	11	12	10	11	11.0
65	10	10	11	10	9	10.0
66	8	9	10	11	11	9.8
67	9	11	11	9	8	9.6
68	10	9	10	9	11	9.8
69	9	9	11	11	11	10.2
70	13	11	11	9	11	11.0
71	12	10	8	8	9	9.4
72	13	7	12	9	10	10.2
73	9	10	9	8	9	9.0
74	11	11	10	9	10	10.2
75	9	11	14	9	11	10.8
76	14	10	11	12	12	11.8
77	8	12	10	10	9	9.8
78	8	10	13	9	8	9.6
79	11	11	11	13	10	11.2
80	12	10	11	12	9	10.8
81	10	9	10	10	13	10.4
82	11	10	9	9	12	10.2
83	11	11	10	10	10	10.4
84	11	10	11	9	9	10.0
85	10	11	10	9	7	9.4
86	7	11	10	9	11	9.6
87	10	11	10	10	10	10.2
88	9	8	11	10	12	10.0
89	14	9	12	10	9	10.8
90	9	12	9	10	10	10.0
91	10	10	8	6	11	9.0
92	8	9	11	9	10	9.4
93	8	10	9	9	11	9.4

Sample	Length (to nearest inch)					$\bar{x}$ = Sample Mean
94	12	11	12	13	10	11.6
95	11	11	9	9	9	9.8
96	8	12	8	11	10	9.8
97	13	11	11	12	8	11.0
98	10	11	8	10	11	10.0
99	13	10	7	11	9	10.0
100	9	9	10	12	12	10.4

- *Comment:* Techniques of Section 2.3 dictate a class width of 0.4. However, this choice results in the tenth class being beyond the data. Consequently, we shortened the class width slightly and also started the first class with a value slightly lower than the smallest data value.

Table 7-2 Frequency Table for 100 Values of $\bar{x}$

Class	Class Limits		f = Frequency	$f/100$ = Relative Frequency
	Lower	Upper		
1	8.39	8.76	1	0.01
2	8.77	9.14	5	0.05
3	9.15	9.52	10	0.10
4	9.53	9.90	19	0.19
5	9.91	10.28	27	0.27
6	10.29	10.66	18	0.18
7	10.67	11.04	12	0.12
8	11.05	11.42	5	0.05
9	11.43	11.80	3	0.03

The far right column of Table 7-2 contains relative frequencies $f/100$. Recall that the relative frequencies may be thought of as probabilities, so we effectively have a probability distribution. Since $\bar{x}$ represents the mean length of a trout (based on samples of five trout caught by each child), then we estimate the probability of $\bar{x}$ falling into each class by using the relative frequencies. Figure 7-1 is a relative frequency or probability distribution of the $\bar{x}$ values. For convenience, we have labeled the horizontal axis of the histogram with the class limits.

The bars of Figure 7-1 represent our estimated probabilities of $\bar{x}$ values based on the data of Table 7-1. The bell-shaped curve represents the theoretical probability distribution which would be obtained if the number of children (i.e., number of $\bar{x}$ values) were much larger.

Figure 7-1 represents a *probability sampling distribution* for the sample mean $\bar{x}$ of trout lengths based on random samples of size 5. We see that the distribution is mound-shaped and even somewhat bell-shaped. Irregularities

Figure 7–1 Estimates of Probabilities of $\bar{x}$ Values

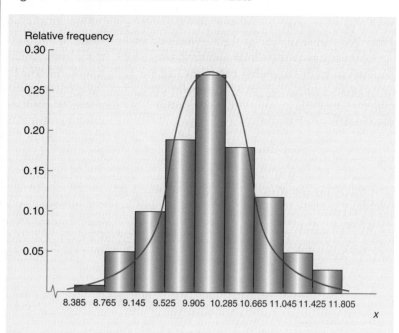

are due to the small number of samples used (only 100 sample means) and the rather small sample size (5 trout per child). These irregularities would become less obvious and even disappear if the sample of children became much larger, if we used a larger number of classes in Figure 7–1, and if the number of trout used in each sample became larger. In fact, the curve would eventually become a perfect bell-shaped curve. We will discuss this property at some length in the next section, which introduces the *central limit theorem*.

There are other sampling distributions besides the $\bar{x}$ distribution. In the chapters ahead we will see that other statistics have different sampling distributions. However, the $\bar{x}$ sampling distribution is very important. It will serve us well in our inferential work in Chapters 8 and 9 on estimation and testing.

Let us summarize the information about sampling distributions in the following exercise.

GUIDED EXERCISE 1

(a) What is a population parameter? Give an example.

(b) What is a sample statistic? Give an example.

(a) A population parameter is a numerical descriptive measure of a population. Examples are μ, σ, and p.

(b) A sample statistic or a statistic is a numerical descriptive measure of a sample. Examples are $\bar{x}$, s, and $\hat{p}$.

(c) What is a sampling distribution?

(c) A sampling distribution is a probability distribution for the sample statistic we are using.

(d) In Table 7–1, what makes up the members of the sample? What is the sample statistic corresponding to each sample? What is the sampling distribution? To which population parameter does this sampling distribution correspond?

(d) There are 100 samples, each of which has five trout lengths. The first sample of five trout has lengths 11, 10, 10, 12, and 11. The sample statistic is the sample mean $\bar{x} = 10.8$. The sampling distribution is shown in Figure 7–1. This sampling distribution relates to the population mean μ of all lengths of trout taken from the Pinedale children's pond (i.e., trout over 6 inches long).

(e) Where will sampling distributions be used in our study of statistics?

(e) Sampling distribution will be used for statistical inference. (Chapter 8 will concentrate on the method of inference called *estimation*. Chapter 9 will concentrate on a method of inference called *testing*.)

Section 7.1 Problems

This is a good time to review several important concepts, some of which we have studied earlier. Please write out a careful but brief answer to each of the following questions.

1. What is a population? Give three examples.
2. What is a random sample from a population? (*Hint:* See Section 2.1.)
3. What is a population parameter? Give three examples.
4. What is a sample statistic? Give three examples.
5. What is the meaning of the term *statistical inference*? What types of inferences will we make about population parameters?
6. What is a sampling distribution?
7. How do frequency tables, relative frequencies, and histograms using relative frequencies help us understand sampling distributions?
8. How can relative frequencies be used to help us estimate probabilities occurring in sampling distributions?
9. How do sampling distributions help us make inferences about population parameters?
10. Give an example of a specific sampling distribution we studied in this section. Outline other possible examples of sampling distributions from areas such as business administration, economics, finance, psychology, political science, sociology, biology, medical science, sports, engineering, chemistry, linguistics, and so on.

Section 7.2   The Central Limit Theorem

In Section 7.1 we began a study of the distribution of $\bar{x}$ values, where $\bar{x}$ was the (sample) mean length of five trout caught by children at the Pinedale children's fishing pond. Let's consider this example again in the light of a very important theorem of mathematical statistics.

Properties of $\bar{x}$ Distribution, Assuming x Has Normal Distribution

- **Theorem 7.1:** Let x be a random variable with a *normal distribution* whose mean is μ and standard deviation is σ. Let $\bar{x}$ be the sample mean corresponding to random samples of size n taken from the x distribution. Then the following are true:

  (a) The $\bar{x}$ distribution is a *normal distribution*.
  (b) The mean of the $\bar{x}$ distribution is μ.
  (c) The standard deviation of the $\bar{x}$ distribution is $\sigma/\sqrt{n}$.

We conclude from Theorem 7.1 that when x has a normal distribution, the $\bar{x}$ distribution will be normal *for any sample size n*. Furthermore, we can convert the $\bar{x}$ distribution to the standard normal z distribution using the following formulas.

$$\mu_{\bar{x}} = \mu$$

$$\sigma_{\bar{x}} = \frac{\sigma}{\sqrt{n}}$$

$$z = \frac{\bar{x} - \mu_{\bar{x}}}{\sigma_{\bar{x}}} = \frac{\bar{x} - \mu}{\sigma/\sqrt{n}} \quad \text{or} \quad \frac{\sqrt{n}(\bar{x} - \mu)}{\sigma}$$

where n is the sample size,
  μ is the mean of the x distribution, and
  σ is the standard deviation of the x distribution.

Theorem 7.1 is a wonderful theorem! It says that the $\bar{x}$ distribution will be normal provided the x distribution is normal. The sample size n could be 2, 3, 4, or any (fixed) sample size we wish. Furthermore, the mean of the $\bar{x}$ distribution is μ (same as for the x distribution), but the standard deviation is $\sigma/\sqrt{n}$ (which is, of course, smaller than σ). The next example illustrates Theorem 7.1.

Example 2

Suppose a team of biologists has been studying the Pinedale children's fishing pond. Let x represent the length of a single trout taken at random from the pond. This group of biologists has determined that x has a normal distribution with mean $\mu = 10.2$ in. and standard deviation $\sigma = 1.4$ in.

(a) What is the probability that a *single trout* taken at random from the pond is between 8 and 12 in. long?

Solution: We use the methods of Chapter 6 with $\mu = 10.2$, $\sigma = 1.4$ to get

$$z = \frac{x - \mu}{\sigma} = \frac{x - 10.2}{1.4}$$

Therefore,

$$P(8 < x < 12) = P\left(\frac{8 - 10.2}{1.4} < \frac{x - 10.2}{1.4} < \frac{12 - 10.2}{1.4}\right)$$

$$= P(-1.57 < z < 1.29)$$

$$= 0.4418 + 0.4015 = 0.8433$$

Therefore, the probability is about 0.8433 that a *single* trout taken at random is between 8 and 12 in. long.

(b) What is the probability that the *mean length* $\bar{x}$ of five trout taken at random is between 8 and 12 in.?

Solution: If we let $\mu_{\bar{x}}$ represent the mean of the distribution, then Theorem 7.1 part b tells us that

$$\mu_{\bar{x}} = \mu = 10.2$$

If $\sigma_{\bar{x}}$ represents the standard deviation of the $\bar{x}$ distribution, then Theorem 7.1 part c tells us that

$$\sigma_{\bar{x}} = \sigma/\sqrt{n} = 1.4/\sqrt{5} = 0.63$$

To create a standard normal z variable from $\bar{x}$, we subtract $\mu_{\bar{x}}$ and divide by $\sigma_{\bar{x}}$:

$$z = \frac{\bar{x} - \mu_{\bar{x}}}{\sigma_{\bar{x}}} = \frac{\bar{x} - \mu}{\sigma/\sqrt{n}} = \frac{\bar{x} - 10.2}{0.63}$$

To standardize the interval $8 < \bar{x} < 12$, we use 8 and then 12 in place of $\bar{x}$ in the preceding formula for z.

$$8 < \bar{x} < 12$$

$$\frac{8 - 10.2}{0.63} < z < \frac{12 - 10.2}{0.63}$$

$$-3.49 < z < 2.86$$

Theorem 7.1 part a tells us that $\bar{x}$ has a normal distribution. Therefore,

$$P(8 < \bar{x} < 12) = P(-3.49 < z < 2.86)$$

$$= 0.4998 + 0.4979 = 0.9977$$

The probability is about 0.9977 that the mean length based on a sample size 5 is between 8 and 12 in.

(c) Looking at the results of parts a and b, we see that the probabilities (0.8433 and 0.9977) are quite different. Why is this the case?

Solution: According to Theorem 7.1, both x and $\bar{x}$ have a normal distribution, and both have the same mean of 10.2 in. The difference is in the standard deviation for x and $\bar{x}$. The standard deviation of the x distribution is $\sigma = 1.4$. The standard deviation of the $\bar{x}$ distribution is

$$\sigma_{\bar{x}} = \sigma/\sqrt{n} = 1.4/\sqrt{5} = 0.63$$

The standard deviation of $\bar{x}$ is less than half the standard deviation of x. Figure 7-2 shows the distribution of x and $\bar{x}$.

Figure 7–2 General Shapes of the x and $\bar{x}$ Distributions

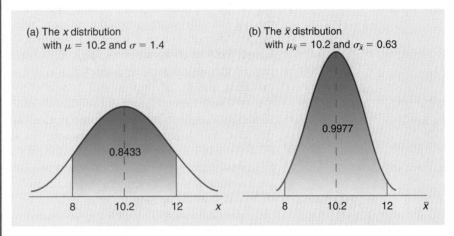

(a) The x distribution with $\mu = 10.2$ and $\sigma = 1.4$

0.8433

8   10.2   12 x

(b) The $\bar{x}$ distribution with $\mu_{\bar{x}} = 10.2$ and $\sigma_{\bar{x}} = 0.63$

0.9977

8   10.2   12 $\bar{x}$

Looking at Figure 7-2 (a) and (b), we see that both curves use the same scale on the horizontal axis. The means are the same, and the shaded area is above the interval from 8 to 12 on each graph. It becomes clear that the smaller standard deviation of the $\bar{x}$ distribution has the effect of gathering together much more of the total probability into the region over its mean. Therefore, the region from 8 to 12 has a much higher probability for the $\bar{x}$ distribution.

Standard Error of the Mean

Theorem 7.1 describes the distribution of a statistic: namely, the distribution of sample means $\bar{x}$. The standard deviation of a statistic is referred to as the *standard error* of that statistic. For the $\bar{x}$ sampling distribution, the standard error of $\bar{x}$ is $\sigma_{\bar{x}}$ or $\sigma/\sqrt{n}$. In other words, the standard error of the mean is $\sigma/\sqrt{n}$. In Minitab, the output

SE MEAN

refers to the standard error of the $\bar{x}$ distribution.

Central Limit Theorem

Theorem 7.1 gives complete information about the $\bar{x}$ distribution, provided the original x distribution is known to be normal. What happens if we don't have information about the shape of the original x distribution? The *central limit theorem* tells us what to expect.

- *Theorem 7.2 The Central Limit Theorem:* If x possesses *any* distribution with mean μ and standard deviation σ, then the sample mean $\bar{x}$ based on a random sample of size n will have a distribution that approaches the distribution of a normal random variable with mean μ and standard deviation $\sigma/\sqrt{n}$ as n increases without limit.

The central limit theorem is indeed surprising! It says that x can have *any* distribution whatever, but as the sample size gets larger and larger, the distribution of $\bar{x}$ will approach a *normal* distribution. From this relation, we begin to appreciate the scope and significance of the normal distribution.

In the central limit theorem, the degree to which the distribution of $\bar{x}$ values fits a normal distribution depends on both the selected value of n and the original distribution of x values. A natural question is: How large should the sample size be if we want to apply the central limit theorem? After a great deal of theoretical as well as empirical study, statisticians agree that if n is 30 or larger, the $\bar{x}$ distribution will appear to be normal and the central limit theorem will apply. However, this rule should not be applied blindly. If the x distribution is definitely not symmetrical about its mean, then the $\bar{x}$ distribution also will display a lack of symmetry. In such a case, a sample size larger than 30 may be required to get a reasonable approximation to the normal.

In practice, it is a good idea, when possible, to make a histogram of sample x values. If the histogram is approximately mound-shaped and if it is more or less symmetrical, then we may be assured that, for all practical purposes, the $\bar{x}$ distribution will be well approximated by a normal distribution and the central limit theorem will apply when the sample size is 30 or larger. The main thing to remember is that in almost all practical applications, a sample size of 30 or more is adequate for the central limit theorem to hold. However, in a few rare applications you may need a sample size larger than 30 to get good results.

Let's summarize this information for convenient reference:

For almost all x distributions, if we use a random sample of size 30 or larger, the $\bar{x}$ distribution will be approximately normal, and the larger the sample size becomes, the closer the $\bar{x}$ distribution gets to the normal. Furthermore, we may convert the $\bar{x}$ distribution to a standard normal distribution using the formulas shown below.

$$\mu_{\bar{x}} = \mu$$

$$\sigma_{\bar{x}} = \frac{\sigma}{\sqrt{n}}$$

$$z = \frac{\bar{x} - \mu_{\bar{x}}}{\sigma_{\bar{x}}} = \frac{\bar{x} - \mu}{\sigma/\sqrt{n}} \text{ or } \frac{\sqrt{n}\,(\bar{x} - \mu)}{\sigma}$$

where n is the sample size ($n \geq 30$),
μ is the mean of the x distribution, and
σ is the standard deviation of the x distribution.

GUIDED EXERCISE 2

(a) Suppose x has a *normal* distribution with mean $\mu = 18$ and standard deviation $\sigma = 3$. If we draw random samples of size 5 from the x distribution and $\bar{x}$ represents the sample mean, what can you say about the $\bar{x}$ distribution? How could you standardize the $\bar{x}$ distribution?

(a) Since the x distribution is given to be *normal*, the $\bar{x}$ distribution also will be normal even though the sample size is much less than 30. The mean is $\mu_{\bar{x}} = \mu = 18$. The standard deviation is

$$\sigma_{\bar{x}} = \sigma/\sqrt{n} = 3/\sqrt{5} = 1.3$$

We could standardize $\bar{x}$ as follows:

$$z = \frac{\bar{x} - \mu}{\sigma/\sqrt{n}}$$

$$z = \frac{\bar{x} - 18}{1.3}$$

(b) Suppose we know that the x distribution has mean $\mu = 75$ and standard deviation $\sigma = 12$, but we have no information as to whether or not the x distribution is normal. If we draw samples of size 30 from the x distribution and $\bar{x}$ represents the sample mean, what can you say about the $\bar{x}$ distribution? How could you standardize the $\bar{x}$ distribution?

(b) Since the sample size is large enough, the $\bar{x}$ distribution will be approximately a normal distribution. The mean of the $\bar{x}$ distribution is

$$\mu_{\bar{x}} = \mu = 75$$

The standard deviation of the distribution is

$$\sigma_{\bar{x}} = \sigma/\sqrt{n} = 12/\sqrt{30} = 2.2$$

We could standardize $\bar{x}$ as follows:

$$z = \frac{\bar{x} - \mu}{\sigma/\sqrt{n}} = \frac{\bar{x} - 75}{2.2}$$

(c) Suppose you did not know that x had a normal distribution. Would you be justified in saying that the $\bar{x}$ distribution is approximately normal if the sample size was $n = 8$?

(c) No, the sample size should be 30 or larger if we don't know that x has a normal distribution.

Now let's look at an example that demonstrates the use of the central limit theorem in a decision-making process.

Example 3 | A certain strain of bacteria occurs in all raw milk. Let x be the bacteria count per milliliter of milk. The health department has found that if the milk is not contaminated, then x has a distribution that is more or less mound-shaped and symmetrical. The mean of the x distribution is $\mu = 2500$, and the standard deviation is $\sigma = 300$. In a large commercial dairy, the health inspector takes 42 random samples of the milk produced each day. At the end of the day, the bacteria count in each of the 42 samples is averaged to obtain the sample mean bacteria count $\bar{x}$.

(a) Assuming that the milk is not contaminated, what is the distribution of $\bar{x}$?

Solution: The sample size is $n = 42$. Since this value exceeds 30, the central limit theorem applies, and we know that $\bar{x}$ will be approximately normal with mean

$$\mu_{\bar{x}} = \mu = 2500$$

and standard deviation

$$\sigma_{\bar{x}} = \sigma/\sqrt{n} = 300/\sqrt{42} = 46.3$$

(b) Assuming that the milk is not contaminated, what is the probability that the average bacteria count $\bar{x}$ for one day is between 2350 and 2650 bacteria per milliliter?

Solution: We convert the interval

$$2350 \leq \bar{x} \leq 2650$$

to a corresponding interval on the standard z *axis*.

$$z = \frac{\bar{x} - \mu}{\sigma/\sqrt{n}} = \frac{\bar{x} - 2500}{46.3}$$

$$\bar{x} = 2350 \quad \text{converts to} \quad z = \frac{2350 - 2500}{46.3} = -3.24$$

$$\bar{x} = 2650 \quad \text{converts to} \quad z = \frac{2650 - 2500}{46.3} = 3.24$$

Therefore,

$$
\begin{aligned}
P(2350 \leq \bar{x} \leq 2650) &= P(-3.24 \leq z \leq 3.24) \\
&= 2P(0 \leq z \leq 3.24) \\
&= 2(0.4994) \\
&= 0.9988
\end{aligned}
$$

The probability is 0.9988 that $\bar{x}$ is between 2350 and 2650.

(c) At the end of each day, the inspector must decide to accept or reject the accumulated milk that has been held in cold storage awaiting shipment. Suppose that the 42 samples taken by the inspector have a mean bacteria count $\bar{x}$ that is *not* between 2350 and 2650. If you were the inspector, what would be your comment on this situation?

Solution: The probability that $\bar{x}$ is between 2350 and 2650 is very high. If the inspector finds that the average bacteria count for the 42 samples is not between 2350 and 2650, then it is reasonable to conclude that there is something wrong with the milk. If $\bar{x}$ is less than 2350, you might suspect someone added chemicals to the milk to artificially reduce the bacteria count. If $\bar{x}$ is above 2650, you might suspect some other kind of biologic contamination.

GUIDED EXERCISE 3

In mountain country, major highways sometimes use tunnels instead of long, winding roads over high passes. However, too many vehicles in a tunnel at the same time can cause a hazardous situation. Traffic engineers are studying a long tunnel in Colorado. If x represents the time for a vehicle to go through the tunnel, it is known that the x distribution has mean $\mu = 12.1$ minutes and standard deviation $\sigma = 3.8$ minutes under ordinary traffic conditions. From a histogram of x values, it was found that the x distribution is mound-shaped with some symmetry about the mean.

Engineers have calculated that *on average,* vehicles should spend from 11 to 13 minutes in the tunnel. If the time is less than 11 minutes, traffic is moving too fast for safe travel in the tunnel. If the time is more than 13 minutes, there is a problem of bad air (too much carbon monoxide and other pollutants).

Under ordinary conditions, there are about 50 vehicles in the tunnel at one time. What is the probability that the mean time for 50 vehicles in the tunnel will be from 11 to 13 minutes?

We will answer this question in steps.

(a) Let $\bar{x}$ represent the sample mean based on samples of size 50. Describe the $\bar{x}$ distribution.

(a) From the central limit theorem we expect the $\bar{x}$ distribution to be approximately normal with mean

$$\mu_{\bar{x}} = \mu = 12.1$$

and standard deviation

$$\sigma_{\bar{x}} = \frac{\sigma}{\sqrt{n}} = \frac{3.8}{\sqrt{50}} = 0.54$$

(b) Find $P(11 < \bar{x} < 13)$.

(b) We convert the interval

$$11 < \bar{x} < 13$$

to a standard z interval and use the standard normal probability table to find our answer. Since

$$z = \frac{\bar{x} - \mu}{\sigma/\sqrt{n}} = \frac{\bar{x} - 12.1}{0.54}$$

then $\bar{x} = 11$ converts to

$$z = \frac{11 - 12.1}{0.54} = -2.04$$

and $\bar{x} = 13$ converts to

$$z = \frac{13 - 12.1}{0.54} = 1.67$$

9. Let x be a random variable that represents the cost of repairing a VCR. Based on information from *Consumer Reports* (January 1994), the mean of the x distribution is $\mu = \$80$, and the estimated standard deviation is $\sigma = \$19$. Suppose that we can assume that x has a normal distribution.
   (a) What is the probability that the cost of repair for one VCR is between $70 and $90?
   (b) If we have $n = 10$ VCRs, what can we say about the average cost $\bar{x}$ for repairs? What is the mean? What is the standard deviation for the $\bar{x}$ distribution. *Hint:* See Theorem 7.1. What is the probability that $\bar{x}$ is between $70 and $90?
   (c) Suppose we cannot assume that x has a normal distribution. However, a histogram of x values is more or less symmetrical and mound-shaped. What can we say about the $\bar{x}$ probability distribution? How large should the sample size be? If the sample size is sufficiently large, what is the mean and standard deviation of the $\bar{x}$ distribution?
   (d) If we have $n = 30$ VCRs, what is the probability that $\bar{x}$ is between $70 and $90?
   (e) Compare your answers for parts a, b, and d. Did the probabilities increase as n increased? Explain why you expect this to happen.

10. Let x be a random variable that represents daily high temperatures (degrees Fahrenheit) in January. The following information is based on a report from the U.S. Department of Commerce Environmental Data Services. For Miami, Florida, the mean of the x distribution is $\mu = 76$ and the standard deviation is approximately $\sigma = 1.9$. For Fairbanks, Alaska, the mean of the x distribution is $\mu = 0$ with approximate standard deviation $\sigma = 5.3$. Assume that x has a normal distribution.
    (a) For one day chosen at random in January, what is the probability that the high temperature in Miami will be less than 77°F? What is the probability the high temperature in Fairbanks will be less than 3°F?
    (b) If we choose $n = 7$ days in January, what can we say about the probability distribution of $\bar{x}$, the average high temperature? What is the probability that $\bar{x}$ is less than 77°F for Miami? less than 3°F for Fairbanks?
    (c) Suppose that we cannot assume that x has a normal distribution, but we can say that the distribution is approximately symmetrical and mound-shaped. In this case what can we say about the $\bar{x}$ probability distribution? If we use all 31 days in January, what is the probability $\bar{x} < 77$°F in Miami? less than 3°F in Fairbanks?

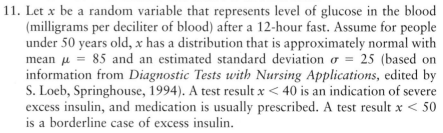

11. Let x be a random variable that represents level of glucose in the blood (milligrams per deciliter of blood) after a 12-hour fast. Assume for people under 50 years old, x has a distribution that is approximately normal with mean $\mu = 85$ and an estimated standard deviation $\sigma = 25$ (based on information from *Diagnostic Tests with Nursing Applications*, edited by S. Loeb, Springhouse, 1994). A test result $x < 40$ is an indication of severe excess insulin, and medication is usually prescribed. A test result $x < 50$ is a borderline case of excess insulin.

(a) What is the probability that on a single test $x < 40$? What is the probability of $x < 50$?

(b) Suppose that a doctor uses the average $\bar{x}$ for two tests taken about a week apart. What can we say about the probability distribution of $\bar{x}$? *Hint:* See Theorem 7.1. What is the probability $\bar{x} < 40$? What is the probability $\bar{x} < 50$?

(c) Repeat part b for $n = 3$ tests taken a week apart.

(d) Repeat part b for $n = 5$ tests taken a week apart.

(e) Compare your answers for parts a, b, c, and d. Did the probabilities decrease as n increased? Explain what this might say if you were a doctor or a nurse. If a patient had a test result of $\bar{x} < 40$ based on five tests, explain why you are either looking at an extremely rare event or (more likely) the person has a case of excess insulin.

12. Let x be a random variable that represents white blood cell count per cubic millimeter of whole blood. Assume x has a distribution that is approximately normal with mean $\mu = 7500$ and estimated standard deviation $\sigma = 1750$ (see reference in Problem 11). A test result of $x < 3500$ is an indication of leukopenia. This indicates bone marrow depression that may be the result of a viral infection. A test result of $x < 4000$ indicates borderline leukopenia.

(a) What is the probability that on a single test x is less than 3500? What is the probability that x is less than 4000?

(b) Suppose that a doctor uses the average $\bar{x}$ for two tests taken about a week apart. What can we say about the probability distribution of $\bar{x}$? What is the probability of $\bar{x} < 3500$? What is the probability of $\bar{x} < 4000$?

(c) Repeat part b for $n = 3$ tests taken a week apart.

(d) Compare your answers for parts a, b, and c. How did the probabilities change as n increased? If a person had $\bar{x} < 3500$ based on three tests, what conclusion would you draw as a doctor or a nurse?

13. Let x be a random variable that represents weights in kilograms (kg) of healthy adult female deer (does) in December in Mesa Verde National Park. Then x has a distribution that is approximately normal with mean $\mu = 63.0$ kg and standard deviation $\sigma = 7.1$ kg (reference: *The Mule Deer of Mesa Verde National Park,* by G. W. Mierau and J. L. Schmidt, Mesa Verde Museum Association, 1981). Suppose that a doe that weighs less than 54 kg is considered undernourished.

(a) What is the probability that a single doe captured at random in December (weighed and released) is undernourished.

(b) If the park has about 2200 does, what number do you expect to be undernourished in December.

(c) To estimate the health of the December doe population, park rangers use the rule that the average weight of $n = 50$ does should be more than 60 kg. If the average weight is less than 60 kg, it is thought that the entire population of does might be undernourished. What is the

Figure 7–5

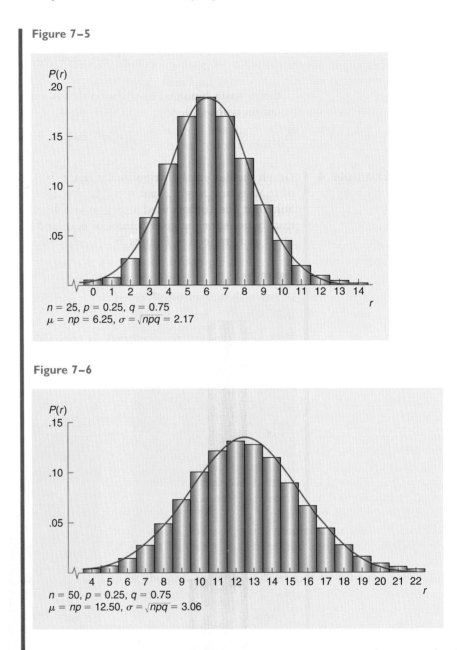

$n = 25, p = 0.25, q = 0.75$
$\mu = np = 6.25, \sigma = \sqrt{npq} = 2.17$

Figure 7–6

$n = 50, p = 0.25, q = 0.75$
$\mu = np = 12.50, \sigma = \sqrt{npq} = 3.06$

When $n = 3$, the outline of the histogram does not even begin to take the shape of a normal curve. But when $n = 10, 25,$ or 50, it does begin to take a normal shape, indicated by the dashed curve.

From a theoretical point of view, the histograms in Figures 7–4, 7–5, and 7–6 would have bars for all values of r from $r = 0$ to $r = n$. However, in the construction of these histograms, the bars of height less than 0.001 unit have been omitted—i.e., in Examples 4 and 5 probabilities less than 0.001 have been rounded to 0.

Example 5

The owner of a new apartment building must install 25 water heaters. From past experience in other apartment buildings, she knows that Quick Hot is a good brand. It is guaranteed for 5 years only, but from her past experience she knows that the probability it will last 10 years is 0.25.

(a) What is the probability that 8 or more of the 25 water heaters will last at least 10 years?

Solution: In this example $n = 25$ and $p = 0.25$, so Figure 7–5 represents the probability distribution we will use. Let r be the binomial random variable corresponding to the number of successes out of $n = 25$ trials. We want to find $P(r \geq 8)$ by using the normal approximation. This probability is represented graphically (Figure 7–5) by the area of the bar over 8 and all bars to the right of the bar over 8.

Let x be a normal random variable corresponding to a normal distribution with $\mu = np = 25(0.25) = 6.25$ and $\sigma = \sqrt{npq} = \sqrt{25(0.25)(0.75)} \approx 2.17$. This normal curve is represented by the dashed line in Figure 7–5. The area under the normal curve from $x = 7.5$ to the right is approximately the same as the area of the bars from the bar over $r = 8$ to the right. It is important to notice that we start with $x = 7.5$ because the bar over $r = 8$ really starts at $x = 7.5$.

The area of the bars and the area under the corresponding dashed (normal) curve are approximately equal, so we conclude that $P(r \geq 8)$ is approximately equal to $P(x \geq 7.5)$.

When we convert $x = 7.5$ to standard units, we get

$$z = \frac{x - \mu}{\sigma} = \frac{7.5 - 6.25}{2.17} = 0.58$$

The probability we want is

$$P(x \geq 7.5) = P(z \geq 0.58) = 0.5 - P(0 \leq z \leq 0.58)$$
$$= 0.5 - 0.2190$$
$$= 0.2810$$

(b) How does this result compare with the result we can obtain by using the formula for the binomial probability distribution with $n = 25$ and $p = 0.25$?

Solution: Using a programmable calculator and the binomial distribution, the authors computed that $p(r \geq 8) = 0.2735$. This means that the probability is approximately 0.27 that 8 or more water heaters will last at least 10 years.

(c) How do the results of parts a and b compare?

Solution: The error of approximation is the difference between the approximate value (0.2810) and the true value (0.2735). The error is only $0.2810 - 0.2735 = 0.0075$, which is negligible for most practical purposes.

We knew in advance that the normal approximation to the binomial probability would be good, since $np = 25(0.25) = 6.25$ and $nq = 25(0.75) = 18.75$ are both greater than 5. These are the conditions that asssure us that the normal approximation will be sufficiently close to the binomial probability for most practical purposes.

Converting r values to x values

Remember that when using the normal distribution to approximate the binomial, we are computing the areas under bars. The bar over r goes from $r - 0.5$ to $r + 0.5$. If r is a *left* endpoint of an interval, we *subtract* 0.5 to get the corresponding normal variable x. If r if a *right* endpoint of an interval, we *add* 0.5 to get the corresponding variable x. For instance, $P(6 \le r \le 10)$ where r is a binomial variable is approximated by $P(5.5 \le x \le 10.5)$ where x is the corresponding normal variable.

- *Comment:* Both the binomial and Poisson distributions are for *discrete* random variables. Therefore, adding or subtracting 0.5 to r was not necessary when we approximated the binomial distribution by the Poisson distribution (Section 5.4). However, the normal distribution is for a *continuous* random variable. In this case, adding or subtracting 0.5 (as appropriate) to r will improve the approximation of the normal to the binomial distribution.

GUIDED EXERCISE 4

From many years of observation a biologist knows the probability is only 0.65 that any given Arctic tern will survive the migration from its summer nesting area to its winter feeding grounds. A random sample of 500 Arctic terns were banded at their summer nesting area. Use the normal approximation to the binomial and the following steps to find the probability that between 310 and 340 of the banded Arctic terns will survive the migration. Let r be the number of surviving terns.

(a) To approximate $P(310 \le r \le 340)$, we use the normal curve with $\mu =$ _____ and $\sigma =$ _____.

(a) We use the normal curve with
$$\mu = np = 500(0.65) = 325$$
$$\sigma = \sqrt{npq} = \sqrt{500(0.65)(0.35)} = 10.67$$

(b) $P(310 \le r \le 340)$ is approximately equal to $P($ _____ $\le x \le$ _____ $)$ where x is a variable from the normal distribution described in part a.

(b) Since 310 is the left endpoint, we subtract 0.5, and since 340 is the right endpoint, we add 0.5. Consequently,
$$P(310 \le r \le 340) \approx P(309.5 \le x \le 340.5)$$

(c) Convert the condition $309.5 \le x \le 340.5$ to a condition in standard units.

(c) Since $\mu = 325$ and $\sigma = 10.67$, the condition $309.5 \le x \le 340.5$ becomes
$$\frac{309.5 - 325}{10.67} \le z \le \frac{340.5 - 325}{10.67}$$
or
$$-1.45 \le z \le 1.45$$

(d) $P(310 \leqslant r \leqslant 340) = P(309.5 \leqslant x \leqslant 340.5)$
$ = P(-1.45 \leqslant z \leqslant 1.45)$
$ = \underline{}$

(d) $P(-1.45 \leqslant z \leqslant 1.45) = 2P(0 \leqslant z \leqslant 1.45)$
$ = 2(0.4265)$
$ = 0.8530$

which is approximately the probability we were seeking.

(e) Will the normal distribution make a good approximation to the binomial for this problem? Explain your answer.

(e) Since

$$np = 500(0.65) = 325 \quad \text{and}$$
$$nq = 500(0.35) = 175$$

are both greater than 5, the normal will be a good approximation to the binomial.

Section 7.3 Problems

Note: When we say *between a and b,* we mean every value from *a* to *b, including a and b.*

1. A survey reported in *USA Today* (December 13, 1989) indicates that 65% of small business owners favor drug testing for their employees. In a random sample of 50 small businesses, what is the probability that
   (a) Fewer than 25 of the owners favor drug testing?
   (b) More than 35 favor drug testing?
   (c) Between 30 and 45 favor drug testing?

2. The U.S. Department of Transportation keeps monthly reports on airline performance. Among the data which they collect is the percentage of flights that arrive on time. For November 1989, 78% of the flights by the 12 major carriers arrived on time (that is, within 15 minutes of schedule). For that period, what is the probability that in a random sample of 100 flights
   (a) More than half arrived on time?
   (b) No more than 30 were late?
   (c) Between 80 and 100 arrived on time?

3. In Colorado Springs, a local newspaper ran a full page of nearly 100 mug shots of people the police want to arrest for serious crimes. Within 1 week, the police received enough information to locate and arrest about 17% of these "wanted" people (reported in *Rocky Mountain News,* January 11, 1994). If next month the newspaper runs a full page of 125 mug shots of fugitives, what is the probability that the police will receive enough information to locate and arrest
   (a) At least 15 fugitives?
   (b) 28 or more fugitives?
   (c) Between 15 and 28 fugitives (including 15 and 28)?
   (d) In the solution to this problem, what was *n*? *p*? *q*? Does it appear that both *np* and *nq* are larger than 5? Why is this an important consideration?

DATA HIGHLIGHTS

1. *Iris setosa* is a beautiful wildflower that is found in such diverse places as Alaska, the Gulf of St. Lawrence, much of North America, and even in English meadows and parks. R. A. Fisher, with his colleague Dr. Edgar Anderson, studied these flowers extensively. Dr. Anderson described how he collected information on iris:

   I have studied such irises as I could get to see, in as great detail as possible, measuring iris standard after iris standard and iris fall after iris fall, sitting squat-legged with record book and ruler in mountain meadows, in cypress swamps, on lake beaches, and in English parks. [Anderson, E., "The Irises of the Gaspé Peninsula," *Bulletin, American Iris Society*, 59:2–5, 1935].

   The data in Table 7–3 were collected by Dr. Anderson and were published by his friend and colleague R. A. Fisher in a paper entitled, "The Use of Multiple Measurements in Taxonomic Problems" (*Annals of Eugenics*, part II, 179–188, 1936).

   Table 7–3 Petal Length in Centimeters for *Iris setosa*

1.4	1.4	1.3	1.5	1.4
1.7	1.4	1.5	1.4	1.5
1.5	1.6	1.4	1.1	1.2
1.5	1.3	1.4	1.7	1.5
1.7	1.5	1	1.7	1.9
1.6	1.6	1.5	1.4	1.6
1.6	1.5	1.5	1.4	1.5
1.2	1.3	1.4	1.3	1.5
1.3	1.3	1.3	1.6	1.9
1.4	1.6	1.4	1.5	1.4

   Let x be a random variable representing petal length. Using the TI-82 calculator, it was found that the sample mean is $\bar{x} = 1.46$ cm and the sample standard deviation is $s = 0.17$ cm. Figure 7–7 shows a histogram for the given data generated on a TI-82 calculator.

   (a) Examine the histogram for petal lengths. Would you say that the distribution is approximately mound-shaped and symmetrical? Our sample has only 50 irises; if many thousands of irises had been used, do you think that the distribution would look even more like a normal curve? Let x be the petal length of *Iris setosa*. Research has shown that x has an approximately normal distribution with mean $\mu = 1.5$ cm and standard deviation $\sigma = 0.2$ cm.

   (b) Use the empirical rule with $\mu = 1.5$ and $\sigma = 0.2$ to get an interval in which approximately 68% of the petal lengths will fall. Repeat this for 95% and 99.7%. Examine the raw data and compute the percentage of the raw data that actually falls in each of these intervals (the 68% interval, the 95% interval, and the 99.7% interval). Compare your computed percentages with the theoretical percentages.

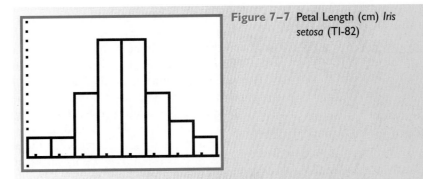

Figure 7–7 Petal Length (cm) *Iris setosa* (TI-82)

(c) Compute the probability that a petal length is between 1.3 and 1.6 cm. Compute the probability that the petal length is greater than 1.6 cm.

(d) Suppose that a random sample of 30 irises is obtained. Compute the probability that the average petal length for this sample is between 1.3 and 1.6 cm. Compute the probability that the average petal length is greater than 1.6.

(e) Compare your answers for parts c and d. Do you notice any differences? Why would you expect these differences?

2. Examine Figure 7–8, "Shopping by the Clock" (*USA Today*, July 14, 1992).

Figure 7–8 Shopping by the Clock (July 14, 1992)

USA SNAPSHOTS®

A look at statistics that shape our lives

Shopping by the clock

People spend an average of 69 minutes each visit to a mall or shopping center:

Time shopping

More than 3 hours
4%

2 – 3 hours
10%

Less than 1 hour
52%

1 – 2 hours
34%

Source: International Council of Shopping Centers

By Elys A. McLean, USA TODAY

Source: Copyright 1992, USA TODAY. Reprinted with permission.

(a) Notice that 52% of the people who go to a shopping center spend less than 1 hour. However, the figure also states that people spend an average of 69 minutes on each visit to a shopping center. How could *both* these claims be correct? Write a brief, complete essay in which you discuss mean, median, and mode in the context of symmetrical distribution. Also discuss mean, median, and mode for distributions that are skewed left, skewed right, or general distributions. Then answer the question: How could 52% of the people spend less than 1 hour in the shopping center while the average (we don't know which average was used) time spent was 69 minutes?

(b) Ala Moana Shopping Center in Honolulu is sometimes advertised as the largest shopping center for 2500 miles and the best shopping center in the middle of the Pacific Ocean. There are many interesting Hawaiian, Asian, and other ethnic shops in Ala Moana, so this center is a favorite of tourists. Suppose that a tour group of 75 people has just arrived at the shopping center. The International Council of Shopping Centers indicates that 86% (52% plus 34%) of the people will spend less than 2 hours in a shopping center. Let us assume this applies to our tour group.

   (i)   For the tour group of 75 people, what is the expected number who finish shopping on or before 2 hours? What is the standard deviation?

   (ii) For the tour group of 75 people, what is the probability that 55 or more will finish shopping in 2 hours or less?

   (iii) For the tour group, what is the probability that 70 or more will finish shopping in 2 hours or less?

   (iv) What is the probability that between 50 and 70 (including 50 and 70) people in the tour group will finish shopping in 2 hours or less?

   (v)   If you are a tour director, how could you use this information to plan an appropriate length of time for the stop at Ala Moana shopping center? You do not want to frustrate your group by allowing too little time for shopping, but you also do not want to spend too much time at the center.

LINKING CONCEPTS

Discuss each of the following topics in class or review the topics on your own. Then write a brief but complete essay in which you summarize the main points. Please include formulas and graphs as appropriate.

1. Most people would agree that increased information should give better predictions. Discuss how sampling distributions actually accomplish better predictions by using more information. Examine Theorem 7.1 again. Suppose that x is a random variable with a *normal* distribution. Then $\bar{x}$,

the sample mean based on random samples of size n, also will have a normal distribution for *any* value of $n = 1, 2, 3, \ldots$.

What happens to the standard deviation of the $\bar{x}$ distribution as n (the sample size) increases? Consider the following table for different values of n.

n	1	2	3	4	10	50	100
$\sigma/\sqrt{n}$	1σ	0.71σ	0.58σ	0.50σ	0.32σ	0.14σ	0.10σ

In this case, "increased information" means a larger sample size n. Give a brief explanation why a large *standard deviation* will usually result in poor statistical predictions, whereas a small standard deviation usually results in much better predictions. Since the standard deviation of the sampling distribution $\bar{x}$ is $\sigma/\sqrt{n}$, we can decrease the standard deviation by increasing n. In fact, if we look at the above table, we see that if we use a sample of only size $n = 4$, we cut the standard deviation of $\bar{x}$ by 50% of the standard deviation σ of x. If we were to use a sample of size $n = 100$, we would cut the standard deviation of $\bar{x}$ to 10% of the standard deviation σ of x.

Give the preceding discussion some thought and explain why you expect to get much better predictions for μ by using $\bar{x}$ from a sample of size n rather than by just using x. Write a brief essay in which you explain why sampling distributions are an important tool in statistics.

2. In a way, the central limit theorem can be thought of as a kind of "grand central station." It is a connecting hub or center for a great deal of statistical work. We will use it extensively in Chapters 8 and 9. Put in a very elementary way, it says that as the sample size n increases, the mean $\bar{x}$ will always approach a normal distribution no matter where the original x variable came from. For most people, it is the complete generality of the central limit theorem that is so awe inspiring: it applies to practically everything. List and discuss at least three variables from everyday life where you expect the variable x itself does *not* follow a normal or bell-shaped distribution. Then discuss what would happen to the sampling distribution $\bar{x}$ as the sample size increased. Sketch diagrams of the $\bar{x}$ distributions as the sample size n increases.

3. From Chapter 5 you no doubt remember we promised you a much better way to compute binomial probabilities when the number of trials is large.

   (a) Using the methods of Section 7.3, compute $P(r \geqslant 285)$ when $n = 500$ and $p = 0.6$.

   (b) Refer back to Problem 2(b) in Linking Concepts of Chapter 5. The preceding method of computing $P(r \geqslant 285)$ is much easier isn't it?

   (c) The normal approximation to the binomial distribution is another example of the importance of the normal distribution in statistics. Including Chapter 7, list general applications of the normal distribution we have made so far in this text.

Using Technology

The problems in this section may be done using statistical computer software or calculators with statistical functions. Displays and suggestions are given for Minitab (Release 9), the TI-82 graphing calculator, and ComputerStat.

Part I: In-Class Project Using Calculators

1. Have a class discussion about how you could use the random number table (Table 2 of Appendix II) to get a random sample of the digits 0, 1, 2, 3, 4, 5, 6, 7, 8, and 9. In our sample we allow repetitions of the digits. Therefore 3, 6, 1, 6, and 8 would be a random sample of size $n = 5$ digits. The mean for this sample would be 4.80.

2. Have each student in class use the random number table to get a random sample of five digits from 0 to 9. Then have each student compute the sample mean of his or her sample of digits. Save these means for use in Problems 3 and 4.

3. We assume the professor has a calculator with mean and standard deviation keys. Have each student read his or her mean (calculated in Problem 2) to the professor. The professor enters each mean into the calculator and finds the grand sample mean $\bar{x}$ and sample standard deviation s of the means provided by the students.

4. Use the numbers $\bar{x}$ and s computed in Problem 3 to create the intervals shown in Column I of Table 7–4. Again have each student read his or her mean (from Problem 2) to the professor. Tally the sample means computed by the students in Problem 2 to determine how many fall in each interval of Column II.

(a) Examine Figure 6–7. Notice the areas under the normal curve in this figure. Compare the percents shown in this figure to those in Column III of Table 7–4 labeled Hypothetical Normal. Percents in the column labeled Hypothetical Normal represent percents of the total sample tally that would fall in each interval if the sampling distribution (based on samples of size $n = 5$) were in fact normal. How does your sample tally compare with the hypothetical normal? (*Hint:* Convert your sample tally to a percent of the total tally.)

(b) Explain how this class project relates to the Central Limit Theorem. If we repeat Problems 2, 3, and 4 with a large class of students and with a sample size n that is fairly large, would you say the sampling distribution should closely approximate the hypothetical normal? Why?

(c) Using the frequency table, construct a histogram with six bars. Some bars may be of zero height depending on how your table turned out. Looking at your histogram, would you say it is approximately mound-shaped and symmetric? Does it seem to give the general outline of a normal curve?

Part II: Computer Demonstration

The activities described in Part II can be done using computer software packages such as ComputerStat or Minitab. ComputerStat has a program *Central Limit Theorem Demonstration* designed to perform the steps of Part I.

A. Using *ComputerStat*

In the ComputerStat menu of topics, select Probability Distributions and Central Limit Theorem. Then use the program Central Limit Theorem Demonstration, to continue our study.

Table 7–4 Frequency Table of Sample Means

I. Interval	II. Frequency	III. Hypothetical Normal
$\bar{x} - 3s$ to $\bar{x} - 2s$	Tally the sample	2 or 3%
$\bar{x} - 2s$ to $\bar{x} - s$	means computed	13 or 14%
$\bar{x} - s$ to $\bar{x}$	by the students	about 34%
$\bar{x}$ to $\bar{x} + s$	in Problem 2 and	about 34%
$\bar{x} + s$ to $\bar{x} + 2s$	place here.	13 or 14%
$\bar{x} + 2s$ to $\bar{x} + 3s$		2 or 3%

The program is set up essentially to parallel the activities of Problems 2, 3, and 4. However, the computer does the work much faster. You may use any sample size n from 2 to 50.

For each sample size you describe, the computer will use a random number generator to obtain a random sample of n real numbers from 0 to 9. It then computes the mean of these numbers. The process is repeated 100 times to get 100 sample means based on samples of size n.

Next the computer finds the grand mean $\bar{x}$ and sample standard deviation s for all 100 sample means. Then it constructs a frequency table similar to Table 7–4 of Problem 4. Finally, the computer constructs a histogram from the frequency table.

5. Run the program for a sample size $n = 2$.

   (a) Examine the frequency table. How close does the sample tally fit a hypothetical normal?

   (b) Examine the histogram. Does the graph appear mound-shaped and symmetric? Does it seem to be approximately normal?

   (c) Pay close attention to the standard deviation s and look at the histogram to see how "spread out" the graph is for this sample size n.

6. Repeat Problem 5 for a sample of size $n = 5$.

7. Repeat Problem 5 for a sample of size $n = 15$.

8. Repeat Problem 5 for a sample of size $n = 30$.

9. In Problems 5–8 the sample standard deviations s got smaller and smaller as n got larger. Also,

the graph became less and less spread as n got larger. Furthermore, the entire graph seemed to strongly "peak out" over 4.5 as n got larger. Look again at the statement of the Central Limit Theorem. Why does the Central Limit Theorem predict all of the above behavior?

10. Notice that the hypothetical normal gives a good approximation even when the sample size is small. This is because the original distribution of numbers from zero to nine is symmetric about the value 4.5 when the numbers are drawn at random. Because of the symmetry of the original distribution, we got good results even for small samples. The Central Limit Theorem says the sampling distribution of means will become a normal distribution even if the original distribution was not symmetric. However, we usually need a sample size of $n \geq 30$ to get reasonably accurate results.

As a library assignment, interested readers are asked to give a report on the article "Understanding the Central Limit Theorem" by David A. Thomas in *The Mathematics Teacher*, vol. 77, no. 7, Oct. 1984, p. 452.

B. Using *Minitab*

Minitab can be programmed to demonstrate the Central Limit Theorem. You may draw random samples from a variety of distributions such as a normal distribution, any binomial distribution, a Poisson distribution, a uniform distribution (as done by ComputerStat), any discrete probability distribution, and so on. A Minitab computer display at the end of this section shows a program that samples from a normal distribution and creates a histogram of the sample means.

Computer Displays

The first display is from ComputerStat. It shows the graph of the binomial probability distribution with $n = 20$ and $p = 0.45$. Since both np and nq are greater than 5, we can use a normal approximation to the binomial distribution. Imagine a normal distribution with mean 9 and standard deviation 2.22 superimposed on the graph shown.

ComputerStat Display Version 4.0: Binomial Distribution, n = 20, p = 0.45

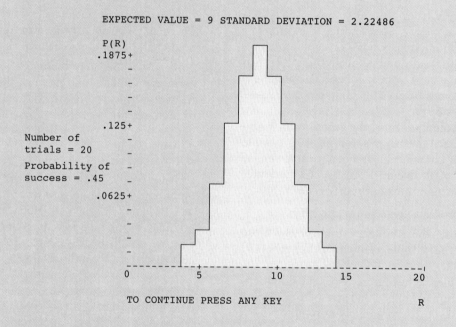

```
          EXPECTED VALUE = 9 STANDARD DEVIATION = 2.22486

          P(R)
          .1875+
              -
              -
              -
              -
          .125+
Number of     -
trials = 20   -
              -
Probability of -
success = .45 -
          .0625+
              -
              -
              -
              -
          --------+----------+----------+-------------+
          0      5         10        15           20

          TO CONTINUE PRESS ANY KEY                     R
```

Minitab permits us to take random samples from a selection of probability distributions. The next display involves 500 random samples of size $n = 5$ taken from a normal distribution with mean 10 and standard deviation 2. The mean $\bar{x}$ of each of the samples was then computed. According to Theorem 7.1, the $\bar{x}$ distribution from *all* possible samples of size $n = 5$ is normal with mean 10 and standard deviation 0.8944. Notice that the histogram of our 500 $\bar{x}$ values is somewhat normal, and the mean and standard deviation of the 500 $\bar{x}$ values are close to those predicted by Theorem 7.1.

Minitab Display:
$\bar{x}$ Distribution from 500 samples of size n = 5
Taken from a Normal Distribution with Mean 10 and
Standard Deviation 2

```
MTB > RANDOM 500 C1-C5;
SUBC> NORMAL MU 10 SIGMA 2.
MTB > NAME C6 'XBAR'
MTB > RMEAN C1-C5 C6
MTB > MEAN C6
   MEAN    =       10.002
MTB > STDEV C6
   ST.DEV. =       0.87045
MTB > Histogram 'XBAR';
SUBC>    MidPoint;
SUBC>    Bar;
SUBC>    Title "XBAR DISTRIBUTION FOR SAMPLES OF SIZE N = 5";
SUBC>    Footnote "MU OF XBAR = 10.00      SIGMA OF XBAR = 0.87".
```

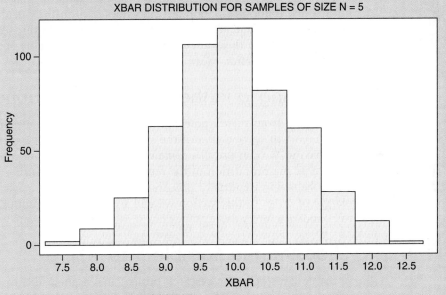

XBAR DISTRIBUTION FOR SAMPLES OF SIZE N = 5

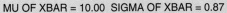

MU OF XBAR = 10.00 SIGMA OF XBAR = 0.87

Section 8.1

Estimating μ with Large Samples

How can we use a sample statistic $\bar{x}$ to get information about the population mean μ? We cannot give an exact value for μ, but we can give an interval of values which is likely to contain μ. Such an interval is called a *confidence interval*. In this section we introduce levels of confidence, critical values, error of estimate, and confidence intervals for the population mean μ of a distribution. Our methods require large samples (samples of size 30 or larger) so that we may utilize the central limit theorem.

Section 8.2

Estimating μ with Small Samples

When our sample statistic $\bar{x}$ is based on *small* samples, we cannot use the normal distribution to obtain critical values used in the calculation of confidence intervals for μ. We need another distribution. In this section we explore properties of the *Student's t distribution* and develop confidence intervals for the population mean μ based on *small* samples.

Section 8.3

Estimating p in the Binomial Distribution

Information from survey polls is a popular item in the news media. Polls often report the proportion of the surveyed sample with a certain opinion or behavior. We can use this sample information to create confidence intervals for p, the proportion of the respective population with a certain opinion or behavior. Reports of poll results often include information about the *margin of error*. In this section we will see how the margin of error relates to confidence intervals.

Section 8.4

Choosing the Sample Size

In the design stages of a research project, it is a good idea to decide in advance on the maximum error of estimate E and the confidence level c you want for your project. How you make these choices depends on the requirements and practical nature of your project. Whatever specifications you make, the next step is to determine the sample size that meets your needs.

Section 8.5

Estimating $\mu_1 - \mu_2$ and $p_1 - p_2$

In this section we study independent random samples from two populations. Based on data obtained from such samples, we compute confidence intervals for the difference of population parameters $\mu_1 - \mu_2$ and $p_1 - p_2$. We will see conditions under which we use large-sample or small-sample techniques.

CHAPTER EIGHT

Robert Lee Frost
(1874–1963)

This celebrated American poet drew poetic symbols largely from common experiences observed in his rural New England

Estimation

We dance round in a ring and suppose,
But the Secret sits in the middle and knows.
Robert Frost, "The Secret Sits"*

In Chapter 1 we said that statistics is the study of how to collect, organize, analyze, and interpret numerical data. That part concerned with analysis, interpretation, and forming conclusions about the source of the data is called *statistical inference*. Problems of statistical inference require us to draw a *sample* of observations from a larger *population*. A sample usually contains incomplete information, so in a sense we must "dance round in a ring and suppose." Nevertheless, conclusions about the population can be obtained from sample data by use of statistical estimates. This chapter will introduce you to several widely used methods of estimation.

Focus Problem ▶ The Trouble with Wood Ducks

The National Wildlife Federation published an article entitled, "The Trouble with Wood Ducks" (*National Wildlife*, Vol. 31, No. 5, Aug.–Sept. 1993). In this article, wood ducks are described as beautiful birds living in forested areas such as the Pacific Northwest and Southeast United States. Because of over-hunting and habitat destruction, these birds were in danger of extinction. A federal ban on hunting wood ducks in 1918 helped save the species from extinction. Wood ducks like to nest in tree cavities. However, many such trees were disappearing due to heavy timber cutting. For a period of time it seemed that nesting boxes were the solution to disappearing trees. At first, the wood duck population grew, but after a few seasons, the population declined sharply. Good biology research combined with good statistics provided an answer to this disturbing phenomenon.

Cornell University professors of ecology Paul Sherman and Brad Semel found that the nesting boxes were placed too close to each other. Female wood

---

* Source: From *The Poetry of Robert Frost*, edited by Edward Connery Lathem. Copyright 1942 by Robert Frost. Copyright © 1969 by Holt, Rinehart and Winston. Copyright © 1970 by Lesley Frost Ballantine. Reprinted by permission of Henry Holt and Company, Inc.

ducks prefer a secluded nest that is a considerable distance from the next wood duck nest. In fact, female wood duck behavior changed when the nests were too close to each other. Some females would lay their eggs in another female's nest. The result was too many eggs in one nest. The biologists found that if there were too many eggs in a nest, the proportion of eggs that hatched was considerably reduced. In the long run, this meant a decline in the population of wood ducks.

In their study, Sherman and Semel used two placements of nesting boxes. Group I had boxes that were well separated from each other and well hidden by available brush. Group II had boxes that were highly visible and grouped closely together.

In Group I boxes, there were a total of 474 eggs, of which a field count showed that about 270 hatched. In Group II boxes, there were a total of 805 eggs, of which a field count showed that, again, about 270 hatched.

The material in Chapter 8 will enable us to answer many questions about the hatch ratios of eggs from nests in the two groups.

(a) Find a point estimate $\hat{p}_1$ for p_1, the proportion of eggs that hatch in group I nest box placements. Find a 95% confidence interval for p_1.

(b) Find a point estimate $\hat{p}_2$ for p_2, the proportion of eggs that hatch in group II nest box placements. Find a 95% confidence interval for p_2.

(c) Find a 95% confidence interval for $p_1 - p_2$. Does the interval indicate that the proportion of eggs hatched from group I nest box placements is higher than, lower than, or not different from the proportion of eggs hatched from group II nest boxes?

(d) What conclusions about placement of nest boxes can be drawn? In the article, additional concerns are raised about the higher cost of placing and maintaining group I nest box placement. At issue is also the cost efficiency per successful wood duck hatch. Data in the article do not include information that would help us answer questions of *cost* efficiency. However, the data presented do help us answer questions about proportion of successful hatches in the two nest box configurations.

Section 8.1   Estimating μ with Large Samples

Basic Terminology

An estimate of a population parameter given by a single number is called a *point estimate* of that parameter. It should be no great surprise that we use $\bar{x}$ (the sample mean) as a point estimate for μ (the population mean) and s (the sample standard deviation) as a point estimate for σ (the population standard deviation). In this section we will discuss estimates of μ and σ from large samples ($n \geq 30$).

Statistical theory and empirical results show that if a distribution is approximately mound-shaped and symmetrical, then when the sample size is 30 or larger, we are safe, for most practical purposes, if we estimate σ by s. The error resulting from taking the population standard deviation σ to be equal to the sample standard deviation s is negligible. However, when the sample size is less than 30, we will use special small sample methods, which we will study later in Section 8.2.

For large samples of size $n \geqslant 30$,

$$\sigma \approx s$$

is a good estimate, for most practical purposes.

Using $\bar{x}$ to estimate μ is not quite so simple, even when we have a large sample size. The *error of estimate* is the magnitude of the difference between the point estimate and the true parameter value. Using $\bar{x}$ as a point estimate for μ, the error of estimate is the magnitude of $\bar{x} - \mu$. If we use absolute-value notation, we can indicate the error of estimate for μ by the notation $|\bar{x} - \mu|$.

We cannot say exactly how close $\bar{x}$ is to μ when μ is unknown. Therefore, the exact error of estimate is unknown when the population parameter is unknown. Of course, μ is usually not known or there would be no need to estimate it. In this section we will use the language of probability to give us an idea of the size of the error of estimate when we use $\bar{x}$ as a point estimate of μ.

First, we need to learn about *confidence levels*. The reliability of an estimate will be measured by the confidence level.

Finding the Critical Value

Suppose we want a confidence level of c (see Fig. 8–1). Theoretically, you can choose c to be any value between 0 and 1, but usually c is equal to 0.90, 0.95, or 0.99. In each case, the value z_c is the number such that the area under

Figure 8–1 Confidence Level c and Corresponding Critical Value z_c Shown on the Standard Normal Curve

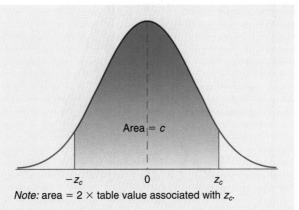

$$-z_c \qquad 0 \qquad z_c$$

Note: area = 2 × table value associated with z_c.

the standard normal curve falling between $-z_c$ and z_c is equal to c. The value z_c is called the *critical value* for a confidence level of c.

The area under the normal curve from $-z_c$ to z_c is the probability that the standardized normal variable z lies in that interval. This means that

$$P(-z_c < z < z_c) = c$$

Example 1

Let us use Table 6 in Appendix II to find a number $z_{0.95}$ so that 95% of the area under the standard normal curve lies between $-z_{0.95}$ and $z_{0.95}$. That is, we will find $z_{0.95}$ so that

$$P(-z_{0.95} < z < z_{0.95}) = 0.95$$

Solution: Table 6 in Appendix II gives the area under the normal curve from the mean 0 to any point z. The condition $P(-z_{0.95} < z < z_{0.95}) = 0.95$ is the same as the condition $2P(0 < z < z_{0.95}) = 0.95$, since the standard normal curve is symmetrical about the mean 0. When we divide both sides of the last equation by 2, we get

$$P(0 < z < z_{0.95}) = \frac{0.95}{2} = 0.4750$$

Note that 0.4750 is an entry in Table 6. Table 8–1 is an excerpt from Table 6 in Appendix II.

Table 8–1 Excerpt from Table 6 of Areas Under the Standard Normal Curve from 0 to z (Appendix II)

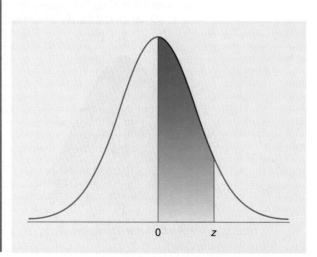

z	0.00	0.01	0.02	0.03	0.04	0.05	0.06	0.07...
0.0								
.								
.								
.								
1.8	0.4641	0.4649	0.4656	0.4664	0.4671	0.4678	0.4686	0.4693
1.9	0.4713	0.4719	0.4726	0.4732	0.4738	0.4744	0.4750	0.4756

Area is 0.4750 for $z = 1.96$

We will use Table 8–1 to find $z_{0.95}$. From Table 8–1 we see that $z_{0.95} = 1.96$, so the probability is 0.95 that the standardized statistic z lies between -1.96 and 1.96. In symbols, we have

$$P(-1.96 < z < 1.96) = 0.95$$

GUIDED EXERCISE 1

(a) Is it true that the condition

$$P(-z_{0.99} < z < z_{0.99}) = 0.99$$

is equivalent to the condition

$$2P(0 < z < z_{0.99}) = 0.99?$$

Why?

(b) Use the information of part a and Table 6 in Appendix II to find the value of $z_{0.99}$.

(a) It is true that the conditions are equivalent because the standard normal curve is symmetrical about its mean 0.

(b) To complete the computation, we divide both sides of the equation

$$2P(0 < z < z_{0.99}) = 0.99$$

by 2 and get the equivalent equation

$$P(0 < z < z_{0.99}) = \frac{0.99}{2} = 0.4950$$

We look up the area 0.4950 in Table 6 and then find the z value that produces that area. The value 0.4950 is not in the table; however, the values 0.4949 and 0.4951 are in the table. Even though 0.4950 is exactly halfway between the two values, the two values are so close together we use the higher value 0.4951. This gives us

$$z_{0.99} = 2.58$$

The results of Example 1 and Guided Exercise 1 will be used a great deal in our later work. For convenience, Table 8–2 gives some levels of confidence and corresponding critical values z_c.

Table 8–2 Some Levels of Confidence and Their Corresponding Critical Values	
Level of Confidence c	Critical Value z_c
0.75	1.15
0.80	1.28
0.85	1.44
0.90	1.645
0.95	1.96
0.99	2.58

Error of Estimate

An estimate is not very valuable unless we have some kind of measure of how "good" it is. Now that we have studied confidence levels and critical values, the language of probability can give us an idea of the size of the error of estimate caused by using the sample mean $\bar{x}$ as an estimate for the population mean.

Remember that $\bar{x}$ is a random variable. Each time we draw a sample of size n from a population, we can get a different value for $\bar{x}$. According to the central limit theorem, if the sample size is large, then $\bar{x}$ has a distribution that is approximately normal with mean $\mu_{\bar{x}} = \mu$, the population mean we are trying to estimate. The standard deviation is $\sigma_{\bar{x}} = \sigma/\sqrt{n}$.

This information, together with our work on confidence levels, leads us (as shown in the optional derivation) to the probability statement

$$P\left(-z_c\frac{\sigma}{\sqrt{n}} < \bar{x} - \mu < z_c\frac{\sigma}{\sqrt{n}}\right) = c \tag{1}$$

Equation (1) uses the language of probability to give us an idea of the size of the error of estimate for the corresponding confidence level c. In words, Equation (1) says that the probability is c that our point estimate $\bar{x}$ is within a distance $\pm z_c(\sigma/\sqrt{n})$ of the population mean μ. This relationship is shown in Figure 8–2.

In the following optional discussion, we derive Equation (1). If you prefer, you may jump ahead to the summary about the error of estimate.

Optional Derivation of Equation (1)

For a c confidence level, we know

$$P(-z_c < z < z_c) = c \tag{2}$$

Figure 8-2 Distribution of Sample Means $\bar{x}$

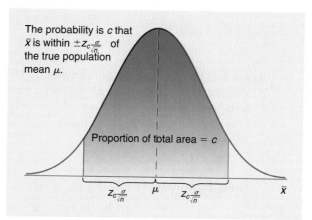

The probability is c that $\bar{x}$ is within $\pm z_c \frac{\sigma}{\sqrt{n}}$ of the true population mean μ.

Proportion of total area = c

$$z_c\frac{\sigma}{\sqrt{n}} \qquad \mu \qquad z_c\frac{\sigma}{\sqrt{n}} \qquad\qquad \bar{x}$$

This statement gives us information about the size of z, but we want information about the size of $\bar{x} - \mu$. Is there a relationship between z and $\bar{x} - \mu$? The answer is yes since, by the central limit theorem, $\bar{x}$ has a distribution that is approximately normal with mean μ and standard deviation $\sigma/\sqrt{n}$. We can convert $\bar{x}$ to a standard z score by using the formula

$$z = \frac{\bar{x} - \mu}{\sigma/\sqrt{n}} \tag{3}$$

Substituting this expression for z in Equation (2) gives

$$P\left(-z_c < \frac{\bar{x} - \mu}{\sigma/\sqrt{n}} < z_c\right) = c \tag{4}$$

Multiplying all parts of the inequality in (4) by $\sigma/\sqrt{n}$ gives us

$$P\left(-z_c \frac{\sigma}{\sqrt{n}} < \bar{x} - \mu < z_c \frac{\sigma}{\sqrt{n}}\right) = c \tag{1}$$

Equation (1) is precisely the equation we set out to derive.

- **Summary:** The *error of estimate* using $\bar{x}$ as a point estimate for μ is $|\bar{x} - \mu|$. In most practical problems, μ is unknown, so the error of estimate is also unknown. However, Equation (1) allows us to compute an *error tolerance* E, which serves as a bound on the error of estimate. Using a $c\%$ level of confidence, we can say the point estimate $\bar{x}$ differs from the population mean μ by a maximal error tolerance of

$$E = z_c \frac{\sigma}{\sqrt{n}}$$

Since $\sigma \approx s$ for large samples, we have

$$E \approx z_c \frac{s}{\sqrt{n}} \qquad \text{when } n \geq 30 \qquad (5)$$

where E is the *maximal error tolerance* on the error of estimate for a given confidence level c (i.e., $|\bar{x} - \mu| < E$ with probability c); z_c is the critical value for the confidence level c (see Table 8–2); s is the sample standard deviation; n is the sample size.

Using Equations (1) and (5), we conclude that

$$P(-E < \bar{x} - \mu < E) = c \qquad (6)$$

Equation (6) says that the probability is c that the difference between $\bar{x}$ and μ is no more than the maximal error tolerance E.

If we use a little algebra on the inequality

$$-E < \bar{x} - \mu < E \qquad (7)$$

for μ, we can rewrite it in the following mathematically equivalent way:

$$\bar{x} - E < \mu < \bar{x} + E \qquad (8)$$

Confidence Intervals (Large Sample)

Since (7) and (8) are mathematically equivalent, their probabilities are the same. Therefore, from (6), (7), and (8) we obtain

$$P(\bar{x} - E < \mu < \bar{x} + E) = c \qquad (9)$$

Equation (9) says that there is a chance of c that the population mean μ lies in the interval from $\bar{x} - E$ to $\bar{x} + E$. We call this interval a *c confidence interval for* μ. We may get a different confidence interval for each different sample that is taken. Some intervals will contain the population mean μ and others will not. However, in the long run, the proportion of confidence intervals that contains μ is c.

• *Summary:* For large samples ($n \geq 30$) taken from a distribution that is approximately mound-shaped and symmetrical, and for which the population standard deviation σ is unknown, a *c confidence interval for the population mean* μ is given by

c Confidence Interval for μ (Large Samples)

$$\bar{x} - E < \mu < \bar{x} + E \qquad (10)$$

where $\bar{x}$ = sample mean

$$E \approx z_c \frac{s}{\sqrt{n}}$$

> s = sample standard deviation
> c = confidence level $(0 < c < 1)$
> z_c = critical value for confidence level c
>   (See Table 8–2 for frequently used values.)
> n = sample size $(n \geqslant 30)$

- ***Important Comment:*** What if you could assume
  (i) you were drawing your samples from a *normal* population *and*
  (ii) the population standard deviation σ was known to you?
  Under these assumptions, a c confidence interval for the population mean
  would be $\bar{x} - E < \mu < \bar{x} + E$, where

$$E = z_c \frac{\sigma}{\sqrt{n}}$$

  and the condition that we must have a large sample $(n \geqslant 30)$ could be
  dropped.

In most practical situations we don't know the population standard deviation σ. In these situations, we use Equation (10) with large samples $(n \geqslant 30)$ to find a c confidence interval, or we use small samples $(n < 30)$ and the methods of the next section to find a c confidence interval.

Example 2 | Julia enjoys jogging. She has been jogging over a period of several years, during which time her physical condition has remained constantly good. Usually she jogs 2 miles/day. During the past year Julia has sometimes recorded her times required to run 2 miles. She has a sample of 90 of these times. For these 90 times the mean was $\bar{x} = 15.60$ minutes and the standard deviation was $s = 1.80$ minutes. Let μ be the mean jogging time for the entire distribution of Julia's 2-mile running times (taken over the past year). Find a 0.95 confidence interval for μ.
Solution: The interval from $\bar{x} - E$ to $\bar{x} + E$ will be a 95% confidence interval for μ. In this case, $c = 0.95$, so $z_c = 1.96$ (see Table 8–2). The sample size $n = 90$ is large enough that we may approximate σ as $s = 1.80$ minutes. Therefore,

$$E \approx z_c \frac{s}{\sqrt{n}}$$

$$E = 1.96\left(\frac{1.80}{\sqrt{90}}\right)$$

$$E = 0.37$$

Using Equation (10), the given value of $\bar{x}$, and our computed value for E, we get the 95% confidence interval for μ.

$$\bar{x} - E < \mu < \bar{x} + E$$
$$15.60 - 0.37 < \mu < 15.60 + 0.37$$
$$15.23 < \mu < 15.97$$

We conclude that there is a 95% chance that the population mean μ of jogging times for Julia is between 15.23 and 15.97 minutes.

A few comments are in order about the general meaning of the term *confidence interval*. It is important to realize that the endpoints $\bar{x} \pm E$ are really statistical *variables*. Equation (9) says we have a chance c of obtaining a sample such that the interval, once it is computed, will contain the parameter μ. Of course, after the confidence interval is numerically fixed, it either does or does not contain μ. So the probability is 1 or 0 that the interval, when it is fixed, will contain μ. A nontrivial probability statement can be made only about variables, not constants. Therefore, Equation (9) really says that if we repeat the experiment many times and get lots of confidence intervals (for the same sample size), then the proportion of all intervals that will turn out to contain the mean μ is c.

In Figure 8–3, the horizontal lines represent 0.90 confidence intervals for various samples of the same size from a distribution. Some of these intervals contain μ, and others do not. Since the intervals are 0.90 confidence intervals, about 90% of all such intervals should contain μ. For each sample the interval goes from $\bar{x} - E$ to $\bar{x} + E$.

- *Comment:* Please see "Using Technology" at the end of this chapter for a computer demonstration of this discussion about confidence intervals.

Figure 8–3 0.90 Confidence Intervals for Samples of the Same Size

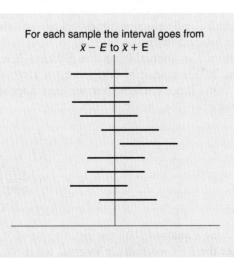

For each sample the interval goes from $\bar{x} - E$ to $\bar{x} + E$

GUIDED EXERCISE 2

Walter usually meets Julia at the track. He prefers to jog 3 miles. While Julia kept her record, he also kept one for his time required to jog 3 miles. For his 90 times, the mean was $\bar{x} = 22.50$ minutes and the standard deviation was $s = 2.40$ minutes. Let μ be the mean jogging time for the entire distribution of Walter's 3-mile running times over the past several years. How can we find a 0.99 confidence interval for μ?

(a) What is $z_{0.99}$? (See Table 8–2.)

(a) $z_{0.99} = 2.58$

(b) Since the sample size is large, what can we use for σ?

(b) $\sigma \approx s = 2.40$

(c) What is the value of E?

(c) $E = z_c \dfrac{\sigma}{\sqrt{n}} \approx 2.58 \left(\dfrac{2.40}{\sqrt{90}} \right) = 0.65$

(d) What are the endpoints for a 0.99 confidence interval for μ?

(d) The endpoints are given by

$$\bar{x} - E \approx 22.50 - 0.65$$
$$= 21.85$$
$$\bar{x} + E \approx 22.50 + 0.65$$
$$= 23.15$$

GUIDED EXERCISE 3

A large loan company specializes in making automobile loans for used cars. The board of directors wants to estimate the average amount loaned for cars during the past year. The company takes a random sample of 225 customer files for this period. The mean amount loaned for this sample of 225 loans is $\bar{x} = \$8200$ and the standard deviation is $s = \$750$. Let μ be the mean of all car loans made over the past year.

Find a 0.95 confidence interval for μ.

Since $n = 225$ is a large sample, we take $\sigma \approx s = 750$. From Table 8–2, we see that $z_{0.95} = 1.96$. Then

$$E \approx z_c \dfrac{s}{\sqrt{n}} = 1.96 \left(\dfrac{750}{\sqrt{225}} \right) = 98$$
$$\bar{x} - E \approx 8200 - 98 = \$8102$$
$$\bar{x} + E \approx 8200 + 98 = \$8298$$

The interval from \$8102 to \$8298 is a 0.95 confidence interval for μ.

GUIDED EXERCISE 4

We have said that a sample of size 30 or larger is a large sample. In this section we indicated two important reasons why our methods require large samples.

What are these reasons?

Reason 1: Our methods require $\bar{x}$ to have approximately a normal distribution. We know from the central limit theorem that this will be the case for large samples.

Reason 2: Unless we somehow know σ, our methods require us to approximate σ with the sample standard deviation s. This approximation will be good only if the sample size is large.

When we use samples to estimate the mean of a population, we generate a small error. However, samples are useful even when it is possible to survey the entire population because the use of a sample may yield savings of time or effort in collecting data.

Section 8.1 Problems

1. *Consumer Reports* (October 1993) gave the following data about calories in a 30-gram serving of chocolate chip cookies. Both fresh-baked such as Duncan Hines and Pillsbury and packaged cookies such as Pepperidge Farm and Nabisco were included.

153	152	146	138	130	146	149	138	168
147	140	156	155	163	153	155	160	145
138	150	135	155	156	150	146	129	127
171	148	155	132	155	127	150	110	

   (a) Use a calculator with mean and standard deviation keys to verify that the sample mean number of calories is $\bar{x} = 146.5$ with sample standard deviation $s = 12.7$ calories.
   (b) We take the point of view that the preceding data are representative of the population of all chocolate chip cookies. Find an 80% confidence interval for the mean calories μ in a 30-gram serving of all chocolate chip cookies. Find the length of this interval.
   (c) Repeat part b using a 90% confidence interval.
   (d) Repeat part b using a 99% confidence interval.
   (e) Compare the lengths from parts b, c, and d. Comment on how these lengths change as c, the confidence level, increases.

2. In Roosevelt National Forest, the rangers took random samples of live aspen trees and measured the base circumference of each tree.
   (a) The first sample had 30 trees with a mean circumference of $\bar{x} = 15.71$ in. and a sample standard deviation of $s = 4.63$ in. Find a 95% confidence interval for the mean circumference of aspen trees from these data.

    (b) The next sample had 90 trees with a mean of $\bar{x} = 15.58$ in. and a sample standard deviation of $s = 4.61$ in. Again, find a 95% confidence interval from these data.

    (c) The last sample had 300 trees with a mean of $\bar{x} = 15.59$ in. and a sample standard deviation of $s = 4.62$ in. Again, find a 95% confidence interval from these data.

    (d) Find the length of each interval of parts a, b, and c. Comment on how these lengths change as the sample size increases.

3. *Forbes* (January 3, 1994) gave the following data about percentage return on capital (12 months) for representative stocks in the entertainment/information sector. Stocks such as CBS, Turner Broadcasting, Walt Disney, Time Warner, Gannett, and so on were included.

29.7	21.1	6.5	10.0	9.0	3.6	2.4	23.5
9.3	9.7	10.6	5.5	12.3	1.7	22.0	21.7
28.9	26.9	14.9	13.7	9.6	2.3	7.1	12.9
10.3	10.9	8.1	8.1	10.8	8.2	7.0	11.0
10.0	5.5	3.0	4.8	6.5	19.1	17.2	4.6
14.5							

    (a) Use a calculator with mean and standard deviation keys to verify that the sample mean is $\bar{x} = 11.57$ percentage return with sample standard deviation $s = 7.3$ percentage return.

Let us say that these stocks are representative of the entire sector of entertainment/information stocks.

    (b) Find an 80% confidence interval for μ, the average percentage return on capital for all stocks in this sector. In the investment business, sometimes the low end of a confidence interval is called a *support* (the quantity is not likely to go below this value). The high end of a confidence interval is called a *resistance* (the quantity is not likely to rise above this value). At the 80% confidence level, what would you use for support and resistance for percentage return on capital in this stock sector?

    (c) If someone told you that the average return on capital in the entertainment/information stock sector was soon going to have a percentage return above 24, would you have reason to suspect that this might not happen? Explain using the confidence interval of part b.

    (d) Repeat parts b and c for an 85% level of confidence.

4. *Forbes* (January 3, 1994) gave the following information about percentage return on capital (12 months) for representative stocks in the drug/health care sector. Stocks such as Merck, Bristol-Myers, Upjohn, QualMed, Humana, and so on were included.

32.7	34.9	17.8	19.9	19.3	40.7	29.8
36.0	37.0	27.0	20.5	16.8	23.6	14.9
12.3	10.2	6.3	5.5	16.4	20.3	33.1
40.9	51.8	13.3	27.1	16.8	17.6	14.4
29.2	17.6					

(a) Use a calculator with mean and standard deviation keys to verify that the sample mean is $\bar{x} = 23.46$ percentage return and the sample standard deviation is $s = 11.17$ percentage return.

(b) Find an 80% confidence interval for μ, the average percentage return on capital for all stocks in this sector. What would you estimate for a support? for a resistance? (See Problem 3 for a description of these terms.)

(c) If someone told you that the average return on capital in the drug/health care sector was soon going to drop below 5 percentage or rise above 40 percentage, might you have reason to be skeptical? Explain using the confidence interval of part b.

(d) Repeat parts b and c for a 90% level of confidence.

5. The U.S. Department of Commerce Environmental Data Service gave the following information about average temperature (°F) in January in Phoenix, Arizona, for the past 40 years.

52.8	43.2	52.6	50.7	54.6	53.3	52.4
51.7	49.9	50.4	49.6	48.5	51.6	43.7
49.7	51.9	51.4	54.5	52.3	48.7	56.0
54.0	53.0	53.8	48.5	54.2	51.5	48.4
46.7	52.7	42.8	50.7	52.4	54.9	52.1
52.2	51.4	51.2	54.0	52.3		

(a) Use a calculator with mean and standard deviation keys to verify that the sample mean is $\bar{x} = 51.16°F$ and the sample standard deviation is $s = 3.04°F$.

(b) Find a 90% confidence interval for the January mean temperature in Phoenix.

(c) Find a 99% confidence interval for the January mean temperature in Phoenix.

(d) If someone told you that the earth was heating up and the average January temperature in Phoenix was now 53°F, what might you think about such a claim? Is it possible that a few more years of observation might be needed before such a claim could be made? Explain.

6. The Roman Arches is an Italian restaurant. The manager wants to estimate the average amount a customer spends on lunch Monday through Friday. A random sample of 115 customers' lunch tabs gave a mean of $\bar{x} = \$9.74$ with standard deviation $s = \$2.93$.

(a) Find a 95% confidence interval for the average amount spent on lunch by all customers.

(b) For a day when the Roman Arches has 115 lunch customers, use part a to estimate a range of dollar values for the total lunch income that day.

7. In the clothing department of a local dry goods store, a random sample of 100 customers had an average cash register receipt (total bill) of $\bar{x} = \$77.54$ with standard deviation $s = \$16.25$.

    (a) Find a 90% confidence interval for the average cash register receipt in the clothing department.

    (b) For a group of 100 customers, estimate a range of dollar values for the total cash register receipts in the clothing department.

8. How hot is the air in the top (crown) of a hot air balloon? Information from *Ballooning: The Complete Guide to Riding the Winds*, by Wirth and Young (Random House, 1991), claims that the air in the crown should be an average of 100°C for a balloon to be in a state of equilibrium. However, the temperature does not need to be exactly 100°C. What is a reasonable and safe range of temperatures? This may vary with the size and (decorative) shape of the balloon. All balloons have a temperature gauge in the crown. Suppose that 56 readings (for a balloon in equilibrium) gave a mean temperature $\bar{x} = 97$°C with sample standard deviation $s = 17$°C.

    (a) Compute a 95% confidence interval for the average temperature for which this balloon will be in a steady-state equilibrium.

    (b) If the average temperature in the crown of the balloon goes above the high end of your confidence interval, do you expect the balloon will go up or down? Explain.

9. How long does it take to fall asleep at night? This depends on what happened the night before. Alexander Borbely is a professor at the University of Zurich Medical School and director of the Sleep Laboratory. The following is adapted from the book, *Secrets of Sleep*, by Professor Borbely.

    (a) Suppose that a random sample of 38 college students was kept awake all night and the next day (24 hours total). The mean time for this group to go to sleep the next night was $\bar{x} = 2.5$ minutes with standard deviation $s = 0.7$ minutes. Compute a 90% confidence interval for the mean time of all such (sleep-deprived) students to fall asleep. What is the length of this interval?

    (b) Suppose that a random sample of 38 college students had a normal (8-hour) sleep and a normal (16-hour) day. The mean time for this group to go to sleep the next night was $\bar{x} = 15.2$ minutes with sample standard deviation $s = 4.8$ minutes. Compute a 90% confidence interval for the mean time to go to sleep for all people in this (normal) group. What is the length of this interval?

    (c) Suppose that a random sample of 38 college students stayed in bed at least 12 hours and then after another 12 hours went back to bed. The mean time for this group to fall asleep was $\bar{x} = 25.7$ minutes with sample standard deviation $s = 8.3$ minutes. Compute a 90% confidence interval for all people in this group to fall asleep. What is the length of this interval?

    (d) Compare the lengths of the intervals in parts a, b, and c. As the sample standard deviations got larger, did the intervals get longer? Why would you expect this from the method of calculation? Explain.

10. Dr. Edgar Anderson was a botanist who collected vast amounts of data for several species of wild iris (see Data Highlights in Chapter 7). *Iris*

virginica, a lovely wildflower spread over most of the American continent and much of Europe, is one of the species Dr. Anderson studied. His friend R. A. Fisher published the data in a paper entitled, "The Use of Multiple Measurements in Taxonomic Problems," *Annals of Eugenics* 7 (pt II):179–188, 1936. For a sample of 50 *Iris virginica,*

(a) The sample mean petal length was $\bar{x} = 5.55$ cm with sample standard deviation $s = 0.57$ cm. Compute an 85% confidence interval for the population mean petal length.

(b) The sample mean petal width was $\bar{x} = 2.03$ cm with sample standard deviation $s = 0.27$ cm. Compute a 90% confidence interval for the population mean petal width.

11. A sociologist is studying the length of courtship before marriage in a rural district near Kyoto, Japan. A random sample of 56 middle-income families was interviewed. It was found that the average length of courtship was 3.4 years with sample standard deviation 1.2 years. Find an 85% confidence interval for the length of courtship for the population of all middle-income families in this district.

12. A sociologist by the name of N. Keyfitz studied the age of first marriage of women in the providence of Quèbec, Canada. The following is based on information from *American Journal of Sociology,* 53:470–480.

(a) In a large rural district of Quèbec far from any towns, a study of 75 families showed that the approximate sample mean age at which a woman married was $\bar{x} = 19.5$ years with sample standard deviation $s = 2.25$ years. Find a 95% confidence interval for the mean age of marriage for all married women in this district.

(b) In another study, only families from medium-sized and larger cities in Quèbec were used. This study of 89 families showed that the approximate mean age at which a woman married was $\bar{x} = 22.8$ years with sample standard deviation $s = 2.79$ years. Find a 99% confidence interval for the mean age of marriage for all married women in these communities.

13. Irv and Nancy are thinking about buying the Rockwood Motel located on Interstate 70. Before they make up their mind, they want to estimate the average number of vehicles that go by the motel each day in the summer. Fortunately, the highway department has been counting vehicles on I-70 near the motel. A random sample of 36 summer days shows an average of 16,000 cars per day with a standard deviation of 2400 cars. Find a 0.90 confidence interval for the mean number of cars per summer day going past the Rockwood Motel.

14. In September, a biological research team caught, weighed, and released a random sample of 54 chipmunks in Rocky Mountain National Park. The mean of the sample weights was $\bar{x} = 8.7$ ounces with a standard deviation of $s = 1.4$ ounces.

(a) Find a *c* confidence interval for the mean September weight of all Rocky Mountain chipmunks when $c = 0.80, 0.90, 0.95,$ and 0.99.

(b) Find the length of each interval of part a, and comment on how these lengths change as *c* increases.

15. In an article exploring blood serum levels of vitamins and lung cancer risks (*The New England Journal of Medicine,* November 13, 1986), the mean serum level of vitamin E in the control group was 11.9 mg/liter with standard deviation 4.30 mg/liter. There were 196 patients in the control group. (These patients were free of all cancer, except possibly skin cancer, in the subsequent 8 years.) Using this information, find a 95% confidence interval for the mean serum level of vitamin E in all persons similar to the control group.

16. In the same article as cited in Problem 15, 99 patients who were cancer-free at the time the blood was drawn later developed lung cancer. For these patients, the mean blood serum level of vitamin E was 10.5 mg/liter with standard deviation 3.2 mg/liter. Using this information, find a 95% confidence interval for the mean serum level of vitamin E in the population of all persons with similar lung cancer risks.

17. The *Denver Post* (January 18, 1994) stated that the average cost of a room (hotel or motel) was $62.50 per night. Suppose that you are a reporter for a competing paper and you question the statement by the *Post.*

    (a) Let us (hypothetically) say that you used the Yellow Pages to get a random sample of 40 hotels and motels. You called the lodges to get the price per night of a room. The sample mean room rate was $\bar{x} = \$55.98$ with sample standard deviation $s = \$10.73$. Use this information to compute a 99% confidence interval for the mean room rate for all Denver hotel and motel rooms.

    (b) Is the *Denver Post* figure of $62.50 in your confidence interval in part a? Do you suspect that the *Post* average might be high or low? Explain.

18. *Consumer Reports* (January 1994) stated that the average cost to repair a vacuum cleaner was $40.

    (a) Suppose that you interview a random sample of 35 people in your community who had their vacuum cleaners fixed. The sample mean cost was $\bar{x} = \$49.29$ with sample standard deviation $s = \$6.41$. Compute a 99% confidence interval for the population mean cost to fix a vacuum cleaner in this community.

    (b) Do you think that the *Consumer Reports* figure is correct in your community? Do you think that the *Consumer Reports* figure is too high or too low for your community? Explain using the confidence interval in part a.

Section 8.2   Estimating μ with Small Samples

For samples of size 30 or larger we can approximate the population standard deviation σ by *s,* the sample standard deviation. Then we can use the central limit theorem to find bounds on the error of estimate and confidence intervals for μ.

There are many practical and important situations, however, where large samples are simply not available. Suppose an archaeologist discovers only seven fossil skeletons from a previously unknown species of miniature horse. Reconstructions of the skeletons of these seven miniature horses show their mean shoulder heights to be $\bar{x} = 46.1$ cm. Let μ be the mean shoulder height for this entire species of miniature horse. How can we find the maximal error of estimate $|\bar{x} - \mu|$? How can we find a confidence interval for μ? We will return to this problem later in this section.

Student's t Distribution

To avoid the error involved in replacing σ by s—i.e., approximating σ by s—when the sample size is small (less than 30), we introduce a new variable called *Student's t variable*. The t variable and its corresponding distribution, called *Student's t distribution*, were discovered in 1908 by W. S. Gosset. He was employed as a statistician by a large Irish brewing company that frowned on the publication of research by its employees, so Gosset published his research under the pseudonym Student. Gosset was the first to recognize the importance of developing statistical methods for obtaining reliable information from small samples. It might be more fitting to call this *Gosset's t distribution*; however, in the literature of mathematical statistics it is known as *Student's t distribution*.

The t variable is defined by the following formula.

$$t = \frac{\bar{x} - \mu}{\dfrac{s}{\sqrt{n}}} \tag{11}$$

where $\bar{x}$ is the mean of a random sample of n measurements, μ is the population mean of the x distribution, and s is the sample standard deviation.

• **Comment:** You should note that our t variable is just like

$$z = \frac{\bar{x} - \mu}{\dfrac{\sigma}{\sqrt{n}}}$$

except that we replace σ with s. Unlike our methods for large samples, σ cannot be approximated by s when the sample size is less than 30 and we cannot use the normal distribution. However, we will be using the same methods as in Section 8.1 to find the maximal error of estimate and to find confidence intervals, but we use the student's t distribution.

If many random samples of size n are drawn, then we get many t values from Equation (11). These t values can be organized into a frequency table and a histogram can be drawn, thereby giving us an idea of the shape of the t distribution (for a given n).

Fortunately, all this work is not necessary because mathematical theories can be used to obtain a formula for the *t* distribution. However, it is important to observe that these theories say that the shape of the *t* distribution depends only on *n*, provided the basic variable *x* has a normal distribution. So *when we use the t distribution, we will assume that the x distribution is normal.*

Degrees of Freedom

Table 7 in Appendix II gives values of the variable *t* corresponding to what we call the number of *degrees of freedom*, abbreviated *d.f.* For the methods used in this section, the number of degrees of freedom is given by the formula

$$d.f. = n - 1 \tag{12}$$

where *d.f.* stands for the degrees of freedom and *n* is the sample size being used.

Each choice for *d.f.* gives a different *t* distribution. However, for *d.f.* larger than about 30, the *t* distribution and the standard normal *z* distribution are almost the same.

The graph of a *t* distribution is always symmetrical about its mean, which (as for the *z* distribution) is 0. The main observable difference between a *t* distribution and the standard normal *z* distribution is that a *t* distribution has somewhat thicker tails.

Figure 8–4 shows a standard normal *z* distribution and student's *t* distribution with *d.f.* = 3 and *d.f.* = 5.

Using Table 7 to Find Critical Values for Confidence Intervals

Table 7 of Appendix II gives various *t* values for different degrees of freedom *d.f.* We will use this table to find critical values t_c for a *c* confidence level. In other words, we want to find t_c so that an area equal to *c* under the *t* distribution for a given number of degrees of freedom falls between $-t_c$ and

Figure 8–4 A Standard Normal Distribution and Student's *t* Distribution with *d.f.* = 3 and *d.f.* = 5.

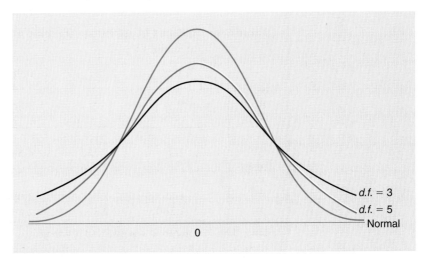

d.f. = 3
d.f. = 5
Normal

0

t_c. In the language of probability, we want to find t_c so that

$$P(-t_c < t < t_c) = c$$

This probability corresponds to the area shaded in Figure 8–5.

Figure 8–5 Area Under the t Curve Between $-t_c$ and t_c

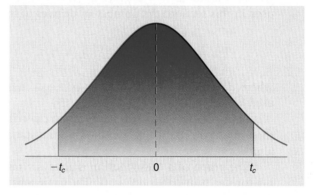

Table 7 in Appendix II has been arranged so that c is one of the column headings, and the degrees of freedom $d.f.$ are the row headings. To find t_c for any specific c, we find the column headed by that c value and read down until we reach the row headed by the appropriate number of degrees of freedom $d.f.$ (You will notice two other column headings: α' and α''. We will use these later, but for the time being, ignore them.)

Example 3   Use Table 8–3 (an excerpt from Table 7 in Appendix II) to find the critical value t_c for a 0.99 confidence level for a t distribution with sample size $n = 5$.

Table 8–3 Student's t Distribution (Excerpt from Table 7, Appendix II)

c	... 0.90	0.95	0.98	0.99
α'	—	—	—	—
α''	—	—	—	—
$d.f.$				
⋮				
3	... 2.353	3.182	4.541	5.841
4	... 2.132	2.776	3.747	4.604←
⋮				
7	... 1.895	2.365	2.998	3.499
8	... 1.860	2.306	2.896	3.355

Source: Table 7, Appendix II, was generated by *Minitab*.

Solution:

(a) First, we find the column with c heading 0.99. This is the last column.

(b) Next, we compute the number of degrees of freedom: $d.f. = n - 1 = 5 - 1 = 4$.

(c) We read down the column under the heading $c = 0.99$ until we reach the row headed by 4 (under $d.f.$). The entry is 4.604. Therefore, $t_{0.99} = 4.604$.

GUIDED EXERCISE 5

Use Table 7 of Appendix II to find t_c for a 0.90 confidence level of a t distribution with sample size $n = 9$.

(a) We find the column headed by $c =$ _____. This is the _____ (first, second, third, fourth, fifth, sixth) column.

    (a) $c = 0.90$. This is the fourth column.

(b) The degrees of freedom are given by

$$d.f. = n - 1 = \text{\_\_\_\_\_}$$

    (b) $d.f. = n - 1 = 9 - 1 = 8$

(c) Read down the column found in part a until you reach the entry in the row headed by $d.f. = 8$. The value of $t_{0.90}$ is _____ for a sample size of 9.

    (c) $t_{0.90} = 1.860$ for a sample size $n = 9$.

(d) Find t_c for a 0.95 confidence level of a t distribution with sample size $n = 9$.

    (d) $t_{0.95} = 2.306$ for a sample of size $n = 9$.

Maximal Error of Estimate

In Section 8.1 we found bounds $\pm E$ on the error of estimate for a c confidence level. Using the same basic approach, we arrive at the conclusion that

$$E = t_c \frac{s}{\sqrt{n}}$$

is the maximal error of estimate for a c confidence level with small samples (i.e., $|\bar{x} - \mu| < E$ with probability c). The analogue of Equation (1) in Section 8.1 is

$$P\left(-t_c \frac{s}{\sqrt{n}} < \bar{x} - \mu < t_c \frac{s}{\sqrt{n}}\right) = c \tag{13}$$

- *Comment:* Comparing Equation (13) with Equation (1) in Section 8.1, it becomes evident that we are using the same basic method on the t distribution that we did on the z distribution.

Likewise, for small samples from normal populations, Equation (9) of Section 8.1 becomes

$$P(\bar{x} - E < \mu < \bar{x} + E) = c \qquad (14)$$

where $E = t_c (s/\sqrt{n})$. Let us organize what we have been doing in a convenient summary.

Confidence Interval for μ
(Small Sample)

- **Summary:** For small samples ($n < 30$) taken from a normal population where σ is unknown, a c confidence interval for the population mean μ is as follows

---

c Confidence Interval for μ (Small Sample)

$$\bar{x} - E < \mu < \bar{x} + E \qquad (15)$$

where $\bar{x}$ = sample mean

$$E = t_c \frac{s}{\sqrt{n}}$$

c = confidence level ($0 < c < 1$)

t_c = critical value for confidence level c,
        and degrees of freedom $d.f. = n - 1$
        taken from t distribution

n = sample size (small samples, $n < 30$)

s = sample standard deviation

- **Comment:** In our applications of Student's t distribution we have made the basic assumption that x has a normal distribution. However, the same methods apply even if x is only approximately normal. In fact, the main requirement for using the Student's t distribution is that the distribution of x values be reasonably symmetrical and mound-shaped. If this is the case, then the methods we employ with the t distribution can be considered valid for most practical applications.

Example 4

Let's return to our archaeologist and the newly discovered (but extinct) species of miniature horse discussed at the beginning of this section. There are only seven known existing skeletons with shoulder heights (in centimeters) 45.3, 47.1, 44.2, 46.8, 46.5, 45.5, and 47.6. For this sample data the mean is $\bar{x} = 46.14$ and the sample standard deviation is $s = 1.19$. Let μ be the mean shoulder height (in centimeters) for this entire species of miniature horse and assume the population of shoulder heights is approximately normal.

Find a 99% confidence interval for μ, the mean shoulder height of the entire population of such horses.

Solution: In this case, $n = 7$, so $d.f. = n - 1 = 7 - 1 = 6$. For $c = 0.99$, Table 7 in Appendix II gives $t_{0.99} = 3.707$ (for $d.f. = 6$). The sample standard deviation is $s = 1.19$.

$$E = t_c \frac{s}{\sqrt{n}} = (3.707)\frac{1.19}{\sqrt{7}} = 1.67$$

The 99% confidence interval is

$$\bar{x} - E < \mu < \bar{x} + E$$
$$46.14 - 1.67 < \mu < 46.14 + 1.67$$
$$44.5 < \mu < 47.8$$

GUIDED EXERCISE 6

A company has a new process for manufacturing large artificial sapphires. The production of each gem is expensive, so the number available for examination is limited. In a trial run 12 sapphires are produced. The mean weight for these 12 gems is $\bar{x} = 6.75$ carats and the sample standard deviation is $s = 0.33$ carats. Let μ be the mean weight for the distribution of all sapphires produced by the new process.

(a) What is *d.f.* for this setting?

(a) *d.f.* $= n - 1$ where n is the sample size. Since $n = 12$, *d.f.* $= 12 - 1 = 11$.

(b) Use Table 7 in Appendix II to find $t_{0.95}$.

(b) Using Table 7 with *d.f.* $= 11$ and $c = 0.95$, we find $t_{0.95} = 2.201$.

(c) Find E.

(c) $E = t_{0.95}\dfrac{s}{\sqrt{n}} = (2.201)\dfrac{0.33}{\sqrt{12}} = 0.21$

(d) Find a 95% confidence interval for μ.

(d)
$$\bar{x} - E < \mu < \bar{x} + E$$
$$6.75 - 0.21 < \mu < 6.75 + 0.21$$
$$6.54 < \mu < 6.96$$

(e) What assumption about the distribution of all sapphires had to be made to obtain these answers?

(e) The population of artificial sapphire weights is approximately normal.

We have several formulas for confidence intervals for the population mean μ. How do we choose an appropriate one? We need to look at the sample size, the distribution of the original population, as well as whether or not the population standard deviation σ is known. There are essentially four cases for which we have the tools to find c confidence intervals for the mean μ.

Summary

Confidence Intervals for the Mean

Large Sample Cases

$n \geqslant 30$

1. If σ is not known, then a c confidence interval for μ is

$$\bar{x} - z_c \frac{s}{\sqrt{n}} < \mu < \bar{x} + z_c \frac{s}{\sqrt{n}}$$

2. If σ is known, then a c confidence interval for μ is

$$\bar{x} - z_c \frac{\sigma}{\sqrt{n}} < \mu < \bar{x} + z_c \frac{\sigma}{\sqrt{n}}$$

Small Sample Case

$$n < 30$$

If the population is approximately normal and σ is not known, then a c confidence interval for μ is

$$\bar{x} - t_c \frac{s}{\sqrt{n}} < \mu < \bar{x} + t_c \frac{s}{\sqrt{n}}$$

For Any Sample Size

If the population *is normal* and σ is known, then for any sample size (large or small) a c confidence interval for μ is

$$\bar{x} - z_c \frac{\sigma}{\sqrt{n}} < \mu < \bar{x} + z_c \frac{\sigma}{\sqrt{n}}$$

Section 8.2 Problems

In all the following problems, assume that the population of x values has an approximately normal distribution.

1. Use Table 7 in Appendix II to find t_c for a 0.95 confidence level when the sample size is 18.

2. Use Table 7 in Appendix II to find t_c for a 0.99 confidence level when the sample size is 4.

3. Use Table 7 in Appendix II to find t_c for a 0.90 confidence level when the sample size is 22.

4. Use Table 7 in Appendix II to find the value of t_c for a 0.95 confidence level when the sample size is 12.

5. At Burnt Mesa Pueblo, the method of tree ring dating gave the following dates A.D. for an archeological excavation site (*Bandelier Archaeological Excavation Project: Summer 1990 Excavations at Burnt Mesa Pueblo*, edited by Kohler, Washington State University, 1992):

1189	1267	1268	1275	1275
1271	1272	1316	1317	

   (a) Use a calculator with mean and standard deviation keys to verify that the sample mean date is $\bar{x} = 1272$ with sample standard deviation $s = 37$ years.

(b) Find a 90% confidence interval for the mean of all tree ring dates from this archaeological site.

6. *Consumer Reports* (November 1991) gave the following information about the life (hours) of size AA batteries in toys:

2.3	2.5	4.2	6.1	5.7	5.5	1.3
1.5	5.4	5.3	1.8	1.9	5.2	1.8
5.1	1.6					

(a) Use a calculator with mean and standard deviation keys to verify that the sample mean of the data is $\bar{x} = 3.58$ hours with sample standard deviation $s = 1.85$ hours.

(b) Find a 95% confidence interval for the mean life μ hours for all brand name AA batteries used in toys.

7. *Consumer Reports* (July 1993) gave the following information about annual premiums (in dollars) for 18 renewable life insurance policies with similar benefits:

300	345	328	426	660	388	410	563
303	360	395	278	455	577	470	455
373	365						

(a) Use a calculator with mean and standard deviation keys to verify that the sample mean is $\bar{x} = \$413.94$ with sample standard deviation $s = \$102.88$.

(b) Find a 90% confidence interval for the population of all annual premiums for such life insurance policies.

8. *USA Today* (June 16, 1993) reported the following information about pounds of candy consumed annually per person in the United States over the past several years:

18.4	18.3	19.2	20.8
20.4	20.1	20.3	20.4

(a) Use a calculator with mean and standard deviation keys to verify that the sample mean is $\bar{x} = 19.74$ pounds per person with sample standard deviation $s = 0.97$ pound per person.

(b) Compute a 95% confidence interval for the population mean annual per person consumption of candy in the United States.

(c) If a friend ate (on average) more than 2 pounds of candy each month, would that be considered above average consumption? Explain.

9. The *P/E* ratio is the price of a share of stock divided by the company's total earnings per share. If a company is fundamentally sound, then a low *P/E* ratio may indicate a bargain stock, whereas a high *P/E* ratio could indicate that the stock is overpriced. What is a large *P/E* ratio? This depends on the type of stock you have in mind. A random sample of 10 energy stocks (Exxon, Chevron, Mobil, Apache, and so on) listed in the *Wall Street Journal* gave the following *P/E* ratios:

14.1	12.2	19.3	15.4	10.0
13.2	22.4	16.3	15.1	17.2

(a) Use a calculator with mean and standard deviation keys to verify that the sample mean P/E ratio is $\bar{x} = 15.5$ with sample standard deviation $s = 3.56$.

(b) Assume that the data are representative of all energy stocks. Find a 95% confidence interval for the mean P/E ratio of all energy stocks.

(c) Does a mean P/E value of 10 seem to be below average for energy stocks? Explain.

10. The P/E ratios (see Problem 9) for retail stocks such as J. C. Penney, Sears, Gap, U.S. Shoe, and so on also can be found in the *Wall Street Journal*. A random sample of 15 such stocks gave the following P/E ratios:

7.4	5.1	6.6	4.1	3.3	6.1	8.5
6.2	4.4	8.1	10.2	7.0	8.4	6.3
5.1						

(a) Use a calculator with mean and standard deviation keys to verify that the sample mean P/E ratio is $\bar{x} = 6.45$ with sample standard deviation $s = 1.88$.

(b) Assume that the data are representative of all retail stocks. Find a 99% confidence interval for the mean P/E ratio of all retail stocks.

11. The shoulder height for a random sample of six fawns (less than 5 months old) in Mesa Verde National Park was $\bar{x} = 79.25$ cm with sample standard deviation $s = 5.33$ cm (*The Mule Deer of Mesa Verde National Park*, edited by G. W. Mierau and J. L. Schmidt, Mesa Verde Museum Association, 1981). Compute an 80% confidence interval for the mean shoulder height of the population of all fawns (less than 5 months old) in Mesa Verde National Park.

12. How many calories are there in 3 ounces of french fries? It depends on where you get them. *Good Cholesterol Bad Cholesterol*, by Roth and Streicher, gives the data from eight popular fast-food restaurants. The data are (in calories)

222	255	254	230	249	222	237	287

Use these data to create a 99% confidence interval for the mean calorie count in 3 ounces of french fries obtained from fast-food restaurants.

13. In *Hospitals* (July 20, 1989), 18 economic forecasters made predictions about the average length of stay (in days) in hospitals for 1995. The mean of the predictions was 6.7 days, with standard deviation 0.5. Using this information, construct a 90% confidence interval for the predicted mean length of a hospital stay in 1995.

14. In the same article cited in Problem 13, the 18 economists also made predictions as to the cost of health care as a percentage of GNP for 1995. The predicted mean was 13.1%, and the standard deviation was 1.09%.

Use this information to construct a 95% confidence interval for the predicted mean percent of GNP that health care will represent.

15. The number of pups in wolf dens of the southwestern United States is recorded below for 16 wolf dens (*The Wolf in the Southwest: The Making of an Endangered Species*, edited by D. E. Brown, University of Arizona Press, 1988).

5	8	7	5	3	4	3	9
5	8	5	6	5	6	4	7

    (a) Use a calculator with mean and standard deviation keys to verify that the sample mean is $\bar{x} = 5.63$ pups with sample standard deviation $s = 1.78$ pups.
    (b) Compute an 85% confidence interval for the population mean number of wolf pups per den in the southwestern United States.

16. The following information is taken from *Academe, Bulletin of the American Association of University Professors* (March 1993).
    (a) The percentage increases in annual salary for professors in a random sample of 10 colleges and universities in the western United States are shown below.

5.0	6.0	7.0	3.0	1.2
2.4	5.0	3.9	9.8	5.8

    Use a calculator with mean and standard deviation keys to verify that the sample mean is $\bar{x} = 4.91$ percentage increase with sample standard deviation $s = 2.47$ percentage increase. Compute a 90% confidence interval for the percentage increase in annual salary for professors in all colleges and universities in the western United States.
    (b) The percentage increases in annual salary for professors in a random sample of 15 colleges and universities on the East Coast of the United States are shown below.

6.3	8.6	6.6	4.8	4.5
7.5	4.6	6.3	8.0	3.5
4.9	5.2	6.4	3.9	5.0

    Use a calculator with mean and standard deviation keys to verify that the sample mean is $\bar{x} = 5.74$ percentage increase with sample standard deviation $s = 1.51$ percentage increase. Compute a 90% confidence interval for the percentage increase in annual salary for professors in all colleges and universities on the East Coast of the United States.
    (c) Compute the length of the confidence intervals in parts a and b. One interval is shorter than the other. Explain why. (*Hint:* Look at the sample sizes and sample standard deviations for both.)

17. André is head waiter at a famous gourmet restaurant in San Francisco. The Internal Revenue Service is doing an audit on his tax return this year.

In particular, the IRS wants to know the average amount André gets for a tip. In an effort to satisfy the IRS, André took a random sample of eight credit card receipts, each of which indicated his tip. The results were

$10.00	$11.93	$15.70	$ 9.10
$12.75	$11.15	$14.50	$13.65

(a) Use a calculator to verify that the sample mean is $12.35 and the sample standard deviation is $2.25.
(b) Find a 90% confidence interval for the population mean of tips received by André.

18. A random sample of records of 10 night shifts at the Emergency Medical Center gave the following information about the number of people admitted each night:

18   23   15   19   21   19   24   22   23   22

(a) Use a calculator to verify that the sample mean is 20.6 and the sample standard deviation is 2.8.
(b) Find a 95% confidence interval for the mean number of people admitted to the Emergency Medical Center during the night shift.

19. Error of depth perception is very important in dental work. A certain aptitude test asks subjects to estimate the distances between a fixed object and a second object of variable position. A random sample of 14 subjects gave the following information about errors in a particular depth perception test (units in millimeters):

1.1	1.5	0.9	2.1	1.4	1.7	0.8
1.3	1.8	1.1	1.6	1.9	1.2	1.6

(a) Use a calculator to verify that the sample mean of the above data is 1.43 mm and the sample standard deviation is 0.38 mm.
(b) Find a 90% confidence interval for the population mean of errors for this depth perception test.

Section 8.3   Estimating p in the Binomial Distribution

The binomial distribution is completely determined by the number of trials n and the probability p of success in a single trial. For most experiments, the number of trials is chosen in advance. Then the distribution is completely determined by p. In this section we will consider the problem of estimating p under the assumption that n has already been selected.

Basic Criteria

Again, we are employing what are called *large-sample methods*. We will assume that the normal curve is a good approximation to the binomial distribution, and when necessary, we will use sample estimates for the standard deviation. Empirical studies have shown that these methods are quite good provided that *both*

$$np > 5 \quad \text{and} \quad nq > 5 \quad \text{where } q = 1 - p$$

Let r be the number of successes out of n trials in a binomial experiment. We will take the proportion of successes $\hat{p} = r/n$ as our *point estimate* for p.

Point estimate for p

$$\hat{p} = \frac{r}{n}$$

Point estimate for q

$$\hat{q} = 1 - \hat{p}$$

For example, suppose 800 students are selected at random from a student body of 20,000 students and they are each given shots to prevent a certain type of flu. These 800 students are then exposed to the flu, and 600 of them do not get the flu. What is the probability p that the shot will be successful for any single student selected at random from the entire population of 20,000 students? We estimate p for the entire student body by computing r/n from the sample of 800 students. The value $\hat{p} = r/n$ is 600/800 or 0.75. The value $\hat{p} = 0.75$ is then the estimate for p.

Error of Estimate

The difference between the actual value of p and the estimate $\hat{p}$ is the size of our error caused by using $\hat{p}$ as a point estimate for p. The magnitude of $\hat{p} - p$ is called the *error of estimate* for $\hat{p} = r/n$ as a point estimate for p. In absolute value notation, the error of estimate is $|\hat{p} - p|$.

To compute the bounds for the error of estimate, we need some information about the distribution of $\hat{p} = r/n$ values for different samples of the same size n. It turns out that, for large samples, the distribution of $\hat{p}$ values is well approximated by a *normal curve with*

$$\text{mean } \mu = p \quad \text{and} \quad \text{standard error } \sigma = \sqrt{pq/n}$$

Since the distribution of $\hat{p} = r/n$ is approximately normal, we use features of the standard normal distribution to find the bounds for the difference $\hat{p} - p$. Recall that z_c is the number such that an area equal to c under the standard normal curve falls between $-z_c$ and z_c. Then, in terms of the language of probability,

$$P\left(-z_c\sqrt{\frac{pq}{n}} < \hat{p} - p < z_c\sqrt{\frac{pq}{n}}\right) = c \tag{16}$$

Equation (16) says that the chance is c that the numerical difference between $\hat{p}$ and p is between $-z_c\sqrt{pq/n}$ and $z_c\sqrt{pq/n}$. With the c confidence level, our estimate $\hat{p}$ differs from p by no more than

---

$$E = z_c\sqrt{pq/n}$$

As in Section 8.1, we call E the *maximal error tolerance* of the error of estimate $|\hat{p} - p|$ for a confidence level c.

Optional Derivation of Equation (16)

First we need to show that $\hat{p} = r/n$ has a distribution that is approximately normal with $\mu = p$ and $\sigma = \sqrt{pq/n}$. From Section 7.3 we know that, for sufficiently large n, the binomial distribution can be approximated by a normal distribution with mean $\mu = np$ and standard deviation $\sigma = \sqrt{npq}$. If r is the number of successes out of n trials of a binomial experiment, then r is a binomial random variable with a binomial distribution. When we convert r to standard z units, we obtain

$$z = \frac{r - \mu}{\sigma} = \frac{r - np}{\sqrt{npq}}$$

For sufficiently large n, r will be approximately normally distributed, so z will be too.

If we divide both numerator and denominator of the last expression by n, the value of z will not change.

$$z = \frac{\dfrac{r - np}{n}}{\dfrac{\sqrt{npq}}{n}}$$

When we simplify, we find

$$z = \frac{\dfrac{r}{n} - p}{\sqrt{\dfrac{pq}{n}}} \qquad (17)$$

The last equation tells us that the $\hat{p} = r/n$ distribution is approximated by a normal curve with $\mu = p$ and $\sigma = \sqrt{pq/n}$.

The probability is c that z lies in the interval between $-z_c$ and z_c because an area equal to c under the standard normal curve lies between $-z_c$ and z_c. Using the language of probability, we write

$$P(-z_c < z < z_c) = c$$

From Equation (17), we know that

$$z = \frac{\hat{p} - p}{\sqrt{\dfrac{pq}{n}}}$$

If we put this expression for z into the previous equation, we obtain

$$P\left(-z_c < \frac{\hat{p} - p}{\sqrt{\dfrac{pq}{n}}} < z_c\right) = c$$

If we multiply all parts of the inequality by $\sqrt{pq/n}$, we obtain the equivalent statement

$$P\left(-z_c \sqrt{\frac{pq}{n}} < \hat{p} - p < z_c \sqrt{\frac{pq}{n}}\right) = c \tag{16}$$

Confidence Interval for *p*

To find a c confidence interval for p, we will use E in place of the expression $z_c\sqrt{pq/n}$ in Equation (16). Then we get

$$P(-E < \hat{p} - p < E) = c \tag{18}$$

Some algebraic manipulation produces the mathematically equivalent statement

$$P(\hat{p} - E < p < \hat{p} + E) = c \tag{19}$$

Equation (19) says that the probability is c that p lies in the interval from $\hat{p} - E$ to $\hat{p} + E$. Therefore, the interval from $\hat{p} - E$ to $\hat{p} + E$ is the c confidence interval for p that we wanted to find.

There is one technical difficulty in computing the c confidence interval for p. The expression $E = z_c\sqrt{pq/n}$ requires that we know the values of p and q. In most situations, we will not know the actual values of p or q, so we will use our point estimates

$$p \approx \hat{p} \quad \text{and} \quad q = 1 - p \approx 1 - \hat{p}$$

to estimate E. These estimates are safe for most practical purposes, since we are dealing with large sample theory ($np > 5$ and $nq > 5$).

For convenient reference, we'll summarize the information about c confidence intervals for p, the probability of success.

- *Summary:* Consider a binomial distribution where n = number of trials, r = number of successes out of the n trials, p = probability of success on each trial, and q = probability of failure on each trial.

If n, p, and q are such that

$$np > 5 \quad \text{and} \quad nq > 5$$

then a c confidence interval for p is

$$\hat{p} - E < p < \hat{p} + E$$

where $\hat{p} = \dfrac{r}{n}$

$$E \approx z_c \sqrt{\frac{\hat{p}(1 - \hat{p})}{n}}$$

z_c = critical value for confidence level c taken from a normal distribution (see Table 8–2).

Example 5

Let's return to our flu shot experiment described at the beginning of this section. Suppose that 800 students were selected at random from a student body of 20,000 and given shots to prevent a certain type of flu. All 800 students were exposed to the flu, and 600 of them did not get the flu. Let p represent the probability that the shot will be successful for any single student selected at random from the entire population of 20,000. Let q be the probability that the shot is not successful.

(a) What is the number of trials n? What is the value of r?
   Solution: Since each of the 800 students receiving the shot may be thought of as a trial, then $n = 800$, and $r = 600$ is the number of successful trials.

(b) What are the point estimates for p and q?
   Solution: We estimate p by

$$\hat{p} = \frac{r}{n} = \frac{600}{800} = 0.75$$

We estimate q by

$$\hat{q} = 1 - \hat{p} = 1 - 0.75 = 0.25$$

(c) Would it seem that the number of trials is large enough to justify a normal approximation to the binomial?
   Solution: Since $n = 800$, $p \approx 0.75$, and $q \approx 0.25$, then

$$np \approx (800)(0.75) = 600 > 5 \quad \text{and} \quad nq \approx (800)(0.25) = 200 > 5$$

A normal approximation is certainly justified.

(d) Find a 99% confidence interval for p.
   Solution:

$$z_{0.99} = 2.58 \text{ (see Table 8–2)}$$

$$E \approx z_{0.99} \sqrt{\frac{\hat{p}(1 - \hat{p})}{n}}$$

$$\approx 2.58 \sqrt{\frac{(0.75)(0.25)}{800}}$$

$$\approx 0.0395$$

The 99% confidence interval is then

$$\hat{p} - E < p < \hat{p} + E$$

$$0.75 - 0.0395 < p < 0.75 + 0.0395$$

$$0.71 < p < 0.79$$

GUIDED EXERCISE 7

A random sample of 188 books purchased at a local bookstore showed that 66 of the books were murder mysteries. Let p represent the proportion of books sold by this store that are murder mysteries.

(a) What is a point estimate for p?

(a) $\hat{p} = \dfrac{r}{n} = \dfrac{66}{188} = 0.35$

(b) Find a 90% confidence interval for p.

(b) $E = z_c \sqrt{\dfrac{\hat{p}(1 - \hat{p})}{n}}$

$= 1.645 \sqrt{\dfrac{(0.35)(1 - 0.35)}{188}}$

$= 0.0572$

The confidence interval is

$$\hat{p} - E < p < \hat{p} + E$$
$$0.35 - 0.0572 < p < 0.35 + 0.0572$$
$$0.29 < p < 0.41$$

(c) What is the meaning of the confidence interval you just computed?

(c) If we had computed the interval for many different sets of 188 books, we would find that about 90% of the intervals actually contained p, the population proportion of mysteries. Consequently, we can be 90% sure that our interval contains the unknown value p.

(d) To compute the confidence interval, we used a normal approximation. Does this seem justified?

(d) $n = 188$
$p \approx 0.35$ and $q \approx 0.65$
Since $np \approx 65.8 > 5$ and $nq \approx 122.2 > 5$, the approximation is justified.

It is interesting to note that our point estimate $\hat{p} = r/n$ and the confidence interval for p do not depend on the size of the population. In our bookstore example, it made no difference how many books the store sold. On the other hand, the size of the sample does affect the accuracy of a statistical estimate. In the next section we will study the effect of sample size on the reliability of our estimate.

Margin of Error

Newspapers frequently report the results of an opinion poll. In articles that are more complete, a statement about the margin of error accompanies the poll results. The *margin of error* is the maximal error of estimate E for a confidence interval. Usually a 95% confidence interval is assumed. Some articles clarify the meaning of the margin of error further by saying that it is an error due to sampling. For instance, the following comments accompany results of a political poll reported in the October 29, 1993 issue of the *Wall Street Journal*.

How Poll Was Conducted

The *Wall Street Journal*/NBC News poll was based on nationwide telephone interviews of 1508 adults conducted last Friday through Tuesday by the polling organizations of Peter Hart and Robert Teeter.

The sample was drawn from 315 randomly selected geographic points in the continental U.S. Each region was represented in proportion to its population. Households were selected by a method that gave all telephone numbers, . . . an equal chance of being included.

One adult, 18 years or older, was selected from each household by a proce-dure to provide the correct number of male and female respondents.

Chances are 19 of 20 that if all adults with telephones in the U.S. had been surveyed, the findings would differ from these poll results by no more than 2.6 percentage points in either direction. A limited number of questions were asked of half the sample; for these, the margin of error was 3.7 percentage points. The margin for any subgroup would depend on the size of that group.

GUIDED EXERCISE 8

Read the last paragraph of the article, "How Poll Was Conducted."

(a) What confidence level corresponds to the phrase "chances are 19 of 20 that if . . . ."

(a) $\dfrac{19}{20} = 0.95$

A 95% confidence interval is being discussed.

(b) The article indicates that everyone in the sam-ple was asked the question, "Which party, the Democratic Party or the Republican Party, do you think would do a better job handling . . . education?" Possible responses were Demo-crats, neither, both, or Republicans. The poll reported that 32% of the respondents said "Democrats." Does 32% represent the sample statistic $\hat{p}$ or the population parameter p for the proportion of adults responding "Democrat?"

(b) 32% represents a sample statistic $\hat{p}$ because 32% represents the percentage of the adults in the *sample* who responded "Democrats."

(c) Continue reading the last paragraph of the ar-ticle. It goes on to state, ". . . if all adults with telephones in the U.S. had been surveyed, the findings would differ from these poll results by no more than 2.6 percentage points in either direction." Use this information together with parts a and b to find a 95% confidence interval for the proportion p of the specified popula-tion who would respond "Democrat" to the question.

(c) The value 2.6 percentage points represents the margin of error. Since the margin of error is equivalent to E, the maximal error of estimate for a 95% confidence interval, the confidence interval is

$$32\% - 2.6\% < p < 32\% + 2.6\%$$
$$29.4\% < p < 34.6\%$$

The poll indicates that at the time of the poll, between 29.4% and 34.6% of the specified population think Democrats do a better job handling education.

Section 8.3 Problems

For all these problems, carry at least four digits after the decimal in your calculations.

1. Isabel Myers was a pioneer in the study of personality types. The following information is taken from *A Guide to the Development and Use of the Myers-Briggs Type Indicator*, by Myers and McCaulley (Consulting Psychologists Press, Inc., 1990). In a random sample of 62 professional actors, it was found that 39 were extroverts.
   (a) Let p represent the proportion of all actors who are extroverts. Find a point estimate for p.
   (b) Find a 95% confidence interval for p. Give a brief interpretation of the meaning of the confidence interval you have found.
   (c) Do you think the conditions $np > 5$ and $nq > 5$ are satisfied in this problem? Explain why this would be an important consideration.

2. In a random sample of 519 judges, it was found that 285 were introverts (see reference of Problem 1).
   (a) Let p represent the proportion of all judges who are introverts. Find a point estimate for p.
   (b) Find a 99% confidence interval for p. Give a brief interpretation of the meaning of the confidence interval you have found.
   (c) Do you think the conditions $np > 5$ and $nq > 5$ are satisfied in this problem? Explain why this would be an important consideration.

3. A random sample of 5222 permanent dwellings on the entire Navajo Indian Reservation showed that 1619 were traditional Navajo hogans (*Navajo Architecture: Forms, History, Distributions*, by Jett and Spencer, University of Arizona Press, 1981).
   (a) Let p be the proportion of all permanent dwellings on the entire Navajo Reservation that are traditional hogans. Find a point estimate for p.
   (b) Find a 99% confidence interval for p. Give a brief interpretation of the confidence interval.
   (c) Do you think that $np > 5$ and $nq > 5$ are satisfied for this problem? Explain why this would be an important consideration.

4. Santa Fe black on white is a type of pottery commonly found at archaeological excavations in Bandelier National Monument. At one excavation site a sample of 592 potsherds were found, of which 360 were identified as Santa Fe black on white (*Bandelier Archaeological Excavation Project: Summer 1990 Excavations at Burnt Mesa Pueblo and Casa del Rito*, edited by Kohler and Root, Washington State University, 1992).
   (a) Let p represent the population proportion of Santa Fe black on white potsherds at the excavation site. Find a point estimate for p.
   (b) Find a 95% confidence interval for p. Give a brief statement of the meaning of the confidence interval.
   (c) Do you think that the conditions $np > 5$ and $nq > 5$ are satisfied in this problem? Why do you think this is important?

5. The past few years a nursery has kept records of blue spruce trees they

have replanted. Over this period it was found that 421 out of 518 blue spruce trees survived replanting.

(a) Let p be the proportion of blue spruce trees that survive replanting in the population of all such trees replanted by this nursery. Find a point estimate for p.

(b) Find a 99% confidence interval for p. Give a brief interpretation of the meaning of your confidence interval.

(c) Do you think that the conditions $np > 5$ and $nq > 5$ are satisfied in this problem? Why is this important?

6. The manager of the dairy section of a large supermarket took a random sample of 250 egg cartons and found that 40 cartons had at least one broken egg.

(a) Let p be the proportion of egg cartons with at least one broken egg out of the population of all egg cartons stocked by this store. Find a point estimate for p.

(b) Find a 90% confidence interval for p. Give a brief interpretation of the meaning of your confidence interval.

(c) Do you think that the conditions $np > 5$ and $nq > 5$ will be satisfied? Why is this important?

7. "Fugitive Task Force Runs 99 Photos in (Colorado) Springs News Paper: Police Make 17 Arrests." This was a headline in the *Rocky Mountain News* (January 11, 1994).

(a) Let p represent the population proportion of fugitives arrested after their photos are displayed in the newspaper. Find a point estimate for p.

(b) Find an 85% confidence interval for p. Give a brief statement of the meaning of the confidence interval.

(c) Do you think that the conditions $np > 5$ and $nq > 5$ are satisfied in this problem? Why do you think this is important?

8. Case studies showed that out of 10,351 convicts who escaped from U.S. prisons, only 7867 were recaptured (*The Book of Odds*, by Shook and Shook, Signet, 1993).

(a) Let p represent the proportion of all escaped convicts who will eventually be recaptured. Find a point estimate for p.

(b) Find a 99% confidence interval for p. Give a brief statement of the meaning of the confidence interval.

(c) Is use of the normal approximation to the binomial justified in this problem? Explain.

9. In a survey of 2503 men and women aged 18 to 75 years and representative of the nation as a whole, 1927 people said the homeless are not adequately assisted by the government ("Parade Magazine," *Rocky Mountain News*, January 9, 1994).

(a) Let p represent the proportion of adults in the general population who agree with the statement that the homeless are not adequately assisted by the government. Find a point estimate for p.

(b) Find a 90% confidence interval for p. Is use of the normal approximation to the binomial justified in this problem? Explain.

10. The survey in "Parade Magazine" (see Problem 9) also indicated that 1602 people out of the 2503 surveyed said they would donate money for the homeless if there were a place on their tax return to do so.
    (a) Let p represent the proportion of adults in the general population who say that they would donate money for the homeless on their tax return. Find a point estimate for p.
    (b) Find a 90% confidence interval for p. Is use of the normal approximation to the binomial justified in this problem? Explain.

11. Coors Brewing Company and its 5-year literacy campaign commissioned a poll of 1000 adults to promote national literacy. One of the results of this study indicated that 250 of the adults surveyed had the habit of reading at least 30 minutes before going to bed every night (*USA Today*, September 27, 1993).
    (a) Let p represent the proportion of all adults who read at least 30 minutes before going to bed every night. Find a point estimate for p.
    (b) Find a 95% confidence interval for p. Is use of the normal approximation to the binomial justified in this problem? Explain.

12. A national survey of 1034 parents showed that 848 claimed pizza was their children's favorite food (*USA Today*, January 14, 1992).
    (a) Let p represent the proportion of all parents who claim that pizza is their children's favorite food. Find a point estimate for p.
    (b) Find an 85% confidence interval for p. Is use of the normal approximation to the binomial justified in this problem? Explain.

13. The *Wall Street Journal* (January 3, 1994) published a list of interest-rate forecasts by 51 well-known economic forecasters. Of these 51 forecasters, it was found that 36 had overestimated the actual interest rate, 9 were very close to the actual interest rate, and 6 had underestimated the interest rate in January of 1994. The forecast was made in July of 1993. Assume that these data are representative of the population of all economic forecasters.
    (a) Construct a 90% confidence interval for the proportion of all economic forecasters who would overestimate the interest rate during this period.
    (b) Repeat part a for the proportion of all economic forecasters who would be close to the actual interest rate for this period.
    (c) Repeat part a for the proportion of all economic forecasters who would be below the actual interest rate for this period.
    (d) Is the normal approximation to the binomial justified in parts a, b, and c? Explain.

14. In a survey of 1000 large corporations, 250 said that given a choice between a job candidate who smokes and an equally qualified nonsmoker, the nonsmoker will get the job (*USA Today*).

(a) Let p represent the proportion of all corporations preferring a non-smoking candidate. Find a point estimate for p.

(b) Find a 0.90 confidence interval for p.

15. The U.S. Department of the Interior is checking cattle on the Windgate open range in Montana. A random sample of 900 cattle shows that 54 are undernourished.

    (a) Let p represent the proportion of undernourished cattle on the Windgate range. Find a point estimate for p.

    (b) Find a 0.99 confidence interval for p.

16. A random sample of 683 fish taken from a popular fishing lake in Maine showed that 217 were yellow perch.

    (a) Let p be the proportion of fish taken from the lake that are yellow perch. Find a point estimate for p.

    (b) Find a 0.95 confidence interval for p.

17. Attending sporting events is a popular source of entertainment. When 1000 people were surveyed, 590 said that getting together with friends was an important reason for attending a sporting event (*USA Today,* December 4, 1989).

    (a) Let p be the proportion of all people attending a sporting event to be with friends. Find a point estimate for p.

    (b) Find a 99% confidence interval for p.

18. The Postmaster in Atlanta, Georgia, found that 44 out of a random sample of 400 packages had insufficient postage.

    (a) Let p be the probability that a package selected at random has insufficient postage. Find a point estimate for p.

    (b) Find a 0.99 confidence interval for p.

19. The Roper Organization conducted a poll of 2000 adults and found that 382 regularly listen to an AM radio station at home (*USA Today,* June 10, 1992).

    (a) Let p represent the proportion of the adult population that regularly listens to an AM radio station at home. Find a point estimate for p.

    (b) Find an 80% confidence interval for p. Is use of the normal approximation to the binomial justified in this problem? Explain.

20. If you were writing a report on some of the results of the poll commissioned by the Coors Brewing Company and its 5-year literacy campaign (see Problem 11), how would you report the percentage of adults who have a habit of reading at least 30 minutes before going to bed every night? What is the margin of error based on a 95% confidence interval?

21. A January 1994 *New York Times*/CBS Poll asked the question, "What do you think is the most important problem facing this country today?" Nineteen percent of the respondents answered "crime and violence." The margin of sampling error was plus or minus 3 percentage points. Following the convention that the margin of error is based on a 95% confidence interval, find a 95% confidence interval for the percentage of the population that would respond "crime and violence" to the question asked by the pollsters.

Section 8.4   Choosing the Sample Size

In the design stages of statistical research projects, it is a good idea to decide in advance on the confidence level you wish to use and to select the *maximum* error of estimate E you want for your project. How you choose to make these decisions depends on the requirements of the project and the practical nature of the problem. Whatever specifications you make, the next step is to determine the sample size. In this section we will assume that the distribution of sample means $\bar{x}$ is approximately normal, and when necessary, we will approximate σ by the sample standard deviation s. These methods are technically justifiable since our samples will be of size at least 30.

Sample Size for Estimating μ

Let's say that at a confidence level of c, we want our point estimate $\bar{x}$ for μ to be in error either way by less than some quantity E. In other words, E is the maximum error of estimate we can tolerate. Using the language of probability, we want the following to be true:

$$P(-E < \bar{x} - \mu < E) = c \tag{20}$$

This is essentially the same as Equation (1) of Section 8.1. Let's compare them.

$$P(-E < \bar{x} - \mu < E) = c \tag{20}$$

$$\downarrow \qquad \downarrow \qquad \downarrow$$

$$P\left(-z_c\frac{\sigma}{\sqrt{n}} < \bar{x} - \mu < z_c\frac{\sigma}{\sqrt{n}}\right) = c \tag{1}$$

From this comparison, we see that we want E to be

$$E = z_c\frac{\sigma}{\sqrt{n}}$$

Solving this equation for n, we get

$$n = \left(\frac{z_c\sigma}{E}\right)^2 \tag{21}$$

To compute n from Equation (21), we must know the value of σ. If the value of σ is not previously known, we do a preliminary sampling to approximate it. For most practical purposes, a preliminary sample of size 30 or larger will give a sample standard deviation s, which we may use to approximate σ.

Example 6

A wildlife study is designed to find the mean weight of salmon caught by an Alaskan fishing company. As a preliminary study, a random sample of 50 freshly caught salmon is weighed. The sample standard deviation of the weights of these 50 fish is $s = 2.15$ lb. How large a sample should be taken to be 99% confident that the sample mean $\bar{x}$ is within 0.20 lb of the true mean weight μ?

Solution: In this problem $z_{0.99} = 2.58$ (see Table 8–2) and $E = 0.20$. The preliminary study of 50 fish is large enough to permit a good approximation of σ by $s = 2.15$. Therefore, Equation (21) becomes

$$n = \left(\frac{z_c \sigma}{E}\right)^2 \approx \left(\frac{(2.58)(2.15)}{0.20}\right)^2 = 769.2$$

In determining sample size, any fraction value of n is always rounded to the *next higher whole number.* We conclude that a sample size of 770 will be enough to satisfy the specifications. Of course, a sample size larger than 770 also will work.

Example 7 A certain company makes light fixtures on an assemblyline. An efficiency expert wants to determine the mean time it takes an employee to assemble the switch on one of these fixtures. A preliminary study used a random sample of 45 observations and found that the sample standard deviation was $s = 78$ seconds. How many more observations are necessary for the efficiency expert to be 95% sure that the point estimate $\bar{x}$ will be "off" from the true mean μ by at most 15 seconds?
Solution: In this example we approximate σ by $s = 78$. We use $z_{0.95} = 1.96$ (see Table 8–2). The maximum error of estimate is specified to be $E = 15$ seconds. Equation (21) gives us

$$n = \left(\frac{z_c \sigma}{E}\right)^2 = \left(\frac{(1.96)(78)}{15}\right)^2 = 103.9$$

The efficiency expert should use a sample of minimum size 104. Since the preliminary study has 45 observations, an additional $104 - 45 = 59$ observations are necessary.

GUIDED EXERCISE 9

A large state college has over 1800 faculty members. The dean of faculty wants to estimate the average teaching experience (in years) of the faculty members. A preliminary random sample of 60 faculty members yields a sample standard deviation of $s = 3.4$ years. The dean wants to be 99% confident that the sample mean $\bar{x}$ does not differ from the population mean by more than half a year. How large a sample should be used? Let's answer this question in parts.

(a) What value can we use to approximate σ? Why can we do this?

(b) What is $z_{0.99}$? (*Hint:* See Table 8–2.)

(c) What is E for this problem?

(d) Which is the correct formula for n:

$$\left(\frac{z_c \sigma}{n}\right)^2, \left(\frac{z_c \sigma}{E}\right)^2, \text{ or } \left(\frac{z_c E}{\sigma}\right)^2$$

(a) $s = 3.4$ years is a good approximation because a preliminary sample of 60 is fairly large.

(b) $z_{0.99} = 2.58$

(c) $E = 0.5$ year

(d) $n = \left(\frac{z_c \sigma}{E}\right)^2$

(e) Use the formula for n to find the minimum sample size. Should your answer be rounded up or down to a whole number?

(e) $n = \left(\dfrac{(2.58)(3.4)}{0.5}\right)^2 = (17.54)^2 = 307.8$

Always round n up to the next whole number. Our final answer $n = 308$ is the minimum size.

Sample Size for Estimating
$\hat{p} = r/n$

(If you omitted the binomial distribution, omit the rest of this section.)

Next, we will determine the minimum sample size when we use r/n as a point estimate for p in a binomial distribution. We will use the methods of normal approximation (large samples) discussed in Section 8.3. Suppose for a confidence level c we want the estimate $\hat{p} = r/n$ for p to be in error either way by less than some quantity E. Using the language of probability, we want the following to be true.

$$P(-E < \hat{p} - p < E) = c \tag{22}$$

Let's compare this with Equation (16) of Section 8.3. For convenience, they both are written together:

$$P(-E < \hat{p} - p < E) = c \tag{22}$$

$$P\left(-z_c \sqrt{\dfrac{pq}{n}} < \hat{p} - p < z_c \sqrt{\dfrac{pq}{n}}\right) = c \tag{16}$$

The comparison of the two equations gives a formula for E:

$$E = z_c \sqrt{\dfrac{pq}{n}}$$

Solving the last equation for n, we get

$$n = pq\left(\dfrac{z_c}{E}\right)^2$$

Since $q = 1 - p$, our equation for n can be written

$$n = p(1 - p)\left(\dfrac{z_c}{E}\right)^2 \tag{23}$$

Equation (23) cannot be used unless we already have a preliminary estimate for p. To get around this difficulty, we will use the equation $p(1 - p) = \frac{1}{4} - (p - \frac{1}{2})^2$. This is an algebraic identity that you are asked to verify in an optional exercise at the end of this section. In this exercise you are also asked to use a little logical deduction to show that the maximum possible value of

2. Root depth for grasses and shrubs in a type of soil known as glacial out-wash was studied in Yellowstone National Park by D. G. Despain (see reference in Problem 1). Let x be a random variable representing root depth in this type of soil. It was found that the standard deviation of x values is approximately $\sigma = 8.94$ in. In a proposed study region of glacial outwash, how many plants should be carefully dug up and studied to be 90% sure that the sample mean root depth $\bar{x}$ is within 0.5 in. of the population mean root depth?

*3. Suppose that you live near a McDonald's restaurant and you want to estimate the proportion p of all people in your neighborhood who go to McDonald's on a typical day.
   (a) If you had no preliminary estimate for p, how many people should you include in a random sample to be 85% sure that the point estimate $\hat{p}$ will be within a distance of 0.05 from p?
   (b) Answer part a if you use the preliminary estimate that nationally about 1 in 20 Americans goes to McDonald's every day (*Fascinating McFacts*, provided by McDonald's Corporation).

4. A random sample of 41 basketball players from the "All-Time Player Directory" of *The Official NBA Basketball Encyclopedia* (Villard Books) gave a sample standard deviation for height of players $s = 3.32$ in. How many more basketball players from the "All-Time Player Directory" should be included in the sample to be 95% sure that the sample mean $\bar{x}$ is within 0.75 in. of the population mean μ of all players listed in the NBA encyclopedia?

5. The NBA "All-Time Player Directory" also gives the weight of each basketball player. A random sample of 56 basketball players from the directory (see the reference in Problem 4) gave a sample standard deviation $s = 26.58$ pounds for the weights of players. How many more basketball players from the "All-Time Player Directory" should be included in the sample to be 90% sure that the sample mean player weight $\bar{x}$ is within 4 pounds of the population mean μ?

*6. How hard is it to reach a businessperson by phone? Let p be the proportion of calls to businesspeople for which the caller reaches the person being called on the *first* try.
   (a) If you have no preliminary estimate for p, how many business phone calls should you include in a random sample to be 80% sure that the point estimate $\hat{p}$ will be within a distance of 0.03 from p?
   (b) *The Book of Odds*, by Shook and Shook (Signet, 1993), reports that businesspeople can be reached by a single phone call approximately 17% of the time. Using this (national) estimate for p, answer part a.

*7. What percentage of the campus student body is female? Let p be the proportion of women students on your campus.
   (a) If no preliminary study is made to estimate p, how large a sample is

*Omit problems marked with an asterisk if you omitted the binomial distribution.

needed to be 99% sure that a point estimate $\hat{p}$ will be within a distance of 0.05 from p?

(b) The *Statistical Abstract of the United States*, 112th ed., indicates that approximately 54% of college students are females. Answer part a using this estimate for p.

*8. At many gasoline stations customers have the option of using self-service pumps and receiving a discount instead of using full-service pumps. The question is: What proportion of customers in your neighborhood take advantage of this option and use the self-service pumps?

(a) If no preliminary study is made to estimate p, how large a sample of customers is necessary to be 90% sure that the point estimate $\hat{p}$ will be within a distance 0.08 of p?

(b) Nationally, about 81% of the gasoline customers use self-service pumps (source: Amoco Oil Corporation). Answer part a for your neighborhood using this estimate for p.

9. At the site of a nuclear waste spill, cleanup crews were working to bring the mean radiation level down to 16 microcuries, with a maximum error tolerance of ±0.5 microcuries. A random sample of 30 readings around the spill area gave a sample standard deviation $s = 1.75$ microcuries. How many more sample readings should be taken to be 99% confident that the sample mean $\bar{x}$ is within ±0.5 microcuries of the population mean radiation μ?

10. Logan's Pharmacy wants to estimate the average amount a customer pays for a prescription. A preliminary random sample of 150 customers shows the sample standard deviation to be $3.62. How many *more* customers should be included in a random sample to be 99% confident that the sample mean $\bar{x}$ is within $0.50 of the population mean cost μ?

*11. A ponderosa pine forest in Colorado has a pine beetle infestation. The beetles bore into a tree and carry a fungus which ultimately kills the tree. Let p be the proportion of trees in the forest that are infested.

(a) If no preliminary sample is taken to estimate p, how large a sample is necessary to be 85% sure that a point estimate $\hat{p}$ will be within a distance of 0.06 from p?

(b) A preliminary study of 58 trees showed that 19 were infested. How many *more* trees should be included in the sample to be 85% sure that a point estimate $\hat{p}$ will be within a distance of 0.06 from p?

12. Gordon is thinking of buying a combination hardware/sporting goods store in Dove Creek, Montana. However, daily cash flow is an important consideration. A random sample of 40 business days from the past year was taken from the store records. For each day the net income was determined. The sample standard deviation was found to be $57.19. How many *more* business days should be included in the sample to be 85%

---

* Omit problems marked with an asterisk if you omitted the binomial distribution.

confident that the sample mean $\bar{x}$ of daily net incomes is within $10 of the population mean μ of daily net incomes?

*13. David is doing a research project in political science to determine the proportion p of voters in his district who favor capital punishment.
   (a) If no preliminary sample of voters is taken to estimate p, how large a sample is necessary to be 99% sure that a point estimate $\hat{p}$ will be within a distance of 0.01 from p?
   (b) The National Opinion Research Center at the University of Chicago found that approximately 67% of people in the United States favor capital punishment. Use this estimate to answer part a.

14. A sociologist is studying marriage customs in a rural community in Denmark. A random sample of 35 women who have been married was used to determine the age of the woman at the time of her first marriage. The sample standard deviation of these ages was 2.3 years. The sociologist wants to estimate the population mean age of a woman at the time of her first marriage. How many *more* women should be included in the sample to be 95% confident that the sample mean $\bar{x}$ of ages is within 0.25 year of the population mean μ?

15. When customers phone an airline to make reservations, they usually find it irritating if they are kept on hold for a long time. In an effort to determine how long phone customers are kept on hold, one airline took a random sample of 167 phone calls and determined the length of time (in minutes) each was kept on hold. The sample standard deviation was 3.8 minutes. How many more phone customers should be included in the sample to be 99% sure that the sample mean $\bar{x}$ of hold times is within 30 seconds of the population mean μ of hold times?

*16. The National Council of Small Businesses is interested in the proportion of small businesses that declared Chapter 11 bankruptcy last year. Since there are so many small businesses, the National Council intends to estimate the proportion from a random sample. Let p be the proportion of small businesses that declared Chapter 11 bankruptcy last year.
   (a) If no preliminary sample is taken to estimate p, how large a sample is necessary to be 95% sure that a point estimate $\hat{p}$ will be within a distance of 0.10 from p?
   (b) In a preliminary random sample of 38 small businesses, it was found that 6 had declared Chapter 11 bankruptcy. How many *more* small businesses should be included in the sample to be 95% sure that a point estimate $\hat{p}$ will be within a distance of 0.10 from p?

*17. Let p be the proportion of all pickup truck owners in Cheyenne, Wyoming, who are women.
   (a) If no preliminary study is made to estimate p, how large a sample is necessary to be 90% sure that a point estimate $\hat{p}$ will be within a distance of 0.1 from p?

* Omit problems marked with an asterisk if you omitted the binomial distribution.

(b) *USA Today* (December 18, 1993) reported that nationally, approximately 24% of all pickup trucks are owned by women. Answer part a using this estimate for p.

*18. Linda Silbers is a social scientist studying voter opinion about a city bond proposal for a light-rail mass transit system in Denver.
  (a) If Linda wants to be 90% sure that her sample estimate of the proportion of voters who favor the bond is within 5% of the population percent p who favor the bond issue, how large a sample should she use?
  (b) If a preliminary study showed that p is approximately 73%, how large a sample is required?

*19. (a) Show that $p(1 - p) = 1/4 - (p - 1/2)^2$.
  (b) Why is $p(1 - p)$ never greater than 1/4?

20. You are working for a local polling firm. Your project involves interviewing a random sample of registered voters to determine the percentage favoring the use of state lottery proceeds for park improvements. The firm wants to ensure that the margin of error is no more than 3 percentage points either way. Assuming that there is no preliminary estimate for the percentage of registered voters favoring this use of lottery funds, what is the *minimum* number of respondents required? (*Hint:* Convert the margin of error to decimal and use the *New York Times*/CBS convention that the margin of error is based on a 95% confidence level.)

Section 8.5   Estimating $\mu_1 - \mu_2$ and $p_1 - p_2$

We have all heard the exclamation, "So what!" Philologists (people who study cultural linguistics) tell us that this expression is a shortened version of "So what is the difference!" They also tell us that there are similar popular or slang expressions about differences in all languages and cultures. It is human nature to challenge the claim that something is better, worse, or just simply different. In this section we will focus on this very human theme by studying probable differences between population means and probable differences between population proportions. In a way this is another example of what the great French mathematician Laplace meant when he said, "the theory of probability is at bottom only common sense reduced to calculation."

Independent Samples and Dependent Samples

In order to make a statistical estimate about the difference between two population parameters, we need to have a sample from each population. Samples may be *independent* or *dependent* according to how they are selected. If the way we take a sample from one population is unrelated to the selection of sample data from the other population, the samples are called *independent*. However, if the samples are chosen in such a way that *each measurement* in one sample can be naturally *paired* with a measurement in the other sample, then the samples are called *dependent*.

* Omit problems marked with an asterisk if you omitted the binomial distribution.

Dependent samples and data pairs occur very naturally in "before and after" situations where the *same object* or item is *measured twice*. We will devote an entire section (9.6) to the study of dependent samples and paired data. However, in this section we will confine our interest to independent samples.

Independent samples occur very naturally when we draw *two random samples*, one from the first population and one from the second population. Because *both* samples are random samples, there is no pairing of measurements between the two populations. All the examples of this section will involve independent random samples.

GUIDED EXERCISE 11

For each experiment, categorize the sampling as independent or dependent, and explain your choice.

(a) In many medical experiments, a sample of subjects is randomly divided into two groups. One group is given a specific treatment, and the other group is given a placebo. After a certain period of time, both groups are measured for the same condition. Do the measurements from these two groups constitute independent or dependent samples?

(a) Since the subjects are *randomly assigned* to the two treatment groups (one a treatment, the other a placebo), the resulting measurements would form independent samples.

(b) In an accountability study, a group of students in an English composition course is given a pretest. After the course, the same students are given a posttest over the same material. Are the two groups of scores independent or dependent?

(b) Since the pretest scores and the posttest scores are from the same students, the samples are dependent. Each student has both a pretest score and a posttest score, so there is a natural pairing of data values.

The $\bar{x}_1 - \bar{x}_2$ Sampling Distribution

In this section we will use probability distributions that arise from a difference of means (or proportions). How do we obtain such distributions? Suppose that we have two statistical variables x_1 and x_2 each with its own distribution. We take *independent* random samples of size n_1 from the x_1 distribution and of size n_2 from the x_2 distribution. Then we compute the respective means $\bar{x}_1$ and $\bar{x}_2$. Now consider the difference $\bar{x}_1 - \bar{x}_2$. This expression represents a difference of means. If we repeat this sampling process over and over, we will create lots of $\bar{x}_1 - \bar{x}_2$ values. Figure 8–6 illustrates the sampling distribution of $\bar{x}_1 - \bar{x}_2$.

The values of $\bar{x}_1 - \bar{x}_2$ that come from repeated (independent) sampling from populations 1 and 2 can be arranged in a relative-frequency table and a relative-frequency histogram (see Section 2.3). This would give us an experimental idea of the theoretical probability distribution of $\bar{x}_1 - \bar{x}_2$.

Figure 8–6 Sampling Distribution of $\bar{x}_1 - \bar{x}_2$

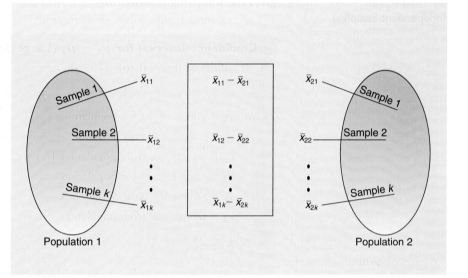

Fortunately, it is not necessary to carry out this lengthy process for each example. The results have been worked out mathematically. The next theorem presents the main results.

- ***Theorem 8.1:*** Let x_1 have a normal distribution with mean μ_1 and standard deviation σ_1. Let x_2 have a normal distribution with mean μ_2 and standard deviation σ_2. If we take independent random samples of size n_1 from the x_1 distribution and of size n_2 from the x_2 distribution, then the variable $\bar{x}_1 - \bar{x}_2$ has

  1. a normal distribution
  2. mean $\mu_1 - \mu_2$
  3. standard deviation

$$\sqrt{\frac{\sigma_1^2}{n_1} + \frac{\sigma_2^2}{n_2}}$$

- ***Comment:*** The theorem requires that x_1 and x_2 have *normal* distributions. However, if *both* n_1 and n_2 are 30 or larger (and the distributions are approximately mound-shaped and symmetrical), then the central limit theorem (Section 7.2) assures us that $\bar{x}_1$ and $\bar{x}_2$ are approximately normally distributed. In this case, the conclusions of the theorem are again valid even if the original x_1 and x_2 distributions are not exactly normal.

  Furthermore, for most practical applications, if $n_1 \geqslant 30$ and $n_2 \geqslant 30$, then the approximation $s_1 \approx \sigma_1$ and $s_2 \approx \sigma_2$ give very usable results (where s_1 and s_2 are the sample standard deviations of populations 1 and 2, respectively).

for the population proportion p of people who favor Standard Time. Report the same information in terms of a margin of error.

4. Examine Figure 8–8, "Coupons: Limited Clipping" (*USA Today,* October 19, 1993).

Figure 8–8 Coupons: Limited Clipping (October 19, 1993)

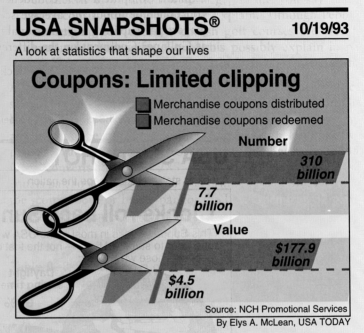

Source: Copyright 1993, USA TODAY.
Reprinted with permission.

(a) Use Figure 8–8 to estimate the percentage of merchandise coupons that were redeemed. Also estimate the percentage of dollar value of the coupons that were redeemed. Are these numbers approximately equal?

(b) Suppose that you are a marketing executive working for a national chain of toy stores. You wish to estimate the percentage of coupons that will be redeemed for the toy stores. How many coupons should you check to be 95% sure that the percentage of coupons redeemed is within 1% of the population proportion of all coupons redeemed for the toy store?

(c) Use the results of part (a) as a preliminary estimate for p, the percentage of coupons that are redeemed, and redo part (b).

(d) Suppose that you sent out 937 coupons and found that 27 were redeemed. Explain why you could be 95% confident that the proportion of such coupons redeemed in the future would be between 1.9% and 3.9%.

(e) Suppose that the dollar value of a collection of coupons was $10,000. Use the data in Figure 8–8 to find the expected value and standard deviation of the dollar value of the redeemed coupons. What is the probability that between $225 and $275 (out of the $10,000) is redeemed?

LINKING CONCEPTS

Discuss each of the following topics in class or review the topics on your own. Then write a brief but complete essay in which you summarize the main points. Please include formulas and graphs as appropriate.

1. In this chapter we have studied confidence intervals. Carefully read the following statements about confidence intervals:

   (a) Once the endpoints of the confidence interval are numerically fixed, then the parameter in question (either μ or p) does or does not fall inside the "fixed" interval.

   (b) A given fixed interval either does or does not contain the parameter μ or p; therefore, the probability is 1 or 0 that the parameter is in the interval.

   Next, read the following statements. Then discuss all four statements in the context of what we actually mean by a confidence interval.

   (c) Nontrivial probability statements can be made only about variables, not constants.

   (d) The confidence level c represents the proportion of all (fixed) intervals that would contain the parameter if we repeated the process many, many times.

2. Throughout Chapter 8 we have used the normal distribution, the central limit theorem, or the student's t distribution.

   (a) Give a brief outline describing how confidence intervals for means use the central limit theorem or student's t distribution in their basic construction.

   (b) Give a brief outline describing how the normal approximation to the binomial distribution is used in the construction of confidence intervals for a proportion p.

   (c) Give a brief outline describing how the sample size for a predetermined error tolerance and level of confidence is determined from the normal distribution or the central limit theorem.

3. When results of a survey or a poll are published, the sample size is usually given as well as the margin of error. For example, suppose the *Honolulu Star Bulletin* reported that they surveyed 385 Honolulu residents and 78% said they favor mandatory jail sentences for people convicted of driving under the influence of drugs or alcohol (with margin of error of 5 percentage points in either direction). Usually the confidence level of the

interval is not given, but it is standard practice to use the margin of error for a 95% confidence interval when no other confidence level is given.

(a) The paper reported a point estimate of 78% with margin of error of ±5%. Write this information in the form of a confidence interval for p, the population proportion of residents favoring mandatory jail sentences for people convicted of driving under the influence. What is the assumed confidence level?

(b) The margin of error is simply the error due to using a sample instead of the entire population. It does not take into account the bias that might be introduced by the wording of the question, by the truthfulness of the respondents, or by other factors. Suppose the question was asked in this fashion: "Considering the devastating injuries suffered by innocent victims in auto accidents caused by drunken or drugged drivers, do you favor a mandatory jail sentence for those convicted of driving under the influence of drugs or alcohol?" Do you think the wording of the questions would influence the respondents? Do you think the population proportion of those favoring mandatory jail sentences is accurately represented by a confidence interval based on responses to such a question? Explain your answer.

Suppose the question had been: "Considering the existing overcrowding of our prisons, do you favor a mandatory jail sentence for people convicted of driving under the influence of drugs or alcohol?" Do you think the population proportion of those favoring mandatory jail sentences is accurately represented by a confidence interval based on responses to such a question? Explain your answer.

Using Technology

The problems in this section may be done using statistical computer software or calculators with statistical functions. Displays and suggestions are given for Minitab (Release 9), the TI-82 graphing calculator, and ComputerStat.

Demonstration of the Meaning of a *c*% Confidence Interval

Suppose you select 30 numbers at random on the line segment from 0 to 1. Then you find the sample mean $\bar{x}$ and sample standard deviation s of the numbers you selected at random. Using the material we learned in this chapter, we realize that we have a large sample and a 90% confidence interval would be given by

$$\bar{x} - 1.645 \frac{s}{\sqrt{30}} < \mu < \bar{x} + 1.645 \frac{s}{\sqrt{30}}$$

where μ is the population mean of all numbers selected at random between 0 and 1.

However, in this special case mathematical theories can be used to show that for the *population* of all random numbers taken from the interval 0 to 1 the population mean is just $\mu = 0.5$. Since in this special case we actually know $\mu = 0.5$, we can use this information to do a little checking up on our theory of confidence intervals. What does it mean to say we have a 90% confidence interval for the population mean μ? It means that if we construct many confidence intervals (from many samples) then in the long run, about 90% of these intervals will in fact contain μ. Figure 8–3 illustrated this property.

Now let's use the computer to check up on this statement. Notice that we cannot use the computer to actually *prove* we have a 90% confidence interval. However, we can use the computer to give a numerical demonstration that we have a 90% confidence interval.

Minitab

In Minitab you can write a brief program to draw random samples from the uniform distribution of all numbers between 0 and 1. Then you can construct *c*% confidence intervals for the mean μ using large samples. Such a program is shown in the Computer Displays for samples of size 35. Modifications of the program can be made to accommodate other sample sizes and other confidence levels.

TI-82

On the TI-82 you can store random numbers between 0 and 1 in a list. Then using the mean and standard deviation of the list and critical values z_c from Table 8–2, you can construct confidence intervals for a given sample size.

ComputerStat

In the ComputerStat menu of topics, select Confidence Intervals. Then select the program Confidence Interval Demonstration. This computer program selects 20 random samples each of size N (you select N from 30 to 500). Each sample consists of N random numbers from 0 to 1. Then the computer finds 90% confidence intervals for each sample and keeps a running tally of how many intervals actually contain the population mean $\mu = 0.5$. As we know from theory, about 90% of the intervals should contain μ. It is interesting to see how our theory shapes up against actual calculations.

Application I

It is easiest to do this application using the Confidence Interval Demonstration program in ComputerStat. However, you can generate programs for Minitab or some graphing calculators to do similar activities.

(a) Run the program for a sample size of $N = 30$. The computer will find 20 confidence intervals for $\mu = 0.5$ based on samples of size 30. Look at the displayed confidence intervals and their graphs. Look at the tally and percent of intervals that contain $\mu = 0.5$. Look at the length of each interval on the graph. Now use the program option to find more confidence intervals of size $N = 30$. Keep on finding intervals until you have 100 of them. In the long run, what percent of the intervals seem to contain $\mu = 0.5$? How is this predicted by what we have learned in this chapter?

(b) Repeat part (a) for a sample size of $N = 60$. Pay close attention to the lengths of the intervals graphed. Are these intervals longer or shorter than those of part (a)? Explain why you should expect them to be longer or shorter. We have a larger sample size than that of part (a) but we still get only about 90% of the intervals containing $\mu = 0.5$. Again explain why we expect only 90% to contain μ and not a higher percent.

(c) Run the program for a sample size of $N = 500$. Just compute 20 intervals and no more (this will take about 90 seconds). Again compare the graphs of these intervals with those of part (a) and part (b). Which are the longest? The shortest? Why do we expect these results? A sample size of 500 is a very large sample, but we still get only about 90% of the intervals containing $\mu = 0.5$. Explain why we expect this to be the case.

Finding a Confidence Interval for a Population Mean *Mu* (Small Sample)

Most statistical software packages for computers have commands to generate confidence intervals for data you have entered. On most graphing calculators, you enter the data, compute the mean and sample standard deviation, and then use values of t_c from a table to compute the endpoints of the confidence intervals.

Minitab

The commands

```
MTB > SET C1 #Enter your data in column 1
MTB > TINTERVAL 90 for C1
```

generate a 90% confidence interval for the mean based on the sample in column C1.

TI-82

To find a confidence interval for μ on the TI-82, enter your data in a list such as L1, and use 1- Var Stats L1 to find the mean and sample standard deviation of the data in L1. Then compute the endpoints of the confidence interval using an appropriate value of t_c or z_c (from Table 7 of Appendix II or Table 8–2 respectively), the values of $\bar{x}$ and s, and the formulas for the endpoints of the confidence interval.

ComputerStat

Under the menu Confidence Intervals, select the program Confidence Intervals for a Population Mean *MU*. Then follow the instructions on the screen to enter your data and your confidence level.

Application 2

Cryptanalysis, the science of breaking codes, makes extensive use of language patterns. The frequency of various letter combinations is an important part of the study. A letter combination consisting of a single letter is a monograph, while combinations consisting of two letters are called digraphs, and those with three letters are called trigraphs. In the English language the most frequent digraph is the letter combination TH.

The characteristic rate of a letter combination is a measurement of its rate of occurrence. To compute the characteristic rate, count the number of occurrences of a given letter combination and divide by the number of letters in the text. For instance, to estimate the characteristic rate of the digraph TH, you could select a newspaper text and pick a random starting place. From that place mark off 2000 letters and count the number of times that TH occurs. Then divide the number of occurrences by 2000.

The characteristic rate of a digraph can vary slightly depending on the style of the author; so to estimate an overall characteristic frequency, you want to consider several samples of newspaper text by different authors. Suppose you did this with a random sample of 15 articles and found the characteristic rate of the digraph TH in the articles. The results follow.

0.0275	0.0290	0.0315	0.0265	0.0255
0.0280	0.0230	0.0295	0.0250	0.0265
0.0240	0.0295	0.0300	0.0275	0.0265

(a) Find a 95% confidence interval for the means characteristic rate of the digraph TH.

(b) Repeat part (a) for a 90% confidence interval. Note: you do not need to enter the data again; simply use the option to rerun the program with data you have already entered.

(c) Repeat part (a) for an 80% confidence interval.

(d) Repeat part (a) for a 70% confidence interval.

(e) Repeat part (a) for a 60% confidence interval.

(f) For each confidence interval in parts (a)–(e) compute the length of the given interval. Do you notice a relation between the confidence level and the length of the interval?

A good reference for cryptanalysis is a book by Sinkov:

Sinkov, Abraham, *Elementary Cryptanalysis,* New York: Random House, 1968

In the book other common digraphs and trigraphs are given.

Finding a Confidence Interval for a Proportion p

To find a confidence interval for a proportion on a calculator or with Minitab, simply evaluate the sample estimate $\hat{p} = r/n$ and then use z_c values from Table 8–2 and the formulas for the endpoints of the confidence intervals. In ComputerStat, select the program Confidence Intervals for the Probability of Success in a Binomial Distribution and follow the instructions on the screen.

Application 3

There must be nurses on duty in hospitals around the clock. Therefore, many nurses work various shifts. Tasto, Colligan, *et al.* did a study of the health consequences of shift work. Their results are published in the following government document:

United States Department of Health, Education, and Welfare, NIOSH Technical Report, Tasto, Colligan, *et al., Health Consequences of Shift Work*. Washington: GPO, 1978. 25.

They used a large random sample of nurses on various shifts in 12 hospitals. Part of the report concerns the number of sick days nurses on various shifts take. A random sample of 315 day-shift nurses showed that 62 took no sick days during a six-month period. During that same period a random sample of 309 nurses on rotating duty showed that 51 took no sick days.

(a) We wish to estimate the proportion p of rotating-shift nurses who take no sick days in a six-month period. Find a $c\%$ confidence interval for p when $c = 98, 90, 85, 75, 60$. Notice that you enter the data only once and rerun the program with the same data for the different c values.

(b) For each confidence interval in part (a) compute the length of the interval. Do you notice a relation between confidence level and length of the interval?

(c) We wish to estimate the proportion p of day-shift nurses who take no sick days in a six-month period. Find a $c\%$ confidence interval for p when $c = 99, 95, 80, 70, 60$. Is there a relation between confidence level and length of these intervals?

Computer Displays

Most statistical software packages will allow you to specify the confidence level for a confidence interval. In general you will also need to specify the appropriate probability distribution (normal, Student's *t*, binomial, etc.)

Minitab Display:
Data from Example 4, Section 8.2

```
MTB > Note Confidence Interval for mean, using small sample and
      t distribution
MTB > Note Data from Example 4, Section 8.2
MTB > SET C1
DATA> 45.3 47.1 44.2 46.8 46.5 45.5 47.6
DATA> END
MTB > TINTERVAL 99 PERCENT C1
    N   MEAN   STDEV   SE MEAN   99.0 PERCENT C.I.
C1  7  46.143  1.190    0.450    (44.475, 47.811)
```

Some software such as Minitab allows you to graph various probability distributions. The Student's *t* distribution with three degrees of freedom is shown next.

Minitab Display:
Student's t Distribution with 3 Degrees of Freedom

```
MTB > SET C1
DATA> -5:5/.01
DATA> END
MTB > NAME C1 'T'
MTB > PDF C1 C2;
SUBC> T  DF = 3.
MTB > Plot C2*C1;
SUBC>  Connect;
SUBC>  Title "T DISTRIBUTION, D.F. = 3".
```

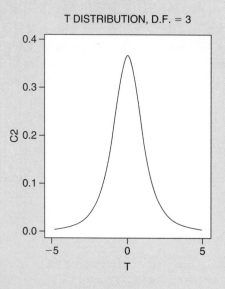

T DISTRIBUTION, D.F. = 3

Minitab Display of Confidence Interval Demonstration

The following program draws random samples of size 35 from a uniform distribution of numbers between 0 and 1. Then it creates 90% confidence intervals for the population mean *mu*.

```
MTB > RANDOM 20 INTO C1-C35;
SUBC> UNIFORM A = 0 TO B = 1.
MTB > RMEAN C1-C35 PUT INTO C50
MTB > RSTDEV C1-C35 PUT INTO C60
MTB > LET C61 = 1.645*C60/SQRT(35)
MTB > LET C70 = C50 - C61 #LOWER BOUND
MTB > LET C71 = C50 + C61 #UPPER BOUND
MTB > SET C73
DATA> 1:20
DATA> END
MTB > NAME C50 = 'MEAN'
MTB > NAME C60 = 'STDEV"
MTB > NAME C61 = 'E'
MTB > NAME C70 = 'LBOUND'
MTB > NAME C71 = 'UBOUND'
MTB > NAME C73 = 'INTNUM'
MTB > Plot 'UBOUND'*'INTNUM';
SUBC>    Symbol;
SUBC>      Type 0;
SUBC>    Project;
SUBC>      Base 'LBOUND'
SUBC>    Title "90% CONFIDENCE INTERVALS; SAMPLE SIZE 35";
```

```
SUBC>    Overlay;
SUBC>    Minimum 2 0.2;
SUBC>    Maximum 2 .7;
SUBC>    Reference 2 .5.
```

90% CONFIDENCE INTERVALS;
SAMPLE SIZE 35

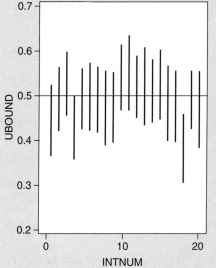

ComputerStat Display:
Data from Guided Exercise 7, Section 8.3

```
****** INFORMATION SUMMARY ******
CONFIDENCE LEVEL = 90%
NUMBER OF TRIALS N = 188
NUMBER OF SUCCESSES R = 66
SAMPLE APPROXIMATION FOR P = R/N = .3510638

SINCE NP = 66>5 AND N(1-P) = 122>5
THE NORMAL APPROXIMATION IS VALID FOR OUR DATA.
A 90% CONFIDENCE INTERVAL FOR P THE PROBABILITY OF SUCCESS ON
A SINGLE BINOMIAL TRIAL IS GIVEN BELOW.
  .2937926 <= P <= .4083351
```

Introduction to Hypothesis Testing

In this section we introduce the basic concept of hypothesis testing and the terminology. You will see how to establish two hypotheses and then how to determine which is most likely to be correct based on the sample data.

Tests Involving the Mean μ (Large Samples)

Last year it took you an average of 15 minutes to drive to campus each day. However, this year you claim that it will take longer because traffic is heavier. How can you use sample data to verify your claim? In this section you will see how to use the normal distribution to draw conclusions about hypotheses regarding the mean when you have large samples.

The *P* Value in Hypothesis Testing

As you gain experience with hypothesis testing, you might notice that the *same sample data* enable you to reject the null hypothesis (initial claim) for some levels of significance, but not for others. A natural question is: What is the smallest level of significance for which the sample data will allow us to reject the null hypothesis? The value is the *P* value.

Tests Involving the Mean μ (Small Samples)

In this section we will again consider hypotheses tests about the mean of a distribution, but this time the samples will be small, a situation which requires the use of the Student's *t* distribution. This section shows you how to conclude a hypothesis test about the mean in the traditional way by using critical values and critical regions, as well as by using *P* values.

Tests Involving a Proportion

Suppose your data are about proportions rather than means. For instance, suppose you want to determine if the proportion of students holding full-time jobs has increased over the past decade. You will see how concepts of hypothesis testing can be applied to problems involving proportions.

Tests Involving Paired Differences

Many research questions center around *dependent samples* such as "before and after" situations, or situations in which there is a natural pairing of data. In such cases, the Student's *t* distribution can be used to test differences in means.

Testing Differences of Two Means or Two Proportions (Independent Samples)

Is there a difference in average automobile insurance costs for California residents compared with residents in South Carolina? To answer such questions, we test the difference of means from independent samples. You also will see how to test the difference of two proportions.

CHAPTER NINE

Charles Lutwidge Dodgson (1832–1898)

Using the pseudonym Lewis Carroll, this English mathematician and author wrote *Alice's Adventures in Wonderland.*

Hypothesis Testing

"Would you tell me, please, which way I ought to go from here?"
"That depends a good deal on where you want to get to," said the Cat.
"I don't much care where—" said Alice.
"Then it doesn't matter which way you go," said the Cat.

Lewis Carroll
Alice's Adventures in Wonderland

Charles Dodgson was an English mathematician who loved to write children's stories in his free time. The above dialogue between Alice and the Cheshire Cat occurs in the masterpiece *Alice's Adventures in Wonderland*, written by Dodgson under the pen name Lewis Carroll. These lines relate to our study of hypothesis testing. Statistical tests cannot answer all of life's questions. They cannot always tell us "where to go," but after this decision is made on other grounds, they can help us find the best way to get there.

Focus Problem ▶ ## Business Opportunities and Start-Up Costs

Be your own boss! Be financially independent with your own business! These are dreams that are within reach if you are willing to do some work and occasionally take some calculated risks. The first step is to evaluate your financial and/or credit position. You do not need a lot of money to start a business, provided you have a reasonable credit rating. Next, you need to decide what kind of business interests you. Then you need to gather data and do a little homework. Some statistics should be helpful here. Where can you get data? Most local or national newspapers have a column called "Business Opportunities." For example, the *Wall Street Journal* has a section called "The Mart: International/National/Regional." Five days a week this section publishes various business opportunities. Most local newspapers such as the *New York Times, Denver Post, Santa Fe New Mexican, Honolulu Advertiser,* and so on have sections that list business opportunities. If you want to look farther, then *Franchise and Business Opportunities Annual Report* (1994) contains over 1500 business start-up opportunities.

To be specific, let's say you want to start a (small) business in advertising services and related products. What should you expect for the start-up costs?

Chapter 9 Hypothesis Testing

Start-up costs are the money required to get the business going and offer your product. Such costs might include rental of building space, needed equipment, supplies, and materials; mailing costs; staff salaries; and so on. In other words, start-up costs are the money you need to begin your new business venture. A random sample of 45 small advertising companies gave the following information about start-up costs (in thousands of dollars):

21.6	17.1	14.8	25.2	11.6
8.7	18.8	16.5	16.8	20.9
20.7	11.2	15.1	14.5	18.2
19.1	16.2	18.1	23.7	22.6
29.1	18.6	19.7	15.3	16.1
17.5	21.3	20.5	17.9	21.2
18.0	17.9	15.3	19.4	27.9
10.1	12.3	13.4	13.7	23.4
25.1	24.2	14.0	14.4	21.3

For these data we have $n = 45$ data values with sample mean $\bar{x} = 18.20$ and sample standard deviation $s = 4.55$.

Suppose that you are taking out a small business loan, and the loan officer claims that the mean start-up costs for your intended advertising business should be only $16,500. However, you want a loan for more than $16,500. Using the preceding data (and in a gentle, persuasive way), could you effectively argue that the mean start-up costs are in fact higher?

The sample data have a mean of $18,200, and this seems to contradict the claim that the mean start-up costs are only $16,500. The question is whether or not the sample mean $18,200, is *significantly* greater than $16,500. Put another way, how likely is it that the population mean start-up costs really are $16,500 and the preceding sample results are due only to chance fluctuations or sampling error? In this chapter we will learn how to answer such questions.

Section 9.1 Introduction to Hypothesis Testing

In Chapter 1 we emphasized the fact that a statistician's most important job is to draw inferences about populations based on samples taken from the population. Most statistical inference centers around the parameters of a population (usually the mean or probability of success in a binomial trial). Methods for drawing inferences about parameters are of two types: Either we make decisions concerning the value of the parameter, or we actually estimate the value of the parameter. When we estimate the value (or location) of a parameter, we are using methods of estimation as studied in Chapter 8. Decisions concerning the value of a parameter are obtained by hypothesis testing, the topic we shall study in this chapter.

Students often ask which method should be used on a particular problem—that is, should the parameter be estimated, or should we test a hypothesis involving the parameter? The answer lies in the practical nature of the problem and the questions posed about it. Some people prefer to test theories concerning the parameters. Others prefer to express their inferences as estimates. Both estimation and hypothesis testing are found extensively in the literature of statistical applications.

Null and Alternate Hypotheses

A *statistical hypothesis*, or a *hypothesis*, is an assumption about one or more population parameters of a probability distribution. The hypothesis will be accepted or rejected on the basis of information taken from a sample of the distribution. Hypothesis *testing* is the procedure whereby we decide whether to accept or reject a hypothesis.

Sometimes we formulate a statistical hypothesis for the sole purpose of trying to reject it. If we want to decide whether one method of doing something is better than another, we might formulate a hypothesis that says that there is no difference in the methods. The term *null hypothesis* is used for any hypothesis which is set up primarily for the purpose of seeing whether it can be rejected.

If the null hypothesis cannot be rejected, we do not claim that it is true beyond all doubt; we just claim that under our method of testing, it cannot be rejected. Any hypothesis which differs from the null hypothesis is called an *alternate hypothesis*. An alternate hypothesis is constructed in such a way that it is the one to be accepted when the null hypothesis must be rejected. The *null hypothesis is denoted by* H_0 and the *alternate hypothesis is denoted by* H_1.

Example 1

A car dealer advertises that its new subcompact models get 47 mpg. Let μ be the mean of the mileage distribution for these cars. You assume the dealer will not underrate the car, but you suspect the mileage might be overrated.

(a) What shall we use for H_0?
We want to see if the dealer's claim $\mu = 47$ can be rejected. Therefore, our null hypothesis is simply that $\mu = 47$. We denote the null hypothesis as

$$H_0: \mu = 47$$

(b) What shall we use for H_1?
From experience with this dealer we have every reason to believe that the advertised mileage is too high. If μ is not 47, we are sure it is less than 47. Therefore, the alternate hypothesis is

$$H_1: \mu < 47$$

GUIDED EXERCISE 1

A company manufactures ball bearings for precision machines. The average diameter of a certain type of ball bearing should be 6.0 mm. To check that the average diameter is correct, the company decides to formulate a statistical test.

(a) What should be used for H_0? (*Hint:* What are they trying to test?)

(a) If μ is the mean diameter of the ball bearings, the company wants to test $\mu = 6.0$ mm. Therefore, H_0: $\mu = 6.0$.

(b) What should be used for H_1? (*Hint:* An error either way, too small or too large, would be serious.)

(b) An error either way could occur and it would be serious. Therefore, H_1: $\mu \neq 6.0$ (μ is either smaller than or larger than 6.0).

GUIDED EXERCISE 2

A package delivery service claims it takes an average of 24 hours to send a package from New York to San Francisco. An independent consumer agency is doing a study to test the truth of this claim. Several complaints have led the agency to suspect that the delivery time is longer than 24 hours.

(a) What should be used for the null hypothesis?

(a) The claim $\mu = 24$ hours is in question, so we take H_0: $\mu = 24$.

(b) Assuming that the delivery service does not underrate itself, what should be used for the alternate hypothesis?

(b) If the delivery service does not underrate itself, then the only reasonable alternate hypothesis is H_1: $\mu > 24$.

Types of Errors

If we *reject the null hypothesis when it is* in fact *true*, we have an error that is called a *type I error*. On the other hand, if we *accept the null hypothesis when it is* in fact *false*, we have made an error that is called a *type II error*. Table 9–1 indicates how these errors occur.

Table 9–1 Type I and Type II Errors

	Our Decision	
Truth of H_0	**And if we do not reject H_0**	**And if we reject H_0**
If H_0 is true	Correct decision; no error	Type I error
If H_0 is false	Type II error	Correct decision; no error

In order for tests of hypotheses to be good, they must be designed to minimize possible errors of decision. (Often we do not know if an error has been made, and therefore, we can only talk about the probability of making an error.) Usually for a given sample size an attempt to reduce the probability of one type of error results in an increase in the probability of the other type of error. In practical applications, one type of error may be more serious than another. In such a case, careful attention is given to the more serious error. If we increase the sample size, it is possible to reduce both types of errors, but increasing the sample size may not be possible.

Level of Significance

The probability with which we are willing to risk a type I error is called the *level of significance* of a test. The level of significance is denoted by the Greek letter α (pronounced "alpha"). In good statistical practice, α is specified in advance before any samples are drawn so that results will not influence the choice for the level of significance.

The probability of making a type II error is denoted by the Greek letter β (pronounced "beta"). Methods of hypothesis testing require us to choose α and β values to be as small as possible. In elementary statistical applications we usually choose α first.

Power of a Test

The quantity $1 - \beta$ is called the *power* of the test and represents the probability of rejecting H_0 when it is in fact false. For a given level of significance, how much power can we expect from a test? The actual value of the power is usually difficult (and sometimes impossible) to obtain, since it requires us to know the H_1 distribution. However, we can make the following general comments:

1. The power of a statistical test increases as the level of significance α increases. A test performed at the $\alpha = 0.05$ level has more power than one at $\alpha = 0.01$. This means that the less stringent we make our significance level α, the more likely we will reject the null hypothesis when it is false. Using a larger value of α will increase the power, but it also will increase the probability of a type I error. In spite of this fact, most business executives, administrators, social scientists, and scientists use *small* α values. This choice reflects the conservative nature of administrators and scientists, who are usually more willing to make an error by failing to reject a claim (i.e., H_0) than to make an error by accepting another claim (i.e., H_1) that is false.

2. The power of a statistical test increases as the sample size n increases. Therefore, the probability of correctly rejecting H_0 when it is false is better when the sample size is larger. Of course, the probability of correctly accepting the null hypothesis when it is true is also larger when the sample size is larger. The difficulty is that sometimes it may be too costly or perhaps even impossible to get a larger sample.

3. Some statistical tests are designed to be more powerful than others. The techniques described in Chapters 9, 10, and 11 are called *parametric tests;* those discussed in Chapter 12 are called *nonparametric tests.* Most parametric tests require special and stringent assumptions about the nature of the data. However, the nonparametric tests make very few restrictive assumptions about the data. In general, parametric tests are more powerful than nonparametric tests because we can employ more theoretical assumptions with parametric tests. However, nonparametric tests are extremely important (although less powerful) when certain theoretical assumptions cannot be made.

Table 9–2 Probabilities Associated with a Statistical Test

	Our Decision	
Truth of H_0	And if we accept H_0 as True	And if we reject H_0 as False
H_0 *is true*	Correct decision, with corresponding probability $1 - \alpha$	Type I error, with corresponding probability α called the *level of significance* of the test
H_0 *is false*	Type II error, with corresponding probability β	Correct decision, with corresponding probability $1 - \beta$ called the *power* of the test

- *Comment:* Since the calculation of the probability of a type II error is treated in advanced statistics courses, we will restrict our attention to the probability of a type I error.

Meaning of Accepting H_0

In most statistical applications, the level of significance is specified to be $\alpha = 0.05$ or $\alpha = 0.01$, although other values can be used. If $\alpha = 0.05$, then we say we are using a 5% level of significance. This means that in 100 similar situations, H_0 will be rejected 5 times, on average, when it should not have been rejected.

When we accept (or fail to reject) the null hypothesis, we should understand that we are *not proving the null hypothesis*. We are only saying that the sample evidence (data) is not strong enough to justify rejection of the null hypothesis. The word *accept* sometimes has a stronger meaning in common English usage than we are willing to give in our application of statistics. Therefore, we often use the expression *fail to reject H_0* instead of accept H_0. *Fail to reject* the null hypothesis simply means the evidence in favor of rejection was not strong enough (see Table 9–3). Often, in the case H_0 cannot be rejected, a confidence interval is used to estimate the parameter in question. The confidence interval gives the statistician a range of possible values for the parameter.

Table 9–3 Meaning of the Terms *Fail to Reject H_0* and *Reject H_0*

Term	Meaning
Fail to reject H_0	There is not enough evidence in the data (and the test being used) to justify a rejection of H_0. This means that we retain H_0 with the understanding that we have not proved it to be true beyond all doubt.
Reject H_0	There is enough evidence in the data (and the test employed) to justify rejection of H_0. This means that we choose the alternate hypothesis H_1 with the understanding that we have not proved H_1 to be true beyond all doubt.

Procedure for Hypothesis Testing

A decision to accept or reject the null hypothesis is made on the basis of sample data. We set up a process to evaluate whether or not the sample data are consistent with the null hypothesis. If they are *too different* from what we expect under the null hypothesis, we reject the null hypothesis. What process do we use to evaluate the difference between a sample mean $\bar{x}$ and a population mean μ proposed by the null hypothesis? Let's look at the next example.

Example 2

Statement of Problem: The St. Louis Zoo wishes to obtain eggs of a rare Mississippi river turtle. The zoo will hatch the eggs and raise the turtles as an exhibit of a rare and endangered species. Carol Wright is the staff biologist at the zoo who has been given the job of finding the eggs to be hatched. Turtles of the area bury their eggs in a nest in sandbanks along the river. Then the nest is abandoned and the eggs hatch by themselves. A number of different species of turtles live in the region, and eggs from each species look much alike. Past research has shown that lengths of turtle eggs are normally distributed, and lengths of the rare turtle eggs have population mean $\mu = 7.50$ cm with standard deviation $\sigma = 1.5$ cm. The rare turtle egg is the only one with mean length 7.50 cm. The mean lengths of eggs from each of the other species are longer than 7.50 cm. The eggs of all the local turtle species have the same standard deviation $\sigma = 1.5$ cm for length.

After searching for some time, Carol found a nest with 36 eggs. The way the nest was constructed makes her suspect that it was made by the rare turtle. The mean length of this collection of 36 eggs is $\bar{x} = 7.74$ cm. Since $\bar{x} = 7.74$ cm is longer than the population mean $\mu = 7.50$ cm of the rare turtle, Carol is a little worried that the eggs may come from a species that lays larger eggs.

Let's use a statistical test to help the biologist make a decision. Pay close attention to this example; it contains principal features common to most statistical tests.

I. *Summary of Known Facts:* In any testing problem it is a good idea to make a short summary of known facts before we start to construct the test.

(a) The distribution of lengths of eggs from the rare turtle is *normal*, with population mean $\mu = 7.50$ cm and standard deviation $\sigma = 1.5$ cm.

(b) The nest contains $n = 36$ eggs with an observed mean $\bar{x} = 7.74$ cm.

(c) Since the population is *normal* and μ and σ are known, Theorem 7.1 tells us that $\bar{x}$ is also normally distributed. The mean and standard deviation of the $\bar{x}$ distribution are

$$\mu_{\bar{x}} = \mu = 7.50 \text{ cm}$$

$$\sigma_{\bar{x}} = \frac{\sigma}{\sqrt{n}} = \frac{1.5}{\sqrt{36}} = 0.25 \text{ cm}$$

II. *Establishing H_0 and H_1:* The null hypothesis H_0 is set up for the primary purpose of seeing whether or not it can be rejected. The alternate hypothesis H_1 will be chosen when the null hypothesis must be rejected.

Let μ be the mean length of the population distribution from which our sample of 36 eggs is drawn. Our biologist suspects that the nest contains the rare turtle eggs; therefore, we will use the null hypothesis

$$H_0:\ \mu = 7.50$$

since the rare turtle eggs are known to have mean length $\mu = 7.50$ cm. However, all other local species lay eggs with a longer population mean. Therefore, the alternate hypothesis is

$$H_1:\ \mu > 7.50$$

III. *Choosing the Level of Significance α:* The null hypothesis says that the eggs in the nest are from the rare turtle. A type I error means that we reject the nest as being formed by the rare turtle when it was in fact formed by the rare turtle. A type II error means that we accept the nest as coming from the rare turtle when it really came from a common species.

A type I error could be serious; we don't want to reject the eggs if they are from the rare turtle. A type II error is not too serious. If the eggs are from a common species, the turtles can be released after they hatch. Naturally, the zoo doesn't want to incubate the wrong eggs, but it would not be too serious if it did.

Although other levels of significance may be used, most researchers use either $\alpha = 0.05$ or $\alpha = 0.01$. Our biologist has agreed to use a level of significance $\alpha = 0.01$. This means that she is willing to risk a type I error with a probability of $\alpha = 0.01$.

IV. *Geometric Model for the Test:* What decision procedure shall we use to test our hypothesis? In a way, the logic of our decision process is similar to that used in a typical courtroom setting, but our methods are mathematical rather than legal. In a courtroom setting, the person charged with a crime is initially considered innocent (null hypothesis). If evidence (data) presented in court can sufficiently discredit the person's innocence, he or she is then judged to be guilty (alternate hypothesis). In a similar way, we will consider the null hypothesis to be *true* until there is enough data (mathematical evidence) to discredit it at the $\alpha = 0.01$ level of significance.

Figure 9–1 shows the geometric model for a test with hypotheses

$$H_0:\ \mu = 7.50$$

$$H_1:\ \mu > 7.50$$

and a large sample. Let us examine the details of Figure 9–1.

(a) First, we determine the *sampling distribution.* By the central limit theorem (Theorem 7.2), the test statistic $\bar{x}$ follows a *normal* distribution. We convert the $\bar{x}$ distribution to the standard normal distribution by the formula

$$z = \frac{\bar{x} - \mu}{(\sigma/\sqrt{n})}$$

Figure 9-1 Geometric Model for a Right-Tailed Test of μ (Large Sample) with $\alpha = 0.01$

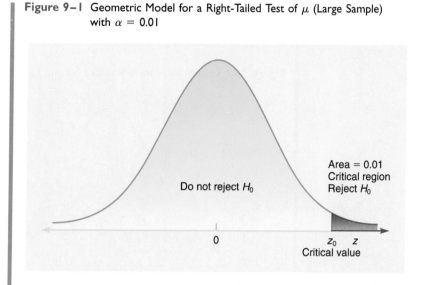

Area = 0.01
Critical region
Reject H_0

Do not reject H_0

0   z_0 z
Critical value

where μ is given in H_0, σ is given or estimated from the sample (large sample), and n is the sample size. In our case, $\mu = 7.50$, $\sigma = 1.5$, and $n = 36$. Figure 9–1 is the standard normal distribution.

(b) Next, we find the critical region. Since H_1: $\mu > 7.50$ claims that μ is greater than 7.50, the *critical region* for this problem is a *right tail* of the standard normal distribution. This tail has an area of $\alpha = 0.01$. If the z value corresponding to the sample statistic $\bar{x} = 7.74$ falls in the critical region, we say that there is enough evidence to discredit the null hypothesis, and we *reject H_0* at the $\alpha = 0.01$ level of significance. If our observed value falls outside the critical region, we conclude that the evidence is not strong enough to reject H_0, so in this case we *fail to reject H_0*. Since H_1: $\mu > 7.50$ claims that μ is greater than 7.50, then an observed sample statistic $\bar{x}$ *far enough* to the *right* of $\mu = 7.50$ discredits the null hypothesis and supports the alternate hypothesis. In the next section we will encounter left-tailed and two-tailed tests.

(c) The value z_0 is called the *critical value* for the test. It is the separation point for the critical region. If the z value of the sample statistic $\bar{x} = 7.74$ falls to the *left* of z_0, we *fail to reject H_0*. If it falls to the *right* of z_0, we *reject H_0*. Once we know z_0 and convert the sample statistic $\bar{x}$ to z, we can quickly finish the test.

V. *Finding the Critical Value, Critical Region, and z value for $\bar{x}$:* In the next section you will be given a table of critical values z_0 to use for tests with sampling distributions that are normal. We find these values as we did in Chapter 6 by using Table 6, "Areas of a Standard Normal Distribution," Appendix II. In this problem we have a right-tailed test with level of significance $\alpha = 0.01$. We want to find the value z_0 so that 1% of the standard normal curve lies to the right of z_0. Since the areas in Table 6 go from 0 to z, we look up z so that the area from 0 to z is $0.5 - \alpha = 0.5 - 0.0100 = 0.4900$. This gives us the value $z_0 = 2.33$. The critical region is all values of z greater than or equal to $z_0 = 2.33$ (see Figure 9–2).

Figure 9–2 Critical Value for a Standard Normal Curve, Right-Tailed Test with $\alpha = 0.01$

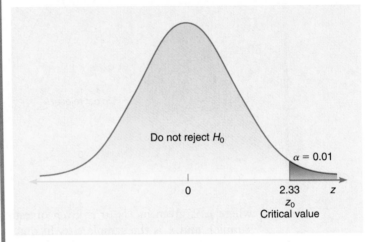

The sample "evidence" we have is $\bar{x} = 7.74$ based on a nest of 36 eggs. We convert $\bar{x}$ to z using the formula in part IV:

$$z = \frac{\bar{x} - \mu}{(\sigma/\sqrt{n})} = \frac{7.74 - 7.50}{(1.5/\sqrt{36})} = 0.96$$

Now we have all the information we need to complete the test.

VI. *Conclusion:* Earlier we pointed out a similarity between the logic of a statistical test and proceedings in a court of law. We are now at the point where all the sample evidence has been presented, and we are awaiting a decision. Who makes the decision? In a court, the jury or judge would make the decision, but in our statistical test, it is Mother Nature who makes the final decision. The observed value $\bar{x} = 7.74$ cm of length for turtle eggs taken from the turtle nest corresponds to the z value 0.96. This z value does not lie in the critical region (see Figure 9–3).

We conclude that there is not enough evidence to discredit the null hypothesis at the $\alpha = 0.01$ level of significance. Therefore, we do not reject H_0: $\mu = 7.50$, and we still think that the nest could have been made by the rare endangered species of turtle. The biologist should collect the eggs and take them to the zoo for incubation. It is important to remember that we do not claim to have *proven* that the eggs are from the rare turtle; all we say is that there is not enough evidence to reject H_0, and therefore, we "accept" it.

VII. *Meaning of α and β:* Remember that β is the probability of accepting H_0 when it is false. In our setting, β is the probability that the zoo incubates and

Figure 9–3 z Value Corresponding to the Observed $\bar{x} = 7.74$ Falls Outside the Critical Region

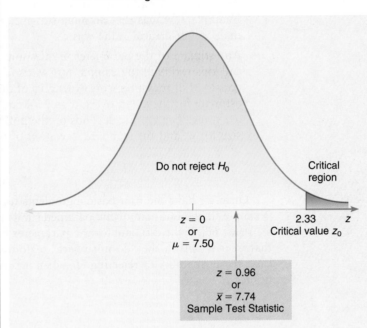

hatches eggs from a common turtle species. To calculate β requires knowledge of the H_1 distribution. Since there are several species of common turtles in the area and we don't know which species made the nest, we really don't know the H_1 distribution. However, a type II error is not too serious because if the wrong eggs (from the common turtle) are hatched, there is little harm done. The baby turtles can simply be released near the place the eggs were found.

The level of significance α is the probability of rejecting H_0 when it is true. This is the probability of saying that the eggs are not from the rare turtle species when they in fact are. It would be a serious mistake to reject the nest of the rare turtle. To guard against such a mistake, we have taken a relatively small α value of 0.01.

Four Basic Ingredients
of a Test

In this section we have introduced you to all the essential ingredients of hypothesis testing. The turtle example contains all the important, basic ideas. For convenience, let's summarize the main points:

A Statistical Test Is a Package of Four Basic Ingredients:

1. H_0, the null hypothesis.
2. H_1, the alternative hypothesis.

3. A critical value and critical region that depend on H_0, H_1, the level of significance α, and the distribution of the sampling statistic. (In Example 2, $\bar{x}$ was the sampling statistic, and its distribution was normal, so our critical value was z_0.)

4. An estimate of the parameter in question obtained from a sample. We call this estimate the *sample test statistic*. (In Example 2, the sample consisted of measurements of lengths of 36 turtle eggs, and the sample estimate for the mean μ was $\bar{x} = 7.74$ cm.) We convert the estimate to a z value. The z value depends on the null hypothesis for μ, the sample size for n, and the standard deviation of the measurements.

Conclusion of Test

Once we have the four basic ingredients for a statistical test, our strategy is simple. If the estimate of the parameter falls inside the critical region, then we reject H_0. If the estimate for the parameter falls outside the critical region, that is, if it falls in the "do not reject" region, we *fail to reject* H_0. In either case, the probability of rejecting H_0 when it is really true is the level of significance α.

GUIDED EXERCISE 3

Suppose that the biologist of Example 2 found a nest with 36 turtle eggs for which the sample mean length of the eggs is $\bar{x} = 8.13$ cm. Is this sample statistic so much longer than the mean length $\mu = 7.50$ specified in H_0 that we should reject H_0? In other words, is the mean length of the turtle eggs in this sample so long that we can be confident that the nest does not contain the eggs of the rare turtle? We will answer this question in several steps. We again use $\alpha = 0.01$.

(a) Since all aspects of this problem are the same as those in Example 2 except for the specific value of $\bar{x}$, we use the same critical region as that shown in Example 2. When we convert $\bar{x} = 8.13$ to z, we get

$$z = \frac{\bar{x} - \mu}{(\sigma/\sqrt{n})}$$

$$= \frac{8.13 - 7.50}{(1.5/\sqrt{36})}$$

$$= 2.52$$

Place this sample z value on the graph of Figure 9–4.

(a) See Figure 9–5 on page 541.

Figure 9–4 Critical Region

Figure 9–5 Critical Region Showing Sample Test Statistic (Completion of Figure 9–4)

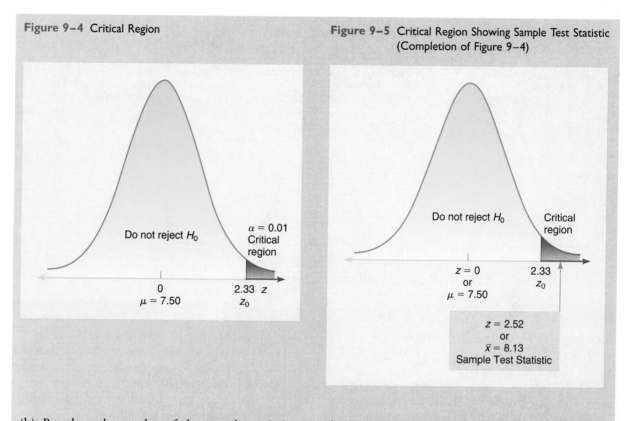

(b) Based on the z value of the sample statistic $\bar{x}$ = 8.13, do we reject or fail to reject H_0 at the 1% level of significance? Explain.

(b) Since the z score corresponding to the sample statistic $\bar{x}$ = 8.13 falls in the critical region, we reject H_0 at the 1% level of significance. The eggs seem to be from the common turtle. There is a 1% chance that we made an error and that the eggs are really those of the rare turtle.

One- and Two-Tailed Tests

In most instances of hypothesis testing, the alternate hypothesis is the condition that the parameter under consideration is less than (<), greater than (>), or not equal to (≠) some specific value. The types of critical regions used with these kinds of alternate hypotheses are shown in Figure 9–6.

Figures 9–6a and b correspond to what are called *one-tailed tests*. A one-tailed test is a statistical test for which the critical region is located in the left tail *or* in the right tail of the distribution (but not in both tails).

Figure 9–6c corresponds to what is called a *two-tailed test*. A two-tailed test is a statistical test for which the critical region is located in *both* tails of the distribution.

Figure 9–6 Alternate Hypothesis and Corresponding Critical Region

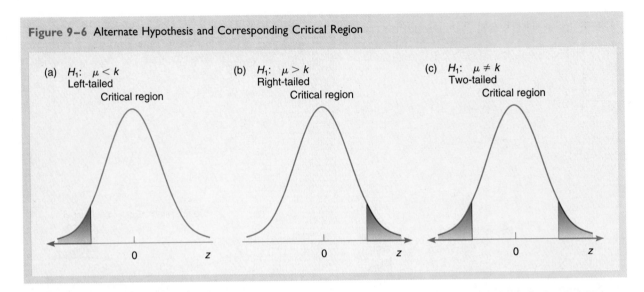

(a) H_1: $\mu < k$
Left-tailed
     Critical region

(b) H_1: $\mu > k$
Right-tailed
     Critical region

(c) H_1: $\mu \neq k$
Two-tailed
     Critical region

GUIDED EXERCISE 4

(a) Suppose an alternate hypothesis is

$$H_1: \mu < \text{some value}$$

Let z_0 be the critical value. Do we have a one-tailed test or a two-tailed test? Shade the critical region in Figure 9–7. If $\alpha = 0.01$, what area is contained in the critical region? If the null hypothesis is true, what is the probability that a z value selected at random will fall in the critical region?

(a) One-tailed test. Since the less than symbol $<$ is used in H_1, we shade the left tail. For $\alpha = 0.01$, the critical region contains an area of 0.01. Under the null hypothesis, the probability that a z value selected at random will fall in the critical region is 0.01.

Figure 9–7 Shade the Critical Region

Figure 9–8 Completion of Figure 9–7

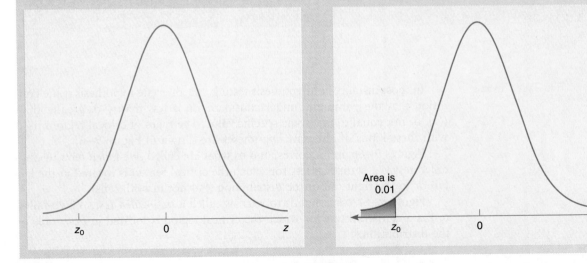

Area is
0.01

(b) Suppose an alternate hypothesis is

$$H_1: \mu \neq \text{some value}$$

There are two critical values. Is this a one-tailed or a two-tailed test? Shade the critical region in Figure 9–9. For $\alpha = 0.05$, what is the total area contained in the critical region? If the null hypothesis is true, what is the probability that a z value selected at random will fall in the critical region?

(b) Two-tailed test. Since the not equal symbol $\neq$ is used in H_1, we shade both tails. The total area contained in the two tails is 0.05. Under the null hypothesis, the probability that a z value selected at random will fall in the critical region is 0.05.

Figure 9–10 Completion of Figure 9–9

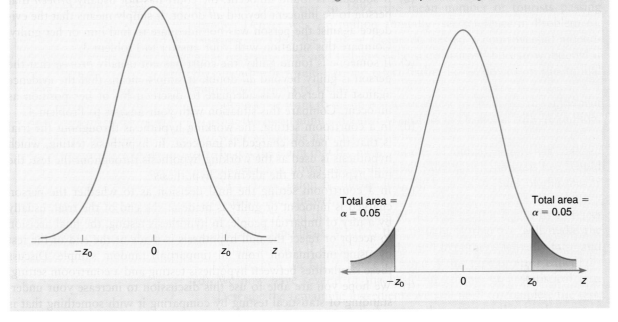

Section 9.1 Problems

1. Write a careful and complete answer to each of the following questions.
   (a) What is a statistical hypothesis?
   (b) What is a null hypothesis H_0?
   (c) What is an alternate hypothesis H_1?
   (d) What is a type I error? a type II error?
   (e) What is the level of significance of a test? What is the probability of a type II error? What is the power of a test?
   (f) For the tests of this section, what do we mean by the sample statistic and sampling distribution?
   (g) What is a critical value? What is a critical region?
   (h) How do we draw a conclusion about rejecting or failing to reject the null hypothesis?

2. In a statistical test we have a choice of a left-tailed critical region, right-tailed critical region, or two-tailed critical region. Is it the null hypothesis

Figure 9-12 Critical Region, $\alpha = 0.05$

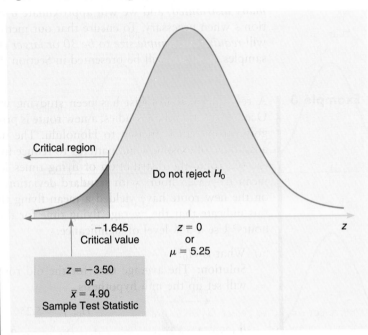

Critical region

Do not reject H_0

-1.645
Critical value

$z = 0$
or
$\mu = 5.25$

z

$z = -3.50$
or
$\bar{x} = 4.90$
Sample Test Statistic

Solution: Let's look at the critical region of Figure 9-12. The sample z value corresponding to the sample test statistic $\bar{x} = 4.90$ falls in the critical region. We reject H_0 and choose H_1 at the $\alpha = 0.05$ level. This means that we conclude that the flying time on the new route is less than the flying time on the old route.

GUIDED EXERCISE 5

Pam likes to practice golf at a driving range. From thousands of shots at the range she knows that her average distance using a number one wood is about 225 yards. A friend asked Pam to experiment with a ball made of a new kind of material to see if it will increase her distance. Using the new type ball for 100 shots, she found that her average distance was 230 yards with a standard deviation of 25 yards. Let us see if we can reject the hypothesis H_0: $\mu = 225$ (the new ball goes no farther on the average than the old ball). We will use the 1% level of significance.

(a) From the statement of the problem, what is a reasonable choice for H_1?

H_1: $\mu < 225$　　H_1: $\mu \neq 225$　　H_1: $\mu > 225$

(a) A reasonable alternate hypothesis is that the new ball increases the average driving distance. Therefore, we choose H_1: $\mu > 225$.

(b) What kind of test should we use: left-tailed test, right-tailed test, or two-tailed test? Find the critical value(s).

(c) What is the z value corresponding to the sample test statistic $\bar{x} = 230$?

(d) Sketch the standard normal distribution and show the critical region on the sketch. Place the sample z value on the sketch. Does the sample test statistic fall in the critical region or not? Do we reject or fail to reject H_0? Is there evidence that the new golf ball increases Pam's average distance? Explain.

(b) Since the alternate hypothesis is H_1: $\mu > 225$, we use a right-tailed test. For $\alpha = 0.01$, the critical value for a right-tailed test is $z_0 = 2.33$.

(c) To find the z value, we use $\mu = 225$ from H_0 and $n = 100$ (sample size). We do not know σ, so we estimate σ by the sample statistic $s = 25$. This estimate is valid because the sample size is large. Then,

$$z = \frac{\bar{x} - \mu}{(\sigma/\sqrt{n})}$$

$$= \frac{230 - 225}{(25/\sqrt{100})}$$

$$= 2.00$$

(d) **Figure 9–13** Critical Region, $\alpha = 0.01$

Do not reject H_0

Critical region

z = 0
or
μ = 225

2.33   z
Critical value

z = 2.00
or
$\bar{x}$ = 230
Sample Test Statistic

The z value corresponding to the sample test statistic falls in the "do not reject H_0" region. This means that we do not have enough evidence to reject H_0. The distances Pam achieved using the new ball were not sufficiently greater than those she achieved with the regular golf ball. The sample evidence does not support the claim that the new golf ball increased her average distance.

Example 4

A large company has branch offices in several major cities of the world. From time to time it is necessary for company employees to move their families from one city to another. From long experience, the company knows that its employees move on the average of once every 8.50 years. However, trends for the past few years have led people to think that a change might have occurred. To determine if such a change has occurred, a random sample was taken of 48 employees (from the entire company). The employees were asked to provide either the number of years since the company asked them to move or the number of years employed by the company if they had never been asked to move. For this sample of 48 employees, the mean time was $\bar{x} = 7.91$ years with sample standard deviation 3.62 years.

Let us see if we can reject the hypothesis H_0: $\mu = 8.50$ at the $\alpha = 0.05$ level of significance. Since we have no way of knowing if the average moving time (μ) has increased or decreased, the alternate hypothesis will simply be H_1: $\mu \neq 8.50$.

(a) Should we use a right-tailed, left-tailed, or two-tailed test? Find the critical values.

Solution: Since the alternate hypothesis uses the $\neq$ symbol, we use a two-tailed test. The sampling distribution $\bar{x}$ is approximately normal by the central limit theorem, so we can look at Figure 9–11 to find the critical values. For $\alpha = 0.05$, Figure 9–11 tells us that the critical values are $z_0 = \pm 1.96$.

(b) Convert the sample test statistic $\bar{x} = 7.91$ to a z value and show the location of the critical region and sample test statistic on the standard normal distribution.

Solution: We convert $\bar{x} = 7.91$ years to a z value using $\mu = 8.50$ from H_0, $n = 48$, and estimating σ by $s = 3.62$ (see Figure 9–14):

$$z = \frac{\bar{x} - \mu}{(\sigma/\sqrt{n})} = \frac{7.91 - 8.50}{(3.62/\sqrt{48})} \approx -1.13$$

Calculator Note It is best to do the entire calculation for z internally on your calculator. For instance, on the TI-82, key in

$$(7.91 - 8.50) \div (3.62 \div \sqrt{48}) \quad \text{ENTER}$$

Then round z to 2 places after the decimal. If you calculate the denominator $3.62/\sqrt{48}$ separately, be sure to carry at least four places after the decimal. Then divide the quantity $(7.91 - 8.50)$ by that number.

(c) Do we reject or fail to reject H_0 at the 5% level of significance?

Solution: The sample test statistic does not fall in the critical region. Therefore, we *fail to reject* H_0. It appears that employees still move on the average of once every 8.50 years.

Figure 9–14 Critical Region, $\alpha = 0.05$

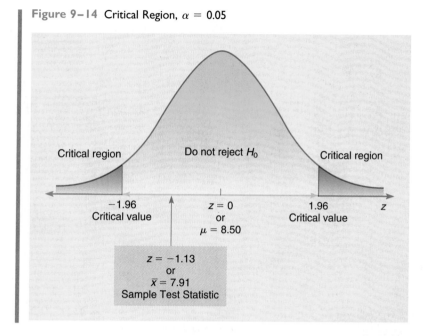

GUIDED EXERCISE 6

A machine makes twist-off caps for bottles. The machine is adjusted to make caps of diameter 1.85 cm. Production records show that when the machine is so adjusted it will make caps with mean diameter 1.85 cm and with standard deviation $\sigma = 0.05$ cm. During production, an inspector checks the diameters of caps to see if the machine has slipped out of adjustment. A random sample of 64 caps is taken. If the mean diameter for this sample is $\bar{x} = 1.87$ cm, does this indicate that the machine has slipped out of adjustment and the average diameter of caps is no longer $\mu = 1.85$ cm? (Use a 1% level of significance.)

(a) What is the null hypothesis?

$H_0: \mu = 0.05 \qquad H_0: \mu = 1.85$
$\qquad H_0: \mu = 1.90$

(a) $H_0: \mu = 1.85$

(b) We want to test the null hypothesis against the hypothesis that the mean diameter is *not* 1.85 cm. Therefore, the alternate hypothesis is

$H_1: \mu < 1.85 \qquad H_1: \mu \neq 1.85$
$\qquad H_1: \mu > 1.85$

(b) $H_1: \mu \neq 1.85$

(c) Should we use a one- or two-tailed test? What are the critical values?

(c) Because the alternate hypothesis uses the $\neq$ symbol, we use a two-tailed test. By the central limit theorem, the sampling distribution of $\bar{x}$ is approximately normal, so we can use Figure 9–11 or Table 6 in Appendix II to find the critical values. For $\alpha = 0.01$, $z_0 = \pm 2.58$.

(d) What is the value of the sample test statistic? Convert it to a z value.

(d) Since we are testing μ, the sample test statistic is $\bar{x}$. The sample of 64 bottle caps yielded a sample mean diameter $\bar{x} = 1.87$ cm. To convert $\bar{x}$ to z, we use $\mu = 1.85$ from H_0, $n = 64$, and $\sigma = 0.05$:

$$z = \frac{\bar{x} - \mu}{(\sigma/\sqrt{n})}$$

$$= \frac{1.87 - 1.85}{(0.05/\sqrt{64})}$$

$$= 3.20$$

(e) Show the critical region and the z value of the sample test statistic on the normal curve. Does the sample test statistic fall in the critical region or not? Do we reject or fail to reject H_0? At the 1% level of significance, can we say that the machine needs adjustment.

(e) **Figure 9–15 Critical Region, $\alpha = 0.01$**

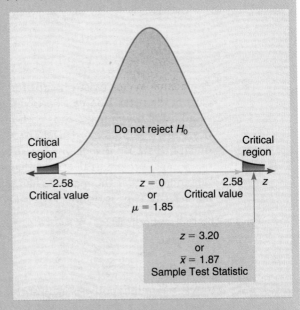

We see that the z value corresponding to the sample test statistic $\bar{x} = 1.87$ falls in the critical region. This means that we reject H_0 and conclude that at the 1% level of significance the machine needs adjustment.

Statistical Significance

• **Comment:** In a sense the sample estimate of the parameter represents the evidence favoring rejection of H_0. For this reason, statisticians say the results of a random sample are *statistically significant* if the estimated parameter falls in the critical region of a test. In Guided Exercise 6 the random sample of 64 caps gave a parameter estimate $\bar{x} = 1.87$. Since the corresponding z value was in the critical region, we say that the results of the sample were statistically significant—that is, there was sufficient evidence to reject H_0 at the specified level of significance.

Section 9.2 Problems

For problems 1 through 17, please provide the requested information.

(a) What is the null hypothesis? What is the alternate hypothesis? Will we use a left-tailed, or right-tailed, or two-tailed test? What is the level of significance?

(b) What sampling distribution will we use? What is the critical value z_0 (or critical values $\pm z_0$)?

(c) Sketch the critical region and show the critical value (or critical values).

(d) Calculate the z value corresponding to the sample statistic $\bar{x}$ and show its location on the sketch of part c.

(e) Based on your answers for parts a to d, shall we reject or fail to reject (i.e., "accept") the null hypothesis? Explain your conclusion in simple nontechnical terms.

1. *Weatherwise* is a magazine published in association with the American Meteorological Society. In the January 1994 issue there is a rating system to classify Nor'easter storms that frequently hit New England states and can cause much damage near the ocean coasts. A *severe* storm has an average peak wave height of 16.4 feet for waves hitting the shore. Suppose that a Nor'easter is in progress at the severe storm class rating. Peak wave heights are usually measured from land (using binoculars) off fixed cement peers. Suppose that a reading of 36 peak waves showed an average wave height of $\bar{x} = 15.1$ feet with sample standard deviation $s = 3.2$ feet. Does this information indicate that the storm is (perhaps temporarily) retreating from its severe rating? Use $\alpha = 0.01$.

2. *Math Horizons* is a publication of the Mathematical Association of America. The 1993 issue reports that in the United States, graduating mathematics majors who also have studied actuarial science (including some statistics) have an average first-year salary of $27,600. Suppose that a random sample of 36 such recent graduates in the Denver/Boulder region showed that they were earning an average of $\bar{x} = \$27,810$ with sample standard deviation $s = \$915$. Does this information indicate that the population mean salary in the Denver/Boulder region is higher than the national average? Use $\alpha = 0.05$.

3. *USA Today* (July 16, 1993) reported that automobile plants in the United States required an average of 24.9 hours to assemble a new car. In order

where $\bar{x}$ = sample mean
        n = sample size
        s = sample standard deviation
follow a Student's t distribution with degrees of freedom $d.f. = n - 1$.

Critical Values from
a t Distribution

In Table 7, "Student's t Distribution," of Appendix II you see the column headings c, α', and α''. (Up to now we have ignored the α' and α'' headings.) In this table, c represents the level of confidence, α' is the significance level of a one-tailed test (α' is the area to the right of t or, equivalently, to the left of $-t$), and α'' is the significance level for a two-tailed test (α'' is the area beyond $-t$ and t, so in fact $\alpha'' = 2\alpha'$). Figure 9–23 illustrates these different values.

To find the critical value(s) t_0, we look in the column headed by the level of significance α' for a *one-tailed test* or α'' for a *two-tailed test*. The critical value t_0 is located in the row headed by degrees of freedom $d.f. = n - 1$.

Example 8

Use Table 7 in Appendix II to find the critical value(s) t_0 and critical region for the described tests of μ with sample size $n = 11$. (Assume that the sample came from a population with a distribution that is mound-shaped and symmetric.)

(a) Suppose that we have a *right-tailed* test of μ with level of significance 0.01.
    Solution: Since the test is a *one-tailed* test, we use the column headed by $\alpha' = 0.01$. The degrees of freedom are $d.f. = 11 - 1 = 10$, so we use the row headed by 10. The critical value is $t_0 = 2.764$ (see Figure 9–24).

Figure 9–24 Critical Region for $\alpha' = 0.01$ and $d.f. = 10$

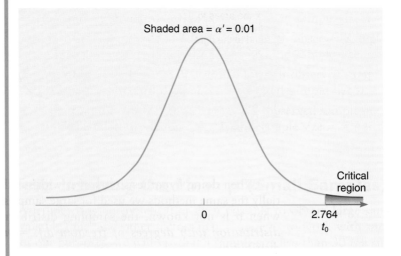

(b) We have a *two-tailed* test of μ with level of significance 0.01.
    Solution: The test is a *two-tailed* test, so we look in the column under $\alpha'' = 0.01$ and the row headed by $d.f. = 11 - 1 = 10$. The critical values are $\pm t_0 = \pm 3.169$ (see Figure 9–25).

Figure 9–25 Critical Region for $\alpha'' = 0.01$ and $d.f. = 10$.

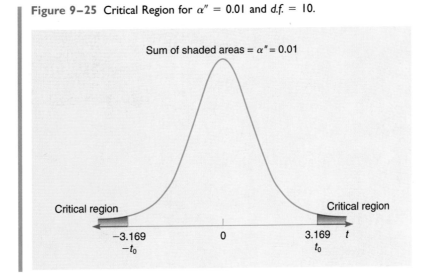

Sum of shaded areas = $\alpha'' = 0.01$

Critical region   Critical region

−3.169   0   3.169 t
$-t_0$ t_0

GUIDED EXERCISE 9

Use Table 7 of Appendix II to find the critical value(s) t_0 and critical region for the test described based on a sample of size $n = 8$.

(a) A *left-tailed* test of μ with level of significance 0.05.

(a) In this case we use the column headed by $\alpha' = 0.05$ and the row headed by $d.f. = n - 1 = 8 - 1 = 7$. This gives us $t = 1.895$. For a left-tailed test, we use the symmetry of the distribution to get $t_0 = -1.895$ (see Figure 9–26).

Figure 9–26 Critical Region for $d.f. = 7$ and $\alpha' = 0.05$

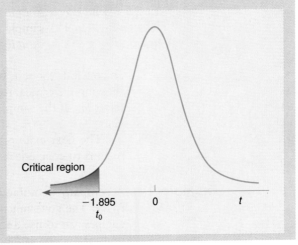

Critical region

−1.895   0 t
t_0

(b) A *two-tailed* test of μ with level of significance 0.05.

(b) Use the column headed by $\alpha'' = 0.05$ and the row headed by $d.f. = n - 1 = 7$. By the symmetry of the curve, the critical values are $\pm t_0 = \pm 2.365$ (see Figure 9–27).

Figure 9–27 Critical Region for $d.f. = 7$ and $\alpha'' = 0.05$

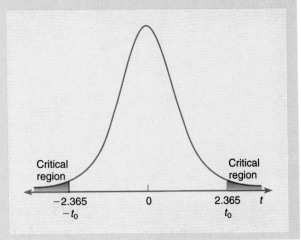

Sample Test Statistic

Once we have the critical value(s) t_0 and critical region, we convert the sample test statistic $\bar{x}$ to a t value using the formula

$$t = \frac{\bar{x} - \mu}{(s/\sqrt{n})}$$

where $\bar{x}$ = sample mean
n = sample size
s = *sample* standard deviation

To conclude the test, we locate the t value of the sample statistic on a diagram showing the critical region. If the sample t value falls in the critical region, we reject H_0. If the sample t value falls outside the critical region, we fail to reject H_0.

The next example demonstrates the traditional method of using critical regions to conclude a test of a mean using small samples.

Example 9 A company manufactures large rocket engines used to project satellites into space. The government buys the rockets, and the contract specifies that these engines are to use an average of 5500 pounds of rocket fuel the first 15 seconds of operation. The company claims that their engines fit specifications. To test the claim, an inspector randomly selects six such engines from the warehouse. These six engines are fired 15 seconds each, and the fuel consumption for each engine is measured. For all six engines, the mean fuel consumption is $\bar{x} = 5690$ pounds and the standard deviation is $s = 250$ pounds. Is the claim justified at the 5% level of significance?

Solution:

(a) We want to see if we can reject the hypothesis $\mu = 5500$ pounds, so the null hypothesis is

$$H_0: \mu = 5500$$

A substantial difference either way from 5500 pounds could be important, so the alternate hypothesis is

$$H_1: \mu \neq 5500$$

(b) Next, we find the critical values. Since our sample is small, we use Table 7 in Appendix II. For a *two-tailed* test with level of significance 0.05, we use the $\alpha'' = 0.05$ column and the row headed by $d.f. = n - 1 = 6 - 1 = 5$. This gives us $\pm t_0 = \pm 2.571$.

(c) Using $\mu = 5500$ from H_0, $s = 250$, and $n = 6$, we convert the sample test statistic $\bar{x} = 5690$ to a t value:

$$t = \frac{\bar{x} - \mu}{(s/\sqrt{n})} = \frac{5690 - 5500}{(250/\sqrt{6})} = 1.862$$

(d) On a diagram show the critical regions and the location of the sample test statistic. (See Figure 9–28.) We see that the t value of the sample test

Figure 9–28 Critical Region for $d.f. = 5$ and $\alpha'' = 0.05$

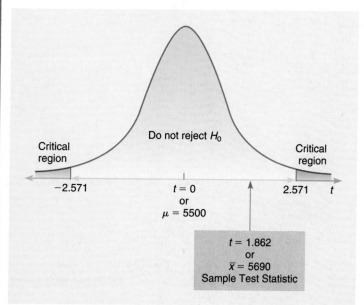

statistic falls outside the critical region. Therefore, we cannot reject H_0. The data do not present sufficient evidence to indicate that the average fuel consumption for the first 15 seconds of operation is different from $\mu = 5500$ pounds.

GUIDED EXERCISE 10

Suppose in Example 9 a random sample of eight engines was used and the mean fuel consumption was $\bar{x} = 5880$ pounds (for the first 15 seconds). Again, the standard deviation was 250 pounds. Use a 1% level of significance to test the claim that the average fuel consumption *exceeds* 5500 pounds.

(a) We will use H_0: $\mu = 5500$. What should we use for H_1?

$$H_1: \mu < 5500 \qquad H_1: \mu \neq 5500$$
$$H_1: \mu > 5500$$

(a) H_1: $\mu > 5500$ because we want to test the claim that the average fuel consumption *exceeds 5500 pounds*.

(b) Find the critical value t_0.

(b) Because the sample size is small, we use Table 7 of Appendix II. For a one-tailed test we look in the column headed by $\alpha' = 0.01$ and the row headed by $d.f. = 8 - 1 = 7$. The critical value is $t_0 = 2.998$.

Figure 9–29 Critical Region for $d.f. = 7$ and $\alpha' = 0.01$

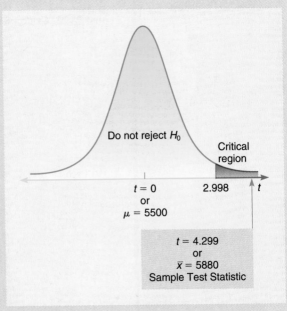

Do not reject H_0

Critical region

$t = 0$
or
$\mu = 5500$

2.998 t

$t = 4.299$
or
$\bar{x} = 5880$
Sample Test Statistic

(c) Convert the sample test statistic $\bar{x}$ to a t value.

(c) We use $\mu = 5500$, $n = 8$, and $s = 250$:

$$t = \frac{\bar{x} - \mu}{(s/\sqrt{n})}$$

$$= \frac{5880 - 5500}{(250/\sqrt{8})}$$

$$= 4.299$$

(d) Sketch the critical region and show the location of the sample test statistic on the diagram. Do we reject H_0 or not at the 1% level of significance?

(d) Since the sample test statistic falls in the critical region, we reject H_0. It seems that the average fuel consumption exceeds 5500 pounds during the first 15 seconds of operation. (See Figure 9–29.)

Using P Values for Tests of μ, Small Samples

Recall that the P value for a statistical test is the probability of getting a sample statistic as far (or even farther) into the tails of the sampling distribution as the observed sample statistic. The smaller the P value, the stronger the evidence is to reject H_0.

In the case of small sample tests of μ, the sample distribution $\bar{x}$ follows a Student's t distribution. Therefore, we will use Table 7 of Appendix II to estimate the P values. However, the areas given in Table 7 are limited. Consequently, when we use Table 7 to estimate P values for $\bar{x}$, we usually find an *interval containing the P value* rather than a single number for the P value.

- *Note Regarding Table 7 of Appendix II:* In Table 7, α' represents the area in *one tail* beyond t. The α'' values represent the area in the *two tails*. Notice that in each column $\alpha'' = 2\alpha'$. Consequently, we use α' values as endpoints of the P value intervals for *one-tailed tests* and α'' values as endpoints of the P value intervals for *two-tailed tests* (see Figure 9–30 below and on page 578).

Figure 9–30 P Values Corresponding to α' and α''

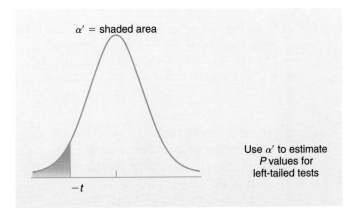

α' = shaded area

Use α' to estimate
P values for
left-tailed tests

$-t$

Figure 9-30 continued

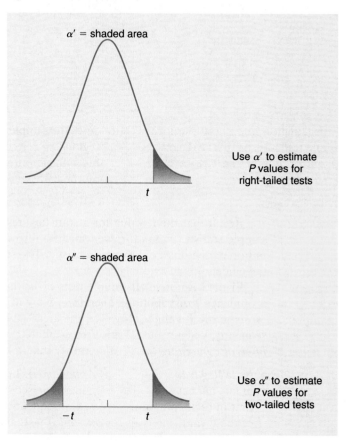

Let's find the *P* values associated with the sample test statistic of Example 9 and of Guided Exercise 10.

Example 10

In Example 9 we tested the rocket manufacturer's claim that its rockets consumed an average of 5500 pounds of fuel in the first 15 seconds of operation. The test was a two-tailed test with sample statistic $\bar{x} = 5690$, $s = 250$, and $n = 6$. Find the *P* value associated with $\bar{x} = 5690$. What does the *P* value tell us?

Solution:

(a) First, we convert $\bar{x} = 5690$ to a *t* value. This was done in Example 9. The corresponding *t* value is 1.862.

(b) To find the associated *P*-value interval, we look in Table 7 in Appendix II in the row headed by *d.f.* $= 6 - 1 = 5$. We find that $t = 1.862$ falls *between* 1.699 and 2.015. Therefore, the *P* value is *between* 0.150 and

0.100 (the α'' labels heading the columns containing 0.150 and 0.100). Figure 9–31 shows these relationships. Note that we use α'' headers because the test is a *two-tailed* test. Thus we have

$$0.100 < P \text{ value} < 0.150$$

Figure 9–31 The *P* Value Is the Shaded Area of a *t* Distribution with *d.f.* = 5

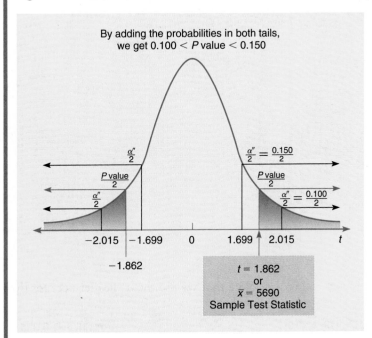

(c) Since the *P* value is less than 0.150, we *reject* H_0 for all levels of significance $\alpha \geq 0.150$ and we *fail to reject* H_0 for all $\alpha < 0.150$. Since 0.05 is greater than 0.150, we reject H_0. This is consistent with the conclusion of Example 9.

Example 11 In Guided Exercise 10 we again looked at the fuel consumption of rockets. This time the sample mean consumption for the first 15 seconds of flight was $\bar{x} = 5880$ pounds with $s = 250$ pounds and $n = 8$ rockets. We used a right-tailed test with H_0: $\mu = 5500$ and H_1: $\mu > 5500$. Find the *P* value associated with the sample statistic $\bar{x}$. What does the *P* value tell you?
Solution:

(a) Again, our first step is to convert the sample statistic $\bar{x} = 5880$ to a *t* value. We did this in Guided Exercise 10 and got $t = 4.299$.

(b) Next, we use Table 7 in Appendix II. We look in the row headed by $d.f. = 8 - 1 = 7$ and find that $t = 4.299$ falls *to the right* of 3.499. Therefore, the *P* value for $t = 4.299$ is *smaller* than 0.005 (the α' label heading the column containing 3.499). Figure 9–32 illustrates these relationships.

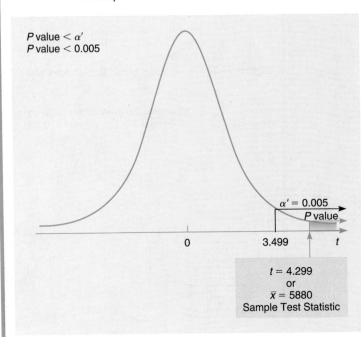

Figure 9–32 The *P* Value Is the Shaded Area of a *t* Distribution with *d.f.* = 7

Note that we use the α' header because the test is a *one-tailed* test. Thus we have

$$P \text{ value} < 0.005$$

(c) Since the *P* value is less than 0.005, we reject H_0 for all $\alpha \geq 0.005$. Since $\alpha = 0.01$ is greater than 0.005, we reject H_0 for a 1% level of significance. This is consistent with the conclusion in Guided Exercise 10.

Section 9.4 Problems

In Problems 1–6, use Table 7 of Appendix II to find the critical value(s) t_0 for the described test of the mean (small sample).

1. Sample size $n = 9$, left-tailed test, level of significance 5%
2. Sample size $n = 13$, right-tailed test, level of significance 1%
3. Sample size $n = 24$, two-tailed test, level of significance 1%
4. Sample size $n = 18$, left-tailed test, level of significance 5%
5. Sample size $n = 12$, two-tailed test, level of significance 5%
6. Sample size $n = 29$, right-tailed test, level of significance 1%

For each of the following problems, please provide the requested information.
  (a) What is the null hypothesis? What is the alternate hypothesis? Will

we use a left-tailed, right-tailed, or two-tailed test? What is the level of significance?

(b) What sampling distribution will we use? What is the critical value t_0 (or critical values $\pm t_0$)?

(c) Sketch the critical region and show the critical value (or critical values).

(d) Calculate the t value corresponding to the sample statistic $\bar{x}$ and show its location on the sketch of part c.

(e) Find the P value (or interval containing the P value) for your test and explain what the P value means in this context.

(f) Based on your answers for parts a to e, shall we reject or fail to reject (i.e., "accept") the null hypothesis? Explain your conclusion in simple nontechnical terms.

7. Let x be a random variable that represents red blood cell count (RBC) in millions per cubic millimeter of whole blood. Then x has a distribution that is approximately normal, and for the population of healthy female adults, the mean of the x distribution is about 4.8 (based on information from *Diagnostic Tests with Nursing Implications,* Springhouse Corporation, 1994). Suppose that a female patient has taken six laboratory blood tests over the past several months and the RBC data sent to the patient's doctor were

    3.5   4.2   4.5   4.6   3.7   3.9

(a) Use a calculator with sample mean and sample standard deviation keys to verify that $\bar{x} = 4.07$ and $s = 0.44$.

(b) Do the given data indicate that the population mean RBC for this patient is lower than 4.8? Use $\alpha = 0.05$.

8. Let x be a random variable that represents white blood cell count (WBC) per cubic millimeter of whole blood. Then x has a distribution that is approximately normal, and for the population of healthy adults, the mean of the x distribution is about 7500 (see reference in Problem 7). Suppose that a patient has taken 8 laboratory blood tests over the past several months and the WBC data sent to the patient's doctor were

    6510   7351   6649   6322
    7015   7418   6824   7109

(a) Use a calculator with sample mean and sample standard deviation keys to verify that $\bar{x} = 6899.75$ and $s = 393.44$.

(b) Does this information indicate that the population mean WBC for this patient is different (either up or down) from 7500? Use $\alpha = 0.05$.

9. Let x be a random variable that represents milligrams of glucose (blood sugar) per deciliter of blood. After a 12-hour fast, x will have a distribution that is approximately normal with mean about 85 for healthy adults under 50 years of age (see reference in Problem 7). Suppose that a

patient has taken 10 laboratory blood tests over the last 6 months and the glucose report sent to the patient's doctor was

93	116	82	80	110
95	79	84	98	72

(a) Use a calculator with sample mean and sample standard deviations keys to verify that $\bar{x} = 90.90$ and $s = 14.18$.

(b) Does this information indicate that the population mean glucose level for this patient is different (either higher or lower) from 85? Use $\alpha = 0.01$.

10. Let x be a random variable that represents hemoglobin count (HC) in grams per 100 milliliters of whole blood. Then x has a distribution that is approximately normal with population mean about 14 for healthy adult women (see reference in Problem 7). Suppose that a female patient has taken 12 laboratory blood tests during the past year. The HC data sent to the patient's doctor were

19	23	15	21	18	16
14	20	19	16	18	21

(a) Use a calculator with sample mean and sample standard deviation keys to verify that $\bar{x} = 18.33$ and $s = 2.71$.

(b) Does this information indicate that the population average HC for this patient is higher than 14? Use $\alpha = 0.01$.

11. *Selasphorus platycerus* is the scientific name of the broad-tailed hummingbird that is commonly found throughout the western United States. It is known that the mean incubation time for eggs of this bird is approximately 16.5 days (based on information from *The Hummingbird Book*, by D. Stokes and L. Stokes, Little, Brown and Company, 1989). Assume that the incubation times are approximately normally distributed. However, at higher elevations (above 8000 feet), it is thought that the average incubation time might be different from 16.5 days. A number of broad-tailed hummingbird nests were located in mountain country above 8000 feet, and incubation times for 18 eggs gave the following information (in days):

15	19	16	16	18	17	21	18	17
16	17	18	19	16	15	21	23	19

(a) Use a calculator with mean and standard deviation keys to verify that $\bar{x} = 17.83$ days and $s = 2.20$ days.

(b) Does this information indicate that the population average incubation time above 8000 feet elevation is different (either more or less) than 16.5 days? Use $\alpha = 0.05$.

12. *The Statistical Abstract of the United States* (109th edition) reported that the average hospital stay for delivering a baby was 3.2 days. At Manoa Community Hospital in Honolulu, records show that a random sample

of 10 women delivering babies spent the following number of days in the hospital:

5   6   2   3   4   3   2   6   5   3

(a) Use a calculator to verify that the sample mean stay is 3.9 days and the sample standard deviation is 1.52.
(b) Use a 5% level of significance to test the claim that the population average length of stay at Manoa Community Hospital is different from the national average.

13. *The Statistical Abstract of the United States* (109th edition) reported that the net average earnings of all M.D.'s was 155.8 thousand dollars per year. A random sample of income tax returns of 9 M.D.'s practicing in rural communities in Nebraska showed their net earnings to be

    93.7   110.5   173.6   123.3   136.8
    142.7   129.9   153.4   140.2

    (a) Use a calculator with mean and standard deviation keys to verify that $\bar{x} = 133.79$ and $s = 23.38$.
    (b) Assuming that the earnings of these M.D.'s follow a distribution that is approximately normal, use a 1% level of significance to test the claim that the population mean earnings of rural Nebraska M.D.'s is different from the national average.

14. *The Statistical Abstract of the United States* (109th edition) reported that the average daily hospital room charge was $687. A random sample of bills from Manoa Community Hospital in Honolulu gave the following information about daily costs:

    693   710   815   642   625   791
    712   685   719   742   788   742

    (a) Use a calculator with mean and standard deviation keys to verify that $\bar{x} = \$722$ and $s = \$57.87$.
    (b) Assuming that the room charges at the hospital follow a distribution that is approximately normal, use a 5% level of significance to test the claim that the population mean room charge at Manoa Community Hospital is higher than the national average.

15. Tree ring dating from archaeological excavation sites is used in conjunction with other chronologic evidence to estimate occupation dates of prehistoric Indian ruins in the southwest United States. It is thought that Burnt Mesa Pueblo was occupied around 1300 A.D. (based on evidence from potsherds and stone tools). The following data give tree ring dates (A.D.) from adjacent archaeological sites (*Bandelier Archaeological Excavation Project: Summer 1990 Excavations at Burnt Mesa Pueblo*, edited by T. Kohler, Washington State University Department of Anthropology, 1992):

    1189   1267   1268   1275   1275
    1271   1272   1316   1317   1230

(a) Use a calculator with mean and standard deviation keys to verify that $\bar{x} = 1268$ and $s = 37.29$ years.

(b) Assuming that the tree ring dates in this excavation area follow a distribution that is approximately normal, does this information indicate the population mean of tree ring dates in the area is different (either high or low) from 1300 A.D.? Use a 1% level of significance.

16. *Consumer Reports* (January 1993) stated that the mean retail cost of an AT&T model 3730 cellular phone was $600. A random sample of 10 stores in Los Angeles, California, gave the following retail prices for this model cellular phone (in dollars):

    593   621   545   561   609
    555   588   575   619   599

(a) Use a calculator with mean and standard deviation keys to verify that $\bar{x} = \$586.50$ and $s = \$26.77$.

(b) Assuming that the retail costs of these cellular phones are distributed approximately normally, does this information indicate that the population mean cost for the AT&T model 3730 cellular phone is less than $600 in Los Angeles? Use a 10% level of significance.

17. *USA Today* (June 16, 1993) reported that the state with the longest mean life span is Hawaii, where the population mean life span is 77 years. A random sample of 20 obituary notices in the *Honolulu Advertizer* gave the following information about life span (in years) of Honolulu residents:

    72   68   81   93   56   19   78   94   83   84
    77   69   85   97   75   71   86   47   66   88

(a) Use a calculator with mean and standard deviation keys to verify that $\bar{x} = 74.45$ years and $s = 18.09$ years.

(b) Assuming that life span in Honolulu is approximately normally distributed, does this information indicate that the population mean life span for Honolulu residents is less than 77 years? Use a 5% level of significance.

18. The mean start-up cost for a windshield repair business is about 6.3 thousand dollars (see reference in Problem 18). A random sample of 5 windshield repair businesses in Phoenix, Arizona, gave the following information about start-up costs (in thousands of dollars):

    8.3   10.2   4.9   5.7   6.2

(a) Use a calculator with mean and standard deviation keys to verify that $\bar{x} = 7.06$ and $s = 2.16$.

(b) Assuming that the start-up costs are approximately normally distributed, do these data indicate that the population mean start-up cost for windshield repair business is more than 6.3 thousand dollars in Phoenix? Use a 5% level of significance.

19. Based on information from *Business Start-Ups Magazine* (March 1994), the mean start-up cost for an automobile paint shop is about 44.9 thou-

sand dollars. A random sample of 7 automobile paint shops in El Paso, Texas, gave the following information about start-up costs (in thousands of dollars):

35.2   51.7   40.9   28.7
43.3   38.9   33.6

(a) Use a calculator with mean and standard deviation keys to verify that $\bar{x} = 38.90$ and $s = 7.45$.
(b) Assuming that the start-up costs are approximately normally distributed, do these data indicate that the population mean start-up cost for automobile paint shops in El Paso is less than 44.9 thousand dollars? Use a 5% level of significance.

Section 9.5   Tests Involving a Proportion

Many situations arise that call for tests of proportions or percentages rather than means. For example, a welfare office claims that the proportion of incomplete applications they receive is now 47%. The office is using this claim to justify a request for two more staff members whose main duty will be to help applicants complete the forms properly. The funding agency wants to test the claim that 47% of the applications are incomplete.

How can we make such a test? In this section we will study tests involving proportions (i.e., percentages or proportions). In principle, such tests are the same as those in Sections 9.2 and 9.4. The main difference is that here we are working with a distribution of proportions instead of means.

Tests for a Single Proportion

Throughout this section we will assume that the situations we are dealing with satisfy the conditions underlying the binomial distribution. In particular, we will let r be a binomial random variable. This means r is the number of successes out of n independent binomial trials (for the definition of binomial trial, see Section 5.1). We will use $\hat{p} = r/n$ as our estimate for p, the probability of success on each trial. The letter q again represents the probability of failure on each trial, and so $q = 1 - p$. We also assume that the samples are large (i.e., $np > 5$ and $nq > 5$).

For large samples, the distribution of $\hat{p} = r/n$ values is well approximated by a *normal curve* with mean μ and standard deviation σ as follows:

$$\mu = p \qquad \sigma = \sqrt{\frac{pq}{n}}$$

The null and alternate hypotheses for tests of proportions are

| H_0: $p = k$ | H_0: $p = k$ | H_0: $p = k$ |
| H_1: $p < k$ | H_1: $p > k$ | H_1: $p \neq k$ |

depending on what is asked for in the problem. Notice that since p is a probability, the value k must be between 0 and 1.

Critical Values for Testing p ($np > 5$ and $nq > 5$)

Since the $\hat{p}$ distribution is approximately normal when n is sufficiently large, we will use the same *critical values* z_0 for our tests as those we used for

Figure 9–33 Critical Values for Tests of Proportions

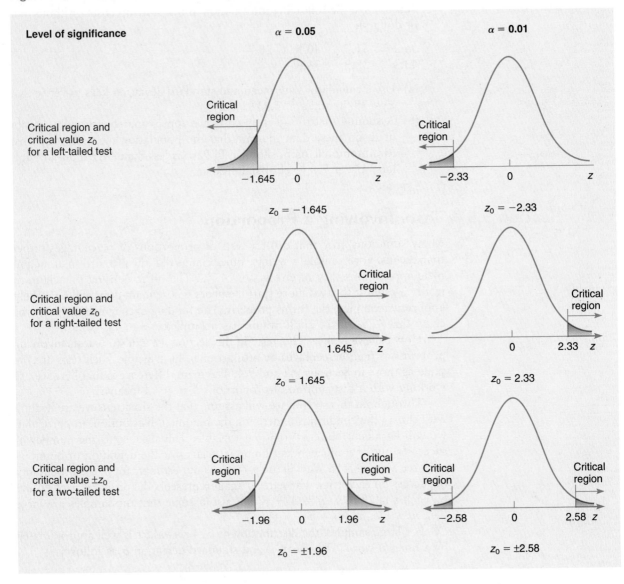

testing the mean with large samples (Section 9.2). These values were shown in Figure 9–11. Figure 9–33 repeats the critical values for convenience.

Sample Test Statistic
For tests of proportions, we need to convert our sample test statistic $\hat{p}$ to a z value. Then we can compare the sample z value with a specified critical value z_0 to determine whether or not to reject H_0. The $\hat{p}$ distribution is approximately normal with mean p and standard deviation $\sqrt{pq/n}$. Therefore, the conversion of $\hat{p}$ to z follows the formula

$$z = \frac{\hat{p} - p}{\sqrt{\dfrac{pq}{n}}}$$

where $\hat{p} = r/n$ is the sample test statistic
p = proportion specified in H_0
$q = 1 - p$ using the proportion p specified in H_0
n = number of trials

Example 12

A team of eye surgeons has developed a new technique for a risky eye operation to restore the sight of people blinded from a certain disease. Under the old method, it is known that only 30% of the patients who undergo this operation recover their eyesight.

Suppose that surgeons in various hospitals have performed a total of 225 operations using the new method and that 88 have been successful (the patients fully recovered their sight). Can we justify the claim that the new method is better than the old one? (Use a 1% level of significance.)

Solution:

(a) Let p be the probability that a patient fully recovers his or her eyesight. The null hypothesis is that p is still 0.30, even for the new method of operation. Therefore,

$$H_0\text{: } p = 0.30$$

(b) The alternate hypothesis is that the new method has improved the patient's chances for eyesight recovery. Therefore,

$$H_1\text{: } p > 0.30$$

(c) Since the alternate hypothesis is H_1: $p > 0.30$, we use a right-tailed test. For $\alpha = 0.01$, Figure 9–33 shows a critical value of $z_0 = 2.33$.

(d) Next, we find the sample test statistic $\hat{p}$ and convert it to a z-value:

$$\hat{p} = \frac{r}{n} = \frac{88}{225} \approx 0.39$$

The z value corresponding to $\hat{p}$ is

$$z = \frac{\hat{p} - p}{\sqrt{\dfrac{pq}{n}}} = \frac{0.39 - 0.30}{\sqrt{\dfrac{0.30(0.70)}{225}}} = 2.95$$

In the formula, the value for p came from the null hypothesis. H_0 specified that $p = 0.30$, so $q = 1 - 0.30 = 0.70$.

table indicate a more positive attitude about smoking.) Do the data indicate that cigarette smokers' attitudes about smoking become less positive after viewing the film? (Use $\alpha = 0.05$ level of significance.)

Person	1	2	3	4	5	6	7
Before film	31	27	25	36	34	29	38
After film	19	30	10	20	28	29	19

12. A new law has been passed giving city police greater powers in apprehending suspected criminals. For six neighborhoods, the numbers of reported crimes 1 year before and 1 year after the new law are shown in the following table:

Neighborhood	1	2	3	4	5	6
Before new law	18	35	44	28	22	37
After new law	21	23	30	19	24	29

Use a 5% level of significance to test the claim that 1 year after the new law, the number of reported crimes has dropped.

13. To test the wearing quality of two brands of automobile tires, one tire of each brand was placed on each of six test cars. The position was determined by using a random number table. The amount of wear (in thousandths of an inch) was determined for each car after 6 months of use. Do the data give sufficient evidence to conclude that the two tire brands show unequal wear? (Use $\alpha = 0.05$ level of significance.)

Car	1	2	3	4	5	6
Soapstone	132	71	90	37	93	107
Bigyear	140	74	110	36	105	119

14. The following data are based on information from the Regis University Psychology Department. In an effort to determine if rats perform certain tasks more quickly if offered larger rewards, the following experiment was performed. On day 1, a group of 3 rats was given a reward of one food pellet each time they ran a maze. A second group of 3 rats was given a reward of five food pellets each time they ran the maze. On day 2, the groups were reversed, so the first group now got five food pellets for running the maze and the second group got only one pellet for running the same maze. The average times in seconds for each rat to run the maze 30 times are shown in the following table.

Rat	A	B	C	D	E	F
Time with one food pellet	3.6	4.2	2.9	3.1	3.5	3.9
Time with five food pellets	3.0	3.7	3.0	3.3	2.8	3.0

Do these data indicate that rats receiving larger rewards tend to run the maze in less time? Use a 5% level of significance.

15. The same experimental design discussed in Problem 14 also was used to test rats trained to climb a sequence of short ladders. Times in seconds for eight rats to do this task are shown in the following table.

Rat	A	B	C	D	E	F	G	H
Time 1 pellet	12.5	13.7	11.4	12.1	11.0	10.4	14.6	12.3
Time 5 pellets	11.1	12.0	12.2	10.6	11.5	10.5	12.9	11.0

Do these data indicate that rats receiving larger rewards tend to perform the ladder climb in less time? Use a 5% level of significance.

16. The following is based on information taken from *Academe: Bulletin of the American Association of University Professors* (April 1993). A random sample of nine small and medium-sized colleges and universities in the western United States gave the following information about numbers of male and female assistant professors in each institution:

Institution	A	B	C	D	E	F	G	H	I
Male Assistant Professors	17	59	7	41	22	25	20	23	14
Female Assistant Professors	16	55	8	36	30	34	15	22	11

Do these data indicate that there is a difference (either higher or lower) in the number of male versus female assistant professors in small and medium-sized colleges in the western United States? Use a 5% level of significance.

17. The following problem is based on information taken from *Diagnostic Tests with Nursing Implications* (Springhouse, 1994). A patient who had undergone a triple coronary artery bypass was tested in the following way. The patient took his pulse at rest and then on a treadmill exercised at a 10% grade at 1.7 mi/h for 2 minutes. This procedure was repeated on six different days. The pulse rate 6 minutes after the test and the pulse rate before the test are shown in the following table (beats per minute):

Test	1	2	3	4	5	6
Pulse before	69	72	75	73	70	74
Pulse after	85	79	83	84	87	78

Do these data indicate that the heart rate 6 minutes after the test is higher than before the test? Use a 5% level of significance.

18. The patient described in Problem 17 also had his systolic blood pressure measured before and after the treadmill tests. The results for the tests are shown in the following table:

Test	1	2	3	4	5	6
Before	135	120	138	127	122	133
After	146	132	144	122	121	130

Does this indicate that the systolic blood pressure is different (either higher or lower) before and 6 minutes after the treadmill test. Use a 5% level of significance.

19. The manager of a sporting goods store offered a bonus commission to his salespeople when they sold more goods. A new manager dropped the bonus system. For a random sample of six salespeople, the weekly sales (in thousands of dollars) are shown in the following table with and without the bonus system:

Salesperson	1	2	3	4	5	6
B: With bonus	2.9	3.0	5.8	4.4	5.3	5.6
A: Without bonus	2.8	2.5	5.9	3.5	4.6	4.6

Use a 5% level of significance to test the claim that the average weekly sales dropped when the bonus system was discontinued.

Section 9.7   Testing Differences of Two Means or Two Proportions (Independent Samples)

Many practical applications of statistics involve a comparison of two population means or two population proportions. In Section 9.6 we considered tests of differences of means for *dependent samples*. With dependent samples, we could pair the data and then consider the difference of data measurements d. In this section we will turn our attention to tests of differences of means from *independent samples*. We will see new techniques for testing the difference of means from *independent samples*.

Independent Samples

First, let's consider independent samples.

> Definition: We say that two sampling distributions are *independent* if there is no relation whatsoever between specific values of the two distributions.

Example 18

A teacher wishes to compare the effectiveness of two teaching methods. Students are randomly divided into two groups: the first group is taught by method 1; the second group, by method 2. At the end of the course, a comprehensive exam is given to all students, and the mean score $\bar{x}_1$ for group 1 is compared with the mean score $\bar{x}_2$ for group 2. Are the samples independent or dependent?

Solution: Because the students were *randomly* divided into two groups, it is reasonable to say that the $\bar{x}_1$ distribution is independent of the $\bar{x}_2$ distribution.

Example 19

In Section 9.6 we considered a situation in which a shoe manufacturer claims that for the general population of adult U.S. citizens, the average length of the left foot is longer than the average length of the right foot. To study this claim, the manufacturer gathers data in this fashion: Sixty adult U.S. citizens are drawn at random, and for these 60 people, both their left and right feet are measured. Let $\bar{x}_1$ be the mean length of the left feet and $\bar{x}_2$ be the mean length of the right feet.

Are the $\bar{x}_1$ and $\bar{x}_2$ distributions independent for this method of collecting data?

Solution: In this method, there is only *one* random sample of people drawn, and both the left and right feet are measured from this sample. The length of a person's left foot is usually related to the length of the right foot, so in this case the $\bar{x}_1$ and $\bar{x}_2$ distributions are *not* independent. In fact, we could pair the data and consider the distribution of the differences, left foot length minus right foot length. Then we would use the techniques of paired difference tests as found in Section 9.6.

GUIDED EXERCISE 14

Suppose the shoe manufacturer of Example 19 gathers data in the following way: Sixty adult U.S. citizens are drawn at random and their left feet are measured; then another 60 adult U.S. citizens are drawn at random and their right feet are measured. Again, $\bar{x}_1$ is the mean of the left foot measurements and $\bar{x}_2$ is the mean of the right foot measurements.

Are the $\bar{x}_1$ and $\bar{x}_2$ distributions independent for this method of collecting data?

For this method of gathering data, two random samples are drawn: one for the left foot measurements and one for the right foot measurements. The first sample is not related to the second sample. The $\bar{x}_1$ and $\bar{x}_2$ distributions are independent.

Testing the Difference of Means for Large, Independent Samples

Properties of $\bar{x}_1 - \bar{x}_2$
Distribution, Large Sample
Size

In this section we will use distributions that arise from a difference of means from independent samples. How do we obtain such distributions? If we have two statistical variables x_1 and x_2, each with its own distribution, we take independent random samples of size n_1 from the x_1 distribution and size n_2 from the x_2 distribution. Then we can compute the respective means $\bar{x}_1$ and $\bar{x}_2$. Consider the difference $\bar{x}_1 - \bar{x}_2$. This represents a difference of means. If

Let us return to Example 18 at the beginning of this section. A teacher wishes to compare the effectiveness of two teaching methods. Students are randomly divided into two groups. The first group is taught by method 1; the second group, by method 2. At the end of the course, a comprehensive exam is given to all students.

The first group consists of $n_1 = 49$ students with a mean score of $\bar{x}_1 = 74.8$ points and standard deviation $s_1 = 14$ points. The second group has $n_2 = 50$ students with a mean score of $\bar{x}_2 = 81.3$ points and standard deviation $s_2 = 15$ points. The teacher claims that the second method will increase the mean score on the comprehensive exam. Is this claim justified at the 5% level of significance?

Let μ_1 and μ_2 be the mean score of the distribution of all scores using method 1 and method 2, respectively.

(a) Which is the null hypothesis?

$H_0\colon \mu_1 = \mu_2 \qquad H_0\colon \mu_1 \neq \mu_2$

$H_0\colon \mu_1 < \mu_2 \qquad H_0\colon \mu_1 > \mu_2$

(a) $H_0\colon \mu_1 = \mu_2$ or $H_0\colon \mu_1 - \mu_2 = 0$

(b) To examine the validity of the teacher's claim, what will we use for the alternate hypothesis?

$H_1\colon \mu_1 \neq \mu_2 \qquad H_1\colon \mu_1 > \mu_2 \qquad H_1\colon \mu_1 < \mu_2$

(b) $H_1\colon \mu_1 < \mu_2$ (the second method gives a higher average score) or $H_1\colon \mu_1 - \mu_2 < 0$

(c) Find the critical value z_0.

(c) By Table 9–7, we see that for a left-tailed test where $\alpha = 0.05$, $z_0 = -1.645$.

(d) Compute the sample test statistic $\bar{x}_1 - \bar{x}_2$.

(d) $\bar{x}_1 - \bar{x}_2 = 74.8 - 81.3 = -6.5$

(e) Convert $\bar{x}_1 - \bar{x}_2 = -6.5$ to a z value.

(e) By the null hypothesis, $\mu_1 - \mu_2 = 0$. From the problem, we have $s_1 = 14$ and $s_2 = 15$. Since the samples are both large, we can estimate σ_1 and σ_2 by these values, respectively. Also, $n_1 = 49$ and $n_2 = 50$. Putting all these values in the formula gives

$$z = \frac{(x_1 - x_2) - (\mu_1 - \mu_2)}{\sqrt{\dfrac{\sigma_1^2}{n_1} + \dfrac{\sigma_2^2}{n_2}}}$$

$$= \frac{-6.5 - 0}{\sqrt{\dfrac{14^2}{49} + \dfrac{15^2}{50}}}$$

$$= -2.23$$

(f) Show the *z* value of the sample test statistic and the critical region on a diagram, and then conclude the test. Is the claim that method 2 is better justified at the 5% level of significance?

(f) **Figure 9–44** Critical Region

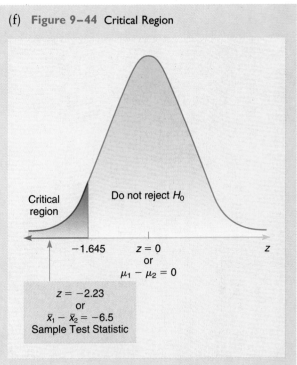

Since the *z* value of the sample test statistic falls in the critical region, we reject H_0, select H_1, and conclude that method 2 is better at the 5% level of significance.

(g) Find the *P* value for the sample test statistic $\bar{x}_1 - \bar{x}_2$. What does the *P* value tell us?

(g) First, we convert $\bar{x}_1 - \bar{x}_2 = -6.5$ to a *z* value. In part e we found that the corresponding *z* value is -2.23. Since the test is a *left-tailed* test, the *P* value is the area to the left of $z = -2.23$ (see Figure 9–45 on page 618). From Table 6 in Appendix II we have

$$P \text{ value} = 0.5 - 0.4871$$
$$= 0.0129$$

This means that we reject H_0 for any $\alpha \geqslant 0.0129$.

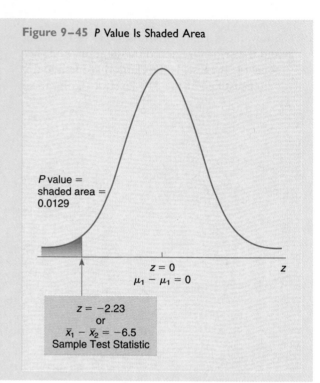

Figure 9–45 P Value Is Shaded Area

P value = shaded area = 0.0129

$z = 0$
$\mu_1 - \mu_1 = 0$

z

$z = -2.23$
or
$\bar{x}_1 - \bar{x}_2 = -6.5$
Sample Test Statistic

Testing Difference of Means for Small Samples

Statistical methods involving small samples and the difference between two means are much like the methods for large samples. However, for small samples, we will use the Student's *t* distribution for critical values instead of the normal distribution.

Independent random samples of size n_1 and n_2, respectively, are drawn from two populations which possess means μ_1 and μ_2. Again, *we assume that the parent populations have normal distributions, and we also assume that the standard deviations σ_1 and σ_2 for the two populations are equal.* The condition $\sigma_1 = \sigma_2$ may seem quite restrictive. However, in a great many practical applications this condition is satisfied. Furthermore, our methods still apply even if the standard deviations are known to be only approximately equal.

Suppose we draw two independent random samples, one from the x_1 population and one from the x_2 population. Say the sample from the x_1 population is of size n_1 and has sample standard deviation s_1. Likewise for the x_2 population, the sample size is n_2 and the sample standard deviation is s_2. We estimate the common standard deviation for the two populations by using a *pooled variance* of the s_1^2 and s_2^2 values. Research shows that the best estimate of the common variance of the x_1 and x_2 populations is given by the formula

$$s^2 = \frac{(n_1 - 1)s_1^2 + (n_2 - 1)s_2^2}{n_1 + n_2 - 2}$$

Pooled Standard Deviation   The best estimate of the common or pooled standard deviation is then

$$s = \sqrt{\frac{(n_1 - 1)s_1^2 + (n_2 - 1)s_2^2}{n_1 + n_2 - 2}}$$

The null hypothesis is usually set up to see if it can be rejected. When testing the difference of means, we first set up the hypothesis H_0 that there is no difference. That is, we take the null hypothesis to be

$$H_0: \mu_1 - \mu_2 = 0$$

or, equivalently,

$$H_0: \mu_1 = \mu_2$$

Table 9–6 on page 613 lists the possibilities for the alternate hypothesis and the type of test to be used with the alternate hypothesis.

Let $\bar{x}_1$ and $\bar{x}_2$ be the sample means for our two random samples from the x_1 and x_2 populations. Then under the assumption that $\sigma_1 = \sigma_2$ and under the null hypothesis $H_0: \mu_1 - \mu_2 = 0$ it is possible to show that

$$t = \frac{\bar{x}_1 - \bar{x}_2}{s\sqrt{\dfrac{1}{n_1} + \dfrac{1}{n_2}}}$$

has a t distribution with degrees of freedom:

$$d.f. = n_1 + n_2 - 2$$

Critical Values   Since the sample statistic $\bar{x}_1 - \bar{x}_2$ follows a Student's t distribution, we find the critical values t_0 and critical regions by using Table 7 in Appendix II. The critical value(s) t_0 are found in the row headed by $d.f. = n_1 + n_2 - 2$. For *one-tailed tests*, we use the column headed by $\alpha' =$ level of significance. For *two-tailed tests*, we use the column headed by $\alpha'' =$ level of significance.

Sample Test Statistic   We use the following two formulas to convert the sample test statistic $\bar{x}_1 - \bar{x}_2$ to a t value:

$$t = \frac{\bar{x}_1 - \bar{x}_2}{s\sqrt{\dfrac{1}{n_1} + \dfrac{1}{n_2}}}$$

where the pooled standard deviation s is

$$s = \sqrt{\frac{(n_1 - 1)s_1^2 + (n_2 - 1)s_2^2}{n_1 + n_2 - 2}}$$

Then we compare the sample t statistic with the critical value(s) t_0 to conclude the test.

Using Technology

The problems in this section may be done using statistical computer software or calculators with statistical functions. Displays and suggestions are given for Minitab (Release 9), the TI-82 graphing calculator, and ComputerStat.

Testing a Mean μ Using Large Samples

Minitab

When testing a single mean using the normal distribution, Minitab requires that the *population* standard deviation be known. If you do not know the population standard deviation and you wish to estimate it by the sample standard deviation s, then you must ask Minitab to compute the sample standard deviation s.

The commands

```
MTB > SET C1 #enter data in column 1
MTB > LET K1 = STDEV C1
MTB > ZTEST MU = 3 SIGMA = K1 on C1
```

perform a two-tailed test with the hypotheses H_0: $\mu = 3$ and H_1: $\mu \neq 3$. The z value of the sample test statistic and the P value of the sample test statistic are given in the output. You compare the P value to your α value to conclude the test.

The default test is a two-tailed test. Use the ALTERNATIVE -1 subcommand to do a left-tailed test and the ALTERNATIVE 1 subcommand to do a right-tailed test. For instance, the commands

```
MTB > ZTEST MU = 3 SIGMA = K1 on C1;
SUBC > ALTERNATIVE -1.
```

do a left-tailed test on the data in column 1.

TI-82

Enter the data in a list, and compute the mean and sample standard deviation for the data. Then use these values in appropriate formulas to convert the sample test statistic to a z value. Use Table 6 in Appendix II to find the P value of the sample test statistic.

ComputerStat

Under the Hypothesis Testing menu, select the program Testing a Single Population Mean. Follow the instructions on the screen.

Application 1

People who do shift work must often adjust their eating habits, sleep habits, exercise habits, family contact, social life, and overall lifestyle to accommodate their job. Extensive rearrangement of a person's habits and lifestyle can sometimes result in tension, anxiety, and overall health problems. An extensive study of the health consequences of shift work can be found in the following publication. Interested readers are referred to this report:

United States Department of Health, Education, and Welfare, NIOSH Technical Report. Tasto, Colligan, et al., *Health Consequences of Shift Work*. Washington GPO, 1978.

In an effort to study mood levels of nurses working in large hospitals, an opinion scale was used. Opinion ratings ranged from 0 = no feeling of tension and anxiety to a rating of 4 = extensive feelings of tension and anxiety. The scale was continuous, so a nurse could mark any number between 0 and 4. Suppose a random sample of 35 nurses on the day shift of a very large hospital gave the ratings shown in the accompanying table of their feelings of tension and anxiety at the end of the day shift.

(a) On a scale of 0 to 4, a moderate (i.e., medium) level of tension and anxiety is 2. Use the null hypothesis that the population mean tension level for nurses after the day shift is 2. Use the alternate hypothesis that the population mean tension level is different (either higher or lower) than 2. Use a 5% level of significance. What is the *P* value? Compare the *P* value with the level of significance. Do you think we should accept or reject the null hypothesis?

(b) Rerun the program with the same data (you do not need to re-enter the data). Use the same null hypothesis, but use a right-tail test with level of significance 0.10. Do we accept or reject the null hypothesis? Look at the *P* value. What is the smallest level of significance that will result in a rejection of the null hypothesis using a right-tail test?

Data for Day-Shift Nurses						
3.50	3.75	2.33	2.16	3.50	0.80	1.25
1.33	2.67	2.50	1.50	0.75	0.00	0.67
4.00	3.75	3.50	3.25	2.40	3.50	2.75
3.50	2.67	2.80	2.33	3.50	3.80	2.75
1.50	1.33	0.00	2.25	1.75	0.50	1.75

Testing a Difference of Means, Independent Samples (large)

Minitab

When testing the difference of means from independent samples, Minitab always uses the *t* distribution regardless of sample size. The *P* value of the sample test statistic will be slightly larger than the *P* value generated using the normal distribution. The commands

```
MTB > SET C1 #Enter data from first sample in column 1
MTB > SET C2 #Enter data from second sample in column 2
MTB > TWOSAMPLE for C1 C2;
SUBC > ALTERNATIVE 1.
```

perform a right-tailed test with the hypotheses H_0: $\mu_1 = \mu_2$ and H_1: $\mu_1 > \mu_2$. Compare the P value to the level of significance α to conclude the test.

Note: In the case of *small samples,* use the command TWOSAMPLE with the subcommand POOLED. This subcommand instructs Minitab to use the common pooled standard deviation s described in Section 9.7. As in Section 9.7, we use the pooled standard deviation s when our samples come from populations that have equal standard deviations.

TI-82

Enter the data for the first sample in list L1 and data for the other sample in list L2. Next, find the mean and sample standard deviations for the two lists. You can use 2-Var Stats if you use the SetUp option to assign L1 to the Xlist and L2 to the Ylist. Then use the appropriate formulas to find the z value of the sample test statistic. To find the P value of the sample test statistic, use Table 6 in Appendix II.

ComputerStat

Under the Hypothesis Testing menu, select the program Testing a Difference of Means (Independent Sample). Then follow the instructions on the screen.

Application 2

Suppose a random sample of 33 nurses on the night shift also was asked to give their opinion about feelings of tension and anxiety at the end of the night shift. They used the same rating scale as described in Application 1. The ratings they gave are in the accompanying table.

Data for Night-Shift Nurses						
3.50	3.75	3.50	3.10	3.20	3.33	1.75
2.75	2.50	2.75	3.20	3.75	4.00	2.00
1.00	0.00	1.80	2.50	3.50	3.00	2.60
3.10	2.75	4.00	2.90	1.75	2.20	3.50
1.00	2.50	0.80	3.70	2.60		

(a) Explain why the samples of Applications 1 and 2 are independent, or at least why it is reasonable to assume they are independent. We want to compare mean tension levels of day- and night-shift nurses.

(b) In this problem let $MU1$ = population mean tension level for the day-shift nurses and let $MU2$ = population mean tension level for the night-shift nurses. What is the null hypothesis?

(c) If we want to test the claim that there is a difference (either way) between tension levels of day-shift and night-shift nurses, which alternate hypothesis do we use? Use a 10% level of significance. What is the P value? Compare the P value with the level of significance. Shall we accept or reject the null hypothesis? What is the smallest level of significance that will result in a rejection of the null hypothesis in this two-tailed test?

(d) Rerun the program with the same data (you do not need to re-enter the data). Use the same null hypothesis, but use a left-tailed test with a level of significance 10%. Do we accept or reject the null hypothesis? What is the smallest level of significance at which we can say the night-shift nurses show a higher average level of tension?

Paired Difference Test

Minitab

Enter the first number in each data pair in column 1 and the second number of corresponding data pair in column 2. Then create column 3 to be the difference of the data in columns 1 and 2. Finally use the command TTEST on the differences in column 3. The commands

```
MTB > READ C1 C2 #Enter the data pairs by row
MTB > LET C3 = C1 - C2 #Create the differences
MTB > TTEST MU = 0 on C3
```

perform a test using H_0: $\mu_d = 0$ and H_1: $\mu_d \neq 0$. To do a left-tailed test, use the subcommand ALTERNATIVE -1 and to do a right-tailed test, use the subcommand ALTERNATIVE 1. The t value corresponding to the sample $\bar{d}$ is given in the results as well as the P value. Compare the P value with the level of significance α to conclude the test.

TI-82

Enter the first number of each data pair in list L1 and the second in list L2. Create L3 by subtracting L2 from L1 and storing the result in L3.

$$L1 - L2 \rightarrow L3$$

The list L3 contains the differences d. Find the mean and sample standard deviation of the differences in L3 by using the 1-Var Stats L3 command. Then use the appropriate formulas to find the t value of the sample test statistic $\bar{d}$. Use Table 7 in Appendix II to approximate the P value.

Application 3

Suppose a random sample of eight nurses were changed from the day shift to a rotating shift of some night work and some day work. For each of these nurses, the information shown in the accompanying table was recorded about feelings of tension and anxiety at the end of a day shift and also at the end of a night shift.

(a) Explain why the sample data for the day shift cannot be thought of as independent of the sample data for the night shift.

(b) Let us say that A is the random variable representing tension levels of night nurses and B is the random variable representing tension levels of day nurses. If we want to test the claim that nurses have a higher level of tension after the night shift, what would we use for the null hypothesis? What would we use for the alternate hypothesis? Choose the appropriate hypothesis and enter your choice on the computer. Use a 2% level of significance. Shall we accept or reject the claim that after a night shift nurses express

Data for Nurses Working Both Shifts								
Nurse	1	2	3	4	5	6	7	8
Day shift (B)	1.5	3	2	3	2	2	1	2
Night shift (A)	3.5	2	4	4	3.5	2	3.5	3

more feelings of tension on the average than they do after a day shift?

(c) What is the smallest level of significance at which this data will allow us to accept the claim that after a night shift nurses express more feelings of tension?

Testing a Proportion or Difference of Proportions

Minitab does not have commands to test proportions. As with the TI-82 calculator, compute $\hat{p}$ for a single proportion or the pooled common $\hat{p}$ for a test of two proportions using the formulas of Section 9.5 or 9.7, respectively. Then use appropriate formulas to compute the z value of the sample test statistic. In ComputerStat, under the Hypothesis Testing menu, select the program Testing a Proportion or the program Testing a Difference of Proportions as appropriate. Then follow the instructions on the screen.

Applications 4 and 5

Data for Applications 4 and 5 are taken from the following source:

Miller, Miller, and Schneider. *American National Election Studies Data Sourcebook 1952–1978*. Cambridge: Harvard University Press, 1980. 250, 261.

1. In a study of support of the American political system, the reference by Miller, Miller, and Schneider reports that the following statement was given to a large random sample of adults:

   People like me don't have any say about what the government does.

   (a) For 1978, Miller, Miller, and Schneider reported that out of 2291 people interviewed, 1214 disagreed with the statement. Let p represent the proportion of all adults in the United States who disagreed with the statement (in 1978). Use the null hypothesis that $p = 0.50$ and the alternate hypothesis that $p > 0.50$ to test the claim that more than half the population in 1978 believed that they had a say in what government does. Use a 1% level of significance.

   (b) Recall that the level of significance is the probability of a type I error, that is, the probability that we are *wrong* in rejecting

the null hypothesis and accepting the alternate hypothesis. Using the data provided, what is the smallest level of significance at which we can accept the claim that more than 50% of the American people believed they had a say in what the government does?

2. In a study similar to that of Application 4, Miller, Miller, and Schneider gave the following statement to a large random sample of American adults:

   (Political) Parties are only interested in people's votes, but not in their opinions.

   For the year 1970 it was reported that 1,487 people were asked about the statement. Of those asked, 803 agreed with the statement. For the year 1978 it was reported that 2278 people were asked about the statement and 1412 agreed with it.

   (a) Let $P1$ = proportion of all American adults who agreed with the statement in 1970 and let $P2$ = proportion of all American adults who agreed with the statement in 1978.
   (i) What value will you use for $N1$ = number of trials in the first distribution?
   (ii) What value will you use for $R1$ =

number of successes in the first distribution?

(iii) What value will you use for N2 = number of trials in the second distribution?

(iv) What value will you use for R2 = number of successes in the second distribution.

(b) What statement will you use for the null hypothesis? If we want to test the claim that a higher proportion of American adults agreed with the statement in 1978 than

agreed with the statement in 1970, what should the alternate hypothesis be?

(c) Use a 2% level of significance and the results of the computer run to complete the test. What is the critical region? Should we accept the claim that a higher proportion of American adults agreed with the statement in 1978 than in 1970?

(d) What is the smallest level of significance at which we can accept the claim that a higher proportion of the American adults agreed with the statement in 1978 than agreed in 1970?

Computer Display

Minitab

Let's look at the output for a test of a single mean, small sample. Consider Problem 16 of Section 9.4. In this problem you are given the prices of 10 AT&T cellular phones purchased at a random sample of 10 retail outlets in Sonoma. You are to test the claim that the mean population retail price for this model of cellular phones is less than $600. Because you are testing a single population mean and you have a small sample (and the population standard deviation is not known), you will use the t distribution. A left-tailed test requires the ALTERNATIVE -1 subcommand.

```
MTB > SET C1
DATA> 593 621 545 561 639 555 588 575 619 599
DATA> END
MTB > TTEST MU = 600 on C1;
SUBC> ALTERNATIVE -1.

TEST OF MU = 600.00 VS MU L.T. 600.00
```

	N	MEAN	STDEV	SE MEAN	T	P VALUE
C1	10	589.50	30.93	9.78	−1.07	0.16

Introduction to Paired Data and Scatter Diagrams

Paired data occur naturally in many areas such as science, business administration, economics, social science, and health sciences. In this section we will construct scatter diagrams for paired data and make a visual estimate of low, moderate, or high linear correlation.

Linear Regression and Confidence Bounds for Prediction

This section develops the mathematical background and formulas for least-squares regression. The standard error of estimate and confidence bounds for forecast y values are presented here.

The Linear Correlation Coefficient

This section develops a mathematical formula for the Pearson product moment correlation coefficient r and the coefficient of determination r^2. Both r and r^2 are important tools for measuring goodness of fit of raw data to our least-squares model.

Testing the Correlation Coefficient

When is a correlation coefficient r significant at a given level of significance α? How do we construct an appropriate statistical test for the significance of a sample correlation coefficient? This section answers these questions.

Multiple Regression

In Sections 10.1 to 10.4 we study simple regression. This means that we use only x and y values as data pairs and construct a least-squares model for these x and y values. However, many real-world applications of statistics involve more than just two variables. In this section we introduce statistical methods of using several x variables to forecast a y value.

G. H. Hardy
(1877–1947)

This English mathematician made significant contributions to number theory, as well as to the mathematics of genetics.

Regression and Correlation

A mathematician, like a poet or painter, is a maker of patterns. If his patterns are more permanent than theirs it is because they are made with ideas.... A mathematician has no material to work with but ideas, and so his patterns are likely to last longer.

G. H. Hardy

In business administration, economics, social science, and natural science we often encounter statistical variables that seem to follow a pattern. In this chapter we study mathematical "patterns" that originate from linear correlations between statistical variables.

Statistical applications often involve several random variables. In this chapter we study the techniques for dealing with data associated with two or more variables. In some problems, variables are studied simultaneously to see how they are interrelated. These are called *correlation* problems. The word *correlation* literally means "related together" or "co-relation."

For other problems, there may be one variable of particular interest. In this case the other variables are used to *predict* how the first variable will behave under given conditions. Problems of this type are called *regression* problems. The methods of regression literally predict the value of one variable by going back to (or regressing to) the values of another related variable.

Focus Problem ▶ ## Getting the Best Price on a New Pickup Truck

Suppose that you want to buy a new pickup truck. To be specific, let us say you are considering a Ford Ranger and the model you are interested in has a list price of $14,990. As the salesperson from the dealership approaches, you wonder how far you can bargain the price down. What is a reasonable estimate for the "best price" you can get? Assume that you do not have a vehicle to trade in. A good answer to this question can be obtained using *Consumers Digest* and statistical methods found in this chapter. Purchasing a vehicle at or near "best price" depends largely on your persistence and negotiating skill. Representatives from *Consumers Digest* (February 1994) obtained the following information, where x = list price and y = best price (both in thousands of dollars), for different representative models of the 1994 Ford Ranger. Remember, the "best price" is the best price representatives for *Consumers Digest* got. Your best price might be higher or lower depending on your ability to negotiate and the dealer's eagerness to sell.

Consumers Digest: List Price and Best Price, 1994 Ford Ranger

List price x:	9.8	11.6	12.3	13.7	16.2	17.7	18.7
Best price y:	8.4	10.4	10.9	12.6	14.4	15.1	16.5

(a) Draw a scatter diagram for these data.

(b) Examine the scatter diagram. Would you say the correlation between x and y values is low? moderate? or high?

(c) Find the equation of the least-squares line, and graph this line on your scatter diagram.

(d) Compute the correlation coefficient r and the coefficient of determination r^2. What percentage of the variation in y can be explained by the corresponding variation in x using the least-squares line? What percentage of the variation is unexplained?

(e) In the least-squares equation of part c, let x = 14.99 (list price of the model you are interested in buying). What does the least-squares equation forecast for y, the best price for this model?

(f) Compute a 90% confidence interval for your forecast y value of part e. Explain the meaning of this confidence interval in the context of this problem.

(g) Use a 5% level of significance to test the claim that the correlation coefficient between list and best price is positive.

Section 10.1   Introduction to Paired Data and Scatter Diagrams

Scatter Diagrams

The study of correlation and regression of two variables usually begins with a table and/or a graph of *paired data values*. Example 1 shows what we mean.

Example 1

Jan is doing a project for her botany class. She wonders if there is a connection between the average weight of watermelons a vine produces and the root depth of the vine. Jan suspects that vines with deeper roots have a better water supply and also larger average melons. From a large watermelon field, 30 vines are chosen at random. At the end of 8 weeks, the watermelons are removed from each vine, and the average weight of watermelons from each vine is determined. Then each plant is carefully dug up and its root depth (or length) is measured. Table 10–1 shows the results.

Table 10–1 Results of a Botany Experiment

x = Root Depth (in.)   y = Mean Wt. of Watermelon (lb)

x	y	x	y	x	y
26.7	20.3	17.5	4.3	9.1	4.5
14.0	4.8	13.1	8.7	17.5	11.1
18.0	9.0	16.5	9.1	20.5	12.3
10.5	9.0	28.4	17.1	4.5	3.1
26.1	10.7	23.9	9.7	23.4	20.8
21.5	17.4	27.0	13.1	27.0	15.2
7.0	8.2	10.2	2.1	24.6	16.1
26.0	7.9	13.1	11.0	15.8	5.7
13.9	3.5	19.1	16.0	27.0	19.3
19.3	8.7	22.6	12.9	21.3	4.2

(a) For each plant there is an ordered pair (x,y) of data values. If we plot the pairs (x,y) as points on a coordinate system, we obtain the graph of Figure 10–1. Figure 10–1 is called a *scatter diagram* for the paired data values of Table 10–1.

Figure 10–1 Scatter Diagram for the Botany Experiment

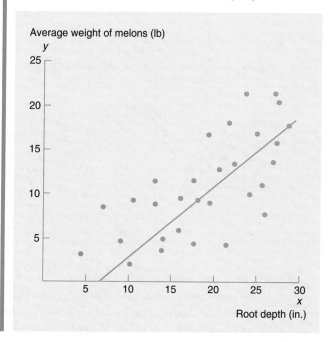

(b) By inspecting Figure 10–1, we see that to some extent larger values of x tend to be associated with larger y values, and smaller x values tend to be associated with smaller y values. Roughly speaking, the general trend seems to be reasonably well represented by the line segment shown in Figure 10–1.

Introduction to Linear
Correlation

Of course, it is possible to draw many curves in Figure 10–1, but the straight line is the simplest and most widely used curve for elementary studies of paired data. We can draw many lines in Figure 10–1, but in some sense the "best" line should be the one that comes closest to each of the points of the scatter diagram. To single out one line as the "best-fitting line," we must find a mathematical criterion for this line and a formula representing the line. This will be done in Section 10.2 by the *method of least squares*.

In some sense there is another problem which precedes that of finding the "best-fitting line." That is the problem of determining how well the points of the scatter diagram are suited for fitting *any* line. Certainly if the points are a very poor fit to *any* line, there is little use in trying to find the "best" line. This problem will be dealt with in Section 10.3 by use of the Pearson product-moment coefficient of correlation.

If the points of a scatter diagram are located so that *no* line is realistically a "good" fit, we then say that the points possess *no linear correlation*. In Figure 10–2 we see some examples of scatter diagrams for which there is no linear correlation.

Figure 10–2 Scatter Diagrams with No Linear
　　　　　　　　Correlation

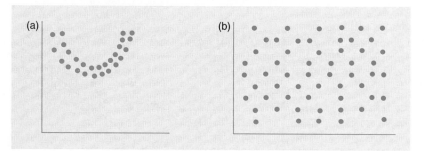

On the other hand, if all the points do in fact lie on a line, then we have perfect *linear correlation*. In Figure 10–3 we see some diagrams with perfect linear correlation. In statistical applications perfect linear correlation almost never occurs.

Figure 10–3 Scatter Diagrams with Moderate and Perfect Linear Correlation

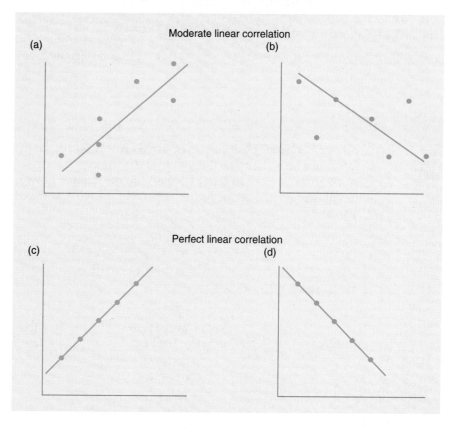

GUIDED EXERCISE 1

Examine the scatter diagrams in Figure 10–4 and then answer the following questions.

Figure 10–4a has perfect linear correlation and can be fitted exactly by a straight line.

Figure 10–4 Scatter Diagrams

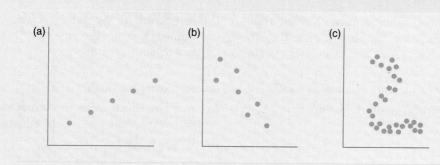

(i)   Which diagram has no linear correlation?
(ii) Which has perfect linear correlation?
(iii) Which can be reasonably fitted by a straight line?

Figure 10–4b can be reasonably fitted by a straight line.

Figure 10–4c has no linear correlation. No straight-line fit should be attempted.

GUIDED EXERCISE 2

A large industrial plant has seven divisions that do the same type of work. A safety inspector visits each division of 20 workers quarterly. The number of work-hours devoted to safety training and the number of work-hours lost due to industry-related accidents are recorded for each separate division in Table 10–2.

Table 10–2 Safety Report

Division	x (No. of Work-Hours in Safety Training)	y (No. of Work-Hours Lost Due to Accidents)
1	10.0	80
2	19.5	65
3	30.0	68
4	45.0	55
5	50.0	35
6	65.0	10
7	80.0	12

(a) Make a scatter diagram for these pairs. Use the x values on the horizontal axis and the y values on the vertical one.

(a) Figure 10–5 shows the scatter diagram.

(b) As the number of hours spent on safety training increases, what happens in general to the number of hours lost due to industry-related accidents?

(b) In general, as the number of hours in safety training goes up, the number of hours lost due to accidents goes down.

(c) Does a line fit the data reasonably well?

(c) A line fits reasonably well.

(d) Draw a line which you think "fits best."

(d) Any line which seems the best fit to you is correct. Later, you will see the equation of a line that is a "best fit."

Figure 10–5 Scatter Diagram for Safety Report

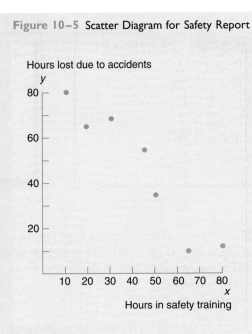

Hours lost due to accidents

Hours in safety training

Calculator Note

Many graphing calculators produce scatter plots. On the TI-82, we first press the STAT key and select EDIT. Then, we enter the x values in list L1 and the y values in list L2. Using the STAT PLOT key, select a scatter plot. Next, set the WINDOW to accommodate all the x and y values. Finally, press GRAPH. Figure 10-6a–d presents TI-82 screens that show how to generate a scatter plot for the data of Guided Exercise 2.

Figure 10–6 TI-82 Scatter Plot for Data of Guided Exercise 2

(a) Enter data in L1 and L2

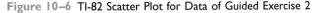

(b) Select a scatter plot

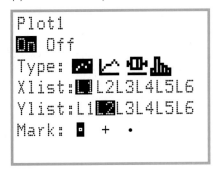

(c) Set the window   (d) Graph

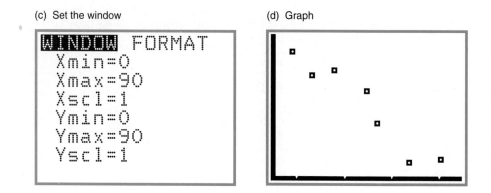

We say a scatter diagram has *high* linear correlation if the points lie close to a straight line. If the points are not close to a straight line, we say the correlation is *moderate* or *low*. If the points fit no straight line, we say there is *no* linear correlation.

Section 10.1 Problems

In Problems 1–6 look at the scatter diagrams and state which of the following conditions you think is true for each diagram:
   (a) High linear correlation
   (b) Moderate or low linear correlation
   (c) No linear correlation

1.   2.

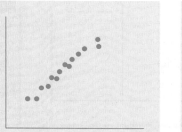

3.   4.

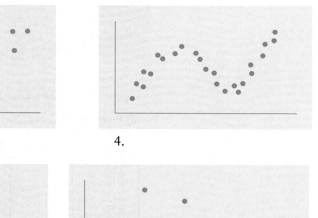

5.

6.

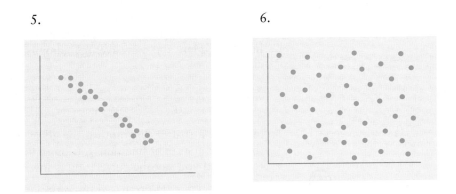

7. *Consumers Digest* (February 1994) gave the following information about x = list price and y = best price (in thousands of dollars) for different models of the Oldsmobile Achieva. The "best price" is the lowest price representatives from *Consumers Digest* negotiated with Oldsmobile dealerships. Your price might be higher or lower depending on your ability to negotiate and the dealer's eagerness to sell.

x = list price	14.1	14.2	17.5	13.5	14.5	16.5
y = best price	12.7	12.8	15.8	12.8	13.8	15.6

(a) Draw a scatter diagram for the given data.
(b) Draw a straight line that you think best fits the data.
(c) Would you say the correlation is low, moderate, or high?

8. *Consumers Digest* (February 1994) gave the following information about x = list price and y = best price (in thousands of dollars) for the Chevrolet Cavalier (see comments in Problem 7).

x = list price	8.8	9.0	10.7	11.3	11.5	17.0	20.0
y = best price	8.4	8.5	10.0	10.6	10.7	15.9	18.1

(a) Draw a scatter diagram for the given data.
(b) Draw a straight line that you think best fits the data.
(c) Would you say the correlation is low, moderate, or high?

9. *Consumers Digest* (February 1994) gave the following information about x = list price and y = best price (in thousands of dollars) for the Dodge Dakota (see comments in Problem 7).

x = list price	9.6	10.7	12.3	14.5	15.7	17.5
y = best price	9.2	10.0	11.2	13.7	14.2	15.8

(a) Draw a scatter diagram for the given data.
(b) Draw a straight line that you think best fits the data.
(c) Would you say the correlation is low, moderate, or high?

10. The following data are based on information from *Domestic Affairs* (Winter, 1993–1994). Let x = average number of employees in a group health insurance plan and y = average administrative cost as a percentage of claims.

x	3	7	15	35	75
y	40	35	30	25	18

(a) Draw a scatter diagram for the given data.
(b) Draw a straight line that you think best fits the data.
(c) Would you say the correlation is low, moderate, or high?

11. The following data are based on information taken from *The Economist* (January 22–28, 1994). Let x = percentage change in wages and y = percentage change in consumer prices for the past year in Australia, Austria, Canada, France, Italy, Spain, and the United States.

x	3.3	4.1	1.9	2.6	3.9	6.3	2.5
y	2.2	3.5	1.9	2.1	4.0	4.9	2.7

(a) Draw a scatter diagram for the given data.
(b) Draw a straight line that you think best fits the data.
(c) Would you say the correlation is low, moderate, or high?

12. The following data are based on information taken from "Increased Incidence of Malignant Melanoma after Peaks of Sunspot Activity" (Houghton, A., Munster, E. W., and Viola, M. V., *The Lancet*, April 8, 1978, p 759ff). Let x = sunspot index (larger numbers mean more sunspots) and y = incidents of malignant melanomas (skin cancer) per 100,000 population.

x	0.5	1.0	5.0	6.0	10.5
y	2.2	2.9	3.9	3.8	4.8

(a) Draw a scatter diagram for the given data.
(b) Draw a straight line that you think best fits the data.
(c) Would you say the correlation is low, moderate, or high?

13. A random sample of 11 Sociology 110 students provided the following data (x = midterm score out of 100 points, y = final exam score out of 150 points):

x	66	71	80	76	63	73	81	68	84	83	79
y	130	132	135	134	129	133	136	132	138	136	135

(a) Draw a scatter diagram for these data.
(b) Draw a straight line that you think best fits the data points.
(c) Would you say the correlation is low, moderate, or high?

14. An ecology class did a project to determine the distance a car will travel on 1 gallon of gas at different rates of speed. A local dealer loaned the

class a new car. The car was given 1 gallon of gasoline and driven around a level track at a constant speed until it ran out of gas. Let x be the speed (mph) and y be the distance the car ran. The following data were obtained:

x	30	35	40	45	50	55	60	65	70	75	80	85
y	36	33	34	32.5	31	32	30	29.5	26.5	27	24.5	24

(a) Draw a scatter diagram for the data.
(b) Draw a straight line that you think best fits the data.
(c) Would you say the correlation is low, moderate, or high?

15. The initial visual impact of a scatter diagram depends on the scales used on the x and y axes. Consider the following data:

x	1	2	3	4	5	6
y	1	4	6	3	6	7

(a) Make a scatter diagram using the same scale on both the x and y axes (i.e., make sure the unit lengths on the two axes are equal).
(b) Make a scatter diagram using a scale on the y axis that is twice as long as that on the x axis.
(c) Make a scatter diagram using a scale on the y axis that is half as long as that on the x axis.
(d) On each of the three graphs, draw the straight line that you think best fits the data points. How does the slope (or direction) of the three lines appear to change? (*Note:* The actual slopes will be the same; they just appear different because of the choice of scale factors.)

Section 10.2   Linear Regression and Confidence Bounds for Prediction

Anyone who has been outdoors on a summer evening has probably heard crickets. Did you know that it is possible to use the cricket as a thermometer? Crickets tend to chirp more frequently as temperatures increase. A Harvard physics professor made a detailed study of this phenomenon. Using sophisticated equipment, Professor George W. Pierce studied the striped ground cricket and compiled the data in Table 10–3.

Do the data indicate a linear relation between chirping frequency and temperature? Is there a way we can use the data to predict the temperature that corresponds to a chirp frequency that is not listed in the table? For instance, how can we use the data to predict the temperature for $x = 19$ chirps per second? Let us first make a scatter diagram (Figure 10–7) for the data of Table 10–3.

Looking at the scatter diagram of Figure 10–7, we ask two questions:

1. Can we find a relationship between x and y?
2. If so, how strong is the relationship?

Table 10–3 Chirping Frequency and Temperature for the Striped Ground Cricket

x (chirps/s)	y (temp., °F)
20.0	88.6
16.0	71.6
19.8	93.3
18.4	84.3
17.1	80.6
15.5	75.2
14.7	69.7
17.1	82.0
15.4	69.4
16.2	83.3
15.0	79.6
17.2	82.6
16.0	80.6
17.0	83.5
14.4	76.3

Reprinted by permission of the publishers from *The Song of Insects* by George W. Pierce, Cambridge, Mass.: Copyright © 1948 The President and Fellows of Harvard College.

Figure 10–7 Scatter Diagram for Table 10–3

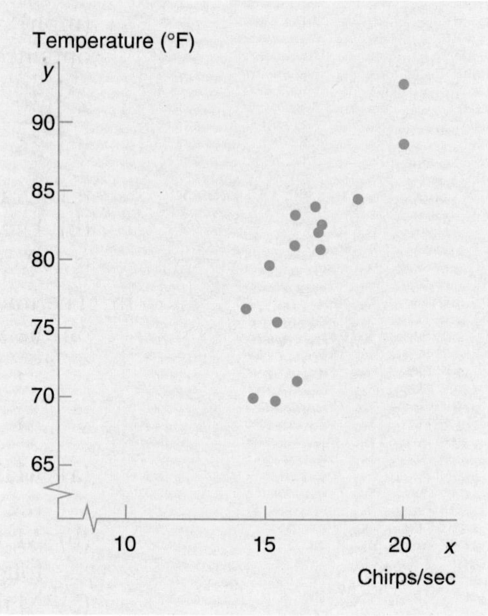

The first step in answering these questions is to try to express the relationship as a mathematical equation. There are many possible equations, but the simplest and most widely used is the linear equation, or the equation of a straight line. Since we will be using this line to predict the y values (temperature) from the x values (chirps per second), we call x the *explanatory variable* and y the *response variable*.

Least-Squares Criterion

Our job is to find a linear equation that is the "best" linear equation representing the points of the scatter diagram. For our criterion of best-fitting line, we use the *least-squares criterion*, which says that the line we fit to the data points must be such that *the sum of the squares of the vertical distances from the points to the line be made as small as possible*. The least-squares criterion is illustrated in Figure 10–8.

In Figure 10–8, d represents the difference between the y coordinate of the data point and the corresponding y coordinate on the line. Thus, if the data point lies above the line, d is positive, but if the data point is below the line, d is negative. As a result, the sum of the d values can be small even if the points are widely spread in the scatter diagram. However, the squares d^2 cannot be negative. By minimizing the sum of the squares, we are in effect not allowing positive and negative d values to "cancel out" one another in the sum. It is in this way that we can meet the least-squares criterion of minimiz-

Figure 10–8 Least-Squares Criterion

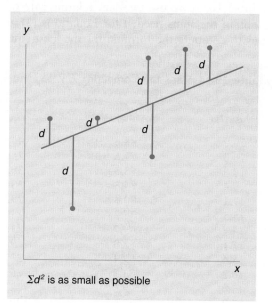

Σd^2 is as small as possible

ing the sum of the squares of the vertical distances between the points and the line over *all* points in the scatter diagram.

Least-Squares Line

Techniques of calculus can be applied to show that the line which meets the least-squares criterion is as follows:

Least-Squares Line

$$y = a + bx \tag{1}$$

where $$b = \frac{SS_{xy}}{SS_x} \qquad b \text{ is the slope} \tag{2}$$

$$a = \bar{y} - b\bar{x} \qquad a \text{ is the } y\text{-intercept} \tag{3}$$

and $\bar{y}$ = mean of y values in scatter diagram
$\bar{x}$ = mean of x values in scatter diagram

$$SS_{xy} = \Sigma xy - \frac{(\Sigma x)(\Sigma y)}{n} \tag{4}$$

$$SS_x = \Sigma x^2 - \frac{(\Sigma x)^2}{n} \tag{5}$$

n = number of points in a scatter diagram.
In Formulas (4) and (5), the sums are taken over all x or y values in the scatter diagram.

The simplest way to find a and b is to organize your work into a table. In Table 10–4 we use the data relating rate of cricket chirps to temperature to obtain the sums needed for Equations (4) and (5). We will then use these sums to compute the formula for the least squares line.

Table 10–4 Sums for Computing $\bar{x}$, $\bar{y}$, SS_x and SS_{xy}

x (chirps/s)	y (°F)	x^2	xy
20.0	88.6	400.0	1,772.0
16.0	71.6	256.0	1,145.6
19.8	93.3	392.0	1,847.3
18.4	84.3	338.6	1,551.1
17.1	80.6	292.4	1,378.3
15.5	75.2	240.3	1,165.6
14.7	69.7	216.1	1,024.6
17.1	82.0	292.4	1,402.2
15.4	69.4	237.2	1,068.8
16.2	83.3	262.4	1,349.5
15.0	79.6	225.0	1,194.0
17.2	82.6	295.8	1,420.7
16.0	80.6	256.0	1,289.6
17.0	83.5	289.0	1,419.5
14.4	76.3	207.4	1,098.7
$\Sigma x = 249.8$	$\Sigma y = 1{,}200.6$	$\Sigma x^2 = 4{,}200.6$	$\Sigma xy = 20{,}127.5$

- **Comment:** The notation SS_x is the same expression used in the computation for the standard deviation of x values (see Section 3.2). Recall that the formula for SS_x is simply a faster way of computing $\Sigma(x - \bar{x})^2$. Likewise, the formula for SS_{xy} is a more efficient way to compute $\Sigma(x - \bar{x})(y - \bar{y})$.

- **Computation Notes**

  1. The formulas used to compute the slope and y intercept of the least-squares line are sensitive to rounding. Answers to the exercises at the end of each section and at the end of the chapter are computer-generated, so you may expect slight differences in your answers depending on how you round intermediate steps.
  2. Do not confuse Σx^2 and $(\Sigma x)^2$. For Σx^2, we *first square* each x value and then find the total sum of these values. For $(\Sigma x)^2$, we *first sum* the x values and then square the total.
  3. On calculators with a statistics mode, you can compute the standard deviation s and then the variance s^2 of the x values. Then

$$SS_x = s^2(n - 1)$$

From Table 10–4 we have

$$SS_x = \Sigma x^2 - \frac{(\Sigma x)^2}{n} = 4200.6 - \frac{(249.8)^2}{15} = 40.6$$

and we also have

$$SS_{xy} = \Sigma xy - \frac{(\Sigma x)(\Sigma y)}{n} = 20{,}127.5 - \frac{(249.8)(1200.6)}{15} = 133.5$$

We also find

$$\bar{x} = \frac{\Sigma x}{n} = \frac{249.8}{15} = 16.7$$

$$\bar{y} = \frac{\Sigma y}{n} = \frac{1200.6}{15} = 80.0$$

Therefore, using Equations (2) and (3), we find a and b in the equation of the least-squares line.

Slope:
$$b = \frac{SS_{xy}}{SS_x} = \frac{133.5}{40.6} = 3.3$$

y intercept:
$$a = \bar{y} - b\bar{x} = (80.0) - (3.3)(16.7) = 24.9$$

We conclude that the least-squares line for the data of Table 10.3 is

$$y = a + bx \tag{6}$$
$$y = 24.9 + 3.3x$$

To graph the least-squares line (6), we have several options available. The slope-intercept method of college algebra is probably the quickest. The slope is $b = 3.3$ and the y intercept is $a = 24.9$. However, if you don't remember this method, it is almost as easy to plot two points and connect them with a straight line. For x values, we usually use any two values in the range of x data values. Corresponding y values are computed from the equation of the least-squares line.

The value of $\bar{x}$, will always be in the range of x values. When we use $x = \bar{x}$ in Equations (1) and (3), we see that the corresponding y value is $\bar{y}$.

Therefore, $(\bar{x}, \bar{y})$ will always be on the least-squares line.

Since we have already computed these values, the point $(\bar{x}, \bar{y})$, is a convenient choice for one of the two points we use to graph the least-squares line. From Table 10–3 we see that $x = 20$ is also in the range of x values. We compute the corresponding y value by using the equation of the least-squares line.

x	$y = 24.9 + 3.3x$
When we choose $x = \bar{x} = 16.7$	$y = 24.9 + 3.3(16.7) = 80.0 = \bar{y}$
When we choose $x = 20.0$	$y = 24.9 + 3.3(20.0) = 90.9$

The line going through the points (16.7, 80.0) and (20.0, 90.9) is the least-squares line for the scatter diagram of Figure 10–7. This line is shown in Figure 10–9.

Figure 10–9 Least-Squares Line $y = 24.9 + 3.3x$

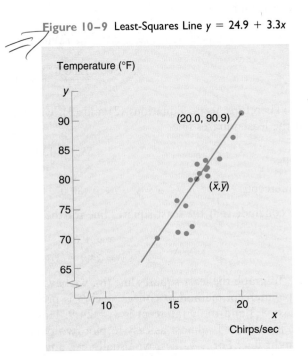

Now suppose we find a striped ground cricket and, with a listening device, discover that it chirps at the rate of 19.0 chirps per second. What should we predict for the temperature? We could read the y value above $x = 19.0$ from the least-squares line graphed in Figure 10–9. But a more accurate estimate can be obtained by using the value $x = 19.0$ in the equation of the least-squares line and computing the corresponding y.

$y = 24.9 + 3.3x$	equation of least-squares line
$y = 24.9 + 3.3(19.0)$	using 19.0 in place of x
$y = 87.6°F$	evaluating y

Rounded to the nearest whole number, we should predict the temperature to be 88°F. Of course, this is just a prediction, and we would be quite happy if the temperature turned out to be relatively close to our prediction. This brings up the natural question: How *good* are predictions based on the least-squares line? This is a fairly difficult question, and much of the answer requires advanced mathematics; however, a partial answer will be given later in this section.

GUIDED EXERCISE 3

The Quick Sell car dealership has been using 1-minute spot ads on a local TV station. The ads always occur during the evening hours and advertise the different models and price ranges of cars on the lot that week. During a 10-week period, the Quick Sell dealer kept a weekly record of the number of TV ads versus the number of cars sold. The results are given in Table 10–5.

Table 10–5

x (No. of Ads in a Week)	y (No. of Cars Sold That Week)
6	15
20	31
0	10
14	16
25	28
16	20
28	40
18	25
10	12
8	15

The manager decided that Quick Sell can only afford 12 ads per week. At that level of advertisement, how many cars can Quick Sell expect to sell each week? We'll answer this question in several steps.

(a) Draw a scatter diagram for the data.

(a) The scatter diagram is shown in Figure 10–10 on page 672.

(b) Look at Equations (1) to (5) pertaining to the least-squares line. Two of the quantities we need to find b are (Σx) and (Σxy). List the others.

(b) We also need n, (Σy), (Σx^2), and $(\Sigma x)^2$.

(c) Complete Table 10–6(a) on page 672.

(c) The missing table entries are shown in Table 10–6(b) on page 672.

(d) Use Table 10–6(a) to compute SS_x, SS_{xy}, $\bar{x}$, and $\bar{y}$.

(d) $SS_x = \Sigma x^2 - \dfrac{(\Sigma x)^2}{n} = 2785 - \dfrac{(145)^2}{10}$

$= 682.5$

$SS_{xy} = \Sigma xy - \dfrac{(\Sigma x)(\Sigma y)}{n} = 3764 - \dfrac{(145)(212)}{10}$

$= 690.0$

$\bar{x} = \dfrac{\Sigma x}{n} = \dfrac{145}{10} = 14.5$

$\bar{y} = \dfrac{\Sigma y}{n} = \dfrac{212}{10} = 21.2$

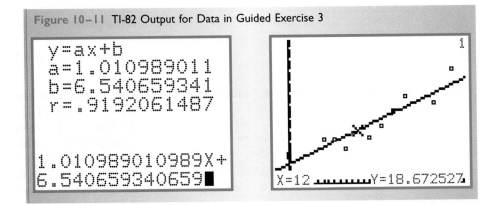

Figure 10–11 TI-82 Output for Data in Guided Exercise 3

We have used the least-squares line to predict y values for x values that were *between* x values observed in the experiment. Predicting y values for x values that are between x values of points in the scatter diagram is called *interpolation*. The least-squares lines can be used for interpolation. Predicting y values for an x value beyond the range of observed x values is a complex problem that is not treated in this book. Prediction beyond the range of observations is called *extrapolation*.

The least-squares line

$$y = a + bx$$

was developed with y as the response variable and x as the explanatory variable. This model can only be used to predict y values from specified x values. If you wish to begin with y values and predict corresponding x values, you must use a different formula. Such a formula would be developed using a model with x as the response variable and y as the explanatory variable. For our purposes, we'll always arrange to predict y values from given x values.

Sometimes a scatter diagram clearly indicates the existence of a linear relationship between x and y, but it can happen that the points are widely scattered around the least-squares line. We need a method (besides just looking) for measuring the spread of a set of points about the least-squares line. There are three common methods of measuring the spread. One method uses the *standard error of estimate*. The others, to be studied in the next section, use the *coefficient of correlation* and the *coefficient of determination*.

Standard Error of Estimate

For the standard error of estimate, we use a measure of spread that is in some ways like the standard deviation of measurements of a single variable. Let

$$y_p = a + bx$$

be the predicted value of y from the least-squares line. Then $y - y_p$ is the difference between the y value of the *data point* (x, y) shown on the scatter diagram (Figure 10–12) and the y value of the point on the *least-squares line* with the same x value. The quantity $y - y_p$ is known as the *residual*. To avoid

Residual

Figure 10–12 The Distance Between Points
(x, y) and (x, y_p)

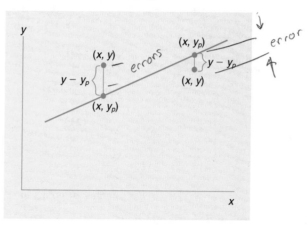

the difficulty of having some positive and some negative values, we square the quantity $(y - y_p)$. Then we sum the squares and, for technical reasons, divide this sum by $n - 2$. Finally, we take the square root to obtain the *standard error of estimate,* which we denote by S_e.

$$\text{Standard error of estimate} = S_e = \sqrt{\frac{\Sigma(y - y_p)^2}{n - 2}}$$

$$\text{where } n \geq 3 \tag{7}$$

Note: To compute the standard error of estimate, we require that there be at least three points on the scatter diagram. If we had only two points, the line would be a perfect fit, since two points determine a line. In such a case, there would be no need to compute S_e.

The nearer the scatter points lie to the least-squares line, the smaller S_e will be. In fact, if $S_e = 0$, it follows that each $y - y_p$ is also zero. This means that all the scatter points lie *on* the least-squares line if $S_e = 0$. The larger S_e becomes, the more scattered the points are.

The formula for the standard error of estimate is reminiscent of the formula for the standard deviation. It too is a measure of dispersion. However, the standard deviation involves differences of data values from a mean, whereas the standard error of estimate involves the differences between experimental and predicted *y* values for a given *x*.

The actual computation of S_e using Equation (7) is quite long because the formula requires us to use the least-squares line equation to compute a predicted value y_p for *each x* value in the data pairs. There is a computational formula that we strongly recommend that you use. However, as with all the computation formulas, be careful about rounding. This formula is sensitive to rounding, and you should carry as many digits as seems reasonable for your problem. Answers will vary depending on rounding used. We give the formula here and follow it with an example of its use.

$$\text{Formula to Calculate } S_e$$

$$S_e = \sqrt{\frac{SS_y - bSS_{xy}}{n-2}} \tag{8}$$

where

$$SS_y = \Sigma y^2 - \frac{(\Sigma y)^2}{n}$$

$$SS_{xy} = \Sigma xy - \frac{(\Sigma x)(\Sigma y)}{n}$$

$$SS_x = \Sigma x^2 - \frac{(\Sigma x)^2}{n}$$

$$b = \frac{SS_{xy}}{SS_x}$$

n = number of points in scatter diagram

Use caution in rounding.

With a considerable amount of algebra, Equations (7) and (8) can be shown to be mathematically equivalent. Equation (7) shows the strong similarity between the standard error of estimate and standard deviation. Equation (8) is a shortcut calculation formula because it involves few subtractions and uses quantities SS_x, b, and SS_{xy} that are also used to determine the least-squares line.

In the next example we show you how to compute the standard error of estimate using the computation formula. Then, in the following example and guided exercise we will show you how to use S_e to create confidence intervals for the y value corresponding to a given x value.

Example 2 | June and Jim are partners in the chemistry lab. Their assignment is to determine how much copper sulfate ($CuSO_4$) will dissolve in water at 10, 20, 30, 40, 50, 60, and 70°C. Their lab results are shown in Table 10–7, where y is the weight in grams of copper sulfate that will dissolve in 100 g of water at x°C.

Table 10–7 Lab Results (x = °C, y = amount of $CuSO_4$)

x	y
10	17
20	21
30	25
40	28
50	33
60	40
70	49

   Sketch a scatter diagram, find the equation of the least-squares line, and compute S_e.

Solution: Figure 10–13 includes a scatter diagram for the data of Table 10–7. To find the equation of the least-squares line and the value of S_e, we set up a computational table (Table 10–8).

Figure 10–13 Scatter Diagram and Least-Squares Line for Chemistry Experiment

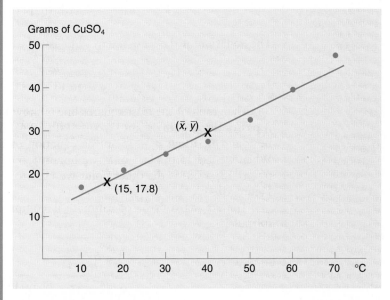

Table 10–8 Computational Table

x	y	x^2	y^2	xy
10	17	100	289	170
20	21	400	441	420
30	25	900	625	750
40	28	1,600	784	1,120
50	33	2,500	1,089	1,650
60	40	3,600	1,600	2,400
70	49	4,900	2,401	3,430
$\Sigma x = 280$	$\Sigma y = 213$	$\Sigma x^2 = 14{,}000$	$\Sigma y^2 = 7{,}229$	$\Sigma xy = 9{,}940$

$$SS_x = \Sigma x^2 - \frac{(\Sigma x)^2}{n} = 14{,}000 - \frac{(280)^2}{7} = 2800$$

$$SS_{xy} = \Sigma xy - \frac{(\Sigma x)(\Sigma y)}{n} = 9940 - \frac{(280)(213)}{7} = 1420$$

$$SS_y = \Sigma y^2 - \frac{(\Sigma y)^2}{n} = 7229 - \frac{(213)^2}{7} = 747.714$$

$$b = \frac{SS_{xy}}{SS_x} = \frac{1420}{2800} = 0.507143 \approx 0.51$$

$$\bar{x} = \frac{280}{7} = 40$$

$$\bar{y} = \frac{213}{7} = 30.43$$

$$a = \bar{y} - b\bar{x} = \frac{213}{7} - (0.507143)\left(\frac{280}{7}\right) \approx 10.14$$

The equation of the least-squares line is

$$y = a + bx$$
$$y = 10.14 + 0.51x$$

The graph of the least-squares line is shown in Figure 10–13. Notice that it passes through the point $(\bar{x}, \bar{y}) = (40, 30.4)$. Another point on the line can be found by using $x = 15$ in the equation of the line $y = 10.14 + 0.51x$. When we use 15 in place of x, we obtain $y = 10.14 + 0.51(15) = 17.8$. The point $(15, 17.8)$ is the other point we used to graph the least-squares line in Figure 10–13.

The standard error of estimate is computed using the computational formula

$$S_e = \sqrt{\frac{SS_y - bSS_{xy}}{n - 2}}$$

$$= \sqrt{\frac{747.714 - (0.507143)(1420)}{5}}$$

$$\approx 2.35$$

Calculator Note

Although most calculators do not provide the value of the standard error of estimate S_e directly, many do provide all the sums needed to evaluate Equation

Figure 10–14 TI-82 2-Var Stats for Data of Example 2

```
2-Var Stats
 x̄=40
 Σx=280
 Σx²=14000
 Sx=21.6046899
 σx=20
↓n=7
■
```

```
2-Var Stats
↑ȳ=30.42857143
 Σy=213
 Σy²=7229
 Sy=11.16329018
 σy=10.33519843
↓Σxy=9940
■
```

(8). For example, the 2-Var Stats command on the TI-82 produces the screens shown in Figure 10–14 for the data of Example 2. Compare these results with those shown in Table 10–8. Using such results from a calculator simplify the work of computing S_e.

Confidence Intervals for y

The least-squares line gives us a predicted value y_p for a specified x value. However, we used sample data to get the equation of the line. The line derived from the population of all data pairs is likely to have a slightly different slope, which we designate by the symbol β for population slope, and a slightly different y intercept, which we designate by the symbol α for population intercept. In addition, there is some random error ϵ, so the true y value would be

$$y = \alpha + \beta x + \epsilon$$

Because of the random variable ϵ, for each x value there is a corresponding distribution of y values. The methods of linear regression were developed so that the distribution of y values for a given x is centered on the population regression line. Furthermore, the distributions of y values corresponding to each x value all have the same standard deviation, which we estimate by the standard error of estimate S_e.

Using all this background, the theory tells us that for a specific x, a c confidence interval for y is given by the next formula.

---

c Confidence Interval for y

$$y_p - E \leq y \leq y_p + E$$

where

$$E = t_c S_e \sqrt{1 + \frac{1}{n} + \frac{(x - \bar{x})^2}{SS_x}}$$

and y_p = the predicted value of y from the least-squares line for the specified x value

t_c = the value from the Student's t distribution for a c confidence level using $n - 2$ degrees of freedom

S_e = the standard error of estimate [see Equation (8)]

$SS_x = \Sigma x^2 - \dfrac{(\Sigma x)^2}{n}$

n = number of data pairs

The formulas involved in the computation of a c confidence interval look complicated. However, they involve quantities we have already computed or values we can easily look up in tables. The next example illustrates this point.

Example 3 | Using the data of Table 10–7, find a 95% confidence interval for the amount of copper sulfate that will dissolve in 100 g. of water at 45°C.
Solution: First, we need to find y_p for $x = 45$°C. We use the equation of the least-squares line that we found in Example 2.

$$y = 10.14 + 0.51x \qquad \text{from Example 2}$$

$$y_p = 10.14 + 0.51(45) \qquad \text{using 45 in place of } x$$

$$y_p \approx 33$$

A 95% confidence interval is then

$$33 - E \leq y \leq 33 + E$$

where

$$E = t_{0.95}S_e\sqrt{1 + \frac{1}{n} + \frac{(x - \bar{x})^2}{SS_x}}$$

Using $n - 2 = 7 - 2 = 5$ degrees of freedom, we find from Table 7 in Appendix II that $t_{0.95} = 2.571$. We computed S_e, SS_x, and $\bar{x}$ in Example 2. Therefore,

$$E = (2.571)(2.35)\sqrt{1 + \frac{1}{7} + \frac{(45 - 40)^2}{2800}}$$

$$= (2.571)(2.35)\sqrt{1.15179}$$

$$\approx 6.5$$

A 95% confidence interval for y is

$$33 - 6.5 \leq y \leq 33 + 6.5$$

$$26.5 \leq y \leq 39.5$$

This means that we are 95% sure that the actual amount of copper sulfate that will dissolve in 100g of water at 45°C is between 26.5 and 39.5 g. The interval is fairly wide but would decrease with more sample data.

GUIDED EXERCISE 4

Let's use the data of Example 2 to compute a 95% confidence interval for y = amount of copper sulfate that will dissolve at $x = 15$°C.

(a) From Example 2 we have

$$y = 10.14 + 0.51x$$

Evaluate y_p for $x = 15$.

(b) The bound E on the error of estimate is

$$E = t_c S_e\sqrt{1 + \frac{1}{n} + \frac{(x - \bar{x})^2}{SS_x}}$$

(a) $y_p = 10.14 + 0.51x$

$$= 10.14 + 0.51(15)$$

$$\approx 17.8$$

(b) $t_{0.95} = 2.571$

$$E = (2.571)(2.35)\sqrt{1 + \frac{1}{7} + \frac{(15 - 40)^2}{2800}}$$

From Example 2 we know that $S_e = 2.35$, SS_x = 2800, and $\bar{x} = 40$. Recall that there were n = 7 data pairs. Find $t_{0.95}$ and compute E.

$$= (2.571)(2.35)\sqrt{1.366071}$$
$$\approx 7.1$$

(c) Find the 95% confidence interval

$$y_p - E \leq y \leq y_p + E$$

(c) The confidence interval is

$$17.8 - 7.1 \leq y \leq 17.8 + 7.1$$
$$10.7 \leq y \leq 24.9$$

As we compare the results of Example 3 and Guided Exercise 4, we notice that the 95% confidence interval of y values for $x = 15°C$ is 7.1 units above and below the least-squares line, while the 95% confidence interval of y values for $x = 45°C$ is only 6.5 units above and below the least-squares line. This comparison reflects the general property that confidence intervals for y are narrower the nearer we are to the mean of the x values. As we move near the extremes of the x distribution, the confidence intervals for y become wider. This is another reason that we should not try to use the least-squares line to predict y values for x values beyond the data extremes of the sample x distribution.

If we were to compute a 95% confidence interval for all x values in the range of the sample x values, the confidence interval band would curve away from the least-squares line, as shown in Figure 10–15.

Figure 10–15 95% Confidence Band for Predicted Values y_p

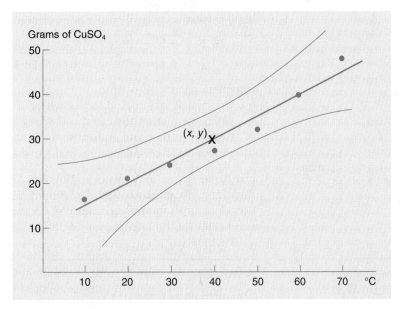

Section 10.2 Problems

Do the following as parts a–d for each problem.
(a) Draw a scatter diagram for the data.
(b) Find $\bar{x}$, $\bar{y}$, and b. Then find the equation of the least-squares line.
(c) Graph the least-squares line on your scatter diagram. Be sure to use the point $(\bar{x}, \bar{y})$ as one of the points on the line.
(d) Find the standard error of estimate S_e.

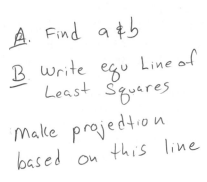

A. Find a & b

B. write equ Line of
   Least Squares

make projedtion
based on this line

1. The following data are based on information from the book *Life in America's Small Cities* (by G. S. Thomas, Prometheus Books). Let x = percentage of those 25 years or older with 4 or more years of college. Let y = per capita income in thousands of dollars. Five small cities in South Carolina (Greenwood, Hilton Head Island, Myrtle Beach, Orangeburg, and Sumpter) reported the following information regarding the x and y variables:

x	13.8	21.9	12.5	12.7	11.5
y	9.0	10.8	8.8	6.9	7.2

Complete parts a through d.
(e) In a small city in South Carolina where x = 20 percent of the population 25 years or older who have had 4 or more years of college, what would the least-squares equation forecast for y = per capita income (in thousands of dollars) in this community.
(f) Find an 80% confidence interval for your forecast y value of part e.

2. Five small cities in California (El Centro, Eureka, Hanford, Madera, and San Luis Obispo–Atascadero) reported the following information. Let x = percentage of 16- to 19-year-olds not in school and not high school graduates. Let y = per capita income in thousands of dollars. The following information was obtained (see reference in Problem 1):

x	16.2	9.9	19.5	19.7	9.8
y	7.2	8.8	7.9	8.1	10.3

Complete parts a through d.
(e) In a small city in California where x = 17, what would the least-squares equation forecast for y = per capita income (in thousands of dollars) in this community.
(f) Find a 75% confidence interval for the forecast y value of part e.

3. Five small cities in Kentucky (Bowling Green, Madisonville, Paducah, Radcliff-Elizabethtown, and Richmond) reported the following information about the random variables x = per capita income and y = per capita retail sales (both in thousands of dollars). See reference in Problem 1.

x	9.0	8.9	9.9	8.2	7.6
y	5.1	4.5	6.2	3.7	4.2

Complete parts a through d.

(e) Suppose that you plan to open a retail store in a small city in Kentucky where the per capita income is $x = 9.5$ (thousand dollars). What does the least-squares equation forecast for $y =$ per capita retail sales (in thousands of dollars)?

(f) Find an 80% confidence interval for the forecast y value of part e.

4. *Consumers Digest* (February 1994) gave the following information about $x =$ list price and $y =$ best price (both in thousands of dollars) for different models of the Ford Ranger. The "best price" is the lowest price representatives from *Consumers Digest* negotiated with Ford dealerships. Your price might be higher or lower depending on your ability to negotiate and the dealer's willingness to sell. We assume that you do not have a trade-in.

x	9.8	11.6	12.3	13.7	16.2	17.7	18.7
y	8.4	10.4	10.9	12.6	14.4	15.1	16.5

Complete parts a through d.

(e) Suppose that you are interested in a Ford Ranger with list price $x = 14.99$ (thousands of dollars). What does the least-squares equation forecast for $y =$ best price?

(f) Find a 90% confidence interval for your forecast y value of part e.

5. For the Dodge Dakota data for $x =$ list price and $y =$ best price in thousands of dollars are given below (see reference and comments in Problem 4):

x	9.6	10.7	12.3	14.5	15.7	17.5
y	9.2	10.0	11.2	13.7	14.2	15.8

Complete parts a through d.

(e) Suppose that you are interested in a Dodge Dakota with list price $x = 16.5$ (thousand dollars). What does the least-squares equation forecast for $y =$ best price?

(f) Find a 95% confidence interval for your forecast y value of part e.

6. The following data are based on information taken from *The Economist* (January 22, 1994). Let $x =$ percentage change in wages and $y =$ percentage change in consumer prices for the past year in Australia, Austria, Canada, France, Italy, Spain, and the United States.

x	3.3	4.1	1.9	2.6	3.9	6.3	2.5
y	2.2	3.5	1.9	2.1	4.0	4.9	2.7

Complete parts a through d.

(e) Suppose that the percentage change in wages is $x = 5$. What does the least-squares equation forecast for y, the corresponding percentage change in consumer prices.

(f) Find an 80% confidence interval for your forecast y value of part e.

7. The number of workers on an assembly line varies due to the level of absenteeism on any given day. In a random sample of production output

from several days of work, the following data were obtained, where x = number of workers absent from the assembly line and y = number of defects coming off the line.

x	3	5	0	2	1
y	16	20	9	12	10

Complete parts a through d.

(e) On a day when four workers are absent from the assembly line, what would the least-squares line predict for the number of defects coming off the line?

(f) Find a 95% confidence interval for the number of defects when four workers are absent.

8. The following data are based on information from the *Harvard Business Review* (January–February 1994). Let x = number of different research programs and y = mean number of patents per program. As in any business, a company can spread itself too thin. For example, too many research programs might lead to a decline in overall research productivity. The following data are for a collection of pharmaceutical companies and their research programs:

x	10	12	14	16	18	20
y	1.8	1.7	1.5	1.4	1.0	0.7

Complete parts a through d.

(e) Suppose that a pharmaceutical company had x = 15 different research programs. What does the least-squares equation forecast for y = mean number of patents per program?

(f) Find an 85% confidence interval for the forecast y value of part e.

9. Data for this problem are based on information taken from *Prehistoric New Mexico: Background for Survey* (by D. E. Stuart and R. P. Gauthier, University of New Mexico Press). It is thought that prehistoric Indians did not take their best tools, pottery, and household items when they visited higher elevations for their summer camps. It is hypothesized that archaeological sites tend to lose their cultural identity and specific cultural affiliation as the elevation of the site increases. Let x = elevation (in thousands of feet) for an archaeological site in the southwestern United States. Let y = percentage of unidentified artifacts (no specific cultural affiliation) at a given elevation. The following data were obtained for a collection of archaeological sites in New Mexico:

x	5.25	5.75	6.25	6.75	7.25
y	19	13	33	37	62

Complete parts a through d.

(e) At an archaeological site with elevation x = 6.5 (thousand feet), what does the least-squares equation forecast for y = percentage of culturally unidentified artifacts.

(f) Find a 75% confidence interval for the forecast y value of part e.

10. A child psychiatrist is studying the mental development of children. A random sample of nine children was given a standard set of questions appropriate to the age of each child. The number of irrelevant responses to the questions was recorded for each child. In the following data, x = age of child in years and y = number of irrelevant responses:

x	2	3	4	5	7	9	10	11	12
y	15	15	12	13	11	10	8	6	5

Complete parts a through d.
(e) If a child is 9.5 years old, what does the least-squares line predict for the number of irrelevant responses?
(f) Find a 99% confidence interval for the number of irrelevant responses for a child who is 9.5 years old.

11. In placing a weekly order for hot dogs, the concessionaire at a large baseball stadium needs to estimate the size of the crowd that will attend the game. Advanced ticket sales often give a good indication of expected attendance at games. Data from six previous weeks of games are shown below, where x = advanced ticket sales (in thousands) and y = number of hot dogs purchased (in thousands) at the game.

x	45	64	37	58	41	29
y	32	46	25	44	32	18

Complete parts a through d.
(e) If advanced ticket sales are 55 thousand this week, how many thousand hot dogs do you recommend the concessionaire be prepared to sell? (Use the predicted value from the least-squares line.)
(f) Find a 75% confidence interval for the number of hot dogs to be prepared when advanced ticket sales are 55 thousand.

12. Data for this problem are based on information from *STATS Basketball Scoreboard*. It is thought that basketball teams that make too many fouls in a game tend to lose the game even if they otherwise play well. Let x = number of fouls more than (i.e., over and above) the opposing team. Let y = percentage of times the team with the larger number of fouls wins the game.

x	0	2	5	6
y	50	45	33	26

Complete parts a through d.
(e) If a team had x = 4 fouls over and above the opposing team, what does the least-squares equation forecast for y?
(f) Find an 80% confidence interval for the forecast of part e.

13. Data for this problem are from *Climatology Report No. 77-3* (by J. F. Benci and T. B. McKee, Department of Atmospheric Science, Colorado

State University). Let x = elevation (in thousands of feet) and y = average number of frost-free days in a year. For Denver, Gunnison, Aspen, Crested Butte, and Dillon, Colorado, the following data were obtained:

x	5.3	7.7	7.9	8.9	9.8
y	162	63	73	49	21

Complete parts a through d.
(e) Colorado Springs is at an elevation of $x = 6$ (thousand feet). What does the least-squares equation forecast for the average number of frost-free days per year in Colorado Springs?
(f) Find an 85% confidence interval for the forecast y value of part e.

14. As director of personnel for a prosperous company, you have just hired a new public relations person. The final salary arrangements are negotiated depending on the number of years of experience the new public relations person brings to the company. After checking with several other companies in your area, you obtain the following data, where x = number of years of experience for a person in public relations and y = annual salary in thousands of dollars:

x	1	2	15	11	9	6
y	33	37	61	57	45	42

Complete parts a through d.
(e) If your candidate for the new public relations position has 8 years of experience, what would the least-squares line suggest for the annual salary?
(f) Estimate a salary range for the candidate so that approximately 90% of the public relations officers with 8 years of experience will be in this range.

15. The following data are taken from the *Handbook of Physics and Chemistry* (CRC Publishing Company). Here x = water temperature in degrees Celsius and y = weight of carbon dioxide in grams that will dissolve in 100 g of water at 1 atmosphere of pressure for the corresponding temperature.

x	3	6	9	12	15
y	0.298	0.268	0.240	0.224	0.210

Complete parts a through d.
(e) If the temperature is 10°C, what does the least-squares line predict for the weight of carbon dioxide that will dissolve in 100 g of water?
(f) Find a 90% confidence interval for your prediction of part e.

16. (a) Suppose that you are given the following x, y data pairs:

x	1	3	4
y	2	1	6

Show that the least-squares equation for these data is $y = 1.071x + 0.143$ (where we round to three digits after the decimal).

(b) Now suppose that you are given these x, y data pairs:

x	2	1	6
y	1	3	4

Show that the least-squares equation for these data is $y = 0.357x + 1.595$ (where we round to three digits after the decimal).

(c) In the data for parts a and b, did we simply exchange the x and y values of each data pair?

(d) Solve $y = 0.143 + 1.071x$ for x. Do you get the least-squares equation of part b with the symbols x and y exchanged?

(e) In general, suppose that we have the least-squares equation $y = a + bx$ for a set of data pairs x and y. If we solve this equation for x, will we *necessarily* get the least-squares equation for the set of data pairs y, x (with x and y exchanged)? Explain using parts a through d.

Section 10.3   The Linear Correlation Coefficient

If we are given a set of data pairs, we know how to find the equation of the line which "best" predicts y from a given x. This equation is called the *least-squares regression line of y on* x. However, we need more information about how well the line "fits" the data. In the last section we saw that the standard error of estimate gives us some measure of how well our predicted values computed from the regression line fit actual experimental data values. The standard error of estimate has the same units of measurement as our y values, and as such, its value is to a certain extent dependent on the unit of measure selected for y. If we compare two different sets of data pairs, we cannot necessarily use the standard error of estimate to say that the regression line from one data set is "better" than the regression line from another data set. Finally, if we exchange the order in our data pairs, we get the regression line of x on y and obtain a different value for the standard error of estimate. In other words, the value of the standard error of estimate changes according to which variable is the explanatory variable and which is the response variable.

Correlation Coefficient, r

We need a unitless measurement to describe the strength of the linear association that exists between two variables regardless of which is listed first. Such a measure is the *correlation coefficient r*. The full name for r is the *Pearson product-moment correlation coefficient*, named in honor of the English statistician Karl Pearson (1857–1936), who is credited with formulating r. We'll develop the defining formula for r and then give a more convenient computation formula.

Development of Formula for *r*

If there is a *positive* linear relation between variables x and y, then high values of x are paired with high values of y and low values of x are paired with low values of y. [See Figure 10–16(a).] In the case of *negative* linear correlation, high values of x are paired with low values of y and low values of x are paired with high values of y. This relation is pictured in Figure 10–16(b). On the other hand, if there is little or no linear correlation between x and y, then we will find both high and low x values sometimes paired with high y values and sometimes paired with low y values. This relation is shown in Figure 10–16(c).

These observations lead us to the development of the formula for the correlation coefficient r. Taking *high* to mean "above the mean," we can express the relationships pictured in Figure 10–16 by considering the products

$$(x - \bar{x})(y - \bar{y})$$

If both x and y are high, both factors will be positive, and the product will be positive as well. The sign of this product will depend on the relative values of x and y compared with their respective means.

$$(x - \bar{x})(y - \bar{y}) \begin{cases} \text{is positive if } x \text{ and } y \text{ are both "high"} \\ \text{is positive if } x \text{ and } y \text{ are both "low"} \\ \\ \text{is negative if } x \text{ is "low," but } y \text{ is "high"} \\ \text{is negative if } x \text{ is "high," but } y \text{ is "low"} \end{cases}$$

In the case of positive linear correlation, most of the products $(x - \bar{x})(y - \bar{y})$ will be positive and so will the sum over all the data pairs

$$\Sigma(x - \bar{x})(y - \bar{y})$$

For negative linear correlation, the products will tend to be negative, so the sum also will be negative. On the other hand, in the case of little, if any, linear correlation, the sum will tend to be zero.

One trouble with the preceding sum is that it will be larger or smaller depending on the units of x and y. Since we want r to be unitless, we standardize both x and y of a data pair by dividing each factor $(x - \bar{x})$ by the sample standard deviation s_x and each factor $(y - \bar{y})$ by s_y. Finally, we take an average of all the products. For technical reasons, we take the average by dividing by $n - 1$ instead of by n. This process leads us to the desired measurement, r.

$$r = \frac{1}{n-1} \Sigma \frac{(y - \bar{y})}{s_y} \cdot \frac{(x - \bar{x})}{s_x}$$

Computation Formula for r

The defining formula for r is awkward to use because of all the subtractions. As before, we can simplify the formula and produce one that is much easier to use. In fact, it should be no surprise that the sums utilized in computing the standard error of estimate and the slope of the least-squares line are also used in the computational formula for r on page 690.

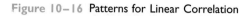

Figure 10–16 Patterns for Linear Correlation

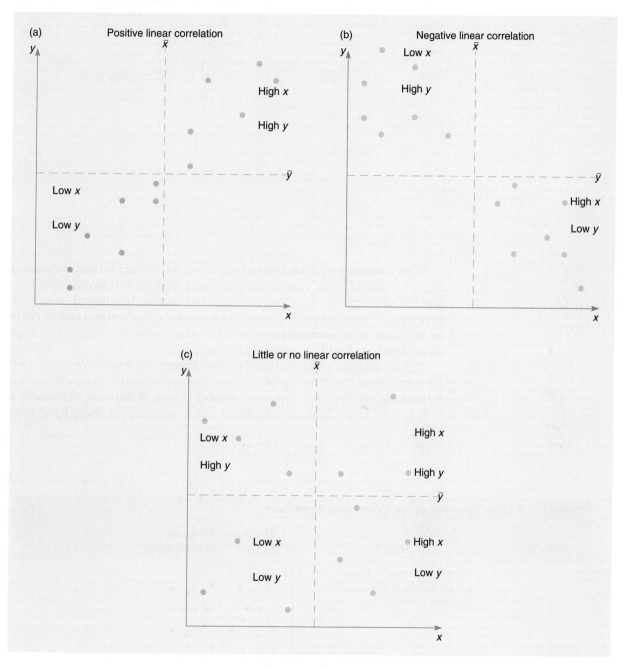

Formula to Calculate Correlation Coefficient, r

$$r = \frac{SS_{xy}}{\sqrt{SS_x \, SS_y}} \tag{9}$$

where $SS_{xy} = \Sigma xy - \dfrac{(\Sigma x)(\Sigma y)}{n}$ *Note:* $SS_{xy} = \Sigma(x - \bar{x})(y - \bar{y})$

$$SS_x = \Sigma x^2 - \frac{(\Sigma x)^2}{n}$$

$$SS_y = \Sigma y^2 - \frac{(\Sigma y)^2}{n}$$

n = number of data pairs in scatter diagram

This formula for r is sensitive to rounding. As in other formulas involving SS_x, SS_{xy}, and SS_y, you want to carry as many digits as is reasonable for your problem until the last step. Again, depending on the rounding process used, answers will vary slightly. The answers for the end-of-section and end-of-chapter exercises were computer-generated, so your answers might differ from them slightly and still be essentially correct.

Let us delay an example showing how to compute r until we know a little more about the meaning of the correlation coefficient. It can be shown mathematically that r is always a number which is between $+1$ and -1 ($-1 \leq r \leq +1$). Table 10–9 gives a quick summary of some basic facts about r.

Table 10–9 Some Facts About the Correlation Coefficient

If r Is	Then	The Scatter Diagram Might Look Something Like
0	There is no linear relation for the points of the scatter diagram.	

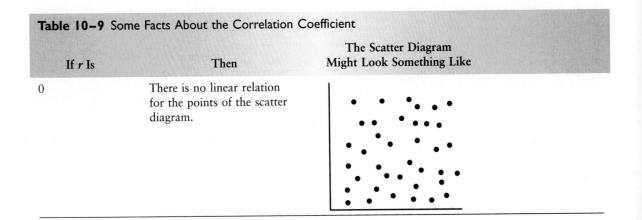

If *r* Is	Then	The Scatter Diagram Might Look Something Like
1 or −1	There is a perfect linear relation between *x* and *y* values; all points lie on the least-squares line.	$r = -1$ $r = 1$
Between 0 and 1 $(0 < r < 1)$	The *x* and *y* values have a *positive correlation*. By this we mean that *large x* values are associated with *large y* values and *small x* values are associated with *small y* values.	As we go from left to right, the least-squares line goes *up*.
Between −1 and 0 $(-1 < r < 0)$	The *x* and *y* values have a *negative correlation*. By this we mean *large x* values are associated with *small y* values and *small x* values are associated with *large y* values.	As we go from left to right, the least-squares line goes *down*.

GUIDED EXERCISE 5

Match the appropriate statement about *r* to each scatter diagram in Figure 10–17 on page 692.

(1) $r = 0$.

(2) $r = 1$.

(3) $r = -1$.

(4) *r* is between 0 and 1.

(5) *r* is between −1 and 0.

(a) $r = 1$ because all the points are on the line and the line goes up from left to right.

(b) $r = 0$ because there is no apparent linear relation among the points.

(c) *r* is between −1 and 0 because the points are fairly close to the line, and as we read from left to right the least-squares line goes down.

Figure 10–17 Scatter Diagrams

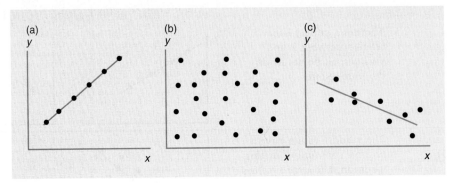

Now let's actually compute r for some data.

Example 4   Most of us have heard someone say that more intelligent people tend to do better in school. Is this always true? Experienced teachers know that it is only partially true. Students with higher IQs (intelligence quotients) often do better schoolwork, but factors other than IQ can affect academic success. However, let's see if there is a correlation between IQ and cumulative grade averages (CGA). The principal of Delta High School chose 12 students from the senior class at random and compiled the data in Table 10–10.

Table 10–10 IQ versus CGA (on a Four-Point Scale) of 12 High School Seniors											
IQ, x	117	92	102	115	87	76	107	108	121	91	113	98
CGA, y	3.7	2.6	3.3	2.2	2.4	1.8	2.8	3.2	3.8	3.0	4.0	3.5

(a) First, make a scatter diagram, and determine if r is positive, close to 0, or negative.
   Solution: The scatter diagram indicates that r is positive. See Figure 10–18.

(b) Compute r.
   Solution: To find r, we must compute Σx, Σy, Σx^2, Σy^2, and Σxy. The values for $(\Sigma x)^2$ and $(\Sigma y)^2$ can be obtained from Σx and Σy. It is easiest to organize our work into a table of five columns (Table 10–11). The first two columns are just a repetition of Table 10–10.

Figure 10–18 Scatter Diagram for Table 10–10

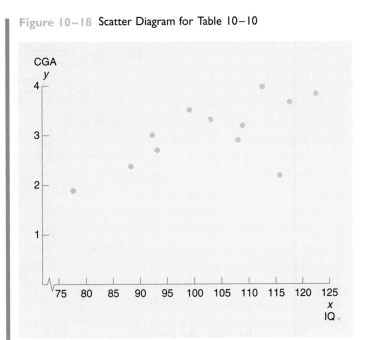

Table 10–11 Information Necessary to Compute r

x(IQ)	y(CGA)	x^2	y^2	xy
117	3.7	13,689	13.7	432.9
92	2.6	8,464	6.8	239.2
102	3.3	10,404	10.9	336.6
115	2.2	13,225	4.8	253.0
87	2.4	7,569	5.8	208.8
76	1.8	5,776	3.2	136.8
107	2.8	11,449	7.8	299.6
108	3.2	11,664	10.2	345.6
121	3.8	14,641	14.4	459.8
91	3.0	8,281	9.0	273.0
113	4.0	12,769	16.0	452.0
98	3.5	9,604	12.3	343.0

$\Sigma x = 1,227$ $\Sigma y = 36.3$ $\Sigma x^2 = 127,535$ $\Sigma y^2 = 114.9$ $\Sigma xy = 3,780.3$
$(\Sigma x)^2 = 1,505,529$ $(\Sigma y)^2 = 1,317.7$

To use Equation (9) to calculate r, we will first compute SS_{xy}, SS_x, and SS_y.

$$SS_{xy} = \Sigma xy - \frac{(\Sigma x)(\Sigma y)}{n}$$

$$= 3780.3 - \frac{(1227)(36.3)}{12}$$

$$= 68.63$$

$$SS_x = \Sigma x^2 - \frac{(\Sigma x)^2}{n}$$

$$= 127{,}535 - \frac{(1227)^2}{12}$$

$$= 2074.25$$

$$SS_y = \Sigma y^2 - \frac{(\Sigma y)^2}{n}$$

$$= 114.9 - \frac{(36.3)^2}{12}$$

$$= 5.09$$

Therefore, the correlation coefficient is

$$r = \frac{SS_{xy}}{\sqrt{SS_x SS_y}}$$

$$= \frac{68.63}{\sqrt{(2074.25)(5.09)}}$$

$$= 0.6679$$

$$\approx 0.67$$

Our correlation coefficient is $r \approx 0.67$. Let's make sure this answer agrees with what we expect from a quick glance at the scatter diagram (Figure 10–18). In Figure 10–18 the general trend is upward as we read from left to right, so we would expect a positive value for r. The value 0.67 is in the expected range—that is, it is between 0 and 1.

It is quite a task to compute r for even 12 data pairs. The use of columns as in Example 4 is extremely helpful. Your value for r should always be between -1 and 1. Use a scatter diagram to get a rough idea of the value of r. If your computed value of r is outside the allowable range or if it disagrees quite a bit with the scatter diagram, recheck your calculations. Be sure you distinguish between expressions such as (Σx^2) and $(\Sigma x)^2$. Negligible rounding errors may occur depending on how you (or your calculator) round.

Calculator Note

Most calculators that support two-variable statistics provide the value of the correlation coefficient r directly. The screens in Figure 10–19 show the results of Example 4 as provided by the TI-82 calculator.

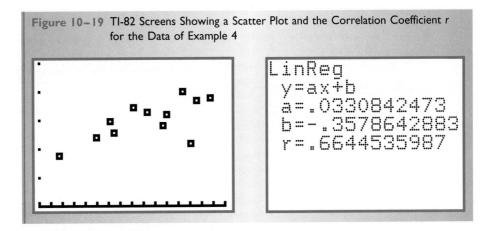

Figure 10–19 TI-82 Screens Showing a Scatter Plot and the Correlation Coefficient *r* for the Data of Example 4

GUIDED EXERCISE 6

In one of the Boston city parks there has been a problem with muggings in the summer months. A police cadet took a random sample of 10 days (out of the 90-day summer) and compiled the following data. For each day, x represents the number of police officers on duty in the park and y represents the number of reported muggings on that day.

x	10	15	16	1	4	6	18	12	14	7
y	5	2	1	9	7	8	1	5	3	6

(a) Construct a scatter diagram of x and y values.

(a) Figure 10–20 shows the scatter diagram.

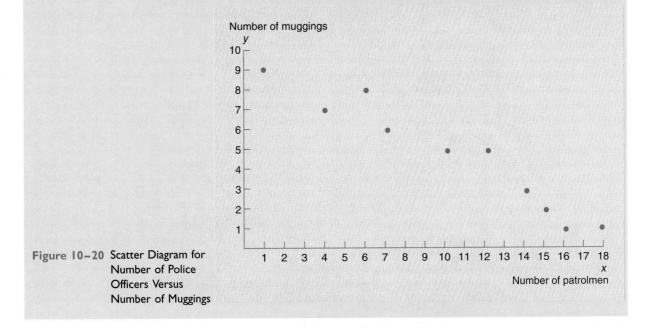

Figure 10–20 Scatter Diagram for Number of Police Officers Versus Number of Muggings

(b) From the scatter diagram, do you think the computed value of r will be positive, negative, or zero? Explain.

(c) Complete Table 10–12.

Table 10–12

x	y	x^2	y^2	xy
10	5	100	25	50
15	2	225	4	30
16	1	256	1	16
1	9	1	81	9
4	7	16	49	28
6	8	——	——	——
18	1	——	——	——
12	5	——	——	——
14	3	——	——	——
7	6	49	36	42
$\Sigma x = 103$	$\Sigma y = 47$	$\Sigma x^2 =$ __	$\Sigma y^2 =$ __	$\Sigma xy =$ __
		$(\Sigma x)^2 =$ __	$(\Sigma y)^2 =$ __	

(d) Compute SS_{xy}, SS_x, SS_y, and then r.

(b) r will be negative. The general trend is that large x values are associated with small y values and vice versa. From left to right, the least-squares line goes down.

(c)

Table 10–13 Completion of Table 10–12

x	y	x^2	y^2	xy
6	8	36	64	48
18	1	324	1	18
12	5	144	25	60
14	3	196	9	42
		$\Sigma x^2 = 1{,}347$	$\Sigma y^2 = 295$	$\Sigma xy = 343$
		$(\Sigma x)^2 = 10{,}609$	$(\Sigma y)^2 = 2209$	

(d) $SS_{xy} = \Sigma xy - \dfrac{(\Sigma x)(\Sigma y)}{n}$

$\qquad = 343 - \dfrac{(103)(47)}{10}$

$\qquad = -141.1$

$SS_x = \Sigma x^2 - \dfrac{(\Sigma x)^2}{n}$

$\qquad = 1347 - \dfrac{(103)^2}{10}$

$\qquad = 286.1$

$SS_y = \Sigma y^2 - \dfrac{(\Sigma y)^2}{n}$

$\qquad = 295 - \dfrac{(47)^2}{10}$

$\qquad = 74.1$

$r = \dfrac{SS_{xy}}{\sqrt{SS_x \, SS_y}}$

$$= \frac{-141.1}{\sqrt{(286.1)(74.1)}}$$

$$= -0.9691$$

$$\approx -0.97$$

The correlation coefficient can be thought of as another measure of how "good" the least-squares line fits the data points of the scatter diagram. (Recall that the standard error of estimate S_e in Section 10.2 is another such measure.) The closer r is to $+1$ or -1, the better the least-squares line "fits" the data. Values of r close to 0 indicate a poor "fit."

Usually our scatter diagram does not contain *all* possible data points that could be gathered. Most scatter diagrams represent only a *random sample* of data pairs taken from a very large population of possible pairs. Because r is computed by Equation (9) on the basis of a random sample of (x, y) pairs, we expect the values of r to vary from one sample to the next (much as sample means $\bar{x}$ varied from sample to sample). This brings up the question of the *significance* of r. Or put another way, what are the chances that our random sample of data pairs indicates a high correlation when in fact the population x and y values are not so strongly correlated? Right now let us just say the significance of r is a separate issue that is left to the next section.

- *Comment:* As we use computing formulas for the slope of the least-squares line, for r, and for standard deviations s_x and s_y, we see many of the same sums used. There is, in fact, a relationship between the correlation coefficient r and the slope of the least-squares line b. In instances when we know r, s_x and s_y, we can use the following formula to compute b.

$$b = r\left(\frac{s_y}{s_x}\right)$$

Coefficient of Determination

There is another way to answer the question, How good is the least-squares line as an instrument of regression? The *coefficient of determination* r^2 is the square of the sample correlation coefficient r.

Suppose we have a scatter diagram and corresponding least-squares line as shown in Figure 10–21 on page 698.

Let us take the point of view that $\bar{y}$ is a kind of baseline for the y values. If you were given an x value and if you were completely ignorant of regression and correlation, but you wanted to predict a value of y corresponding to the given x, a reasonable guess for y would be the mean $\bar{y}$. However, since we do know how to construct the least-squares regression line, we can calculate $y_p = a + bx$, the predicted value corresponding to x. Now in most cases the

Figure 10–21 Explained and Unexplained Deviations

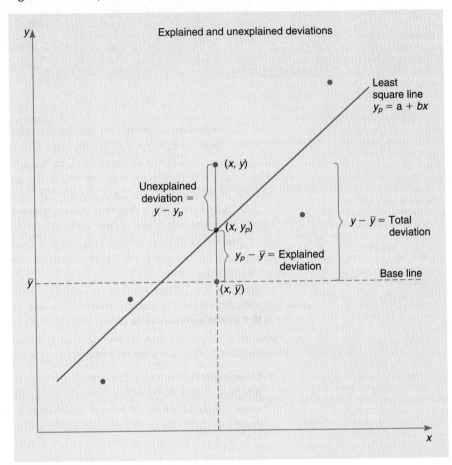

predicted value y_p on the least-squares line will not be the same as the actual data value y. We will measure deviations (or differences) from the base line $\bar{y}$. (See Figure 10–21.)

$$\text{Total deviation} = y - \bar{y}$$
$$\text{Explained deviation} = y_p - \bar{y}$$
$$\text{Unexplained deviation} = y - y_p \quad \text{(also known as the } \textit{residual}\text{)}$$

The total deviation $y - \bar{y}$ is a measure of how far y is from the baseline $\bar{y}$. This can be broken into two parts: the explained deviation $y_p - \bar{y}$ tells us how far the estimated y value "should" be from the baseline $\bar{y}$. (The "explanation" of this part of the deviation is the least-squares line, so to speak.) The unexplained deviation $y - y_p$ tells us how far our data value y is "off." This amount is called *unexplained* because it is due to random chance and other factors that the least-squares line cannot account for.

$$(y - \bar{y}) \quad = \quad (y_p - \bar{y}) \quad + \quad (y - y_p)$$

$$\begin{pmatrix} \text{Total} \\ \text{deviation} \end{pmatrix} = \begin{pmatrix} \text{Explained} \\ \text{deviation} \end{pmatrix} + \begin{pmatrix} \text{Unexplained} \\ \text{deviation} \end{pmatrix}$$

At this point we wish to include all the data pairs and we wish to deal only with nonnegative values (so positive and negative deviations won't cancel out). Therefore, we construct the following equation for the sum of squares. This equation can be derived using some lengthy algebraic manipulations, which we omit.

$$\Sigma(y - \bar{y})^2 \quad = \quad \Sigma(y_p - \bar{y})^2 \quad + \quad \Sigma(y - y_p)^2$$

$$\begin{pmatrix} \text{Total} \\ \text{variation} \end{pmatrix} = \begin{pmatrix} \text{Explained} \\ \text{variation} \end{pmatrix} + \begin{pmatrix} \text{Unexplained} \\ \text{variation} \end{pmatrix}$$

Note that the sum of *squares* is taken over all data points and is then referred to as *variation* (not deviation).

The preceding concepts are connected together in the following important statement (whose proof we omit):

If r is the correlation coefficient [see Equation (9)], then it can be shown that

$$r^2 = \frac{\Sigma(y_p - \bar{y})^2}{\Sigma(y - \bar{y})^2} = \frac{\text{explained variation}}{\text{total variation}}$$

r^2 is called the *coefficient of determination*.

Let us make some comments about the coefficient of determination.

1. The calculation of r is described in Equation (9). The calculation of the coefficient of determination is then very easy; it is simply r^2.
2. The ratio of explained variation over total variation is that fractional amount of total variation in y that can be explained by using the least-squares line and the x variable.

In other words, the coefficient of determination r^2 is a measure of the proportion of variation in y that is explained by the regression line using x as the predicting variable. If $r = 0.90$, then $r^2 = 0.81$ is the coefficient of determination, and we can say that about 81% of the (variation) behavior of the y variable can be explained by the corresponding (variation) behavior of the x variable if we use the equation of the least-squares line. The remaining 19% of the (variation) behavior of the y variable is due to random chance or to the presence of other variables besides the x that influence y.

GUIDED EXERCISE 7

(a) In Example 4 we found the correlation coefficient r of the relationship between IQ and cumulative grade averages. In that case, r was 0.67. How would you describe the strength of this relationship?

(a) The correlation coefficient $r = 0.67$ is moderate, but not extremely high. It seems that other factors besides IQ are significant in determining a cumulative grade point average.

(b) Compute the coefficient of determination for the data of Example 4 and comment on the meaning of this number.

(b) Since $r = 0.67$, then $r^2 = 0.449$ is the value of the coefficient of determination. This says that 44.9% of the variation of y = CGA can be explained by the least-squares line and x = IQ. The remaining $100 - 44.9 = 55.1\%$ of the variation of y is due to random chance or other variables besides x that influence y (possibly, amount of time spent studying!).

(c) In Guided Exercise 6, dealing with the relation between the number of police officers in the park and the number of muggings, we found r to be -0.97. How would you describe the strength of this relationship? Do you think the city is justified in asking for more police officers to be assigned to park duty?

(c) $r = -0.97$ is a high correlation. The relation between the number of police officers in the park and the number of muggings in the park is a strong and dependable negative correlation. The authors feel that the city would be wise to hire more police officers to patrol the park. But many other aspects of the situation must be considered. Perhaps more crimes would be prevented by putting those officers elsewhere.

(d) Compute the coefficient of determination for the data of Guided Exercise 6 and comment on the meaning of this number.

(d) Since $r = -0.97$, then $r^2 = 0.941$ is the coefficient of determination. About 94.1% of the variation of y can be explained by the least-squares line and the x variable. The remaining $100 - 94.1 = 5.9\%$ of the variation of y is due to random chance or other variables besides x that influence y.

Causation

The correlation coefficient is a mathematical tool for measuring the strength of the linear relationship between two variables. As such, it makes no implication about cause or effect. Just because two variables tend to increase or decrease together does not mean a change in one is *causing* a change in the other. A strong correlation between x and y is sometimes due to other (either known or unknown) variables.

Example 5 | Over a period of years, a certain town observed that the correlation between x, the number of people attending churches, and y, the number of people in the city jail, was $r = 0.90$.

Does going to church cause people to go to jail? We hope not. During this period, there was a steady increase in population. Therefore, it is not too surprising that both the number of people attending churches and the number of people in jail increased together. The high correlation between x and y is due to the common effect of the increase in the general population.

Section 10.3 Problems

1. Over the past 10 years, there has been a high positive correlation between the number of South Dakota safety inspection stickers issued and the number of South Dakota traffic accidents.
    (a) Do safety inspection stickers cause traffic accidents?
    (b) What third factor might cause traffic accidents and the number of safety stickers to increase together?

2. There is a high positive correlation in the United States between teachers' salaries and annual consumption of liquor.
    (a) Do you think increasing teachers' salaries has caused increased liquor consumption?
    (b) As teachers' salaries have been going up, most other salaries have been going up too. To some extent this means an upward trend in buying power for everyone. How might this explain the high correlation between teachers' salaries and liquor consumption?

3. Over the past 30 years in the United States there has been a strong negative correlation between number of infant deaths at birth and number of people over age 65.
    (a) Is the fact that people are living longer causing a decrease in infant mortalities at birth?
    (b) What third factor might be decreasing infant mortalities and at the same time increasing life span?

4. Over the past few years, there has been a strong positive correlation between the annual consumption of diet soda pop and the number of traffic accidents.
    (a) Do you think that an increasing consumption of diet pop has led to more traffic accidents?
    (b) What third factor or factors might be causing both the annual consumption of diet pop and the number of traffic accidents to increase together?

For each of the Problems 5–15, do the following:
    (a) Draw a scatter diagram for the data.
    (b) From the scatter diagram, would you estimate the correlation coefficient r to be closest to 1, 0, or -1?
    (c) Compute the correlation coefficient r and the coefficient of determination r^2. What percentage of the variation in y can be *explained* by the corresponding variation in x using the least-squares line? What percentage of the variation is *unexplained*?

5. The following data are based on information from the book *Life in America's Small Cities* (by G. S. Thomas, Prometheus Books). Let x = percentage of 16- to 19-year-olds not in school and not high school graduates. Let y = reported violent crimes per 1000 residents. Six small cities in Arkansas (Blytheville, El Dorado, Hot Springs, Jonesboro, Rogers, and Russellville) reported the following information about x and y:

x	24.2	19.0	18.2	14.9	19.0	17.5
y	13.0	4.4	9.3	1.3	0.8	3.6

Complete parts a through c for these data, and comment on the meaning of r and r^2 in the context of this problem.

6. Let x = per capita income in thousands of dollars. Let y = death rate per 1000 residents. Six small cities in Oregon (Albany, Bend, Corvallis, Grants Pass, Klamath Falls, and Roseburg) gave the following information about x and y values (see reference in Problem 5):

x	8.6	9.3	10.1	8.0	8.3	8.7
y	8.4	7.6	5.4	10.6	8.3	9.3

Complete parts a through c for these data, and comment on the meaning of r and r^2 in the context of this problem.

7. Let x = per capita income in thousands of dollars. Let y = number of medical doctors per 10,000 residents. Six small cities in Oregon (see reference and list of cities in Problem 6) gave the following information about x and y values:

x	8.6	9.3	10.1	8.0	8.3	8.7
y	9.6	18.5	20.9	10.2	11.4	13.1

Complete parts a through c for these data, and comment on the meaning of r and r^2 in the context of this problem.

8. Let x = percentage of 16- to 19-year-olds not in school and not high school graduates. Let y = death rate per 1000 residents. Five small cities in California (El Centro, Eureka, Hanford, Madera, and San Luis Obispo–Atascadero) gave the following information about x and y values (see reference in Problem 5):

x	16.2	9.9	19.5	19.7	9.8
y	7.7	8.8	7.0	8.1	8.4

Complete parts a through c for these data, and comment on the meaning of r and r^2 in the context of this problem.

9. Data for this problem are based on information taken from the *Wall Street Journal* (October 29, 1993). Let x = age in years of a licensed automobile driver. Let y = percentage of all fatal accidents (for a given age) due to speeding. For example, the first data pair indicates that 36% of all fatal accidents of 17-year-olds is due to speeding.

x	17	27	37	47	57	67	77
y	36	25	20	12	10	7	5

Complete parts a through c for these data, and comment on the meaning of r and r^2 in the context of this problem.

10. Let x = age of a licensed driver in years. Let y = percentage of all fatal accidents (for a given age) due to failure to yield the right of way. For example, the first data pair says that 5% of all fatal accidents of 37-year-olds is due to failure to yield the right of way. The *Wall Street Journal* article referenced in Problem 9 reported the following data:

x	37	47	57	67	77	87
y	5	8	10	16	30	43

Complete parts a through c for these data, and comment on the meaning of r and r^2 in the context of this problem.

11. *Consumers Digest* (February 1994) gave the following information about x = list price and y = best price (both in thousands of dollars) for different models of the Ford Ranger. The "best price" is the lowest price representatives from *Consumers Digest* negotiated with Ford dealerships. Your price might be higher or lower depending on your ability to negotiate and the dealer's willingness to sell. We assume that you do not have a trade-in.

x	9.8	11.6	12.3	13.7	16.2	17.7	18.7
y	8.4	10.4	10.9	12.6	14.4	15.1	16.5

Complete parts a through c for these data, and comment on the meaning of r and r^2 in the context of this problem.

12. For the Dodge Dakota data for x = list price and y = best price in thousands of dollars are given below (see reference and comments in Problem 11):

x	9.6	10.7	12.3	14.5	15.7	17.5
y	9.2	10.0	11.2	13.7	14.2	15.8

Complete parts a through c for these data, and comment on the meaning of r and r^2 in the context of this problem.

13. The state criminology laboratory must sometimes estimate a person's height from partial skeleton remains. How strong a correlation is there between body height and bone size? A random sample of eight adult male x-rays gave the following information, where x = length of femur (thigh bone) and y = body height.

x (in.)	17.5	20	21	19	15.5	18.5	16	18
y (in.)	50	80	78	73	63	71	64	71

Complete parts a through c for these data, and comment on the meaning of r and r^2 in the context of this problem.

14. Seven children in the third grade were given a verbal test to study the relationship between the number of words used in a response and the silence interval before the response. A psychologist asked each child a number of questions, and then the total number of words used in answering and the time before the child began answering were recorded. The following data were obtained, where x = total silence time in seconds and y = total number of words in response.

x	25	16	19	27	38	42	31
y	60	55	50	64	73	70	65

Complete parts a through c for these data, and comment on the meaning of r and r^2 in the context of this problem.

15. The following data are taken from the *Statistical Abstract of the United States*. In this data, x = M1 (readily available cash) in tens of billions of dollars and y = passenger car sales (in millions of cars).

x	4.1	4.4	4.8	5.2	5.5	6.2	7.3	7.5
y	6.4	6.3	5.0	6.7	7.6	8.0	7.5	7.1

Complete parts a through c for these data, and comment on the meaning of r and r^2 in the context of this problem.

16. Examine the computation formula for r, the sample correlation coefficient [Equation (9) of this section].
    (a) In the formula for SS_{xy}, if we exchange the symbols x and y, do we get a different result or do we get the same (i.e., equivalent) result? Explain.
    (b) In the formula for r [see Equation (9) of this section], if we exchange the symbols x and y, do we get a different result or do we get the same (equivalent) result? Explain.
    (c) If we have a set of x and y data values and we exchange each corresponding x and y value to get a new data set, should the sample correlation coefficient be the same for both sets of data? Explain.
    (d) Compute the sample correlation coefficient r for each of the following data sets and show that they are the same.

x	1	3	4
y	2	1	6

x	2	1	6
y	1	3	4

What can you say about the least-squares equation for each data set? Are the equations algebraically equivalent? *Hint:* See Problem 16 of Section 10.2.

<table>
<tr><td>

Section 10.4

</td><td>

Testing the Correlation Coefficient

</td></tr>
</table>

The Population Correlation
Coefficient ρ

A basic assumption in the study of economics is that people will spend more if they earn more. Economists claim that there is a high positive linear correlation between x = amount earned and y = amount spent. How could you test this claim? One way would be to obtain all possible (x,y) pairs for all people in the United States with an income. If you did this impossible task, you would have the *population* of all possible (x,y) pairs. You could then compute the *population correlation coefficient*, which we call ρ (a lowercase Greek letter spelled *rho* and pronounced like "row"). If $\rho = 1$, then you have a perfect positive linear correlation. If $\rho = 0$, then you have no linear correlation.

Most people would not even attempt to take the entire population of all incomes and corresponding amounts spent. Usually, we take a random sample and compute the correlation coefficient of the sample. We call this the *sample correlation coefficient r.* If r is near 1, then we have evidence that ρ, the population coefficient, is near 1, or at least greater than 0.

Different random samples will give different values of r. We need a test to decide when a sample value of r is far enough from zero to indicate correlation in the population.

Testing ρ

For simplicity, we will *assume that both the x and y variables are normally distributed.* To test if the (x,y) values are correlated *in the population*, we will set up the null hypothesis that they are not correlated.

> H_0: x and y are not correlated, so $\rho = 0$.

The choice of the alternative hypothesis depends on the belief that the correlation is positive, negative, or simply not zero. (See Table 10–14.)

Table 10–14 Alternate Hypotheses

If You Think	Then Use	Type of Test
$\rho > 0$	H_0: $\rho = 0$ H_1: $\rho > 0$	Right-tailed test
$\rho < 0$	H_0: $\rho = 0$ H_1: $\rho < 0$	Left-tailed test
$\rho \neq 0$	H_0: $\rho = 0$ H_1: $\rho \neq 0$	Two-tailed test

When $\rho = 0$, the distribution of sample correlation coefficients (r values) will be symmetric about $r = 0$. Figure 10–22 shows the distribution for some values of n, where n is the number of data pairs used to compute r.

Figure 10–22 Distribution of r when $\rho = 0$ (No Correlation)

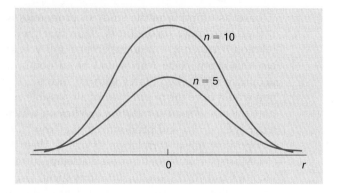

The type of test (left-tailed, right-tailed, or two-tailed) depends on the choice of H_1, as shown in Table 10–14.

To find the critical values for a test, we use Table 8 of Appendix II. The entries in Table 8 are critical values of r corresponding to given n, the number of data points, and α, the level of significance. Each critical value is listed without a sign. The choice of sign, $+$ or $-$, depends on the type of test used. A right-tailed test uses positive critical values, a left-tailed test uses negative critical values, and a two-tailed test uses both. Example 6 shows how to use Table 8 when we have a right-tailed test.

Example 6

In Section 10.2 we examined the relation between x = number of cricket chirps per second and y = temperature (°F). Using the data of Table 10–3, we can find the sample correlation coefficient to be $r = 0.84$. In this case, it seems that if the population data of x and y values are in fact correlated, then $\rho > 0$ (the least-squares line of Figure 10–7 slopes upward). Therefore, we will test

$$H_0: \ \rho = 0$$

$$H_1: \ \rho > 0$$

and so use a right-tailed test. Let us choose $\alpha = 0.01$ as our level of significance.

Solution: Table 10–3 has $n = 15$ data entries that are used to find our sample correlation coefficient r. Therefore, Table 8 in Appendix II gives 0.59 as the critical value to be used in a right-tailed test. (We use a positive critical value because we have a right-tailed test.) Figure 10–23 illustrates the critical region.

The region to the right of 0.59 is the critical, or rejection, region. Because $r = 0.84$ is in the critical region, we reject $H_0: \ \rho = 0$, which says there is no correlation, and conclude that the alternate hypothesis $\rho > 0$ is true. (We conclude that the correlation coefficient of the population is positive.)

Figure 10–23 Critical Region for $n = 15$

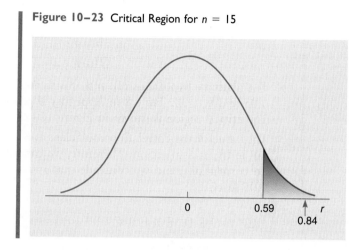

Whenever we reject H_0: $\rho = 0$, we say our r value is *significant*. If we cannot reject H_0, we say our sample r value is *not significant*.

Example 7

For her sociology class, Zelma interviewed a random sample of $n = 30$ married couples. For each couple, Zelma found x = number of years of formal education for the man and y = number of years of formal education for the woman. Assume that both x and y are normally distributed. After collecting the data, Zelma worked out the correlation coefficient to be $r = 0.28$. Determine whether r is significant at the 5% level of significance.
Solution:

(a) Our null hypothesis is H_0: $\rho = 0$. Since Zelma had no reason to believe that ρ is either positive or negative, the alternate hypothesis is H_1: $\rho \neq 0$.

Figure 10–24 Critical Region for $n = 30$

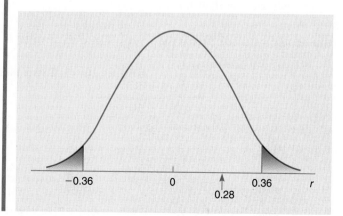

Therefore, we are testing

$$H_0: \rho = 0$$

$$H_1: \rho \neq 0$$

(b) The alternate hypothesis H_1: $\rho \neq 0$ indicates a two-tailed test. Since $\alpha = 0.05$ and $n = 30$, Table 8 in Appendix II gives the critical value of 0.36. The critical region is shown in Figure 10–24 on page 707.

(c) The value of the correlation coefficient is $r = 0.28$. This value does not fall in the critical region. Therefore, we cannot reject H_0: $\rho = 0$ (there is no correlation), and we conclude that $r = 0.28$ is *not significant* at the 0.05 level.

GUIDED EXERCISE 8

Big Rock Life Insurance Company has reason to believe that among white-collar workers, people who earn more money tend to die younger. The Big Rock Company took a random sample of $n = 30$ white-collar workers who died in the past year. For each person x = income in dollars per year and y = age of that person at death. The correlation coefficient was found to be $r = -0.33$. Determine whether r is significant at the 0.05 level of significance.

(a) What is the null hypothesis?

$$H_0: \rho > 0 \qquad H_0: \rho = 0$$

$$H_0: \rho < 0 \qquad H_0: \rho \neq 0$$

(a) H_0: $\rho = 0$; that is, there is no correlation.

(b) Which alternate hypothesis reflects the statement that people who earn more tend to die younger?

$$H_1: \rho = 0 \qquad H_1: \rho > 0 \qquad H_1: \rho < 0$$

(b) The statement indicates a negative correlation between salary and age at death. So we want the alternate hypothesis to claim there is a negative correlation. The appropriate alternate hypothesis is H_1: $\rho < 0$.

(c) Using the alternate hypothesis selected in part b, what kind of test should we use: right-tailed, left-tailed, two-tailed?

(c) Use a left-tailed test.

(d) What critical value should be used? Sketch the critical region.

(d) The critical value is -0.31. See Figure 10–25.

Figure 10–25 Critical Region

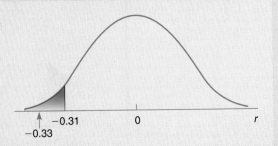

(e) Is $r = -0.33$ significant or not?

(e) Since $r = -0.33$ is in the critical region, we must reject H_0 and conclude that $r = -0.33$ is significant.

(f) What assumptions were made about the x distribution and the y distribution?

(f) We assumed that both x and y had normal distributions.

Even though a significance test indicates the existence of a correlation between x and y in the population, it does *not signify a cause-and-effect relationship*. For instance, a positive correlation between $x =$ cricket chirps per second and $y =$ temperature does *not* imply that crickets chirping more rapidly *causes* temperature to rise. Even after a significant correlation between variables has been established, the cause of the correlation must be identified. In addition, we also must decide if the correlation is high enough to be of practical value for the particular application in which it is to be used.

Problems that require calculating and testing the correlation coefficient must use a *random sample* of data points. This statement means that both x and y are statistical variables whose numerical values are obtained only after the random sample is drawn from the population of all possible data pairs. This procedure is somewhat different from our preceding regression (e.g., least-squares line) problems where the x values can be chosen in advance. In this case, the y values may depend heavily on the choice of x values. The least-squares methods can be applied to random sample data or to data in which the x values are specified in advance. But the interpretation of r as a measure of the linear correlation between x and y *requires* us to use a *random sample* of data points in which both x and y are statistical variables.

P Values

• *Comment:* P values for testing the correlation coefficient can be estimated from Table 8 in Appendix II. For instance, in Guided Exercise 8, the sample value of r is -0.33. The test is a left-tailed test with sample size $n = 30$. We look in the $n = 30$ row and find that the r values indicated for one-tailed (left-tailed) tests are -0.31 and -0.42. Since the sample statistic $r = -0.33$ falls between these values, the corresponding P value falls between the column headers $\alpha = 0.05$ and $\alpha = 0.01$.

$$0.01 < P \text{ value} < 0.05$$

Remember, we reject the null hypothesis when the P value is less than (or equal to) the level of significance α. Consequently, the sample r value is significant when $\alpha = 0.05$ but not significant when $\alpha = 0.01$.

Section 10.4 Problems

For each problem, please do the following:
  (a) State the null and alternate hypotheses.
  (b) Find the critical value or values.
  (c) Sketch the critical region.
  (d) Locate the sample correlation coefficient r on the sketch of part c.

(e) Decide whether you should reject or not reject the null hypothesis at the given level of significance.

(f) In nontechnical terms, summarize the results of the test. If the sample *r* value is *not significant,* what does this mean about the *x* and *y* variables in the context of this problem? If the sample *r* value *is significant,* what can you say about the *x* and *y* variables? In some cases do you think there might be other underlying variables that may help explain a *significant* correlation? Explain your answer.

In the following problems, assume that both *x* and *y* are approximately normally distributed.

1. *The New York Times* (January 5, 1994) did a study of the top 10 movies. Let *x* = number of weeks the movie has been showing in major theaters. Let *y* = total revenues in millions of dollars for that movie. The sample correlation coefficient computed from 10 data pairs printed in the *Times* was *r* = 0.384. Use a 5% level of significance to test the claim that there is a positive population correlation between *x* and *y* variables.

2. It is sometimes claimed that if stocks show a good performance in January, then they will show a good performance for the coming year. For major Standard and Poor's stock groups, *USA Today* (February 1, 1993) listed *x* = January percentage change and *y* = annual percentage change for that same major stock group. A random sample of 15 of these groups showed the sample correlation coefficient for the data pairs to be *r* = 0.646. Use a 5% level of significance to test the claim that there is a positive population correlation between the *x* and *y* variables.

3. *The Economist* (January 22–28, 1994) did a study of seven major free-enterprise countries as regards the variables *x* = percentage change in wages and *y* = percentage change in consumer prices. It was found that the sample correlation coefficient was *r* = 0.918. Use a 5% level of significance to test the claim that there is a positive population correlation between the *x* and *y* variables.

4. *Life in America's Small Cities* is a book by G. S. Thomas. In this book, 10 small cities in New York State were studied as regards the variables *x* = percentage of high school dropouts and *y* = death rate per 1000 residents. It was found that the sample correlation coefficient was *r* = 0.737. Use a 5% level of significance to test the claim that there is a positive population correlation between the *x* and *y* variables.

5. In the same reference as in Problem 4, the same 10 cities in New York State were studied as regards the variables *x* = percentage of population 25-years-old and older who have had 4 or more years of college and *y* = death rate per 1000 residents. It was found that the sample correlation coefficient was *r* = −0.766. Use a 5% level of significance to test the claim that there is a negative population correlation between the *x* and *y* variables.

6. Nor'easter storms have been known to cause much damage to New England coastal regions. *Weatherwise* is a magazine published in associ-

ation with the American Meteorological Society. In the January 1994 issue, a study was reported of the variables x = average peak height of ocean waves (feet) and y = average storm duration (hours). A study of five classifications of storms showed that the sample correlation coefficient for x and y data pairs was $r = 0.999$. Use a 1% level of significance to test the claim that there is a positive population correlation between the x and y variables.

7. *Yellowstone Vegetation* is a book by D. G. Despain, who is a research biologist at Yellowstone National Park. In this book, the following variables are studied: x = elevation in thousands of feet and y = April 1 water content of snowpack in inches. A sample of 12 east-side snow courses showed that the sample correlation coefficient between x and y values was $r = 0.945$. Use $\alpha = 0.01$ to test the claim that there is a positive population correlation between the x and y variables.

8. Let x = total available water in inches and y = root depth in inches. A sample of seven different soil types in Yellowstone National Park showed that the sample correlation coefficient between x and y values was $r = 0.412$ (see reference in Problem 7). Use a 1% level of significance to test the claim that the population correlation between the x and y variables is different from zero.

9. *Consumers Digest* (February 1994) gave 18 data pairs for the variables x = list price and y = best price (both in thousands of dollars) for different models of the GMC Sierra pickup truck. The sample correlation coefficient for these data pairs was found to be $r = 0.982$. Use a level of significance $\alpha = 0.01$ to test the claim that the population correlation coefficient for x and y values is positive.

10. The state medical school has developed a new drug for breaking up cholesterol deposits in blood vessels. A random sample of nine patients with severe cholesterol conditions volunteered to use the new drug. The dosage (x = mg/kg of body weight) and results (y = cholesterol index on a scale of 0 to 100) were determined for each patient. (Each patient started with a cholesterol index above 90.) The correlation coefficient for the x, y values was $r = -0.60$. Use a 1% level of significance to test the claims that there is a negative correlation between drug dosage and cholesterol index.

11. Mr. Tonguetwist owns the Ship Shape Shirt Shop, which makes tailored blouses and shirts. The supervisor of the shop is afraid that the percentage of defective items passing her assembly line during a 20-minute period increases during later hours of the day. Therefore, the supervisor will not give the employees overtime work. However, the employees claim that the more they work the better they get at it, and they want to work overtime.

    To settle the dispute, Mr. Tonguetwist randomly selected sixteen 20-minute periods throughout the day. For each of the 16 periods, the percentage (y) of defective items was determined as well as the number of hours (x) the employees were on the job at the start of the time period. The correlation coefficient between x and y values was $r = 0.48$.

Mr. Tonguetwist says he will take the supervisor's advice if a test indicates $\rho > 0$ at the 1% level of significance. Otherwise, he will let the employees work overtime. What should Mr. Tonguetwist do?

12. A marine biologist is studying the echo effect of whales "talking" to each other. It seems that a whale will send a message on one frequency, and another whale will respond by use of an echo message on another frequency. Let x be the frequency of the first whale and y be the frequency of the second whale. A random sample of 23 pairs of whales were studied, and for this sample the correlation coefficient was found to be $r = 0.71$. Using a 1% level of significance, test the claim that there is a positive correlation between communication frequencies used by whales.

Section 10.5   Multiple Regression

Advantage of Multiple Regression

There are many examples in statistics where one variable can be predicted very accurately in terms of another *single* variable. However, predictions usually improve if we consider additional relevant information. For example, the sugar content y of golden delicious apples taken from an apple orchard in Colorado could be predicted from $x_1 =$ number of days in growing season. If we also included information regarding $x_2 =$ soil quality rating and $x_3 =$ amount of available water, then we would expect our prediction of $y =$ sugar content to be more accurate.

Likewise, the annual net income y of a new franchise auto parts store could be predicted using only $x_1 =$ population size of sales district. However, we would probably get a better prediction of y values if we included the explanatory variables $x_2 =$ size of store inventory, $x_3 =$ dollar amount spent on advertising in local newspapers, and $x_4 =$ number of competing stores in the sales district.

For most statistical applications, we gain a definite advantage in the reliability of our predictions if we include more *relevant* data and corresponding (relevant) random variables in the computation of our predictions. In this section we will give you an idea of how this can be done by methods of multiple regression. You should be aware that an in-depth study of multiple regression requires the use of advanced mathematics. However, if you are willing to let the computer be a "friend who gives you useful information," then you will learn a great deal about multiple regression in this section. We will let the computer do most of the calculating work while we interpret the results.

Basic Terminology and Notation

In statistics, the most commonly used mathematical formulas for expressing linear relationships among more than two variables are *equations* of the form

$$y = b_0 + b_1x_1 + b_2x_2 + \cdots + b_kx_k \qquad (10)$$

Here y is the variable that we want to predict or to forecast. We will employ the usual terminology and call y the *response variable*. The k variables x_1, x_2, ..., x_k are specified variables on which the predictions are going to be based. Once again, we will employ the popular terminology and call x_1, x_2, ..., x_k the *explanatory variables*. This terminology is easy to remember if you just think of the explanatory variables x_1, x_2, ..., x_k as "explaining" the response y.

In Equation (10), b_0, b_1, b_2, ..., b_k are numerical constants (called *coefficients*) that must be mathematically determined from given data. The numerical values of these coefficients are obtained from the *least-squares criterion*, which we will discuss after the following exercise.

GUIDED EXERCISE 9

An industrial psychologist in a hospital supply company is studying the following variables for a random sample of company employees:

x_1 = number of years an employee has been with the company

x_2 = job training level (0 = lowest level and 5 = highest level)

x_3 = interpersonal skills (0 = lowest level and 10 = highest level)

y = job performance rating as given by supervisor (1 = lowest rating, 20 = highest rating)

The psychologist wants to predict y using x_1, x_2, and x_3 together in a least-squares equation.

(a) Identify the response variable and the explanatory variables.

(a) The response variable is what we want to predict. This is y, job performance. The explanatory variables are years of experience x_1, training level x_2, and interpersonal skills x_3. In a sense these variables "explain" the response variable.

(b) After collecting data, the psychologist used a computer with appropriate software to obtain the least-squares linear equation

$$y = 1 + 0.2x_1 + 2.3x_2 + 0.7x_3$$

Identify the constant term and each of the coefficients with its corresponding variable.

(b) The constant term is 1.

Explanatory Variable	Coefficient
x_1	0.2
x_2	2.3
x_3	0.7

(d) If Healthy Crunch receives 15 lbs of mail, how many employees should be assigned mail duty?

(e) Find the standard error of estimate S_e.

(f) Find a 95% confidence interval for the number of employees required to process mail for 15 lbs of mail.

(g) Find r. Find the coefficient of determination.

(h) Test the claim that the population correlation coefficient is positive (use a 1% level of significance).

6. Solve the Chapter Focus Problem found on page 655.

DATA HIGHLIGHTS

A random sample of eight quarterbacks listed in *The Sports Encyclopedia: Pro Football*, 11th Edition, gave the following information. Let x = height of a quarterback in inches, and let y = weight of a quarterback in pounds.

x	75	78	74	73	72	75	76	73
y	205	230	210	210	195	215	203	196

(a) Draw a scatter diagram for the data.

(b) Find the equation of the least-squares line.

(c) Graph the least-squares line on your scatter diagram.

(d) Find the standard error of estimate.

(e) If a quarterback is $x = 76$ inches tall, what does the least-squares equation forecast for the weight of this quarterback?

(f) Find an 80% confidence interval for your forecast of part e.

(g) Compute the correlation coefficient r and the coefficient of determination r^2. What percentage of the variation in y can be explained by the corresponding variation in x using the least-squares model? What percentage of the variation is unexplained?

(h) Use a 5% level of significance to test the claim that there is a positive correlation between x and y values. State the null and alternate hypotheses. Sketch the critical region, and show the critical value and sample correlation coefficient. What is your conclusion?

LINKING CONCEPTS

Discuss each of the following topics in class or review the topics on your own. Then write a brief but complete essay in which you summarize the main points. Please include formulas and graphs as appropriate.

1. What do we mean when we say two variables have a strong positive (or negative) linear correlation? What would a scatter diagram for these variables look like? Is it possible that two variables could be strongly related somehow, but have a low *linear* correlation? Explain and draw a scatter diagram to demonstrate your point.

2. What do we mean by the least-squares criterion? Give a very general description of how the least-squares criterion is involved in the construction of the least-squares line. Why do we say the least-squares line is the "best-fitting" line for the data set?

3. In this chapter we discussed three measures for "goodness of fit" of the least-squares line to given data. These measures were standard error of estimate, correlation coefficient, and coefficient of determination. Discuss the ways these measurements are different and the ways they are similar to each other. Be sure to include a discussion of explained variation, unexplained variation, and total variation in your answer. Draw a sketch and include appropriate formulas.

4. Look at the formula for confidence bounds for least-squares predictions. Which of the following conditions do you think will result in a *shorter* confidence interval for a prediction.

   (a) larger or smaller values for the standard error of estimate
   (b) larger or smaller number of data pairs
   (c) a value of x near $\bar{x}$ or a value of x far away from $\bar{x}$.

   Why would a shorter confidence interval for a prediction be more desirable than a longer interval?

5. If you did not cover Section 10.5, Multiple Regression, then omit this problem.

   For many applications in statistics, more data leads to more accurate results. In multiple regression we have more variables (and data) than we have in most simple-regression problems. Why do you think this will usually lead to more accurate predictions? Will additional variables *always* lead to more accurate predictions? Explain your answer. Discuss the coefficient of multiple determination and its meaning in the context of multiple regression. How do we know if an explanatory variable has a statistically significant influence on the response variable? What do we mean by a regression model?

6. Go to the library and find a magazine or journal article in your field of major interest where the content of this chapter could be applied. List the variables used, method of data collection, and the general type of information and conclusions drawn.

Using Technology

The problems in this section may be done using statistical computer software or calculators with statistical functions. Displays and suggestions are given for Minitab (Release 9), the TI-82 graphing calculator, and ComputerStat.

Simple Linear Regression (One Explanatory Variable)

Minitab

In Minitab, the regression command REGRESS can be used for both simple and multiple regression. The output gives the regression equation, the value of the standard error of estimate S_e labeled s in the output, and the value of the coefficient of determination r^2. An analysis of variance table also is given. The subcommand FITS gives the y_p value predicted by the least-squares line for each x value in the original data pairs. The subcommand PREDICT produces the predicted value y_p for the specified x value as well as a 95% confidence interval for the prediction. This confidence interval is labeled P.I. in the output. In addition, the PLOT command and the LINE subcommand will produce a scatter plot and graph the least-squares line. The following commands will perform all these tasks:

```
MTB > SET C1  #put values of the explanatory variable in column C1
MTB > SET C2  #put corresponding values of the response variable in column C2
MTB > NAME C4 'FITS'
MTB > REGRESS C2 on 1 C1;
SUBC> FITS C4;
SUBC> PREDICT E.  #where E is the x value for which you want a predicted yₚ value and a 95%
                  prediction interval
MTB > PLOT C2*C1;
SUBC> LINE C1 C4.
```

TI-82

Enter the values of the explanatory variable x in list L1 and the corresponding values of the response variable in list L2. Press the STAT key, select CALC, and select item 5: LinReg (ax+b). The coefficients for the regression line will appear as well as the value of the correlation coefficient r.

To draw a scatter plot, press STAT PLOT and select 1:Plot1. Turn the plot On, use Type showing a scatter plot, select L1 for Xlist and L2 for Ylist, and pick the little square for the Mark. Then press WINDOW and set the range of x and y values to accommodate your data. Finally, press GRAPH.

To draw the least-squares line on your scatter plot, press Y=. Then press VARS, select item 5:Statistics. In the menu appearing on the screen, select EQ and then select item 7:RegEQ. This sequence of choices will automatically set Y1= your regression equation. Press GRAPH.

To use the least-squares line to give a prediction for a specified x value, press the CALC key and select item 1:Value. A prompt Eval X = will appear at the bottom of the graph. Enter the desired x value, and the corresponding y value will be computed and displayed.

To find a confidence interval for the predicted y value, use the formulas in Section 10.2

ComputerStat

In ComputerStat, select the program Linear Regression and Correlation, and follow the instructions on the screen.

Applications

The data in this section are taken from this reference:

King, Cuchlaine A. M. *Physical Geography*. Oxford: Basil Blackwell, 1980, 77–86, 196–206. Reprinted with permission of Basil Blackwell Limited, Oxford, England.

Throughout the world, natural ocean beaches are beautiful sights to see. If you have visited natural beaches, you may have noticed that when the gradient or dropoff is steep, the grains of sand tend to be larger. In fact, a manmade beach with the "wrong" size granules of sand tends to be washed away and eventually replaced when the proper size grain is selected by the action of the ocean and the gradient of the bottom. Since manmade beaches are expensive, grain size is an important consideration.

In the data below, x = median diameter (in millimeters) of granules of sand and y = gradient of beach slope in degrees on natural ocean beaches.

In the ComputerStat menu of topics, select Linear Regression and Correlation.

1. We have nine data pairs (x, y). Enter the data shown at the bottom of this page as directed by the computer.

2. Scan the information summary. What is the value of $\bar{x}$? of $\bar{y}$? What are the values of the slope and intercept of the least-squares line?

What is the value of the standard error of estimate? What is the value of the sample correlation coefficient?

3. Select the graphing option. First, graph the data points. Just looking at the scatter diagram, would you expect moderately high correlation and a good fit for the least-squares line? Press return and graph the least-squares line.

4. Next, select the option to test the correlation coefficient. Use a 1% level of significance to test the claim that the population correlation coefficient is positive. The computer program utilizes the P value to conduct the test. For a discussion of P values see Section 9.3, The P Value in Hypothesis Testing. What is the smallest level of significance that will result in our accepting the claim that the population correlation coefficient is positive?

5. Suppose that you have a truckload of sifted sand in which the median size of the granules is 0.38 mm. If you want to put this sand on a beach and you don't want the sand to wash away, then what does the least-squares line predict for the angle of the beach? *Note:* Heavy storms that produce abnormal waves may also wash out the sand. However, in the long run, the size of sand granules that remain on the

x	0.17	0.19	0.22	0.235	0.235	0.30	0.35	0.42	0.85
y	0.63	0.70	0.82	0.88	1.15	1.50	4.40	7.30	11.30

beach or that are brought back to the beach by long-term wave action are determined to a large extent by the angle at which the beach drops off.

To solve the problem, select the option to predict y values from x values. Enter 0.38 for your x value. Next, find a 90% confidence interval for your predicted y value. What range of angles should the beach have if we want to be 90% confident that we are matching the size of our sand granules (0.38 mm) to the proper angle of the beach?

6. Repeat Problem 5 for confidence levels $c = $ 80%, 70%, 60%, 50%. What happens to the length of the confidence interval as the level of confidence decreases?

7. Suppose we now have a truckload of sifted sand where the median size of the granules is 0.45 mm. Repeat Problems 5 and 6 for this new load of sand. What range of angles should the beach have if we want to be 70% confident that we are matching the size of our sand granules (0.45 mm) to the proper angle of the beach.

Problems 8–15 utilize the data at the bottom of the page. Plate tectonics and the spread of the ocean floor are very important in modern studies of earthquakes and earth science in general. The following data give x = age of volcanic islands in the Atlantic and Indian Oceans and y = distance of the island from the center of the mid-oceanic ridge. As you can see, the oldest islands are the farthest from the ridge crest. This fact is explained by the spreading of the ocean floor on which the islands stand. (The following data are adapted by permission of W. H. Freeman and Company.)

As in Problems 1–7, we will use the program Linear Regression and Correlation to solve the following problems.

8. We have 19 data pairs (x, y) (see below). Enter the data as directed by the computer.

9. Scan the information summary. What is the value of $\bar{x}$? of $\bar{y}$? What are the values of the slope and intercept of the least-squares line? What is the value of the standard error of estimate? What is the value of the sample correlation coefficient?

10. Select the graphing option. First graph the scatter diagram. Do you think we will have a good fit for the least-squares line? Press return and graph the least-squares line.

11. Select the option to test the correlation coefficient. Use an 8% level of significance to test the claim that the population correlation coefficient is positive. Again, the computer uses the P value to conclude the test. For an explanation of P values used in hypothesis testing, see Section 9.3. What is the smallest level of significance that will result in our accepting the claim that the population correlation coefficient is positive?

12. Select the option to predict y values from x values. If an island is 70 million years old, how far does the least-squares line predict it will be from the mid-oceanic ridge crest? Find a 95% confidence interval for this predicted distance.

13. Repeat Problem 12 for the confidence levels $c = $ 75%, 60%, 30%. What happens to the length of the confidence interval as the level of confidence decreases?

14. Repeat Problems 12 and 13 for an island that is estimated to be 100 million years old.

15. Consider the number b, which is the slope of the least-squares line. How can this number be used to estimate the rate at which the ocean floor is moving? In one year how many centimeters will the ocean floor be expected to move? (*Hint:* Express the units of b in centimeters per year.)

x (age $\times 10^6$ years)	120	120	120	83	60	50	50	50	35	35	30	20	20	20	17	10	2	1	0
y (distance $\times 10^3$ km)	3.0	2.2	2.0	1.6	1.55	1.45	0.6	0.2	2.2	1.6	1.8	1.2	0.7	0.3	0.0	0.0	0.0	0.2	0.0

Multiple Regression Case Study

Minitab

In Minitab, the command

```
REGRESS C on K pred. C . . . C
```

does multiple regression where the first C is the column containing the response variable, K is the number of explanatory variables, and the explanatory variables are in the columns C . . . C.

Applications

Data values in the following study are taken from *Statistical Abstract of the United States,* U.S. Department of Commerce, 103rd edition, 1982, and 109th edition, 1989 (see Table 10–16).

We will use the following notation:

x_1 = price of a barrel of crude oil in dollars per barrel

x_2 = percent interest on 10-year U.S. Treasury notes

x_3 = total foreign investments in U.S. in billions of dollars

x_4 = Dow Jones Industrial Average (DJIA)

x_5 = Gross National Product, GNP, in billions of dollars

x_6 = purchasing power of U.S. dollar with base 1983 corresponding to $1.000

x_7 = consumer credit (i.e., consumer debt) in billions of dollars

All data values represent annual averages as determined by the U.S. Department of Commerce.

1. Under the menu topic Multiple Regression (in ComputerStat) there are two programs that may be used for this case study. The program MRD asks you to enter the data yourself. The program MRF asks you to give the name of the file in which the data for this problem have been stored. In most cases, having the computer read the data file is simpler. For this problem, the file

Table 10–16 Economic Data 1976 to 1987

Year	x_1	x_2	x_3	x_4	x_5	x_6	x_7
1976	10.9	7.61	31	974.9	1,718	1.757	234.4
1977	12.0	7.42	35	894.6	1,918	1.649	263.8
1978	12.5	8.41	42	820.2	2,164	1.532	308.3
1979	17.7	9.44	54	844.4	2,418	1.380	347.5
1980	28.1	11.46	83	891.4	2,732	1.215	349.4
1981	35.6	13.91	109	932.9	3,053	1.098	366.6
1982	31.8	13.00	125	884.4	3,166	1.035	381.1
1983	29.0	11.11	137	1,190.3	3,406	1.000	430.4
1984	28.6	12.44	165	1,178.5	3,772	0.961	511.8
1985	26.8	10.62	185	1,328.2	4,015	0.928	592.4
1986	14.6	7.68	209	1,792.8	4,240	0.913	646.1
1987	17.9	8.38	244	2,276.0	4,527	0.880	685.5

name to be used is ECON. Use either program and continue on to number 2.

2. Examine Display 1. List the variables in order of increasing coefficient of variation. In your own words explain the meaning of the statement: x_2 has a 22.5% coefficient of variation, whereas x_3 has a 60.8% coefficient of variation. Although x_2 and x_3 have different units, is it possible to make a direct comparison of the coefficients of variation and conclude that x_3 has a much larger data spread than x_2? Explain your answer.

3. Examine Display 2.

   (a) Which variable (other than x_1) seems to have the strongest relationship with the price of oil?

   (b) In increasing order of influence, list the top four variables (not x_3) that seem to have the strongest relationship with total foreign investments.

   (c) In increasing order of influence, list the top three variables (not x_4) that seem to have the strongest relationship with the Dow Jones Industrial Average.

   (d) In increasing order list the top four variables (not x_7) that have the strongest relationship with consumer credit.

4. In part 3 we used the coefficient of determination to measure the strength of the relationship one variable has with another variable. It is important to realize that a high coefficient of determination does *not* imply variables have a cause and effect relationship. That is, we do not claim one variable causes another to change. Examine your answers to part 3 and explain how the variables used may have a high coefficient of determination but still not *cause* a change in other variables.

5. Use the computer to construct a regression model with

   response variable: x_1 (oil)

   explanatory variables:
   x_2 (interest rate) and x_6 (U.S. dollar)

When the computer asks how many explanatory variables we will use, tell it N1 = 2. Then declare x_2 and x_6 as explanatory variables by entering the numbers 2 and 6 as requested. Finally declare x_1 as the response variable by entering the number 1 when requested. Examine Display #3.

What is the coefficient of multiple determination?

   (a) Use level of significance 5% and test each coefficient for significance (two-tailed test).

   (b) Examine the coefficients of the regression equation; then explain why you think the following statement is true or false. If the interest rate on U.S. Treasury notes did not change and the purchasing power of the U.S. dollar increased, we would expect the price of oil to decrease.

   (c) Suppose $x_2 = 9.75$ and $x_6 = 1.420$. Use the option to forecast x_1 values to predict the price of oil. Find an 80% confidence interval for your prediction.

6. Use the option to construct a new regression model. Use

   response variable: x_3 (foreign investments)

   explanatory variables: x_5 (GNP), x_6 (U.S. dollar), and x_7 (consumer credit)

When the computer asks how many explanatory variables we will use, tell it N1 = 3. Then declare x_5, x_6, and x_7 as explanatory variables by entering the numbers 5, 6, and 7 as requested. Finally, declare x_3 as the response variable by entering the number 3 when requested. Examine Display #3.

What is the coefficient of multiple determination?

   (a) Use level of significance 1% and test each coefficient for significance (two-tailed test).

   (b) Examine the coefficients of the regression equation. Then explain why you think the following statement is true or false. If the purchasing power of the U.S. dollar did not change, and the GNP did not change, then an increase in consumer credit would likely be accompanied by a reduction in foreign investments.

(c) Suppose $x_3 = 3500$, $x_6 = 0.975$, and $x_7 = 450$. Use the option to forecast x_3 values to predict the level of foreign investment. Find a 90% confidence interval for your prediction.

7. Use the option to construct a new regression model. Use

response variable: x_4 (DJIA)

explanatory variables: x_3 (foreign investments), x_5 (GNP), and x_7 (consumer credit)

When the computer asks how many explanatory variables we will use, tell it N1 = 3. Then declare x_3, x_5, and x_7 as explanatory variables by entering the numbers 3, 5, and 7 as requested. Finally, declare x_4 as the response variable by entering the number 4 when requested. Examine Display #3.

What is the coefficient of multiple determination?

(a) Use level of significance 5% and test each coefficient for significance (two-tailed test).
(b) Examine the coefficients of the regression equation; then explain why you think the following statement is true or false. If the GNP and consumer credit didn't change but foreign investments increased, the DJIA should show a strong increase.
(c) Suppose $x_3 = 210$, $x_5 = 4260$, and $x_7 = 650$. Use the option to forecast x_4 values to

predict the DJIA and find an 85% confidence interval for your prediction.

8. Use the option to construct a new regression model. Use

response variable: x_7 (consumer credit)

explanatory variables: x_3 (foreign investments), x_5 (GNP), and x_6 (U.S. dollar)

When the computer asks how many explanatory variables we will use, tell it N1 = 3. Then declare x_3, x_5, and x_6 as explanatory variables by entering the numbers 3, 5, and 6 as requested. Finally, declare x_7 as the response variable by entering the number 7 when requested. Examine Display #3.

What is the coefficient of multiple determination?

(a) Use level of significance 1% and test each coefficient for significance (two-tailed test).
(b) Examine the coefficients of the regression equation; then explain why you think each of the following statements is true or false. If both GNP and purchasing power of the U.S. dollar didn't change, then an increase in foreign investments would likely be accompanied by a reduction in consumer credit. If both foreign investments and purchasing power of the U.S. dollar remained fixed, then an increase in GNP would likely be accompanied by an increase in consumer credit.
(c) Suppose $x_3 = 88$, $x_5 = 2750$, and $x_6 = 1.250$. Use the option to forecast x_7 values to predict consumer credit, and find an 80% confidence interval for your prediction.

Computer Displays

Computer software support is very convenient for linear regression problems of every kind.

ComputerStat Display:
Linear Regression Summary for Data of Example 2
(Table 10–7)

```
                ****** INFORMATION SUMMARY ******
NUMBER OF DATA PAIRS = 7
SAMPLE MEAN OF X VALUES = 40
SAMPLE STANDARD DEVIATION OF X VALUES = 21.60247
SMALLEST X VALUE = 10 LARGEST X VALUE = 70
SAMPLE MEAN OF Y VALUES = 30.42857
SAMPLE STANDARD DEVIATION OF Y VALUES = 11.16329
EQUATION OF LEAST SQUARES LINE Y = .5071429 X + 10.14286
STANDARD ERROR OF ESTIMATE = 2.348251
SAMPLE CORRELATION COEFFICIENT = .9813896
COEFFICIENT OF DETERMINATION = .9631256
= = = = = = TO LIST PROGRAM OPTIONS PRESS ANY KEY = = = = = =
```

Minitab Display:
Linear Regression for Cricket Chirps/Sec with Temperature
(Table 10–3 of text)

```
MTB> SET C1
DATA> 20.0 16.0 19.8 18.4 17.1 15.5 14.7 17.1
DATA> 15.4 16.2 15.0 17.2 16.0 17.0 14.4
DATA> END
MTB> SET C2
DATA> 88.6 71.6 93.3 84.3 80.6 75.2 69.7 82.0
DATA> 69.4 83.3 79.6 82.6 80.6 83.5 76.3
DATA> END
MTB> NAME C1 = 'CHIRPS' C2 = 'TEMP'

MTB > REGRESS C2 ON 1 C1;
SUBC> FITS C4;
SUBC> PREDICT 16.
```

```
The regression equation is
TEMP = 25.2 + 3.29 CHIRPS

Predictor        Coef        Stdev      t-ratio          p
Constant        25.23        10.06         2.51      0.026
CHIRPS         3.2911       0.6012         5.47      0.000

s = 3.829       R-sq = 69.7%     R-sq(adj) = 67.4%

Analysis of Variance

SOURCE          DF           SS           MS          F          p
Regression       1       439.29       439.29      29.97      0.000
Error           13       190.55        14.66
Total           14       629.84

    Fit   Stdev.Fit         95% C.I.                  95% P.I.
 77.890       1.064   ( 75.591,  80.188)      ( 69.303,  86.476)

MTB > PLOT C2 * C1;
SUBC> LINE C1 C4.
```

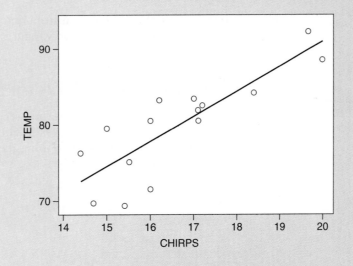

Section 11.1

Chi Square: Tests of Independence

The chi-square probability distribution has many important real-world applications. One of these applications is for testing independence (or dependence) of random variables. In this section we will see how this is done using contingency tables.

Section 11.2

Chi Square: Goodness of Fit

Another application of the chi-square probability distribution is to test for goodness of fit of a given distribution to a distribution of raw data values. This section shows how such a statistical test is constructed.

Section 11.3

Testing and Estimating Variances and Standard Deviations

In this section we use the chi-square distribution to construct statistical tests and confidence intervals for population variances σ^2 and population standard deviations σ.

Section 11.4

ANOVA: Comparing Several Sample Means

How can we test several means using several sets of sample data at once? How is such a test constructed for a given level of significance α? These are questions we will answer in this section using the Fisher F distribution and analysis of variance (ANOVA).

H. G. Wells
(1866–1946)

This English writer and social thinker was the author of the science-fiction novel *The War of the Worlds* (1898).

Chi-Square and *F* Distributions

Statistical thinking will one day be as necessary for efficient citizenship as the ability to read and write.

H. G. Wells

H. G. Wells was an outstanding author of science fiction. At the time his stories were published, they seemed to be completely fictional. Landings on the moon, and interplanetary travel were strictly for the imagination. However, humans have walked on the moon, and space exploration is now in progress. There is no doubt that life in the future will be much more technical than it is today. Effective citizenship means that we must use technology to improve *everyone's* life. Anyone who claims citizenship in modern society will be required to make important decisions based on technical information. These authors feel that effective citizenship requires statistical thinking as much as the ability to read and write.

Focus Problem ▶ Stone Age Tools and Archaeology

Archaeologists at Washington State University did an extensive summer 1990 excavation at Burnt Mesa Pueblo in Bandelier National Monument. Their work is published in the book, *Bandelier Archaeological Excavation Project: Summer 1990 Excavations at Burnt Mesa Pueblo and Casa del Rito*, edited by T. A. Kohler.

One question the archaeologists asked was: Is raw material used by prehistoric Indians for stone tool manufacture independent of the archaeological excavation site? Two different excavation sites at Burnt Mesa Pueblo gave the following contingency table:

Stone Tool Construction Material, Burnt Mesa Pueblo

Material	Site A	Site B	Row Total
Basalt	3,657	1,238	4,895
Obsidian	497	68	565
Pedernal Chert	3,606	232	3,838
Other	357	36	393
Column total	8,117	1,574	9,691

Use a chi-square test with 1% level of significance to test the claim that raw material used for construction of stone tools and excavation site are independent.

(a) State the null and alternate hypotheses.

(b) Find the value of the chi-square statistic.

(c) Find the degrees of freedom and the appropriate critical chi-square value.

(d) Sketch the critical region and locate the sample chi-square and critical chi-square values on the sketch.

(e) Decide whether you should reject or not reject the null hypothesis. State your conclusion in the context of the problem.

Section 11.1

Chi Square: Tests of Independence

Innovative Machines Incorporated has developed two new letter arrangements for typewriter keyboards. They wish to see if there is any relationship between the arrangement of letters on the keyboard and the number of hours it takes a new typing student to learn to type at 20 words per minute. Or, from another point of view, is the time it takes a student to learn to type *independent* of the arrangement of the letters on a typewriter keyboard?

To answer questions of this type, we test the hypotheses

H_0: Keyboard arrangement and learning times *are independent.*

H_1: Keyboard arrangement and learning times *are not independent.*

Chi-square Distribution

In problems of this sort we are testing the *independence* of two factors rather than means or proportions. The probability distribution we use to make the decision is the *chi-square distribution* (*chi* is pronounced like the first two letters of the word *kite*). Chi is a Greek letter denoted by the symbol χ, so chi square is denoted by χ^2.

Because the distribution is of chi-*square* values, the χ^2 values begin at 0 and then are all positive. The graph of the χ^2 distribution is not symmetrical, and like the student's t distribution, it depends on the number of degrees of freedom. Figure 11–1 shows the χ^2 distribution for several degrees of freedom (*d.f.*).

As the degrees of freedom increase, the graph of the chi-square distribution becomes more bell-like and begins to look more and more like the normal

Figure 11–1 The χ^2 Distribution

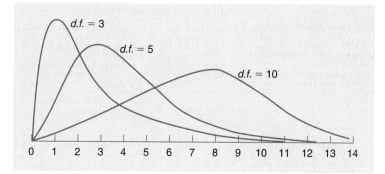

distribution. Notice that the mode, or high point, of the graph with n degrees of freedom occurs over $n - 2$ (for $n \geqslant 3$).

When we use the chi-square distribution to test independence, we always use a *right-tailed test*. Critical values χ_α^2 for a level of significance α, can be found in Table 9 of Appendix II. The critical value depends not only on the level of significance α but also on the degrees of freedom *d.f.*

Now let's return to the problem of typewriter keyboard arrangement and the number of hours it takes a student to learn to type at 20 words per minute (wpm). To test the independence of these two variables we must compute a statistic χ^2 for the sample of typing students used by Innovative Machines Incorporated.

Contingency Table

Innovative Machines took a random sample of 300 beginning typing students and randomly assigned them to learn to type on one of three typewriter keyboards. The learning times for this sample are shown in Table 11–1.

Table 11–1 Keyboard Versus Time to Learn to Type at 20 wpm

Keyboard	21–40 h	41–60 h	61–80 h	Row Total
A	#1 25	#2 30	#3 25	80
B	#4 30	#5 71	#6 19	120
Standard	#7 35	#8 49	#9 16	100
Column total	90	150	60	300 Sample size

Table 11–1 is called a *contingency table*. The *shaded boxes* that contain observed frequencies are called *cells*. The row and column totals are not considered to be cells. This contingency table is of size 3×3 (read, three-by-three), since there are three rows of cells and three columns. When giving the size of a contingency table we always list the number of *rows first*.

GUIDED EXERCISE 1

Give the size of the contingency tables in Figures 11–2 and 11–3. Also count the number of cells in each table. (Remember, each cell is a shaded box.)

(a) **Figure 11–2** Contingency Table

Row total

Column total

(a) There are two rows and four columns, so this is a 2 × 4 table. There are eight cells.

(b) **Figure 11–3** Contingency Table

Row total

Column total

(b) Here we have three rows and two columns, so this is a 3 × 2 table with six cells.

Expected Frequency

We are testing the null hypothesis that the keyboard arrangement and the time it takes a student to learn to type are *independent*. We use this hypothesis to determine the *expected frequency* of each cell.

For instance, to compute the expected frequency of cell 1 in Table 11–1, we observe that cell 1 consists of all the students in the sample who learned to type on keyboard A and who mastered the skill at the 20 word per minute level in 21 to 40 hours. By the assumption (null hypothesis) that the two events are independent, we use the multiplication law to obtain the probability that a student is in cell 1.

$$P(\text{cell 1}) = P(\text{keyboard A } and \text{ skill in 21–40 h})$$
$$= P(\text{keyboard A}) \cdot P(\text{skill in 21–40 h})$$

Since there are 300 students in the sample and 80 used keyboard A,

$$P \text{ (keyboard A)} = \frac{80}{300}$$

Also, 90 of the 300 students learned to type in 21–40 hours, so

$$P \text{ (skill in 21–40 h)} = \frac{90}{300}$$

Using these two probabilities and the assumption of independence,

$$P \text{ (keyboard A } and \text{ skill in 21–40 h)} = \frac{80}{300} \cdot \frac{90}{300}$$

Finally, since there are 300 students in the sample, we have the *expected frequency E* for cell 1.

$$\begin{aligned}
E &= P \text{ (student in cell 1)} \cdot \text{(no. of students in sample)} \\
&= \frac{80}{300} \cdot \frac{90}{300} \cdot 300 \\
&= \frac{80 \cdot 90}{300} \\
&= 24
\end{aligned}$$

We can repeat this process for each cell. However, the next-to-the-last step yields an easier formula for the expected frequency *E*.

Formula for expected frequency *E*

$$E = \frac{\text{(row total)(column total)}}{\text{sample size}}$$

Note: If the expected value is not a whole number, do *not* round it to the nearest whole number.

Let's use this formula in Example 1 to find the expected frequency for cell 2.

Example 1 | Find the expected frequency for cell 2 of contingency Table 11–1.
Solution: Cell 2 is in row 1 and column 2. The row total is 80, and the column total is 150. The size of the sample is still 300.

$$E = \frac{\text{(row total)(column total)}}{\text{sample size}} = \frac{(80)(150)}{300} = 40$$

GUIDED EXERCISE 2

Table 11–2 contains the *observed frequencies O* and *expected frequencies E* for the contingency table giving keyboard arrangement and number of hours it takes a student to learn to type at 20 words per minute. Fill in the missing expected frequencies.

Table 11–2 Complete Contingency Table of Keyboard Arrangement and Time to Learn to Type

Keyboard	21–40 h	41–60 h	61–80 h	Row Total	
A	#1 O = 25 E = 24	#2 O = 30 E = 40	#3 O = 25 E = ___	80	For cell 3 we have $E = \dfrac{(80)(60)}{300} = 16$
B	#4 O = 30 E = 36	#5 O = 71 E = ___	#6 O = 19 E = ___	120	For cell 5 we have $E = \dfrac{(120)(150)}{300} = 60$
Standard	#7 O = 35 E = ___	#8 O = 49 E = 50	#9 O = 16 E = 20	100	For cell 6 we have $E = \dfrac{(120)(60)}{300} = 24$
Column total	90	150	60	300 Sample size	For cell 7 we have $E = \dfrac{(100)(90)}{300} = 30$

Computing χ^2

Now we are in a position to compute the statistic χ^2 for the sample of typing students. The χ^2 value is a measure of the sum of differences between observed frequency O and expected frequency E in each cell. These differences are listed in Table 11–3 for the nine cells.

Table 11–3 Difference Between the Observed and Expected Frequencies

Cell	Observed O	Expected E	Difference (O − E)
1	25	24	1
2	30	40	−10
3	25	16	9
4	30	36	−6
5	71	60	11
6	19	24	−5
7	35	30	5
8	49	50	−1
9	16	20	−4
			$\Sigma(O - E) = 0$

As we see, if we sum the differences between the observed frequencies and the expected frequencies of the cells, we get the value zero. This total certainly does not reflect the fact that there were differences between the observed and expected frequencies. To obtain a measure whose sum does reflect the magnitude of the differences, we square the differences and work with the quantities $(O - E)^2$. But instead of using the terms $(O - E)^2$, we use the values $(O - E)^2/E$. The reason we use this expression is that a small difference between the observed and expected frequency is not nearly as important if the expected frequency is large as it is if the expected frequency is small. For instance, for both cells 1 and 8, the squared difference $(O - E)^2$ is 1. However, this difference is more meaningful in cell 1, where the expected frequency is 24, than it is in cell 8, where the expected frequency is 50. When we divide the quantity $(O - E)^2$ by E, we take the size of the difference with respect to the size of the expected value. We use the sum of these values to form the sample statistic χ^2:

$$\chi^2 = \Sigma \frac{(O - E)^2}{E}$$

where the sum is over all cells in the contingency table.

- *Comment:* If you look up the word *irony* in a dictionary, you will find one of its meanings is described as "the difference between actual (or observed) results and expected results." Since irony is so prevalent in much of our human experience, it is not surprising that statisticians have incorporated a related chi-square distribution into their work. As we will soon see, the chi-square distribution has many applications in social science, business administration, and natural science.

GUIDED EXERCISE 3

(a) Complete Table 11–4 from the data of Table 11–3.

(a) The last two rows of Table 11–4 are

Table 11–4

Cell	O	E	O − E	$(O - E)^2$	$(O - E)^2/E$
1	25	24	1	1	0.04
2	30	40	−10	100	2.50
3	25	16	9	81	5.06
4	30	36	−6	36	1.00
5	71	60	11	121	2.02
6	19	24	−5	25	1.04
7	35	30	5	25	0.83

Cell	O	E	O − E	$(O - E)^2$	$(O - E)^2/E$
8	49	50	−1	1	0.02
9	16	20	−4	16	0.80

$$\Sigma \frac{(O - E)^2}{E} = \text{total of last column} = 13.31$$

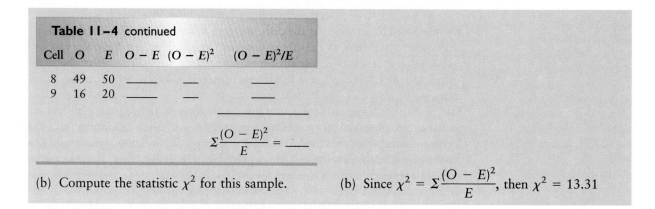

Table 11–4 continued

Cell	O	E	O − E	$(O - E)^2$	$(O - E)^2/E$
8	49	50	___	___	___
9	16	20	___	___	___

$$\Sigma \frac{(O - E)^2}{E} = \underline{\quad}$$

(b) Compute the statistic χ^2 for this sample.   (b) Since $\chi^2 = \Sigma \dfrac{(O - E)^2}{E}$, then $\chi^2 = 13.31$

Critical Value χ^2_α

Notice that when the observed frequency and the expected frequency are very close, the quantity $(O - E)^2$ is close to zero, and so the statistic χ^2 is near zero. As the difference increases, the statistic χ^2 also increases. To determine how large the statistic can be before we must reject the null hypothesis of independence, we find a critical value χ^2_α in Table 9 of Appendix II for the specified level of significance α and the number of degrees of freedom in the sample.

As we saw earlier, the chi-square distribution changes as the degrees of freedom change. To find a critical value χ^2_α we need to know the degrees of freedom in the sample as well as the level of significance designated. To test independence, the degrees of freedom *d.f.* of a sample are determined by the following formula:

Degrees of freedom for independence

Degrees of freedom = (number of rows − 1) · (number of columns − 1)

or $d.f. = (R - 1)(C - 1)$

where R = number of cell rows

                                     C = number of cell columns

GUIDED EXERCISE 4

Determine the number of degrees of freedom in the example of typewriter keyboard arrangements (see Table 11–1). Recall that the contingency table had three rows and three columns.

$d.f. = (R - 1)(C - 1)$
$= (3 - 1)(3 - 1) = (2)(2) = 4$

To test the hypothesis that the letter arrangement on a typewriter keyboard and the time it takes to learn to type at 20 words per minute are independent at the $\alpha = 0.05$ level of significance, we look up the critical value $\chi^2_{0.05}$ in Table 9 of Appendix II. For *d.f.* = 4 and $\alpha = 0.05$, we see $\chi^2_{0.05} = 9.49$. When we compare the sample statistic $\chi^2 = 13.31$ with the critical value $\chi^2_{0.05}$, we see that the sample statistic is larger. Since it is larger, we *reject* the null hypothesis of independence and conclude that keyboard arrangement and learning time are *not* independent. (See Figure 11–4.)

Summary

Let's summarize how we use the chi-square distribution to test the independence of two variables.

Step 1: Set up the hypotheses:

H_0: The variables *are* independent.
H_1: The variables *are not* independent.

Step 2: Compute the expected frequency for each cell in the contingency table by use of the formula

$$E = \text{expected frequency} = \frac{(\text{row total})(\text{column total})}{\text{sample size}}$$

Step 3: Compute the statistic χ^2 for the sample:

$$\chi^2 = \Sigma \frac{(O - E)^2}{E}$$

where O is the observed frequency, E is the expected frequency, and the sum Σ is over all cells.

Step 4: Find the critical value χ^2_α in Table 9 of Appendix II. Use the level of significance α and the number of degrees of freedom *d.f.* to find the critical value.

Figure 11–4 Comparison of Critical Value and Sample Statistic (*d.f.* = 4)

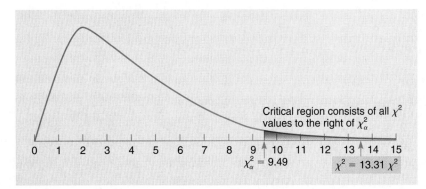

$$d.f. = (R - 1)(C - 1)$$

where R is the number of rows, and C is the number of columns of cells in the contingency table. The critical region consists of all values of χ^2 to the *right* of the critical value χ_α^2.

Step 5: Compare the sample statistic χ^2 of step 3 with the critical value χ_α^2 of step 4. If the sample statistic is *larger,* reject the null hypothesis of independence. Otherwise, do not reject the null hypothesis.

- *Note:* We compare the sample statistic χ^2 with the critical value χ_α^2. But the distribution of sample statistics is only approximately the same as the theoretical distribution whose critical values χ_α^2 are found in Table 9 of Appendix II. In order to safely use critical values χ_α^2, we must be sure that all the cells have an *expected frequency* larger than or equal to 5. If this condition is not met, the sample size should be increased.

GUIDED EXERCISE 5

Super Vending Machines Company is to install soda pop machines in elementary schools and high schools. The market analysts wish to know if flavor preference and school level are independent. A random sample of 200 students was taken. Their school level and soda pop preference are given in Table 11–5. Is independence indicated at the $\alpha = 0.01$ level of significance?

Step 1: State the null and alternate hypotheses.

Step 2: Complete the contingency Table 11–5 by filling in the required expected frequencies.

Table 11–5 School Level and Soda Pop Preference

Soda Pop	High School	Elementary School	Row Total
Kula Kola	O = 33 #1 E = 36	O = 57 #2 E = 54	90
Mountain Mist	O = 30 #3 E = 20	O = 20 #4 E = 30	50
Jungle Grape	O = 5 #5 E = ____	O = 35 #6 E = ____	40
Diet Pop	O = 12 #7 E = ____	O = 8 #8 E = ____	20
Column Total	80	120	200 Sample size

Step 1: H_0: School level and soda pop preference are independent.

H_1: School level and soda pop preference are not independent.

Step 2: The expected frequency

for cell 5 is $\dfrac{(40)(80)}{200} = 16$

for cell 6 is $\dfrac{(40)(120)}{200} = 24$

for cell 7 is $\dfrac{(20)(80)}{200} = 8$

for cell 8 is $\dfrac{(20)(120)}{200} = 12$

Note: In this example the expected frequencies are all whole numbers. If the expected frequency has a decimal part such as 8.45, do *not* round the value to the nearest whole number; rather, give the expected frequency as the decimal number.

Step 3: Fill in Table 11–6 and use the table to find the sample statistic χ^2.

Table 11–6 Computational Table for χ^2

Cell	O	E	O − E	$(O − E)^2$	$(O − E)^2/E$
1	33	36	−3	9	0.25
2	57	54	3	9	0.17
3	30	20	10	100	5.00
4	20	30	−10	100	3.33
5	5	16	−11	121	7.56
6	35	24	11	____	____
7	12	8	____	____	____
8	8	12	____	____	____

Step 4: What is the size of the contingency table? Use the number of rows and columns to determine the number of degrees of freedom. For $\alpha = 0.01$ use Table 9 of Appendix II to find the critical value $\chi^2_{0.01}$.

Step 5: Do we reject or fail to reject the null hypothesis that school level and soda pop flavor preference are independent?

Step 3: The last three rows of Table 11–6 read as follows:

Cell	O	E	O − E	$(O − E)^2$	$(O − E)^2/E$
6	35	24	11	121	5.04
7	12	8	4	16	2.00
8	8	12	−4	16	1.33

$$\chi^2 = \text{total of last column}$$
$$= \Sigma\frac{(O − E)^2}{E} = 24.68$$

Step 4: The contingency table is of size 4 × 2. Since there are four rows and two columns,

$$d.f. = (4 − 1)(2 − 1) = 3$$

For $\alpha = 0.01$ the critical value χ^2_α is 11.34.

Step 5: Since the statistic χ^2 is larger than the critical value χ^2_α we reject the null hypothesis of independence and conclude that school level and soda pop preference are dependent.

P Values

- *Comment: P* values for tests of independence can be estimated from Table 9 of Appendix II. For instance, to estimate the *P* value for the sample statistic $\chi^2 = 24.68$ found in Guided Exercise 5, we look in the row headed by the degrees of freedom for the contingency table, *d.f.* = 3. We see that the sample statistic $\chi^2 = 24.68$ falls to the right of the row entry 12.84. This means that the *P* value is smaller than the column header 0.005 corresponding to the entry 12.84. Therefore,

$$P \text{ value} < 0.005$$

Consequently, we reject H_0 for all $\alpha \geqslant 0.005$. In particular, we reject H_0 for $\alpha = 0.01$. This result is consistent with the conclusion stated in Guided Exercise 5.

Section 11.1 Problems

For each of the problems, do the following:
  (a) State the null and alternate hypotheses.
  (b) Find the value of the chi-square statistic from the sample.

(c) Find the degrees of freedom and the appropriate critical chi-square value.

(d) Sketch the critical region and locate your sample chi-square value and critical chi-square value on the sketch.

(e) Decide whether you should reject or fail to reject the null hypothesis.

Use the expected values, *E*, to the hundredths place.

1. The personnel department of Jupiter Scientific Labs is doing a study about job satisfaction. A random sample of 310 employees was given a test designed to diagnose the level of job satisfaction. Each employee's salary also was recorded. (See Table 11–7 below.) Use a chi-square test to determine if salary and job satisfaction are independent at the 0.05 level of significance.

Table 11–7 Salary Versus Job Satisfaction

Satisfaction	Under $25,000	$25,000–$35,000	Over $35,000	Row Total
High	20	20	10	50
Medium	100	65	35	200
Low	40	15	5	60
Column Total	160	100	50	310

2. The counseling unit of Woodrock College is interested in the relationship between anxiety level and the need to succeed. A random sample of 200 college freshmen was taken. The freshmen were given tests to measure their anxiety level and their need to succeed. The results are given in Table 11–8. Test the hypothesis that anxiety level and need to succeed are independent at the 0.01 level of significance.

Table 11–8 Anxiety Level Versus Need to Succeed

Need	High Anxiety	Medium Anxiety	Low Anxiety	Row Total
High	30	40	5	75
Medium	17	50	33	100
Low	3	10	12	25
Column Total	50	100	50	200

3. Mr. Acosta, a sociologist, is doing a study to see if there is a relationship between the age of a young adult (18 to 35 years old) and the type of movie preferred. A random sample of 93 adults revealed the data in Table 11–9. Test if age and type of movie preferred are independent at the 0.05 level.

Table 11-9 Person's Age Versus Movie Preference

Movie	18–23 yr	24–29 yr	30–35 yr	Row Total
Musical	8	15	11	34
Science Fiction	12	10	8	30
Comedy	9	8	12	29
Column Total	29	33	31	93

4. Ms. Angel is doing a study to see if the type of driving a person prefers to do and the gender of that person are related. A random sample of 100 drivers gave the data in Table 11–10. Test the hypothesis that gender and type of driving preferred are independent at the 0.01 level.

Table 11-10 Person's Gender Versus Driving Preference

Gender	Freeway	Multi-Lane with Traffic Lights	Two-Lane with Traffic Lights	Row Total
Female	18	16	11	45
Male	22	19	14	55
Column Total	40	35	25	100

5. Reading Nook Bookstore has 750 retail outlets across the country. The sales director wanted to see if Christmas music affects book sales in December. She randomly assigned some of the outlets to pipe in music and others not to. Then sales records for the month of December were kept. The results are shown in Table 11–11. Test the hypothesis that sales and Christmas music are independent. Use a 0.05 level of significance.

Table 11-11 Number of Books Sold Versus Use of Christmas Music

Outlet	Less than 10,000	10,000–20,000	More than 20,000	Row Total
With Music	5	18	7	30
Without Music	10	7	3	20
Column Total	15	25	10	50

6. After a large fund drive to help the Boston City Library, the following information was obtained from a random sample of contributors to the library fund (Table 11–12). Using a 1% level of significance, test the claim that the amount contributed to the library fund is independent of ethnic group.

Table 11–12 Contributors to the Library Fund

Number of People Making Contribution

Ethnic Group	$1–50	$51–100	$101–150	$151–200	Over $200	Row Total
A	310	715	201	105	42	1,373
B	619	511	312	97	22	1,561
C	402	624	217	88	35	1,366
D	544	571	309	79	29	1,532
Column Total	1875	2421	1039	369	128	5,832

7. Blue Bird Consolidated Theaters has more than 600 theaters located across the country. Each theater has four separate screens, and a customer can choose from one of four different movies. The president of Blue Bird Consolidated wants to know if a variety of shows (spy, comedy, horror, children's) or a coordinated bill (all spy, all comedy, all horror, all children's) has any effect on the total ticket sales at a theater. The president randomly assigned 47 theaters to use a variety of shows and 53 other theaters to use a coordinated bill of shows. For all theaters, total ticket sales for one week were recorded. Using the data of Table 11–13 and a 5% level of significance, test the claim that total ticket sales are independent of the four shows being varied or coordinated.

Table 11–13 Total Ticket Sales Versus Type of Billing

Ticket Sales for One Week

Type of Billing	Less than 1000	1000 to 2000	2001 to 3000	More than 3000	Row Total
Variety	10	12	18	7	47
Coordinated	6	16	22	9	53
Column Total	16	28	40	16	100

8. "Buddies" is a volunteer social service group that works with disadvantaged children. Adults 18 years and older volunteer from 1 to 6 hours each week to take a disadvantaged child to the zoo, to a museum, to a movie, fishing, ice skating, or some other activity. The Buddies program recruits adults from three main groups: college students, nonstudents living in the inner city, nonstudents living in the suburbs. A random sample of adult volunteers gave the information in Table 11–14. Using a 5% level of significance, test the claim that the number of hours volunteered is independent of the type of volunteer.

Table 11–14 Number of Hours per Week Volunteered to the Buddies Program

Type of Volunteer	Hours Volunteered			Row Total
	1–2	3–4	5–6	
College Student	115	93	47	255
Inner-City Resident	88	150	56	294
Suburban Resident	95	133	60	288
Column Total	298	376	163	837

9. A random sample of senators and representatives in Washington, D.C., gave the following information about party affiliation and number of dollars spent on federal projects in their home districts (Table 11–15). Using a 1% level of significance, test the claim that federal spending level in home districts is independent of party affiliation.

10. Solve the chapter Focus Problem found on page 747.

Table 11–15 Party Affiliation and Dollars Spent in Home District

Party	Dollars Spent on Federal Projects in Home Districts			Row Total
	Less than 5 Million	5 to 10 Million	More than 10 Million	
Democrat	8	15	22	45
Republican	12	19	16	47
Column Total	20	34	38	92

Section 11.2   Chi Square: Goodness of Fit

Last year the labor union bargaining agents listed five items and asked each employee to mark the *one* most important to her or him. The items and corresponding percentage of favorable responses are shown in Table 11–16. The

Table 11–16 Bargaining Items

Item	Percentage of Favorable Responses
Vacation time	4%
Salary	65%
Safety regulations	13%
Health and retirement benefits	12%
Overtime policy and pay	6%

bargaining agents need to determine if the distribution of responses *now* "fits" last year's distribution or if it is different.

In questions of this type, we are asking if a population follows a specified distribution. In other words, we are testing the hypotheses

H_0: The population fits the given distribution.
H_1: The population has a different distribution.

We use the chi-square distribution to test "goodness-of-fit" hypotheses.

Just as with tests of independence, we compute the sample statistic:

$$\chi^2 = \Sigma \frac{(O - E)^2}{E}$$

where E = expected frequency
O = observed frequency
and $\frac{(O - E)^2}{E}$ is summed for each item in the distribution.

Then we compare it with an appropriate critical value χ^2_α from Table 9 of Appendix II. In the case of a *goodness-of-fit test,* we use the null hypothesis to compute the expected values. Let's look at the bargaining item problem to see how this is done.

In the bargaining item problem the two hypotheses are

H_0: The present distribution of responses is the same as last year's.

H_1: The present distribution of responses is different.

The null hypothesis tells us that the expected frequencies of the present response distribution should follow the percentages indicated in last year's survey. To test this hypothesis a random sample of 500 employees was taken. If the null hypothesis is true, then there should be 4%, or 20 responses, out of the 500 rating vacation time as the most important bargaining issue. Table 11–17 gives the other expected values and all the information necessary to compute the sample statistic χ^2.

We see that the sample statistic is

$$\chi^2 = \Sigma \frac{(O - E)^2}{E} = 14.15$$

Again, larger values of the sample statistic χ^2 indicate greater differences between the proposed probability distribution and the one followed by the

Table 11–17 Observed and Expected Frequencies for Bargaining Items

Item	O	E	$(O - E)^2$	$(O - E)^2/E$
Vacation time	30	4% of 500 = 20	100	5.00
Salary	290	65% of 500 = 325	1225	3.77
Safety	70	13% of 500 = 65	25	0.38
Health and retirement	70	12% of 500 = 60	100	1.67
Overtime	40	6% of 500 = 30	100	3.33
	$\Sigma O = 500$	$\Sigma E = 500$		$\Sigma \dfrac{(O - E^2)}{E} = 14.15$

sample. The critical value χ_α^2 tells us how large the sample statistic can be before we reject the null hypothesis that the population does follow the distribution proposed in that hypothesis.

Critical Value χ_α^2

To find the critical value χ_α^2 we need to know the level of significance α and the number of degrees of freedom $d.f.$ In the case of a goodness-of-fit test, the degrees of freedom are found by the following formula:

Degrees of freedom for goodness-of-fit test

$$d.f. = (\text{number of } E \text{ entries}) - 1$$

Notice that when we compute the expected values E, we must use the null hypothesis to compute all but the last one. To compute the last one, we can subtract the previous expected values from the sample size. For instance, for the bargaining issues we could have found the number of responses for overtime policy by adding up the other expected values and subtracting that sum from the sample size 500. We would again get an expected value of 30 responses. The degrees of freedom, then, is the number of E values that *must* be computed by using the null hypothesis.

For the bargaining issues, we have

$$d.f. = 5 - 1 = 4$$

To test the hypothesis at the 0.05 level of significance, we find the critical value $\chi_{0.05}^2$ for four degrees of freedom in Table 9 of Appendix II. The critical value, 9.49, and the sample statistic, 14.15, are shown in Figure 11–5. As shown in the figure, the sample statistic χ^2 is in the critical region. Note that the critical region is always to the right of the critical value χ_α^2. Since the sample statistic is in the critical region, we reject the null hypothesis and conclude that the

Figure 11–5 Critical Value and Test Statistic (*d.f.* = 4)

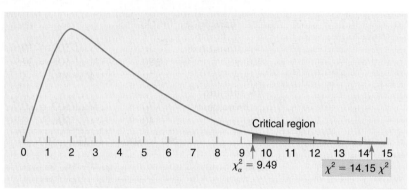

distribution of responses to the bargaining issues now is different from the distribution of last year.

One important application of goodness-of-fit tests is to genetic theories. Such an application is shown in Guided Exercise 6.

GUIDED EXERCISE 6

According to genetics theory, red-green colorblindness in humans is a recessive sex-linked characteristic. In this case, the gene is carried on the X chromosome only. We will denote an X chromosome with the gene by X_c and one without the gene by X_n. Women have two X chromosomes, and they will be red-green colorblind only if both chromosomes have the gene, designated $X_c X_c$. A woman can have normal vision but still carry the colorblind gene if only one of the chromosomes has the gene, designated $X_c X_n$. A man carries an X and Y chromosome; if the X chromosome carries the colorblind gene ($X_c Y$), the man is colorblind.

According to genetics theory, if a man with normal vision ($X_n Y$) and a woman carrier ($X_c X_n$) have a child, the probabilities that the child will have red-green colorblindness, have normal vision and not carry the gene, or have normal vision and carry the gene are given by the equally likely events in Table 11–18.

Table 11–18 Red-Green Colorblindness

Mother \ Father	X_n	Y
X_c	$X_c X_n$	$X_c Y$
X_n	$X_n X_n$	$X_n Y$

P (child has normal vision and is not a carrier) $= P(X_nY) + P(X_nX_n) = \dfrac{1}{2}$

P (child has normal vision and is a carrier) $= P(X_cX_n) = \dfrac{1}{4}$

P (child is red-green colorblind) $= P(X_cY) = \dfrac{1}{4}$

To test this genetics theory, Genetics Labs took a random sample of 200 children whose mothers were carriers of the colorblind gene and whose fathers had normal vision. The results are in Table 11–19. We wish to test the hypothesis that the population follows the distribution predicted by the genetics theory (see Table 11–18).

(a) State the null and alternate hypotheses.

(a) H_0: The population fits the distribution predicted by genetics theory.

H_1: The population does not fit the distribution predicted by genetics theory.

(b) Fill in the rest of Table 11–19 and use the table to compute the sample statistic χ^2.

(b)

Table 11–19 Colorblindness Sample

Event	O	E	$(O-E)^2$	$(O-E)^2/E$
Red-green colorblind	35	50	225	4.50
Normal vision, noncarrier	105	__	__	__
Normal vision, carrier	60	__	__	__

Table 11–20 Completion of Table 11–19

Event	O	E	$(O-E)^2$	$(O-E)^2/E$
Red-green colorblind	35	50	225	4.50
Normal vision, noncarrier	105	100	25	0.25
Normal vision, carrier	60	50	100	2.00

The sample statistic is $\chi^2 = \Sigma \dfrac{(O-E)^2}{E} = 6.75$

(c) There are three expected frequencies listed in Table 11–19. Use this information to compute the degrees of freedom.

(c) $d.f. = $ (no. of E values) $- 1 = 3 - 1 = 2$

(d) Find the critical value $\chi^2_{0.01}$ for a 0.01 level of significance. Do we reject the hypothesis that the population follows the distribution predicted by genetics theory or not?

(d) From Table 9 of Appendix II, we see that for $d.f. = 2$ and level of significance 0.01, the critical value is $\chi^2_{0.01} = 9.21$. Since the sample statistic $\chi^2 = 6.75$ is less than the critical value, we do not reject the null hypothesis that the population follows the distribution predicted by genetics theory.

P Values

● *Comment:* To estimate P values for goodness-of-fit tests, we use Table 9 of Appendix II. As an example, let's find an interval containing the P value of the sample chi-square statistic $\chi^2 = 6.75$ of Guided Exercise 6. The degrees of freedom for this test are $d.f. = 2$. Therefore, we look in the row headed by $d.f. = 2$ in Table 9. Notice that the sample statistic $\chi^2 = 6.75$ falls between the row entries 5.99 and 7.38. Therefore, the P value falls between the corresponding column headers 0.050 and 0.025.

$$0.025 < P \text{ value} < 0.050$$

This means that we reject H_0 for all $\alpha \geqslant 0.050$. In particular, we reject H_0 for $\alpha = 0.05$, but we fail to reject H_0 for $\alpha = 0.01$. This result is consistent with the test conclusion in Guided Exercise 6.

Section 11.2 Problems

For each of the problems, do the following:
  (a) State the null and alternate hypotheses.
  (b) Find the value of the chi-square statistic from the sample.
  (c) Find the degrees of freedom and the appropriate critical chi-square value.
  (d) Sketch the critical region and locate your sample chi-square value and critical chi-square value on the sketch.
  (e) Decide whether you should reject or fail to reject the null hypothesis.

1. In a study done 10 years ago, *Market Trends* magazine discovered that 20% of the new car buyers planned to keep their new cars more than 5 years, 30% planned to keep them between 2 and 5 years, and 50% intended to sell the cars in less than 2 years. This year the magazine did a similar study. A random sample of 200 new car buyers was taken. In this sample 48 people planned to keep their cars more than 5 years, 75 said they would keep them between 2 and 5 years, and 77 indicated that they planned to sell the cars in less than 2 years. Test the hypothesis that the present buyers plan to keep their cars the same length of time as buyers 10 years ago. Use an 0.01 level of significance.

2. Jimmy Nuts Company advertises that their nut mix contains (by weight) 40% cashews, 15% brazil nuts, 20% almonds, and only 25% peanuts. The truth-in-advertising investigators took a random sample (of size 20 lb) of the nut mix and found the distribution to be as follows:

Cashews	Brazil Nuts	Almonds	Peanuts
6 lb	3 lb	5 lb	6 lb

At the 0.01 level of significance, is the claim made by Jimmy Nuts true?

3. Twenty years ago a poll was taken which showed that 70% of the citizens of Alkan City opposed the unionization of city workers, 20% favored it, and 10% had no opinion. Recently, a random sample of 197 Alkan City citizens showed that 145 opposed the unionization, 35 favored it, and 17 had no opinion. At the 0.05 level, has there been a change in opinion about the unionization of city employees?

4. The Fish and Game Department stocked Lake Lulu with fish in the following proportions: 30% catfish, 15% bass, 40% bluegill, and 15% pike. Five years later they sampled the lake to see if the distribution of fish had changed. They found the 500 fish in the sample were distributed as follows:

Catfish	Bass	Bluegill	Pike
120	85	220	75

In the 5-year interval did the distribution of fish change at the 0.05 level?

5. Dr. Gordon is doing a study of the effect of noise on the litter size of coyotes. When the coyotes were subjected to the noise level found in their natural environment, the litter sizes were as follows:

One	Two	Three	Four	Five	More than Five
7%	13%	15%	25%	28%	12%

Under a similar environment, but with the noise level increased by 30 decibels, a random sample of 100 litters showed the sizes to be as follows:

One	Two	Three	Four	Five	More than Five
15%	19%	22%	20%	12%	12%

Is the distribution of litter sizes different under the noise increase? Use a 0.01 level of significance.

6. The director of library services at Walla Woo College did a survey of types of books (by subject) in the circulation library. Then she used library records to take a random sample of 4217 books checked out last term and classified the books in the sample by subject. The results are shown below.

Subject Area	% of Books in Circulation Library on This Subject	Number of Books in Sample on This Subject
Business	32%	1,210
Humanities	25%	956
Natural science	20%	940
Social science	15%	814
All other subjects	8%	297

Using a 5% level of significance, test the claim that the subject distribution of books in the library fits the distribution of books checked out by students.

7. Public Service Company planning office is doing a study of electricity consumption in the north Denver suburbs. In the table on the next page, the second column gives the percentage of total consumption of north Denver suburbs based on data 5 years old. The last column gives the most recent consumption estimates (in millions of kilowatt hours) based on a random sample of readings taken last month.

Area	Old Rate of Total Consumption	Present Consumption Estimates
Northglenn	20%	201
Westminster	10%	97
Thornton	14%	115
Broomfield	22%	245
Commerce City	15%	140
Arvada	12%	105
Henderson	7%	70
		973 total

Using a 1% level of significance, test the claim that the old distribution of electricity consumption is the same as the present distribution of electricity consumption. (*Note:* We are only testing to see if the *distribution* of consumption is the same; the *level* of consumption has, of course, increased because of population growth in the entire region.)

8. The community hospital is studying its distribution of patients. A random sample of 317 patients presently in the hospital gave the following information:

Type of Patient	Old Rate of Occurrence of These Types of Patients	Present Number of This Type Patient in Sample
Maternity ward	20%	65
Cardiac ward	32%	100
Burn ward	10%	29
Children's ward	15%	48
All other wards	23%	75

Using a 5% level of significance, test the claim that the distribution of patients in these wards has not changed.

9. The accuracy of a census report on a city in southern California was questioned by some government officials. A random sample of 1215 people living in the city was used to check the report and the results are shown here:

Ethnic Origin	Census %	Sample Result
Black	10%	127
Asian	3%	40
Anglo	38%	480
Spanish American	41%	502
Native American	6%	56
All others	2%	10

Using a 1% level of significance, test the claim that census distribution and sample distribution agree.

10. Snoop Incorporated is a firm that does market surveys. The Rollum Sound Company hired Snoop to study the age distribution of people who buy compact discs. To check the Snoop report, Rollum used a random sample of 519 customers and obtained the following data:

Customer Age in Years	% of Customers from Snoop Report	Number of Customers in Sample
Less than 14	12%	88
14–18	29%	135
19–23	11%	52
24–28	10%	40
29–33	14%	76
More than 33	24%	128

Using a 1% level of significance, test the claim that the distribution of customer ages in the Snoop report agrees with the sample report.

Section 11.3

Testing σ^2

Testing and Estimating Variances and Standard Deviations

Many problems arise that require us to make decisions about variability. In this section we will study two kinds of problems: (1) we will test hypotheses about the variance (or standard deviation) of a population, and (2) we will find confidence intervals for the variance (or standard deviation) of a population. It is customary to talk about variance instead of standard deviation because our techniques employ the sample variance rather than the standard deviation. Of course, the standard deviation is just the square root of the variance, so any discussion about variance is easily converted to a similar discussion about standard deviation.

Let us consider a specific example in which we might wish to test a hypothesis about the variance. Almost everyone has had to wait in line. In a grocery store, bank, post office, or registration center, there are usually several check-out or service areas. Frequently, each service area has its own independent line. However, many businesses and government offices are adopting a "single-line" procedure.

In a single-line procedure there is only one waiting line for everyone. As any service area becomes available, the next person in line gets served. The old independent-lines procedure has a line at each service center. An incoming customer simply picks the shortest line and hopes it will move quickly. In either procedure, the number of clerks and the rate at which they work is the same, so the average waiting time is the *same*. What is the advantage of the single-line procedure? The difference is in the *attitudes* of people who wait in the lines. A lengthy waiting line will be more acceptable if the variability of

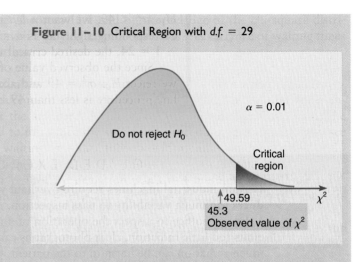

Figure 11–10   Critical Region with d.f. = 29

$\alpha = 0.01$

Do not reject H_0

Critical region

49.59

45.3
Observed value of χ^2

χ^2

(f) Do we reject H_0 or not? Should the inspector recommend that the machine be overhauled?

(f) Since the observed chi-square value 45.3 is not in the critical region, we fail to reject H_0 and conclude that the machine does not need an overhaul at this time.

Confidence Interval for σ^2

Sometimes it is important to have a confidence interval for the variance or standard deviation. Let us look at another example.

Mr. Wilson is a truck farmer in California who makes his living on a large single-vegetable crop of green beans. Because of modern machinery being used, the entire crop must be harvested at once. Therefore, it is important to plant a variety of green beans that matures all at once. This means that Mr. Wilson wants a small standard deviation between maturing times of individual plants. A seed company is trying to develop a new variety of green beans with a small standard deviation of maturing times. To test their new variety, Mr. Wilson planted 30 of the new seeds and carefully observed the number of days required for each plant to arrive at its peak of maturity. The maturing times for these plants had a sample standard deviation of $s = 3.4$ days. How can we find a 95% confidence interval for the population standard deviation of maturing times of this variety of green bean? The answer to this question is based on the following theorem.

- **Theorem 11.2:** Let a random sample of size n be taken from a normal population with population standard deviation σ, and let c be a chosen confidence level ($0 < c < 1$). Then

$$P\left(\frac{(n-1)s^2}{\chi_U^2} < \sigma^2 < \frac{(n-1)s^2}{\chi_L^2}\right) = c$$

and $$P\left(\sqrt{\frac{(n-1)s^2}{\chi_U^2}} < \sigma < \left(\sqrt{\frac{(n-1)s^2}{\chi_L^2}}\right)\right) = c$$

where n = sample size

$s = \sqrt{\dfrac{\Sigma(x-\bar{x})^2}{n-1}}$ is the sample standard deviation

χ_U^2 = chi-square value from Table 9 of Appendix II using
    d.f. = $n-1$ and $\alpha = (1-c)/2$

χ_L^2 = chi-square value from Table 9 of Appendix II using
    d.f. = $n-1$ and $\alpha = (1+c)/2$

From Figure 11–11 we see that a c confidence level on a chi-square distribution with equal probability in each tail does not center the middle of the corresponding interval under the peak of the curve. This is to be expected, since a chi-square curve is skewed to the right.

Figure 11–11 Area Representing a c Confidence Level on a Chi-Square Distribution
with d.f. = $n-1$

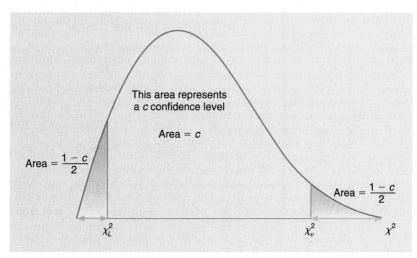

Let us summarize Theorem 11.2 in the following way:
A c confidence interval for σ^2 is

$$\frac{(n-1)s^2}{\chi_U^2} < \sigma^2 < \frac{(n-1)s^2}{\chi_L^2} \tag{1}$$

and a c confidence interval for σ is

$$\sqrt{\frac{(n-1)s^2}{\chi_U^2}} < \sigma < \sqrt{\frac{(n-1)s^2}{\chi_L^2}}$$

Now let us finish our example regarding the variance of maturing times for green beans.

Example 4

A random sample of $n = 30$ plants has a sample standard deviation of $s = 3.4$ days for maturity. Find a 95% confidence interval for the population variance σ^2.

Solution: To find the confidence interval, we use the following values:

$$c = 0.95 \qquad \text{confidence level}$$
$$n = 30 \qquad \text{sample size}$$
$$d.f. = n - 1 = 30 - 1 = 29 \qquad \text{degrees of freedom}$$
$$s = 3.4 \qquad \text{sample standard deviation}$$

To find the value of χ_U^2 we use Table 9 in Appendix II with $d.f. = 29$ and $\alpha = (1 - c)/2 = (1 - 0.95)/2 = 0.025$. From Table 9 we get

$$\chi_U^2 = 45.72$$

To find χ_L^2 we use Table 9 with $d.f. = 29$ and $\alpha = (1 + c)/2 = (1 + 0.95)/2 = 0.975$. From Table 9 we get

$$\chi_L^2 = 16.05$$

Formula (1) tells us that our desired 95% confidence interval for σ^2 is

$$\frac{(n - 1)s^2}{\chi_U^2} < \sigma^2 < \frac{(n - 1)s^2}{\chi_L^2}$$

$$\frac{(30 - 1)(3.4)^2}{45.72} < \sigma^2 < \frac{(30 - 1)(3.4)^2}{16.05}$$

$$7.33 < \sigma^2 < 20.89$$

To find a 95% confidence interval for σ, we simply take square roots; therefore, a 95% confidence interval for σ is

$$\sqrt{7.33} < \sigma < \sqrt{20.89}$$

$$2.71 < \sigma < 4.57$$

GUIDED EXERCISE 9

A few miles off the Kona coast of the island of Hawaii a research vessel lies anchored. This ship makes electrical energy from the solar temperature differential of (warm) surface water versus (cool) deep water. The basic idea is that the warm water is flushed over coils to vaporize a special fluid. The vapor is under pressure and drives electrical turbines. Then some electricity is used to pump up cold water to cool the vapor back to a liquid, and the process is repeated. Even though some electricity is used to pump up the cold water, there is plenty left to supply a moderate size Hawaiian town. The subtropic sun always warms up surface water to a reliable temperature, but ocean currents can change the temperature of the deep, cooler water. If the deep-water temperature is too variable, the power plant cannot operate efficiently or possibly not operate at all. To estimate the variability of deep ocean water temperatures, a random sample of 25 near-bottom readings gave a sample standard deviation of 7.3°C. Find a 99% confidence interval for the variance σ^2 and standard deviation σ of deep-water temperatures.

(a) Determine the following values: $c = $ ____; $n = $ ____; $d.f. = $ ____; $s = $ ____.

(a) $c = 0.99$; $n = 25$; $d.f. = 24$; $s = 7.3$

(b) What is the value of χ_U^2? ____ of χ_L^2 ____

(b) We use Table 9 of Appendix II with $d.f. = 24$. For χ_U^2, $\alpha = (1 - 0.99)/2 = 0.005$

$$\chi_U^2 = 45.56$$

For χ_L^2, $\alpha = (1 + 0.99)/2 = 0.995$

$$\chi_L^2 = 9.89$$

(c) Find a 99% confidence interval for σ^2.

(c) $$\frac{(n-1)s^2}{\chi_U^2} < \sigma^2 < \frac{(n-1)s^2}{\chi_L^2}$$

$$\frac{(24)(7.3)^2}{45.56} < \sigma^2 < \frac{24(7.3)^2}{9.89}$$

$$28.07 < \sigma^2 < 129.32$$

(d) Find a 99% confidence interval for σ.

(d) $\sqrt{28.07} < \sqrt{\sigma^2} < \sqrt{129.32}$

$$5.30 < \sigma \quad < 11.37$$

Section 11.3 Problems

Whenever a test is employed in any of the problems, do the following:
(a) State the null and alternate hypotheses
(b) Find the degrees of freedom and appropriate critical value or critical values.
(c) Find the appropriate chi-square value using the sample standard deviation.
(d) Sketch the critical region and show the critical chi-square value and the value of part c.
(e) Decide whether to reject or fail to reject the null hypothesis.

In each of the following problems, assume a normal population distribution.

1. A new kind of typhoid shot is being developed by a medical research team. The old typhoid shot was known to protect the population for a mean of 36 months with a standard deviation of 3 months. To test the variability of the new shot, a random sample of 24 people was given the new shot. Regular blood tests showed that the sample standard deviation of protection times was 1.9 months.

(a) Using a 0.05 level of significance, test the claim that the new typhoid shot has a smaller variance of protection times.

(b) Find a 99% confidence interval for the population standard deviation of protection times for the new shot.

2. In a Connecticut ship-building yard, a new and faster method of riveting is being used in the production of ship hulls. Although the new method is faster, it is feared there is a greater variability in the shear strength of the new rivets. It is known that for the old method, the rivets had a mean shear strength of 17.2 tons with standard deviation of 4.8 tons. A random sample of 51 new rivets gave a sample standard deviation of 6.1 tons shearing strength.

(a) Using a 0.01 level of significance, test the claim that the new riveting yields rivets with a higher variance of shear strength.

(b) Find a 90% confidence interval for the population variance of shear strengths for the new method.

3. A new car is being advertised as having a highway average of 45 mpg (miles per gallon). However, the ad also says that "your average mileage may vary." A consumer agency decided to estimate the variability a customer might expect. The agency took a random sample of 101 people in the United States who had purchased one of these new cars. Each person reported his or her average highway mileage, and the sample standard deviation was found to be 9.7 miles per gallon.

(a) Find a 95% confidence interval for the population variance of the highway average mpg for the new car.

(b) Use part a to find a 95% confidence interval for the population standard deviation.

4. Kula Cola bottling plant has a machine that fills 12-oz pop cans. The machine is set to put a mean of 12 oz in each can. A variance of 0.007 oz is considered acceptable. However, if the variance becomes too large, we say the machine is out of control. This means that some cans will run over, while other cans will not get enough Kula Cola. During the bottling process, random samples are taken from the production line. Recently, a sample of size 28 gave a sample variance of 0.016. Use a 0.05 level of significance to test the claim that the variance is now larger than 0.007 (i.e., the machine has slipped out of control).

5. The fan blades on commercial jet engines must be replaced when wear on these parts indicates too much variability to pass inspection. If a single fan blade broke during operation, it could severely endanger a flight. A large engine contains thousands of fan blades, and safety regulations require that variability measurements on the population of all blades not exceed $\sigma^2 = 0.15$ mm^2. An engine inspector took a random sample of 61 fan blades from an engine. She measured each blade and found a sample variance of 0.27 mm^2. Using a 0.01 level of significance, is the inspector justified in claiming that all the engine fan blades must be replaced?

6. Jim Hartman is a veterinarian who visits a Vermont farm to examine prize bulls. In order to examine a bull, Jim first gives the animal a tranquilizer shot. The effect of the shot is supposed to last an average of 65 minutes and it usually does. However, Jim sometimes gets chased out of the pasture by a bull that recovers too soon, and other times he becomes worried about prize bulls that take too long to recover. By reading his journals, Jim found that the tranquilizer should have a mean duration of 65 minutes with standard deviation of 15 minutes. A random sample of 10 of Jim's bulls had a mean of close to 65 minutes but a standard deviation of 24 minutes.
   (a) At the 0.01 level of significance, is Jim justified in the claim that the variance is larger than that stated in his journal?
   (b) Using the data Jim collected, find a 95% confidence interval for the population variance.
   (c) Find a 95% confidence interval for the population standard deviation.

7. Happy Acres Apple Farm is considering spraying their apple trees with a plant hormone intended to stabilize the size of apples a tree produces. Very small and very large apples cannot be sold as fresh fruit because the distributor will cull them out as seconds for apple cider. Happy Acres knows that their species of tree will produce apples of mean diameter 8.3 cm with standard deviation 1.7 cm. After spraying a typical test tree with the hormone, a random sample of 71 apples gave a sample standard deviation of 1.5 cm for apple diameter.
   (a) Using a 0.05 level of significance, test the claim that the hormone had no effect on variance against the claim that it made a difference (either way).
   (b) Find a 90% confidence interval for the population variance of apple diameters when the hormone is used.
   (c) Find a 90% confidence interval for the standard deviation of part b.

8. A factor in determining the usefulness of an exam as a measure of demonstrated ability is the amount of spread that occurs in the grades. If the spread or variation of exam scores is very small, it usually means the exam was either too hard or too easy. However, if the variance of scores is moderately large, then there is a definite difference in scores between "better," "average," and "poorer" students. A group of attorneys in a Midwest state has been given the task of making up this year's bar exam for the state. The exam has 500 total possible points, and from the history of past exams, it is known that a standard deviation of around 75 points is desirable. Of course, too large or too small a standard deviation is not good. The attorneys want to test their exam to see how good it is. A preliminary version of the exam (with slight modification to protect the integrity of the real exam) is given to a random sample of 24 newly graduated law students. Their scores give a sample standard deviation of 72 points.

Therefore, using Equation (4), we have

$$SS_{TOT} = \Sigma x_{TOT}^2 - \frac{(\Sigma x_{TOT})^2}{N}$$

$$= 1486 - \frac{(156)^2}{18}$$

$$= 134$$

The numerator for the total variation for all groups in our dream example is $SS_{TOT} = 134$. What interpretation can we give to SS_{TOT}? If we let $\bar{x}_{TOT}$ be the mean of all x values for all groups, then

$$\text{Mean of all } x \text{ values} = \bar{x}_{TOT} = \frac{\Sigma x_{TOT}}{N}$$

Under the null hypothesis (all groups come from the same normal distribution, $SS_{TOT} = \Sigma(x_{TOT} - \bar{x}_{TOT})^2$ represents the numerator of the sample variance for all groups. Therefore, SS_{TOT} represents total variability of the data. Total variability can occur in two ways:

1. Scores may differ from one another because they belong to *different groups* with different means (recall that the alternate hypothesis says the means are not all equal). This difference is called *between-group variability* and is denoted SS_{BET}.

2. Inherent differences unique to each subject and differences due to chance may cause a particular score to be different from the mean of its *own group*. This difference is called *within-group variability* and is denoted SS_W.

Since total variability SS_{TOT} is a sum of between-group variability SS_{BET} and within-group variability SS_W, we may write

$$SS_{TOT} = SS_{BET} + SS_W$$

As we will see, SS_{BET} and SS_W are going to help us decide whether or not to reject the null hypothesis. Therefore, our next two steps are to compute these two quantities.

Step III: Find SS_{BET} Recall that $\bar{x}_{TOT}$ is the mean of all x values from all groups. Between-group variability (SS_{BET}) measures the variability of group means. Since different groups may have different numbers of subjects, we must "weight" the variability contribution from each group by the group size n_i.

$$SS_{BET} = \sum_{\text{all groups}} n_i(\bar{x}_i - \bar{x}_{TOT})^2$$

where n_i = sample size of group i

$\bar{x}_i$ = sample mean of group i

$\bar{x}_{TOT}$ = mean for values from all groups

If we use algebraic manipulations, we can write the formula for SS_{BET} in the following computationally easier form:

$$SS_{BET} = \sum_{\text{all groups}} \left(\frac{(\Sigma x_i)^2}{n_i} \right) - \frac{(\Sigma x_{TOT})^2}{N} \tag{5}$$

where, as before, $N = n_1 + n_2 + \ldots + n_k$

Σx_i = sum of data in group i

Σx_i^2 = sum of data squared in group i

Σx_{TOT} = sum of data from all groups

Using data from Table 11–21 for the dream example, we have

$$SS_{BET} = \sum_{\text{all groups}} \left(\frac{(\Sigma x_i)^2}{n_i} \right) - \frac{(\Sigma x_{TOT})^2}{N}$$

$$= \frac{(\Sigma x_1)^2}{n_1} + \frac{(\Sigma x_2)^2}{n_2} + \frac{(\Sigma x_3)^2}{n_3} + \frac{(\Sigma x_{TOT})^2}{N}$$

$$= \frac{(38)^2}{6} + \frac{(61)^2}{7} + \frac{(57)^2}{5} - \frac{(156)^2}{18}$$

$$= 70.038$$

Therefore, the numerator of between group variation is $SS_{BET} = 70.038$.

■ *Step IV: Find* SS_W We could find the value of SS_W by using the formula relating SS_{TOT} with SS_{BET} and SS_W and solving for SS_W:

$$SS_W = SS_{TOT} - SS_{BET}$$

However, we prefer to compute SS_W a different way and use the preceding formula as a check on our calculations.

SS_W is the numerator of the variation within groups. Inherent differences unique to each subject and differences due to chance create the variability assigned to SS_W. In a general problem with k groups, the variability within the ith group could be represented by

$$SS_i = \Sigma(x_i - \bar{x}_i)^2$$

or by the mathematically equivalent formula

$$SS_i = \Sigma x_i^2 - \frac{(\Sigma x_i)^2}{n_i} \tag{6}$$

Since SS_i represents the variation within the *i*th group and we are seeking SS_W, the variability within *all* groups, we simply add SS_i for all groups:

$$SS_W = SS_1 + SS_2 + \ldots + SS_k \tag{7}$$

Using Equations (6) and (7) and the data of Table 11–21 with $k = 3$, we have

$$SS_1 = \Sigma x_1^2 - \frac{(\Sigma x_1)^2}{n_1}$$

$$= 264 - \frac{(38)^2}{6} = 23.333$$

$$SS_2 = \Sigma x_2^2 - \frac{(\Sigma x_2)^2}{n_2}$$

$$= 551 - \frac{(61)^2}{7} = 19.429$$

$$SS_3 = \Sigma x_3^2 - \frac{(\Sigma x_3)^2}{n_3}$$

$$= 671 - \frac{(57)^2}{5} = 21.200$$

$$SS_W = SS_1 + SS_2 + SS_3$$

$$= 23.333 + 19.429 + 21.200 = 63.962$$

Let us check our calculation by using SS_{TOT} and SS_{BET}.

$$SS_{TOT} = SS_{BET} + SS_W$$

$$134 = 70.038 + 63.962 \quad \text{(from steps II and III)}$$

We see that our calculation checks.

Step V: Find Variance Estimates (Mean Squares)   In steps III and IV we found SS_{BET} and SS_W. Although these quantities represent variability between groups and within groups, they are not yet the variance estimates we need for our ANOVA test. You may recall our study of student's *t* distribution in which we introduced the concept of degrees of freedom. Degrees of freedom represent the number of values that are free to vary once we have placed certain restrictions on our data. In ANOVA there are two types of degrees of freedom: $d.f._{BET}$, representing the degrees of freedom between groups, and $d.f._W$, representing degrees of freedom within groups. A theoretical discussion beyond the scope of this text would show

$$d.f._{BET} = k - 1 \quad \text{where } k \text{ is the number of groups}$$

$$d.f._W = N - k \quad \text{where } N \text{ is the total sample size}$$

(Note: $d.f._{BET} + d.f._W = N - 1$.)

The variance estimates we are looking for are designated as follows:

MS_{BET}, the variance between groups (read *mean square between*)
MS_W, the variance within groups (read *mean square within*)

In the literature of ANOVA, the variances between and within groups are usually referred to as *mean squares* between and within groups, respectively. We will use the mean-square notation because it is so commonly used. However, remember that the notation MS_{BET} and MS_W both refer to *variances*, and you might occasionally see the variance notation S^2_{BET} and S^2_W used for these quantities. The formulas for the variances between and within samples follow the pattern of the basic formula for sample variance.

$$\text{Sample variance} = s^2 = \frac{\Sigma(x - \bar{x})^2}{n - 1} = \frac{SS}{n - 1}$$

Instead of using $n - 1$ in the denominator for MS_{BET} and MS_W variances, we use their respective degrees of freedom.

$$MS_{BET} = \frac{SS_{BET}}{d.f._{BET}} = \frac{SS_{BET}}{k - 1}$$

$$MS_W = \frac{SS_W}{d.f._W} = \frac{SS_W}{N - k}$$

Using these two formulas and the data of Table 11–21, we find the mean squares within and between variances for the dream deprivation example:

$$MS_{BET} = \frac{SS_{BET}}{k - 1} = \frac{70.038}{3 - 1} = 35.019$$

$$MS_W = \frac{SS_W}{N - k} = \frac{63.962}{18 - 3} = 4.264$$

Step VI: Find the F Ratio and Complete the ANOVA Test   The logic of our ANOVA test rests on the fact that one of the variances, MS_{BET}, can be influenced by population differences among means of the several groups whereas the other variance, MS_W, *cannot* be so influenced. For instance, in the dream deprivation and anxiety study, the variance between groups MS_{BET} will be affected if any of the treatment groups has a population mean anxiety score *different* from any other group. On the other hand, the variance within groups MS_W compares anxiety scores of each treatment group to its own group anxiety mean, and the fact that group means might differ *does not* affect the MS_W value.

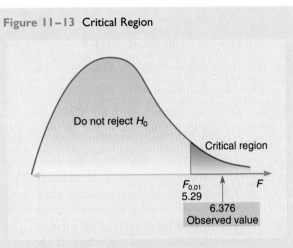

Figure 11-13 Critical Region

significant difference in population means of the four groups. The laboratory setting *does* affect the mean scores.

(k) Make a summary table of this ANOVA test.   (k) (See Table 11-25.)

Table 11-25 Summary of ANOVA Results for Pattern Recognition Experiment

Source of Variation	Sum of Squares	Degrees of Freedom	Mean Square (Variance)	*F* Ratio	F Critical Value	Test Decision
Between Groups	50.617	3	16.872	6.376	5.29	Reject H_0
Within Groups	42.333	16	2.646			
Total	92.950	19				

P Values

• *Comment:* We use Table 10 of Appendix II to estimate *P* values for ANOVA tests. For example, in Guided Exercise 10, the *F* ratio computed from the sample data is $F = 6.376$. To find an interval for the *P* value corresponding to $F = 6.376$, we look in Table 10 of Appendix II in the row headed by degrees of freedom in denominator *d.f.* = 16 and in the column headed by degrees of freedom in the numerator *d.f.* = 3. The table entry 3.24 corresponds to a *P* value of 0.05, while the entry 5.29 corresponds to a *P* value of 0.01. Since the sample *F* ratio $F = 6.376$ is greater than the table entry 5.29, the *P* value for the sample statistic is less than 0.01:

$$P \text{ value} < 0.01$$

This means that we reject H_0 for all $\alpha \geq 0.01$. In particular, we reject H_0 when $\alpha = 0.05$. This conclusion is consistent with the results shown in Guided Exercise 10.

Section 11.4 Problems

In each problem assume that the distributions are normal and have approximately the same population standard deviations. In each problem do the following:

(a) State the null and alternate hypotheses.
(b) Find SS_{TOT}, SS_{BET}, and SS_W and check that $SS_{TOT} = SS_{BET} + SS_W$.
(c) Find $d.f._{BET}$ and $d.f._W$.
(d) Find MS_{BET} and MS_W.
(e) Find the F ratio.
(f) Find the critical value $F_{0.01}$ or $F_{0.05}$ as the problem requires.
(g) Decide if the null hypothesis is to be rejected or not.
(h) Make a summary table for your ANOVA test.

1. Anthropologists working in Central America have found three burial mounds that are somewhat removed from each other but in the same region. Prevailing burial customs did not permit outsiders to be buried in the same mound. Anthropologists know that several tribes lived in the region and have classified them according to length of skull. There were four skulls found in each mound, and their measurements are given in Table 11–26. The question is: Were all three mounds made by the same or different tribes?

Table 11–26 Lengths of Skulls in Three Burial Mounds (cm)

Mound I	Mound II	Mound III
22.3	20.5	25.6
19.1	22.1	25.9
22.5	24.7	26.8
20.7	24.9	22.5

Use an $\alpha = 0.05$ level of significance. Shall we reject the claim that all three mounds were made by the same tribe or not?

2. The quantity of dissolved oxygen is a measure of water pollution in lakes, rivers, and streams. Water samples were taken at four different locations in a river in an effort to determine if water pollution varied from location to location. Location I was 500 m above an industrial plant water discharge and near the shore. Location II was 200 m above the discharge point and in midstream. Location III was 50 m downstream from the discharge point and near the shore. Location IV was 200 m downstream

for the course was also indicated. The results are in Table 11–34. Test the hypothesis that teacher ratings and student grades are independent at the 0.01 level of significance.

Table 11–34 Teacher Ratings and Student Grades

Rating	A	B	C	F (or withdrawal)	Row Total
Excellent	14	18	15	3	50
Average	25	35	75	15	150
Poor	21	27	40	12	100
Column Total	60	80	130	30	300

6. A machine that puts corn flakes in boxes is adjusted to put an average of 15 oz in each box with standard deviation of 0.25 oz. If a random sample of 12 boxes gave a sample standard deviation of 0.38 oz, do these data support the claim that the variance has increased and the machine needs to be brought back into adjustment? (Use a 0.05 level of significance.)

7. A sociologist is studying the age of the population in Blue Valley. Ten years ago the population was such that 20% were under 20 years old, 15% were in the 20–35-year-old bracket, 30% were between 36 and 50, 25% were between 51 and 65, and 10% were over 65. A study done this year used a random sample of 210 residents. This sample showed

Under 20	20–35	36–50	51–65	Over 65
15	25	70	80	20

At the 0.01 level of significance, has the age distribution of the population of Blue Valley changed?

DATA HIGHLIGHTS

The Statistical Abstract of the United States reported information about the percentage of arrests of all drunk drivers according to age group. In the following table, the entry 3.7 in the first row means that in the entire United States about 3.7% of all people arrested for drunk driving were in the age group 16 to 17 years. The Freemont County Sheriff's Office obtained data about the number of drunk drivers arrested in each age group over the past several years. In the following table, the entry 8 in the first row means that eight people in the age group 16 to 17 years were arrested for drunk driving in Freemont County.

Distribution of Drunk Driver Arrests by Age

Age	National Percentage	Number in Freemont County
16–17	3.7	8
18–24	18.9	35
25–29	12.9	23
30–34	10.3	19
35–39	8.5	12
40–44	7.9	14
45–49	8.0	16
50–54	7.9	13
55–59	6.8	10
60–64	5.7	9
65 and over	9.4	15
	100%	174

Use a chi-square test with 5% level of significance to test the claim that the age distribution of drunk drivers arrested in Freemont County is the same as the national age distribution of drunk drivers arrested.

(a) State the null and alternate hypotheses.

(b) Find the value of the chi-square statistic from the sample.

(c) Find the degrees of freedom and the appropriate chi-square critical value.

(d) Sketch the critical region and locate your sample chi-square value and critical chi-square value on the sketch.

(e) Decide whether you should reject or not reject the null hypothesis. State your conclusion in the context of the problem.

LINKING CONCEPTS

Discuss each of the following topics in class or review the topics on your own. Then write a brief but complete essay in which you summarize the main points. Please include formulas and graphs as appropriate.

1. In this chapter you studied the chi-square distribution and three principal applications for the distribution.

   (a) Outline the basic ideas behind the chi-square test of independence. What is a contingency table? What are the null and alternate hypotheses? How are the test statistic and critical region constructed? What basic assumptions underlie this application of the chi-square distribution?

   (b) Outline the basic ideas behind the chi-square test of goodness of fit. What are the null and alternate hypotheses? How are the test statistic and critical region constructed? There are a number of direct similarities between tests of independence and tests for goodness of fit. Discuss and summarize these similarities.

(c) Outline the basic ideas behind the Chi-Square method of testing and estimating a standard deviation. What basic assumptions underlie this process?

2. The Fisher F distribution was used to construct an ANOVA test for comparing several sample means.

(a) Outline the basic purpose of ANOVA. How does ANOVA avoid high risk due to multiple type I errors?

(b) Outline the basic assumption for ANOVA.

(c) What are the null and alternate hypotheses in an ANOVA test? If the test conclusion is to reject the null hypotheses, do we know which of the population means are different from each other?

(d) What is the Fisher F distribution? How are the degrees of freedom for numerator and denominator determined?

(e) What do we mean by a summary table of ANOVA results? What are the main components of such a table? How is the final decision made?

Using Technology

The problems in this section may be done using statistical computer software or calculators with statistical functions. Displays and suggestions are given for Minitab (Release 9), the TI-82 graphing calculator, and ComputerStat.

Tests of Independence

Minitab

In Minitab, you enter data for tests of independence into columns. Then you use the command CHISQUARE followed by a list of the columns containing the data. Minitab generates and displays a contingency table, the sample chi-square value, and the degrees of freedom. The commands

```
MTB > READ C1 C2 . . . CN #enter data by rows
MTB > CHISQUARE C1 C2 . . . CN
```

generate the described output for data in columns C1 through CN.

ComputerStat

Under the main menu item Hypothesis Testing, select Chi-Square Test for Independence. Follow the instructions on the screen to enter data and generate the test results.

Application 1

A study involving people who are food processors gave the following information about work shift and number of sick days.

Table 11–35 Shift Versus Number of Sick Days for Food Processors

Shift	Number Sick Days	0	1	2	3	4 or more
Day		134	44	24	10	61
Aft/Ev		90	39	23	18	99
Night		107	37	21	20	82
Rotating		56	20	14	17	92

Source: United States Department of Health, Education, and Welfare, NIOSH Technical Report. Tasto, Colligan, *et al. Health Consequences of Shift Work.* Washington: GPO, 1978, 29.
(*Note:* This table was adapted from Table 7 on page 25 of the source.)

Use a 1% level of significance to test the null hypothesis that work shift and number of sick days are independent against the alternate hypothesis that they are not independent. What is the sample chi-square value? What is the test conclusion?

Analysis of Variance (ANOVA)

Statistical computer software is especially useful for ANOVA, especially when the data sets are large.

Minitab

Minitab offers extensive support for ANOVA. In Section 11.4 you saw what is called one-way ANOVA. The commands

```
MTB > #enter the data by column using a separate SET command for each
          column of data
MTB > AOVONEWAY C1-CN #where CN is the last column containing the data
```

produce a summary ANOVA table. The term FACTOR is used in place of the expression "between groups." The term ERROR is used in place of the expression "within groups." See the computer displays at the end of Using Technology for a sample of the output from the Minitab command AOVONEWAY.

ComputerStat

Under the main menu Hypothesis Testing, select ANOVA. Then follow the instructions on the screen.

Application 2

The following data are a winter mildness/severity index for three European locations near 50° north latitude. For each decade, the number of unmistakably mild months minus the number of unmistakable severe months for December, January, and February is recorded.

Decade	Britain	Germany	Russia
1930	+4	+4	+5
1940	+1	−1	−1
1950	0	+1	+2

Table is based on data from *Exchanging Climate* by H. H. Lamb, copyright © 1966. Reprinted by permission of Methuen & Co., London.

Decade	Britain	Germany	Russia
1800	−2	−1	+1
1810	−2	−3	−1
1820	0	0	0
1830	−3	−2	−1
1840	−3	−2	+1
1850	−1	−2	+3
1860	+8	+6	+1
1870	0	0	−3
1880	−2	0	+1
1890	−3	−1	+1
1900	+2	0	+2
1910	+5	+6	+1
1920	+8	+6	+2

1. We wish to test the null hypothesis that the mean winter index for Britain, Germany, and Russia are all equal against the alternate hypothesis that they are not all equal. Use a 5% level of significance.

2. Scan the Information Summary. What is the sum of squares between groups? Within groups? What is the sample F ratio? What is the P value? Shall we reject or fail to reject the statement that the mean winter indexes for these locations in Britain, Germany, and Russia are the same?

3. What is the smallest level of significance at which we could conclude that the mean winter indexes for all of these locations are not all equal?

Computer Displays

The calculations involved in tests of independence and ANOVA are extensive, especially when more data are included. Statistical software packages are particularly useful for these statistical procedures.

Our first display shows the results of using ANOVA for Example 5 in Section 11.3, the dream deprivation study. The Minitab terms *factor* and *error* correspond to the respective terms *between* and *within* as used in Section 11.3.

Minitab Display:
Data from Example 5, Table 11–21

Using Minitab, you can generate graphs of the chi-square distribution for different degrees of freedom.

```
MTB > SET C1
DATA> 9 7 3 6 5 8
DATA> END
MTB > SET C2
DATA> 10 9 11 10 7 6 8
DATA> END
MTB > SET C3
DATA> 15 11 12 9 10
DATA> END
MTB > AOVONEWAY C1-C3

ANALYSIS OF VARIANCE
SOURCE      DF          SS         MS        F          p
FACTOR       2       70.04      35.02      8.21      0.004
ERROR       15       63.96       4.26
TOTAL       17      134.00
                                 INDIVIDUAL 95 PCT CI'S FOR MEAN
                                 BASED ON POOLED STDEV
LEVEL    N      MEAN    STDEV  - + ——— + ——— + ——— + —
C1       6     6.333    2.160  (——*——)
C2       7     8.714    1.799               (——*——)
C3       5    11.400    2.302                           (——*——)
                              - + ——— + ——— + ——— + ———
POOLED STDEV = 2.065            5.0      7.5     10.0     12.5
```

Minitab Display:
Graph of Chi-Square Distribution with d.f. = 5

```
MTB > SET C1
DATA> 0:20/.1
DATA> END
MTB > PDF C1 put in C2;
SUBC> CHISQUARE d.f. = 5.
MTB > Plot C2*C1;
SUBC>   Connect;
SUBC>   Title "Chi Square Distribution d.f. = 5".
```

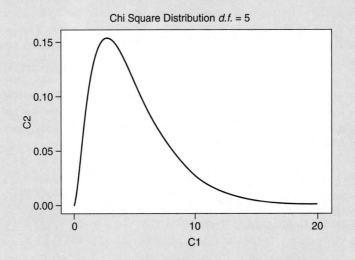

The accompanying ComputerStat display is for a chi-square test of independence using the data in Table 11–1 (example of different typewriter keyboards and the time required to learn to type). Notice that the data are displayed in column format, with observed and expected values given. The original row and column position of each item of data is also noted.

ComputerStat Display:
Table 11–1, Keyboard Versus Time to Learn to Type

```
  = = = = = = COMPLETED CONTINGENCY TABLE = = = = = =
CELL    ROW     COLUMN     OBSERVED FREQ.     EXPECTED FREQ.
1       1       1             25                 24
2       1       2             30                 40
3       1       3             25                 16
4       2       1             30                 36
5       2       2             71                 60
6       2       3             19                 24
7       3       1             35                 30
8       3       2             49                 50
9       3       3             16                 20

****** INFORMATION SUMMARY ******

NULL HYPOTHESIS
H0: THE VARIABLES ARE INDEPENDENT
ALTERNATE HYPOTHESIS
H1: THE VARIABLES ARE NOT INDEPENDENT

TOTAL SAMPLE SIZE N = 300
NUMBER OF ROWS IN CONTINGENCY TABLE R = 3
NUMBER OF COLUMNS IN CONTINGENCY TABLE C = 3
DEGREES OF FREEDOM D.F. = 4

LEVEL OF SIGNIFICANCE, ALPHA = .05

SAMPLE CHI SQUARE VALUE = 13.31583

P-VALUE = 9.83137E-03
```

The Sign Test

Nonparametric tests require no assumptions about the population distribution from which the data are drawn. Such tests have obvious advantages and some notable disadvantages which will be discussed in this section. In any case, several nonparametric tests are very popular and widely used. Our first nonparametric test is the sign test, which is used in many "before-and-after" situations.

The Rank-Sum Test

Whenever data values are not paired as in a "before-and-after" setting, the sign test should not be used. However, the rank-sum test is widely used for the case of independent samples drawn from unknown populations.

Spearman Rank Correlation

In Chapter 10 we studied the Pearson correlation coefficient, which is used for interval- or ratio-type data. Suppose that we are only interested in rank data (ordinal-type data). In this case, the Spearman correlation coefficient is often used. We will learn how to compute and construct a statistical test for the Spearman correlation coefficient.

Albert Einstein (1879–1955)
This brilliant German-born American physicist formulated the theory of relativity.

Nonparametric Statistics

Make everything as simple as possible, but no simpler.
Albert Einstein

Focus Problem ▶ Are the Nation's Highways Getting Safer to Drive?

Are cars getting safer to drive and highways safer to travel? *The Statistical Abstract of the United States* gave data by state for the number of auto deaths per 100 million vehicle miles in both 1985 and 1990. For 16 states, here are the results:

State	1985	1990
ME	2.4	1.8
VT	2.5	1.5
DE	2.2	2.3
MA	1.9	1.3
NY	2.3	2.0
PA	2.4	1.9
IL	2.3	1.9
SD	2.3	2.3
FL	3.4	2.7
NV	3.9	3.6
KY	2.6	2.6
AZ	4.4	2.5
HI	2.0	2.3
CA	2.6	2.0
MS	3.2	3.3
WY	2.7	2.2

Use a 5% level of significance to test the claim that the mean deaths per 100 million miles was less in 1990 than it was in 1985.

(a) State the null and alternate hypotheses.

(b) Find all critical values.

(c) Sketch the critical region, and show the location of the critical value and the sample statistic.

(d) Decide whether to reject or not reject the null hypothesis. State your conclusion in the context of the problem.

Section 12.1   The Sign Test

There are many situations where very little is known about the population from which samples are drawn. Therefore, we cannot make assumptions about the population distribution, such as the distribution is normal or binomial. In this chapter we will study methods that come under the heading of *nonparametric statistics*. These methods are called *nonparametric* because they require no assumptions about the population distributions from which samples are drawn. The obvious advantages of these tests are that they are quite general and (as we shall see) not difficult to apply. The disadvantages are that they tend to waste information and tend to result in acceptance of the null hypothesis more often than they should; nonparametric tests are sometimes less sensitive than other tests.

Criteria for Sign Test

The easiest of all the nonparametric tests is probably the *sign test*. The sign test is used when we compare sample means from two populations which are *not independent*. This occurs when we measure the sample twice, as done in "before-and-after" studies. The following example shows how the sign test is constructed and used.

As part of their training, police cadets took a special course on identification awareness. To determine how the course affects a cadet's ability to identify a suspect, the 15 cadets were first given an identification awareness exam

Table 12–1 Scores for 15 Police Cadets

Cadet	Postcourse Score	Precourse Score	Sign of Difference
1	93	76	+
2	70	72	−
3	81	75	+
4	65	68	−
5	79	65	+
6	54	54	No difference
7	94	88	+
8	91	81	+
9	77	65	+
10	65	57	+
11	95	86	+
12	89	87	+
13	78	78	No difference
14	80	77	+
15	76	76	No difference

and then after the course were tested again. The police school would like to use the results of the two tests to see if the identification awareness course *improves* a cadet's score. Table 12–1 gives the scores for each exam.

The sign of the difference is obtained by subtracting the precourse score from the postcourse score. If the difference is positive, we say the sign of the difference is +, and if the difference is negative, we indicate it with −. No sign is indicated if the scores are identical; in essence such scores are ignored when using the sign test.

To use the sign test, we need to compute the *proportion r of plus signs* to all signs. This is done in Guided Exercise 1.

GUIDED EXERCISE 1

Look at Table 12–1 under the *sign of difference* column.

(a) How many plus signs do you see?

(a) 10

(b) How many plus and minus signs do you see?

(b) 12

(c) The *proportion of plus signs* is

$$r = \frac{\text{number of plus signs}}{\text{total number of plus and minus signs}}$$

Use parts a and b to find r.

(c) $r = \dfrac{10}{12} = \dfrac{5}{6} = 0.833$

Hypotheses

We let μ_2 be the population mean of all precourse scores and μ_1 be the population mean of all postcourse scores (for all police cadets). The null hypothesis

$$H_0: \mu_1 = \mu_2$$

means that the identification awareness course does *not* affect the mean scores. Under the null hypothesis, we expect that the number of plus signs and minus signs should be about equal. Thus r, the proportion of plus signs, should be approximately 0.5 under the null hypothesis.

The police department wants to see if the course *improves* a cadet's score. Therefore, the alternate hypothesis will be

$$H_1: \mu_1 > \mu_2$$

To test the null hypothesis $H_0: \mu_1 = \mu_2$ against the alternate hypothesis $H_1: \mu_1 > \mu_2$, we let p be the population proportion of plus signs for all police cadets. Then we use methods of Section 9.5 for tests involving proportions. As in Section 9.5, we will assume that all our samples are sufficiently large to permit a good normal approximation to the binomial distribution. For most

Critical Value(s)

practical work, this will be the case if the total number of plus and minus signs is 12 or more ($n \geqslant 12$).

When the total number of plus and minus signs is 12 or more, the sample statistic r (proportion of plus signs) has a distribution that is approximately normal with mean p and standard deviation $\sqrt{pq/n}$. Therefore, the critical values for the sign test are z values, as in Figure 9–33. For convenience, we repeat these critical values in Table 12–2.

Table 12–2 Critical Values for the Sign Test

Alternate Hypothesis	$\alpha = 0.05$	$\alpha = 0.01$
$H_0: \mu_1 < \mu_2$ or $\mu_1 - \mu_2 < 0$	$z_0 = -1.645$	$z_0 = -2.33$
$H_0: \mu_1 > \mu_2$ or $\mu_1 - \mu_2 > 0$	$z_0 = 1.645$	$z_0 = 2.33$
$H_0: \mu_1 \neq \mu_2$ or $\mu_1 - \mu_2 \neq 0$	$z_0 = \pm 1.96$	$z_0 = \pm 2.58$
n = total number of plus and minus signs ($n \geqslant 12$)		

Suppose that the police department wants to test the hypothesis that the identification awareness course *improves* a police cadet's score at the $\alpha = 0.05$ level of significance. This means that we want to test that $\mu_1 > \mu_2$. Table 12–2 indicates that the critical value for the right-tailed test is $z_0 = 1.645$.

Sample Test Statistic

Under the null hypothesis $H_0: \mu_1 = \mu_2$, meaning that there is no difference in means, we assume that the population proportion p of plus signs is 0.5. Therefore, the z value corresponding to the sample test statistic r is

$$z = \frac{r - p}{\sqrt{\dfrac{pq}{n}}} = \frac{r - 0.5}{\sqrt{\dfrac{(0.5)(0.5)}{n}}} = \frac{r - 0.5}{\sqrt{\dfrac{0.25}{n}}}$$

where n is the total number of plus and minus signs.

In the police cadet example, we found $r = 0.833$ in Guided Exercise 1. The value of n is 12. (Note that of the 15 cadets in the sample, 3 had no difference in precourse and postcourse test scores, so there are no signs for these 3. The z value corresponding to $r = 0.833$ is then

$$z = \frac{0.833 - 0.5}{\sqrt{\dfrac{0.25}{12}}} = 2.31$$

Test Conclusion

To conclude the test, we show the critical region on a sketch and locate the z value of the sample test statistic on the sketch. If the z value of the sample test statistic falls in the critical region, we reject H_0. The critical region for the police cadet example is shown in Figure 12–1. We see that the z value corresponding to $r = 0.833$ falls in the critical region. Therefore, we reject H_0 and conclude that the identification awareness course improves the cadets' mean score.

Figure 12–1 Critical Region for Police Cadet Example

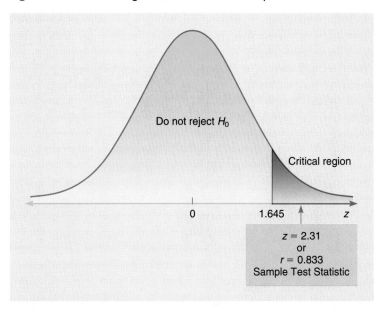

Do not reject H_0

Critical region

0   1.645 z

$z = 2.31$
or
$r = 0.833$
Sample Test Statistic

GUIDED EXERCISE 2

Dr. Kick-a-poo's Traveling Circus made a stop at Middlebury, Vermont, where the doctor opened a booth and sold bottles of Dr. Kick-a-poo's Magic Gasoline Additive. The additive is supposed to increase gas mileage when used according to instructions. Twenty local people purchased bottles of the additive and used it according to instructions. These people carefully recorded their mileage with and without the additive. The results are shown in Table 12–3.

(a) In Table 12–3, complete the column headed "Sign of Difference." How many plus signs are there? How many total plus and minus signs are there? What is r, the proportion of plus signs?

(a) There are 7 plus signs and 17 total plus and minus signs. The proportion of plus signs is

$$r = \frac{7}{17} = 0.412$$

Table 12–3 Mileage Before and After Kick-a-poo's Additive

Car	With Additive	Without Additive	Sign of Difference
1	17.1	16.8	+
2	21.2	20.1	+
3	12.3	12.3	No difference (N.D.)
4	19.6	21.0	−
5	22.5	20.9	+
6	17.0	17.9	_____

(continued)

Car	With Additive	Without Additive	Sign of Difference
7	24.2	25.4	___
8	22.2	20.1	___
9	18.3	19.1	___
10	11.0	12.3	___
11	17.6	14.2	___
12	22.1	23.7	___
13	29.9	30.2	___
14	27.6	27.6	___
15	28.4	27.7	___
16	16.1	16.1	___
17	19.0	19.5	___
18	38.7	37.9	___
19	17.6	19.7	___
20	21.6	22.2	___

Table 12–4 Completion of Table 12–3

Car	Sign of Difference
6	−
7	−
8	+
9	−
10	−
11	+
12	−
13	−
14	N.D.
15	+
16	N.D.
17	−
18	+
19	−
20	−

(b) Most people claim that the additive has no effect. Let's use a 0.05 level of significance to test this claim against the alternate hypothesis that the additive did have an effect (one way or the other). State the null and alternate hypotheses. Use Table 12–2 to find the critical values and shade the critical region. Convert the sample r

(b) Let μ_1 = mpg with additive and μ_2 = mpg without additive.

$$H_0: \mu_1 = \mu_2$$
$$H_1: \mu_1 \neq \mu_2$$

For $\alpha = 0.05$, the critical values for a two-tailed test are $z_0 = \pm 1.96$. To find the z value corre-

value $r = 0.412$ to a z value. Does the z value of the sample test statistic fall in the critical region or not? Do we reject or fail to reject H_0? What conclusion do we draw regarding the effect of the additive?

sponding to $r = 0.412$, we use $n = 17$ (total number of signs):

$$z = \frac{r - 0.5}{\sqrt{0.25/n}}$$

$$= \frac{0.412 - 0.5}{\sqrt{0.25/17}}$$

$$= -0.73$$

Since the z value of the sample test statistic does not fall in the critical region, we do not reject H_0. We conclude that the additive seems to have no effect (at the 5% level of significance). See Figure 12–2.

Figure 12–2 Critical Region

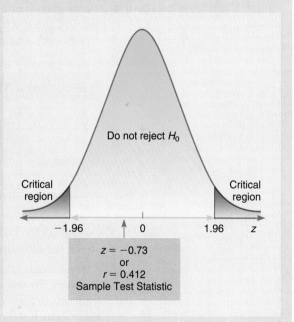

Comment: Since the sampling distribution for r, the proportion of plus signs, follows a normal distribution, you compute P values for the sample test statistic using the methods of Section 9.3. Recall that if the P value is less than or equal to the level of significance α, we reject H_0.

Section 12.1 Problems

For each of the problems, please provide the requested information.

(a) What is the null hypothesis? What is the alternate hypothesis? Will we use a left-tailed, right-tailed, or two-tailed test? What is the level of significance?

(b) What sampling distribution will we use? What is the critical value z_0 (or critical values $\pm z_0$)?

(c) Sketch the critical region, and show the critical value (or critical values).

(d) Calculate the z value corresponding to the sample test statistic r, and show its location on the sketch of part c.

(e) Based on your answers for parts a to d, shall we reject or fail to reject the null hypothesis? State the conclusion in the context of the problem.

1. The Daisy Pen Company has developed a new tip for their felt-tip pens. Twelve pens are filled with ink and fitted with the old tip. Each pen is attached to one of 12 motor-driven paper-covered drums, and the writing life of each pen is determined (in hours). Then each pen is refilled with ink and fitted with a new type tip. Again, the writing life of each pen is determined. The results follow (in hours):

Pen	New Tip	Old Tip	Pen	New Tip	Old Tip
1	52	50	7	47	46
2	47	55	8	57	53
3	56	51	9	56	52
4	48	45	10	46	40
5	51	57	11	56	49
6	59	54	12	47	51

Use a 0.05 level of significance to test the hypothesis that the mean writing life of the new tip is longer than that of the old tip.

2. A psychologist claims that students' pulse rates tend to increase just before an exam. To test this claim, she used a random sample of 14 psychology students and took their pulses before an ordinary class meeting and then again before a class meeting that consisted of an examination. The results follow:

Student	Pulse Rate Before Exam	Pulse Rate Before Ordinary Class
1	88	81
2	77	77

Student	Pulse Rate Before Exam	Pulse Rate Before Ordinary Class
3	72	75
4	74	79
5	81	79
6	70	68
7	75	77
8	80	73
9	68	71
10	75	73
11	82	76
12	61	66
13	77	68
14	64	60

Use a 0.05 level of significance to test the psychologist's claim.

3. A high-school science teacher decided to give a series of lectures on current events. To determine if the lectures had any effect on student awareness of current events, an exam was given to the class before the lectures, and another similar exam was given after the lectures. The scores follow. Use a 0.05 level of significance to test the claim that the lectures made no difference against the claim that the lectures did make some difference (either up or down).

Student	After Lectures	Before Lectures
1	107	111
2	115	110
3	120	93
4	78	75
5	83	88
6	56	56
7	71	75
8	89	73
9	77	83
10	44	40
11	119	115
12	130	101
13	91	110
14	99	90
15	96	98
16	83	76
17	100	100
18	118	109

4. A manufacturer of lens filters is using two production lines to make lens filters for cameras. The same production process is used on each line, and the only difference is in the employees working the lines. Employees on line A are experienced at their work, whereas those on line B are new on the job. The number of defective lens filters produced by each line for a period of 15 days follows:

Day	Line A	Line B	Day	Line A	Line B
1	389	517	9	300	222
2	412	610	10	444	357
3	509	430	11	392	412
4	420	420	12	306	580
5	471	415	13	319	289
6	171	310	14	510	505
7	460	370	15	240	350
8	650	618			

Use a 0.01 level of significance to test the claim that there is no difference in defective production against the claim that there is a difference (one way or the other).

5. To compare two elementary schools in teaching of reading skills, 12 sets of identical twins were used. In each case one child was selected at random and sent to school A and his or her twin was sent to school B. Near the end of fifth grade, an achievement test was given to each child. The results follow:

Twin Pair	School A	School B	Twin Pair	School A	School B
1	177	86	7	86	93
2	150	135	8	111	77
3	112	115	9	110	96
4	95	110	10	142	130
5	120	116	11	125	147
6	117	84	12	89	101

Use a 0.05 level of significance to test the hypothesis that the two schools have the same effectiveness in teaching reading skills against the alternate hypothesis that the schools are not equally effective.

6. A chemical company is testing two types of food preservatives to be used in bread. Twenty bakeries each bake two similar batches of bread, one with preservative A and the other with preservative B. The shelf life for each batch was determined as follows (shelf life in days):

Bakery	Preservative A	Preservative B
1	5	6
2	7	3
3	3	3
4	5	7
5	5	6
6	3	5
7	5	4
8	6	8
9	5	7
10	6	4
11	7	6
12	5	8
13	6	4
14	9	7
15	3	4
16	5	7
17	8	6
18	4	6
19	5	8
20	7	3

Use a 0.05 level of significance to test the claim that bread with preservative B has a longer shelf life.

7. One program to help people stop smoking cigarettes uses the method of posthypnotic suggestion to remind subjects to avoid smoking. A random sample of 18 subjects agreed to test the program. All subjects counted the number of cigarettes they usually smoke a day; then they counted the number of cigarettes smoked the day after hypnosis. (*Note:* It usually takes several weeks for the subject to stop smoking completely, and the method does not work for everyone.) The results follow:

	Number of Cigarettes Smoked per Day	
Subject	After Hypnosis	Before Hypnosis
1	28	28
2	15	35
3	2	14
4	20	20
5	31	25
6	19	40
7	6	18
8	17	15

(continued)

	Number of Cigarettes Smoked per Day	
Subject	After Hypnosis	Before Hypnosis
9	1	21
10	5	19
11	12	32
12	20	42
13	30	26
14	19	37
15	0	19
16	16	38
17	4	23
18	19	24

Using a 1% level of significance, test the claim that the mean number of cigarettes smoked per day was less after hypnosis.

8. Some fishermen claim that eating a clove of garlic will help keep mosquitoes away from your skin. To test this claim, Gary collected a large, clear plastic tube of hungry mosquitoes. He took a random sample of 16 students, each of whom agreed to put a bare arm in the tube and count the number of mosquitoes that landed on the skin during a 2-minute time interval. Then each student ate a clove of garlic. After 3 hours (when the effect of the garlic was in the blood stream), each student again put his or her arm in the tube and counted mosquitoes landing on the skin during a 2-minute time interval. The results follow. Using a 5% level of significance, test the claim that garlic tends to reduce the mean number of mosquitoes on the skin.

	Number of Mosquitoes Landing on Skin	
Student	After Garlic	Before Garlic
1	15	75
2	8	63
3	30	42
4	16	91
5	56	56
6	44	39
7	12	88
8	42	72
9	0	94
10	40	37
11	19	48
12	16	66
13	0	58
14	12	77
15	42	110
16	51	49

9. A pediatrician is studying the pulse rate of babies before and after birth. A random sample of 17 babies gave the following information (pulse rate = heart beats per minute). Using a 1% level of significance, test the claim that the mean pulse rates are different (either up or down).

	Pulse Rate	
Baby	24 Hours After Birth	24 Hours Before Labor Starts
1	70	61
2	73	72
3	82	80
4	80	83
5	58	58
6	88	77
7	80	80
8	60	65
9	71	73
10	60	52
11	63	59
12	58	64
13	79	67
14	71	71
15	73	60
16	72	75
17	85	81

10. The Know-It-All Encyclopedia Company sent a team of 15 sales people to Garden City, Kansas, for door-to-door sales. After 1 week of sales efforts, the company decided to buy local spot TV ads for their encyclopedia and then continue the sales effort another week. The results follow:

	Number of Sales	
Salesperson	After TV Ads	Before TV Ads
1	4	3
2	1	0
3	0	1
4	3	4
5	3	2
6	0	0
7	6	5
8	4	3
9	3	2
10	0	1

(continued)

	Number of Sales	
Salesperson	After TV Ads	Before TV Ads
11	1	0
12	4	3
13	4	4
14	5	6
15	3	2

Using a 5% level of significance, test the claim that mean sales before and after the TV ads are different (either up or down).

11. Solve the chapter Focus Problem found on page 811.

Section 12.2 The Rank-Sum Test

Criteria for Rank-Sum Test

The sign test is used when we have paired data values coming from dependent samples as in "before-and-after" studies. However, if the data values are *not* paired, the sign test should *not* be used.

For the situation where we draw independent random samples from two populations, there is another nonparametric method for testing the difference between sample means; it is called the *rank-sum test* (also called the *Mann-Whitney test*). The rank-sum test can be used when assumptions about *normal* populations are not satisfied or when assumptions about *equal population variances* are not satisfied. To fix our thoughts on a definite problem, let's consider the following example.

When a scuba diver makes a deep dive, nitrogen builds up in the diver's blood. After returning to the surface, the diver must wait in a decompression chamber until the nitrogen level of the blood returns to normal. A physiologist working with the Navy has invented a pill that a diver takes 1 hour before diving. The pill is supposed to have the effect of reducing the waiting time spent in the decompression chamber. Nineteen Navy divers volunteered to help the physiologist determine if the pill has any effect. The divers were randomly divided into two groups: group A had 9 divers who each took the pill, and group B had 10 divers who did not take the pill. All the divers worked the same length of time on a deep salvage operation and returned to the decompression chamber. A monitoring device in the decompression chamber measured the waiting time for each diver's nitrogen level to return to normal. These times are recorded in Table 12–5.

Table 12–5 Decompression Times for 19 Navy Divers (in min)

Group A (had pill)	41	56	64	42	50	70	44	57	63	
				Mean time = 54.1 min						
Group B (no pill)	66	43	72	62	55	80	74	75	77	78
				Mean time = 68.2 min						

Rank the Data

The means of our two samples are 54.1 and 68.2 minutes. We will use the rank-sum test to decide whether the difference between the means is significant. First, we arrange the two samples jointly in order of increasing time. To do this, we use the data of groups A and B as if they were one sample. The times, groups, and ranks are shown in Table 12–6.

Table 12–6 Ranks for Decompression Time

Time	Group	Rank	Time	Group	Rank
41	A	1	64	A	11
42	A	2	66	B	12
43	B	3	70	A	13
44	A	4	72	B	14
50	A	5	74	B	15
55	B	6	75	B	16
56	A	7	77	B	17
57	A	8	78	B	18
62	B	9	80	B	19
63	A	10			

Group A occupies the ranks 1, 2, 4, 5, 7, 8, 10, 11, and 13, and group B occupies the ranks 3, 6, 9, 12, 14, 15, 16, 17, 18, and 19. We add up the ranks of the group with the *smaller* sample size, in this case group A.

The sum of the ranks is denoted by R:

$$R = 1 + 2 + 4 + 5 + 7 + 8 + 10 + 11 + 13 = 61$$

Let n_1 be the size of the *smaller sample* and n_2 be the size of the *larger sample*. In the case of the divers, $n_1 = 9$ and $n_2 = 10$. So R is the sum of the ranks from the smaller sample. If both samples are of the same size, then $n_1 = n_2$ and R is the sum of the ranks of either group (but not both groups).

Distribution of Ranks

When both n_1 and n_2 are sufficiently large (each of size eight or more), advanced mathematical statistics can be used to show that R is approximately normally distributed with mean

$$\mu_R = \frac{n_1(n_1 + n_2 + 1)}{2}$$

and standard deviation

$$\sigma_R = \sqrt{\frac{n_1 n_2(n_1 + n_2 + 1)}{12}}$$

For the Navy divers, compute μ_R and σ_R. (Recall that $n_1 = 9$ and $n_2 = 10$.)

$$\mu_R = \frac{n_1(n_1 + n_2 + 1)}{2} = \frac{9(9 + 10 + 1)}{2} = 90$$

$$\sigma_R = \sqrt{\frac{n_1 n_2(n_1 + n_2 + 1)}{12}}$$

$$= \sqrt{\frac{9 \cdot 10(9 + 10 + 1)}{12}}$$

$$= \sqrt{150}$$

$$= 12.25$$

Testing R

To determine if the difference between sample means is significant, we use a (two-sided) rank-sum test. Table 12–7 indicates the critical values to be used.

Table 12–7 Critical Values for the Rank-Sum Test (Each Sample Size $\geqslant 8$)

When α is	We Use the Critical Values
0.05	$z_0 = \pm 1.96$
0.01	$z_0 = \pm 2.58$

We convert the sample test statistic R to a z value using the formula

$$z = \frac{R - \mu_R}{\sigma_R}$$

Let's use the rank-sum test with $\alpha = 0.05$ level of significance for the problem of the Navy divers.

H_0: Mean decompression time for divers is same.

H_1: Mean decompression time for divers is different.

Since $n_1 = 9$ and $n_2 = 10$, the samples are large enough to use Table 12–7 to find the critical values. For $\alpha = 0.05$, the critical values are $z_0 = \pm 1.96$. The critical region is shown in Figure 12–3.

To find the z value corresponding to the sample rank $R = 61$, we use the values $\mu_R = 90$ and $\sigma_R = 12.25$ found in Guided Exercise 3. Then

$$z = \frac{R - \mu_R}{\sigma_R} = \frac{61 - 90}{12.25} = -2.37$$

Figure 12-3 Critical Region with *z* Value of Sample Rank *R*

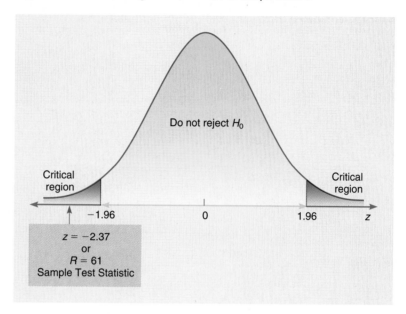

We note that the *z* value of the sample statistic *R* falls in the critical region shown in Figure 12–3. Therefore, we reject H_0 at the 5% level of significance and conclude that the pill does make a difference in decompression time.

GUIDED EXERCISE 4

A biologist is doing research on elk in their natural Colorado habitat. Two regions are under study, both with about the same amount of forage and natural cover. However, region A seems to have more predators than region B. To determine if elk tend to live longer in either region, a sample of 10 elk from each region are tranquilized and have a tooth removed. A laboratory examination of the teeth reveals the ages of the elk. Results for each sample are given in Table 12–8.

Table 12-8 Ages of Elk

Group A	11	6	21	23	16	1	3	10	13	8
Group B	12	7	5	24	4	14	19	22	18	2

(a) Make a table showing the ages, groups, and ranks for the combined data.

(a)

Table 12-9 Ranks of Elk

Age	Group	Rank	Age	Group	Rank
1	A	1	12	B	11
2	B	2	13	A	12
3	A	3	14	B	13
4	B	4	16	A	14
5	B	5	18	B	15
6	A	6	19	B	16
7	B	7	21	A	17
8	A	8	22	B	18
10	A	9	23	A	19
11	A	10	24	B	20

(b) Find μ_R, σ_R, and R.

(b) Since $n_1 = 10$ and $n_2 = 10$,

$$\mu_R = \frac{(10)(10 + 10 + 1)}{2} = 105$$

and
$$\sigma_R = \sqrt{\frac{10 \cdot 10(10 + 10 + 1)}{12}} = 13.23$$

Since $n_1 = n_2 = 10$, we can use either the sum of the ranks of the A group or the B group. Let's use the sum of the ranks of the A group. The A group ranks are 1, 3, 6, 8, 9, 10, 12, 14, 17, and 19. Therefore,

$$R = 1 + 3 + 6 + 8 + 9 + 10 + 12 + 14 + 17 + 19$$
$$= 99$$

(c) Using an $\alpha = 0.05$ level of significance, what critical values should we use for a (two-sided) rank-sum test? Compute the z value corresponding to the sample rank $R = 99$ found in part b. Sketch the critical region, and show the location of the z value of sample rank on the sketch.

(c) The samples are large enough to use the critical values in Table 12-7. They are $z_0 = \pm 1.96$. Using the values for μ_R and σ_R found in part b, we find the z value for $R = 99$ to be

$$z = \frac{R - \mu_R}{\sigma_R}$$

$$= \frac{99 - 105}{13.23}$$

$$= -0.45$$

(See Figure 12-4.)

(d) Do the data support the null hypothesis (mean lifetimes are different for the two regions)?

(d) Since the z value corresponding to the sample rank $R = 99$ does not fall in the critical region, we cannot reject the null hypothesis. The data do not indicate that elk live longer in one region.

Figure 12–4 Critical Region

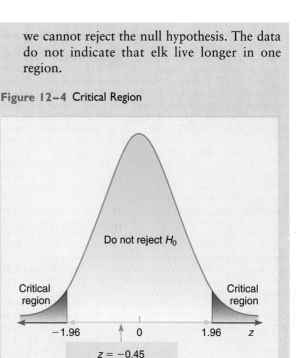

- **Comment:** Since the sampling distribution for the sum of ranks R follows a normal distribution, you compute P values for the sample test statistic using the methods of Section 9.3. Recall that if the P value is less than or equal to the level of significance α, we reject H_0.

- **Note:** In Guided Exercise 4 there were no ties for any rank. If a tie does occur, then each of the tied observations is given the *mean* of the ranks that they occupy. For example, if we rank the numbers

41   42   44   44   44   44

we see that 44 occupies ranks three, four, five, and six. Therefore, we give each of the 44s a rank which is the mean of 3, 4, 5, and 6:

$$\text{Mean of ranks} = \frac{3 + 4 + 5 + 6}{4} = 4.5$$

The final ranking would then be that shown in Table 12–10 on page 830.

For samples where n_1 or n_2 is less than 8, there are statistical tables which give appropriate critical values for the rank-sum test. Most libraries contain such tables, and the interested reader can find such information by looking under the *Mann-Whitney U Test.*

Table 12–10	
Observation	Rank
41	1
42	2
44	4.5
44	4.5
44	4.5
44	4.5

Section 12.2 Problems

In Problems 1–5, use a 0.05 level of significance to test the null hypothesis that there is no difference between average performance of the groups against the alternate hypothesis that there is a difference either way.

1. Two groups of ninth-grade students are given a reading comprehension exam. Group A students are from Windy Heights Public School, and group B students are from Califf, a neighboring private school. The following table shows the results:

Group A	71	65	70	44	81	73	50	60	88	
Group B	69	45	66	85	75	90	63	84	77	55

2. A psychologist tested two adult groups for boredom tolerance. Group A consisted of 12 females, and group B consisted of 10 males. Their scores are in the following table.

Group A	73	68	41	103	92	88	50	111	120	66	75	115
Group B	150	99	85	77	35	69	100	135	54	72		

3. A horse trainer teaches horses to jump by using two methods of instruction. Horses being taught by method A have a lead horse that accompanies each jump. Horses being taught by method B have no lead horse. The table shows the number of training sessions required before each horse would do the jumps properly.

Method A	28	35	19	41	37	31	38	40	25	
Method B	42	33	26	24	44	46	34	20	48	39

4. A French teacher teaches verbs using two different methods. Two groups of 10 students were taught a list of verbs using the two different methods, one method for each group. The time required to learn the list using each method is shown in the following table (in minutes):

Method A	18	25	41	22	56	20	15	30	33	44
Method B	15	28	19	46	55	30	63	58	40	29

5. A cognitive aptitude test consists of putting together a puzzle. Nine people in group A took the test in a competitive setting (first and second to finish received a prize). Twelve people in group B took the test in a noncom-

petitive setting. The results follow (in minutes required to complete the puzzle):

Group A	7	12	10	15	22	17	18	13	8			
Group B	9	16	30	11	33	28	19	14	24	27	31	29

In Problems 6–10, use a 0.01 level of significance to test the null hypothesis that there is no difference between average performance of the groups against the alternate hypothesis that there is a difference either way.

6. A psychologist has developed a mental alertness test. She wishes to study the effects (if any) of type of food consumed on mental alertness. Twenty-one volunteers were randomly divided into two groups. Both groups were told to eat the amount they usually eat for lunch at noon. At 2:00 P.M., all subjects were given the alertness test. Group A had a low-fat lunch with no red meat, lots of vegetables, carbohydrates, and fiber. Group B had a high-fat lunch with red meat, vegetable oils, and low fiber. The only drink for both groups was water. The test scores are shown below:

Group A	76	93	52	81	68	79	88	90	67	85	60
Group B	44	57	60	91	62	86	82	65	96	42	

7. Dr. Winchester is studying the effect of Vitamin B52 on the common cold. A group of 19 Army personnel with common colds was randomly divided into two groups. Group A subjects were given 500-milligram doses of B52 three times a day. Group B subjects were given the same doses of placebos (sugar pills). For each group, the duration of the subject's cold is given (in days).

Group A	14	19	12	21	25	16	20	28	10
Group B	9	15	24	26	18	17	31	8	22	11

8. A group of 18 cross-country ski racers was randomly divided into two groups. Group A used modern no-wax "fish-scale" type Teflon ski bottoms. Group B used the traditional wood-bottom skis with tar and wax. The times for these skiers to complete a 10-km run (with hills) are shown below in minutes:

Group A	45	41	52	47	58	55	40	38	33
Group B	44	39	30	61	37	42	36	50	31

9. Sixteen fourth-grade children were randomly divided into two groups. Group A was taught spelling by a phonetic method. Group B was taught spelling by a memorization method. At the end of the fourth grade, all children were given a standard spelling exam. The scores are shown as follows:

Group A	77	95	83	69	85	92	61	79
Group B	62	90	70	81	63	75	80	72

10. Dr. Hansen, an industrial chemist, has discovered a new catalyst that may affect the setting time of wet cement. Two groups of test slabs of cement

were studied. Group A had no catalyst, and Group B used the catalyst. The setting time for each slab was measured by Dr. Hansen. The results follow (in hours):

Group A	2.7	2.4	1.9	2.9	3.4	1.6	3.6	4.1
Group B	2.5	1.8	1.6	2.2	4.0	3.8	1.4	2.8

Section 12.3   Spearman Rank Correlation

Data given in ranked form (ordinal type) are different from data given in measurement form (interval or ratio type). For instance, if we compare the test performance of three students and, say, Elizabeth did the best, Joel did next best, and Sally did the worst, we are giving the information in ranked form. We cannot say how much better Elizabeth did than Sally or Joel, but we do know how the three scores compare. If the actual test scores for the three tests were given, we would have data in measurement form and could tell exactly how much better Elizabeth did than Joel or Sally. In Chapter 10 we studied linear correlation of data in measurement form. In this section we will study correlation of data in ranked form.

As a specific example of a situation in which we might want to compare ranked data from two sources, consider the following. Hendricks College has a new faculty position in its political science department. A national search to fill this position has resulted in a large number of qualified candidates. The political science faculty reserves the right to make the final hiring decision. However, the faculty is interested in comparing its opinion with student opinion about the teaching ability of the candidates. A random sample of nine equally qualified candidates was asked to give a classroom presentation to a large class of students. Both faculty and students attended the lectures. At the end of each lecture, both faculty and students filled out a questionnaire about the teaching performance of the candidate. Based on these questionnaires, each candidate was given an overall rank from the faculty and an overall rank from the students. The results are shown in Table 12–11. Higher ranks mean better teaching performance.

Using data in ranked form, how can we answer the following questions:

1. Do candidates getting higher ranks from the faculty tend to get higher ranks from students?
2. Is there any relation between faculty rankings and student rankings?
3. Do candidates getting higher ranks from faculty tend to get lower ranks from students?

We will use the Spearman rank correlation to answer such questions. In the early 1900s, Charles Spearman of the University of London developed the techniques that now bear his name. The Spearman test of rank correlation requires us to use *ranked variables*. Because we are only using ranks, we cannot use the Spearman test to check on the existence of a linear relation-

Table 12–11 Faculty and Student Ranks
of Candidates

Candidate	Faculty Rank	Student Rank
1	3	5
2	7	7
3	5	6
4	9	8
5	2	3
6	8	9
7	1	1
8	6	4
9	4	2

ship between the variables, as we did with the Pearson correlation coefficient
(Section 10.3). The Spearman test only checks on the existence of a *monotone* relationship between variables. (See Figure 12–5.) By a *monotone*

Figure 12–5 Examples of Monotone Relations

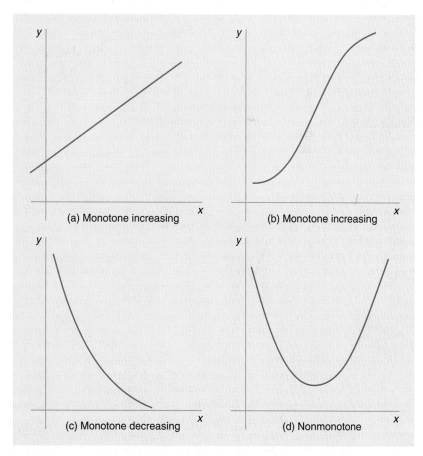

(a) Monotone increasing

(b) Monotone increasing

(c) Monotone decreasing

(d) Nonmonotone

relationship * between variables x and y, we mean a relationship in which

1. as x increases, y also increases, or
2. as x increases, y decreases.

The relationship shown in Figure 12–5d is a nonmonotone relationship because as x increases, y at first decreases, but later starts to increase. Remember, for a relation to be monotone, as x increases, y must *always* increase or *always* decrease. In a nonmonotone relation, as x increases, y sometimes increases and sometimes decreases or stays unchanged.

GUIDED EXERCISE 5

Identify each of the relations in Figure 12–6 as monotone increasing, monotone decreasing, or nonmonotone.

Figure 12–6

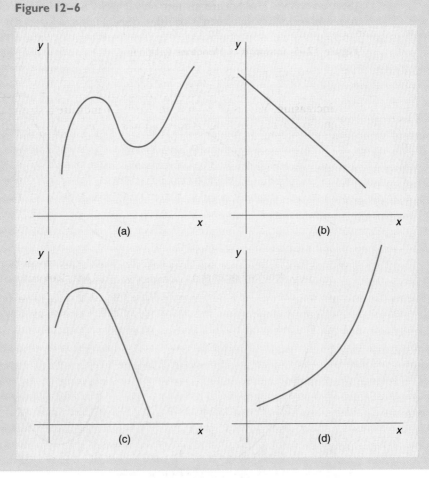

---

* Some advanced texts call the monotone relationship we describe *strictly monotone*.

> *Answers:* (a) nonmonotone, (b) monotone decreasing, (c) nonmonotone, (d) monotone increasing

Spearman Rank Correlation
Coefficient

Before we can complete the solution of our problem about the political science department at Hendricks College, we need the following information.

If we have a sample of size n of randomly obtained ordered pairs (x, y) where both x and y values are from *ranked variables,* and if there are no ties in the ranks, then the Pearson product moment correlation coefficient (Section 10.3) can be reduced to the simpler equation.

$$r_s = 1 - \frac{6\Sigma d^2}{n(n^2 - 1)} \qquad \text{where } d = x - y$$

We call r_s the *Spearman rank correlation coefficient.*

The Spearman rank correlation coefficient r_s has the following important properties:

1. $-1 \leqslant r_s \leqslant 1$ If $r_s = -1$, the relation between x and y is perfectly monotone decreasing. If $r_s = 0$, there is no monotone relation between x and y. If $r_s = 1$, the relation between x and y is perfectly monotone increasing. Values of r_s close to 1 or -1 indicate a strong tendency for x and y to have a monotone relationship (increasing or decreasing as the case may be), and values of r_s close to 0 indicate a very weak (or perhaps nonexistent) monotone relationship.

2. The probability distribution of r_s depends on the sample size n. Table 11 in Appendix II gives critical values for certain left- and right-tailed tests of r_s. It is important to note that we make no assumptions that x and y are normally distributed variables and we make no assumption about the x and y relationship being linear.

3. The Spearman rank correlation coefficient r_s is our *sample* estimate for ρ_s, the *population* Spearman rank correlation coefficient. We will construct a test of significance for the Spearman rank correlation coefficient in much the same way that we tested the Pearson correlation coefficient (Section 10.4). The null hypothesis is

Hypothesis

$$H_0: \rho_s = 0$$

In effect, the null hypothesis says that there is no monotone relation (either increasing or decreasing). The alternate hypothesis depends on the type of test we want to use.

$H_1: \rho_s < 0$ (left-tailed test):   The alternate hypothesis claims that there is a monotone-decreasing relation between x and y. The critical region is shown in Figure 12–7.

Table 11 of Appendix II with $n = 9$ gives a critical value of 0.834. Figure 12–10 shows the critical region.

Figure 12–10 Critical Region for r_s.

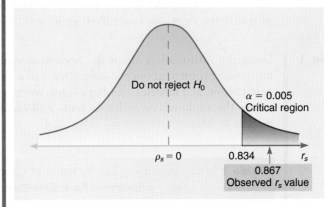

Do not reject H_0

$\alpha = 0.005$
Critical region

$\rho_s = 0$　　　　　0.834　　r_s

0.867
Observed r_s value

Since the observed r_s value is in the critical region, we reject H_0: $\rho_s = 0$ and conclude that the relation between faculty and student ranks is monotonic increasing $\rho_s > 0$. This means that faculty and students tend to rank the teaching performance of candidates in the same way.

GUIDED EXERCISE 6

Fishermen in the Adirondack Mountains are complaining that acid rain caused by air pollution is killing fish in their region. To study this claim, a biology research team studied a random sample of 12 lakes in the region. For each

Table 12–13 Acid Rain and Density of Fish

Lake	Acidity x	Fish Density y	$d = x - y$	d^2
1	5	8	-3	9
2	8	6	2	4
3	3	9	-6	36
4	2	12	-10	100
5	6	7	-1	1
6	1	10	-9	81
7	10	2	8	64
8	12	1	___	___
9	7	5	___	___
10	4	11	___	___
11	9	4	___	___
12	11	3	___	___
				$\Sigma d^2 = $ ___

lake, they measured the level of acidity of rain in the drainage leading into the lake and the density of fish in the lake (number of fish per acre foot of water). Then they did a ranking of x = acidity and y = density of fish. The results are shown in Table 12–13. Higher x ranks mean more acidity, and higher y ranks mean higher density of fish.

(a) Complete the entries in the d and d^2 columns of Table 12–13, and find Σd^2.

(a)

Lake	x	y	d	d^2
8	12	1	11	121
9	7	5	2	4
10	4	11	-7	49
11	9	4	5	25
12	11	3	8	64
				$\Sigma d^2 = 558$

(b) Compute r_s.

(b) $$r_s = 1 - \frac{6\Sigma d^2}{n(n^2 - 1)}$$

$$= 1 - \frac{6(558)}{12(144 - 1)}$$

$$= -0.951$$

(c) The fishermen are claiming that more acidity means lower density of fish. Would this claim say that x and y have a monotone-increasing or monotone-decreasing relation or no monotone relation?

(c) The claim says that as x increases, y decreases, so the claim is that the relation of x and y is monotone decreasing.

(d) To test the fishermen's claim, what should we use for the null hypothesis? What should we use for the alternate hypothesis?

(d) $H_0: \rho_s = 0$ (no monotone relation)
$H_1: \rho_s < 0$ (monotone-decreasing relation)

(e) Using a 0.001 level of significance, find a critical value and sketch the critical region for the test of part d.

(e) $n = 12; \alpha = 0.001$

By Table 11 of Appendix II, the critical value for a left-tailed test is $r_s = -0.826$. Figure 12–11 shows the critical region.

Figure 12–11 Critical Region

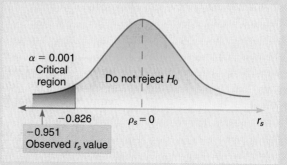

$\alpha = 0.001$
Critical region

Do not reject H_0

−0.826 $\rho_s = 0$ r_s

−0.951
Observed r_s value

(f) Do the data indicate that we should reject the claim that more acidity means fewer fish? Explain.

(f) Since the observed value $r_s = -0.951$ is in the critical region, we reject H_0 and conclude that the level of acidity has a very significant ($\alpha = 0.001$) monotone-decreasing relation with fish density.

Ties of Ranks

If ties occur in the assignment of ranks, we follow the usual method of averaging tied ranks. This method was discussed in Section 12.2 (the Rank-Sum Test). The next example illustrates the method.

- *Comment:* Technically, the use of the given formula for r_s requires that there be no ties in rank. However, if the number of ties in rank is small relative to the number of ranks, the formula can be used with quite a bit of reliability.

Example 2

Do people who smoke more tend to drink more cups of coffee? The following data were obtained from a random sample of $n = 10$ cigarette smokers who also drink coffee.

Person	Cigarettes Smoked Per Day	Cups of Coffee Per Day
1	8	4
2	15	7
3	20	10
4	5	3
5	22	9
6	15	5
7	15	8
8	25	11
9	30	18
10	35	18

To use the Spearman rank correlation test, we need to rank the data. It does not matter if we rank from smallest to largest or largest to smallest. The only requirement is that we be consistent in our rankings. Let us rank from smallest to largest.

First, we rank data as though there were no ties; then we average the ties as shown in Tables 12–14 and 12–15:

Table 12-14 Rankings of Cigarettes Smoked per Day

Person	Cigarettes Smoked per Day		Rank		Average Rank x	
4	5		1		1	
1	8		2		2	
2	15 ⎫		3 ⎫		4 ⎫	
6	15 ⎬ Ties		4 ⎬ Average rank		4 ⎬ Use the average
7	15 ⎭		5 ⎭ is 4.		4 ⎭ rank for tied data.
3	20		6		6	
5	22		7		7	
8	25		8		8	
9	30		9		9	
10	35		10		10	

Table 12-15 Rankings of Cups of Coffee per Day

Person	Cups of Coffee per Day		Rank		Average Rank y	
4	3		1		1	
1	4		2		2	
6	5		3		3	
2	7		4		4	
7	8		5		5	
5	9		6		6	
3	10		7		7	
8	11		8		8	
9	18 ⎫		9 ⎫		9.5 ⎫	
10	18 ⎭ Ties		10 ⎭ Average rank is 9.5.		9.5 ⎭ Use the average rank for tied data.

Next, we compute the observed value:

$$r_s = 1 - \frac{6\Sigma d^2}{n(n^2 - 1)}$$

$$= 1 - \frac{6(4.5)}{10(100 - 1)} = 0.973$$

Using 0.001 as a level of significance, test the claim that x and y have a monotone-increasing relationship. In other words, test the claim that people who tend to smoke more tend to drink more cups of coffee (Table 12-16).

Table 12–16 Ranks to Be Used for a Spearman Rank Correlation Test

Person	Cigarette Rank x	Coffee Rank y	$d = x - y$	d^2
1	2	2	0	0
2	4	4	0	0
3	6	7	−1	1
4	1	1	0	0
5	7	6	1	1
6	4	3	1	1
7	4	5	−1	1
8	8	8	0	0
9	9	9.5	−0.5	0.25
10	10	9.5	0.5	0.25
				$\Sigma d^2 = 4.5$

$$H_0:\ \rho_s = 0 \qquad \text{(There is no monotone relation.)}$$
$$H_1:\ \rho_s > 0 \qquad \text{(Right-tailed test)}$$

From Table 11 of Appendix II, we find that when $n = 10$ and $\alpha = 0.001$, the critical value is $r_s = 0.879$. The resulting critical region is shown in Figure 12–12.

Figure 12–12 Critical Region

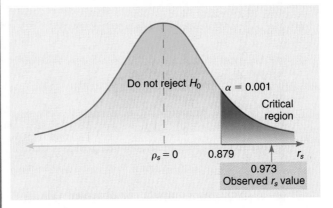

Since the observed value $r_s = 0.973$ is in the rejection region, we reject H_0 and conclude that x and y have a monotone-increasing relation. People who smoke more cigarettes tend to drink more coffee.

Section 12.3 Problems

1. A data processing company has a training program for new sales people. After completing the training program, each trainee is ranked by his or her instructor. After a year of sales, the same class of trainees is again ranked by a company supervisor according to net value of the contracts

they have acquired for the company. The results for a random sample of 11 sales people trained in the last year follow, where x is rank in training class and y is rank in sales after 1 year. Lower ranks mean higher standing in class and higher net sales.

Person	1	2	3	4	5	6	7	8	9	10	11
x Rank	6	8	11	2	5	7	3	9	1	10	4
y Rank	4	9	10	1	6	7	8	11	3	5	2

Using a 0.05 level of significance, test the claim that the relation between x and y is monotone (either increasing or decreasing).

2. As an economics class project, Debbie studied a random sample of 14 stocks. For each of these stocks she found the cost per share (in dollars) and ranked each of the stocks according to cost. After 3 months, she found the earnings per share on each stock (in dollars). Again, Debbie ranked each of the stocks according to earnings. The way Debbie ranked, higher ranks mean higher cost and higher earnings. The results follow, where x is the rank in cost, and y is the rank in earnings.

Stock	1	2	3	4	5	6	7	8	9	10	11	12	13	14
x	5	2	4	7	11	8	12	3	13	14	10	1	9	6
y	5	13	1	10	7	3	14	6	4	12	8	2	11	9

Using a 0.01 level of significance, test the claim that there is a monotone relation, either way, between ranks of cost and earnings.

3. A psychology professor is studying the relation between overcrowding and violent behavior in a rat colony. Eight colonies with different degrees of overcrowding are being used. By using a television monitor, lab assistants record incidents of violence. Each colony has been ranked for crowdedness and violence. A rank of 1 means most crowded or most violent. The results for the eight colonies are in the following table, with x being the population density rank and y the violence rank.

Colony	1	2	3	4	5	6	7	8
x Rank	3	5	6	1	8	7	4	2
y Rank	1	3	5	2	8	6	4	7

Using a 0.05 level of significance, test the claim that lower crowding ranks mean lower violence ranks (i.e., the variables have a monotone-increasing relation).

4. A history professor claims that students who finish exams quicker tend to get higher scores. The following data show the order of finish and score for 10 students selected at random:

Important Words and Symbols

	Section
Nonparametric statistics	12.1
Sign test	12.1
Rank-sum test	12.2
Spearman rank correlation coefficient r_s	12.3

Chapter Review Problems

For each problem do the following:

(a) Decide whether you should use a sign test, rank-sum test, or Spearman test.

(b) State the null and alternate hypotheses.

(c) Find all critical values.

(d) Sketch the critical region, the critical values, and the sample statistic value.

(e) Decide whether you should reject or fail to reject the null hypothesis.

1. In the production of synthetic motor lubricant from coal, a new catalyst has been discovered that seems to affect the viscosity index of the lubricant. In an experiment consisting of 21 production runs, 10 used the new catalyst and 11 did not. After each production run the viscosity index of the lubricant was determined to be as follows:

With Catalyst	1.6	3.2	2.9	4.4	3.7	2.5	1.1	1.8	3.8	4.2	
Without Catalyst	3.9	4.6	1.5	2.2	2.8	3.6	2.4	3.3	1.9	4.0	3.5

Use a 0.05 level of significance to test the null hypothesis that the mean viscosity index is unchanged by the catalyst against the alternate hypothesis that the mean viscosity index has changed.

2. Professor Adams wrote a book called *Improving Your Memory*. The professor claims that if you follow the program outlined in the book, your memory will definitely improve. Fifteen people took the professor's course in which the book and its program were used. On the first day of class everyone took a memory exam, and on the last day everyone took a similar exam. Their scores were as follows:

Last Exam	225	120	115	275	85	76	114	200	99	135	170	110	216	280	78
First Exam	175	110	115	200	60	85	160	190	70	110	140	10	190	200	92

Use a 0.05 level of significance to test the null hypothesis that the mean scores are the same whether or not people have taken the course against the alternate hypothesis that the mean scores of people who have taken the course are higher.

3. A chain of hardware stores is trying to sell more paint by mailing pamphlets describing the paint. In 15 communities containing one of these hardware stores, the paint sales (in dollars) were recorded for the month before and the month after the ads were sent out. The results are given in Table 12–17.

Table 12–17 Sales Before and After Advertising Campaign

Sales After	Sales Before	Sales After	Sales Before
610	460	500	370
150	216	118	118
790	640	265	117
288	250	365	360
715	685	93	93
465	430	217	291
280	220	280	430
640	470		

Use a 0.01 level of significance to test the null hypothesis that the advertising had no effect on average sales against the alternate hypothesis that it improved sales.

4. An obedience school for dogs experimented with two methods of training. One method involved rewards (food, praise); the other involved no rewards. The number of sessions required for training each of 19 dogs follows:

With Rewards	12	17	15	10	16	20	9	23	8	14
No Rewards	19	22	11	18	13	25	24	28	21	

Use a 0.05 level of significance to test the hypothesis that the mean number of sessions was the same for the two groups against the alternate hypothesis that they were not the same.

5. At McDouglas Hamburger stands, each employee must undergo a training program before he or she is hired. A group of nine people went through the training program and were hired to work in the Teton Park McDouglas Hamburger stand. Rankings in performance for the training program and after one month on the job are shown (a rank of 1 is for best performance).

Employee	1	2	3	4	5	6	7	8	9
Rank, Training Program	8	9	7	3	6	4	1	2	5
Rank on Job	9	8	6	7	5	1	3	4	2

Using a 0.05 level of significance, test the claim that there is a monotone-increasing relation between rank in the training program and rank in performance on the job.

6. Two expert French chefs judged chocolate mousse made by students in a Paris cooking school. Each chef ranked the best chocolate mousse as 1.

Student	1	2	3	4	5
Rank by Chef Pierre	4	2	3	1	5
Rank by Chef André	4	1	2	3	5

Use a 0.10 level of significance to test the claim that there is a monotone relation (either way) for ranks given by Chef Pierre and Chef André.

DATA HIGHLIGHTS

You do not have to be rich to make money in stocks, but you do need to make good investment choices. Suppose that you have some money to invest and you are interested in retail stocks. You request the prospectuses for the following nine retail company stocks. Is there a rank correlation between 5-year average growth and 5-year average earnings per share? The following table is based on information taken from *Forbes* (January 3, 1994). A rank of 1 means highest average earnings or highest average growth.

Company	Rank for 5-Year Earnings	Rank for 5-Year Growth
Yonkers	6	9
Dillard	4	3
Gap	1	2
Limited	5	5
Nordstrom	9	7
May	8	8
Ross	3	6
Burlington Coat	7	4
Merry-Go-Round	2	1

(a) Compute the Spearman rank correlation coefficient for these data.
(b) Using a 5% level of significance, test the claim that there is a monotone-increasing relation between the ranks of earnings and growth.
(c) State the null and alternate hypotheses.
(d) Sketch the critical region, and show the critical value and sample Spearman value on the sketch.
(e) Decide whether you should reject or not reject the null hypothesis. State your conclusion in the context of the problem.

Linking Concepts

Discuss each of the following topics in class or review the topics on your own. Then write a brief but complete essay in which you summarize the main points. Please include formulas and graphs as appropriate.

1. (a) What do we mean by the term *nonparametric statistics*? What do we mean by the term *parametric statistics*? How do nonparametric methods differ from the methods we have studied earlier?

    (b) What are the advantages of nonparametric statistical methods? How can they be used in problems where other methods we have learned would not apply?

    (c) Are there disadvantages to nonparametric statistical methods? What do we mean when we say nonparametric methods tend to be wasteful of information? Why do we say nonparametric methods are not as *sensitive* as parametric methods?

    (d) List three random variables from ordinary experience for which you think nonparametric methods would definitely apply and parametric methods would be questionable.

2. Outline the basic logic and ideas behind the sign test. Describe how the binomial probability distribution was used in the construction of the sign test. What assumptions must be made about the sign test? Why is the sign test so extremely general in its possible applications? Why is it a special test for "before-and-after" studies?

3. Outline the basic logic and ideas behind the rank-sum test. Under what conditions would you use the rank-sum test and *not* the sign test? What assumptions must be made about the rank-sum test? List two advantages the rank-sum test has that the methods of Section 9.7 do not have. List some advantages the methods of Section 9.7 have that the rank-sum test does not have.

4. What do we mean by a monotone relationship between two variables x and y? What do we mean by ranked variables? Give a graphic example of two variables x and y that have a monotonic relationship but do *not* have a linear relationship. Does the Spearman test check on a monotonic relationship or a linear relationship? Under what conditions does the Pearson product-moment correlation coefficient reduce to the Spearman rank correlation coefficient? Summarize the basic logic and ideas behind the test for Spearman rank correlation. List variables x and y from daily experience for which you think a strong Spearman rank correlation coefficient exists but the variables are *not* linearly related.

Appendix I Additional Topics

Part I Bayes's Theorem

The Reverend Thomas Bayes (1702–1761) was an English mathematician who discovered an important relation for conditional probabilities. This relation is referred to as Bayes's rule or Bayes's theorem. It uses conditional probabilities to adjust calculations so that we can accommodate new relevant information. We will restrict our attention to a special case of Bayes's theorem in which an event B is partitioned into only *two* mutually exclusive events (see Figure AI–1). The general formula is a bit complicated but is a straight-forward extension of the basic ideas we will present here. Most advanced texts contain such an extension.

Note: We use the following compact notation in the statement of Bayes's theorem:

Notation	Meaning
A^c	complement of A; *not A*
$P(B\|A)$	probability of event B, *given* event A; $P(B, \text{ given } A)$
$P(B\|A^c)$	probability of event B, *given* the complement of A; $P(B, \text{ given not } A)$

We will use Figure AI–1 to motivate Bayes's theorem. Let A and B be events in a sample space that have probabilities not equal to zero or one. Let A^c be the complement of A.

Figure AI–1 A Typical Setup for Bayes's Theorem

Sample space

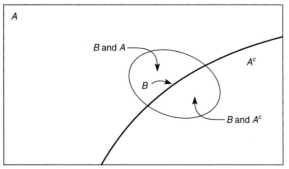

A1

We see that there is a better than 3.3% chance of getting 3 out of 4 bad pins in the top part of the hanger.

(b) Suppose that all the hanger kits are like the one described in part a. On a long bridge that used 200 such hangers, how many do you expect are held up by only 1 good pin? How might this affect the safety of the bridge?

Solution: We would expect

$$200(0.0333) = 6.66$$

That is, between 6 and 7 hangers are expected to be held up by only 1 good pin. As time goes on, this pin will corrode and show signs of wear as the bridge vibrates. With only one good pin, there is much less margin of safety.

Professor Petroski discusses the bridge on I-95 across the Mianus River in his book mentioned earlier. He points out that this dramatic accidental collapse resulted in better quality control (for hangers and pins) as well as better overall design of bridges. In addition to this, the government has greatly increased programs for maintenance and inspection of bridges.

GUIDED EXERCISE 2

The biology club weekend outing has two groups. One group with 7 people will camp at Diamond Lake. The other group with 10 people will camp at Arapahoe Pass. Seventeen duffels were prepacked by the outing committee, but 6 of these had the tents accidentally left out of the duffel. The group going to Diamond Lake picked up their duffels at random from the collection and started off on the trail. The group going to Arapahoe Pass used the remaining duffels. What is the probability that all 6 duffels without tents were picked up by the group going to Diamond Lake?

(a) What is success? Are the duffels selected with or without replacement? Which probability distribution applies?

(a) Success is taking a duffel without a tent. The duffels are selected without replacement. The hypergeometric distribution applies.

(b) Use the hypergeometric distribution to compute the probability of $r = 6$ successes in the sample of 7 people going to Diamond Lake.

(b) To use the hypergeometric distribution, we need to know the values of
a = number of successes in population = 6
b = number of failures in population = 11
n = sample size = 7, since 7 people are going to Diamond Lake
r = number of successes in sample = 6
Then,

$$P(r = 6) = \frac{C_{6,6}C_{11,1}}{C_{17,7}}$$
$$= \frac{1 \cdot 11}{19488} = 0.0006$$

The probability that all 6 duffels without tents are taken by the 7 hikers to Diamond Lake is 0.0006.

Appendix II Tables

1. Random Numbers
2. Factorials
3. Binomial Coefficients $C_{n,r}$
4. Binomial Probability Distribution $C_{n,r}p^r q^{n-r}$
5. Poisson Probability Distribution
6. Areas of a Standard Normal Distribution
7. Student's t Distribution
8. Critical Values of Pearson Product-Moment Correlation, r
9. The χ^2 Distribution
10. The F Distribution
11. Critical Values for Spearman Rank Correlation, r_s

Table I Random Numbers

92630	78240	19267	95457	53497	23894	37708	79862	76471	66418
79445	78735	71549	44843	26104	67318	00701	34986	66751	99723
59654	71966	27386	50004	05358	94031	29281	18544	52429	06080
31524	49587	76612	39789	13537	48086	59483	60680	84675	53014
06348	76938	90379	51392	55887	71015	09209	79157	24440	30244
28703	51709	94456	48396	73780	06436	86641	69239	57662	80181
68108	89266	94730	95761	75023	48464	65544	96583	18911	16391
99938	90704	93621	66330	33393	95261	95349	51769	91616	33238
91543	73196	34449	63513	83834	99411	58826	40456	69268	48562
42103	02781	73920	56297	72678	12249	25270	36678	21313	75767
17138	27584	25296	28387	51350	61664	37893	05363	44143	42677
28297	14280	54524	21618	95320	38174	60579	08089	94999	78460
09331	56712	51333	06289	75345	08811	82711	57392	25252	30333
31295	04204	93712	51287	05754	79396	87399	51773	33075	97061
36146	15560	27592	42089	99281	59640	15221	96079	09961	05371
29553	18432	13630	05529	02791	81017	49027	79031	50912	09399
23501	22642	63081	08191	89420	67800	55137	54707	32945	64522
57888	85846	67967	07835	11314	01545	48535	17142	08552	67457
55336	71264	88472	04334	63919	36394	11196	92470	70543	29776
10087	10072	55980	64688	68239	20461	89381	93809	00796	95945
34101	81277	66090	88872	37818	72142	67140	50785	21380	16703
53362	44940	60430	22834	14130	96593	23298	56203	92671	15925
82975	66158	84731	19436	55790	69229	28661	13675	99318	76873
54827	84673	22898	08094	14326	87038	42892	21127	30712	48489
25464	59098	27436	89421	80754	89924	19097	67737	80368	08795
67609	60214	41475	84950	40133	02546	09570	45682	50165	15609
44921	70924	61295	51137	47596	86735	35561	76649	18217	63446
33170	30972	98130	95828	49786	13301	36081	80761	33985	68621
84687	85445	06208	17654	51333	02878	35010	67578	61574	20749
71886	56450	36567	09395	96951	35507	17555	35212	69106	01679
00475	02224	74722	14721	40215	21351	08596	45625	83981	63748
25993	38881	68361	59560	41274	69742	40703	37993	03435	18873
92882	53178	99195	93803	56985	53089	15305	50522	55900	43026
25138	26810	07093	15677	60688	04410	24505	37890	67186	62829
84631	71882	12991	83028	82484	90339	91950	74579	03539	90122

Table 1 continued

34003	92326	12793	61453	48121	74271	28363	66561	75220	35908
53775	45749	05734	86169	42762	70175	97310	73894	88606	19994
59316	97885	72807	54966	60859	11932	35265	71601	55577	67715
20479	66557	50705	26999	09854	52591	14063	30214	19890	19292
86180	84931	25455	26044	02227	52015	21820	50599	51671	65411
21451	68001	72710	40261	61281	13172	63819	48970	51732	54113
98062	68375	80089	24135	72355	95428	11808	29740	81644	86610
01788	64429	14430	94575	75153	94576	61393	96192	03227	32258
62465	04841	43272	68702	01274	05437	22953	18946	99053	41690
94324	31089	84159	92933	99989	89500	91586	02802	69471	68274
05797	43984	21575	09908	70221	19791	51578	36432	33494	79888
10395	14289	52185	09721	25789	38562	54794	04897	59012	89251
35177	56986	25549	59730	64718	52630	31100	62384	49483	11409
25633	89619	75882	98256	02126	72099	57183	55887	09320	73463
16464	48280	94254	45777	45150	68865	11382	11782	22695	41988

Reprinted from *A Million Random Digits with 100,000 Normal Deviates* by the Rand Corporation (New York: The Free Press, 1955). Copyright 1955 and 1983 by the Rand Corporation. Used by permission.

Table 2 Factorials

n	$n!$
0	1
1	1
2	2
3	6
4	24
5	120
6	720
7	5040
8	40320
9	362880
10	3628800
11	39916800
12	479001600
13	6227020800
14	87178291200
15	1307674368000
16	20922789888000
17	355687428096000
18	6402373705728000
19	121645100408832000
20	2432902008176640000

Table 3 Binomial Coefficients $C_{n,r}$

n \ r	0	1	2	3	4	5	6	7	8	9	10
1	1	1									
2	1	2	1								
3	1	3	3	1							
4	1	4	6	4	1						
5	1	5	10	10	5	1					
6	1	6	15	20	15	6	1				
7	1	7	21	35	35	21	7	1			
8	1	8	28	56	70	56	28	8	1		
9	1	9	36	84	126	126	84	36	9	1	
10	1	10	45	120	210	252	210	120	45	10	1
11	1	11	55	165	330	462	462	330	165	55	11
12	1	12	66	220	495	792	924	792	495	220	66
13	1	13	78	286	715	1,287	1,716	1,716	1,287	715	286
14	1	14	91	364	1,001	2,002	3,003	3,432	3,003	2,002	1,001
15	1	15	105	455	1,365	3,003	5,005	6,435	6,435	5,005	3,003
16	1	16	120	560	1,820	4,368	8,008	11,440	12,870	11,440	8,008
17	1	17	136	680	2,380	6,188	12,376	19,448	24,310	24,310	19,448
18	1	18	153	816	3,060	8,568	18,564	31,824	43,758	48,620	43,758
19	1	19	171	969	3,876	11,628	27,132	50,388	75,582	92,378	92,378
20	1	20	190	1,140	4,845	15,504	38,760	77,520	125,970	167,960	184,756

Table 4 Binomial Probability Distribution $C_{n,r} \, p^r \, q^{n-r}$

This table shows the probability of r successes in n independent trials, each with probability of success p.

n	r	.01	.05	.10	.15	.20	.25	.30	.35	.40	.45	.50	.55	.60	.65	.70	.75	.80	.85	.90	.95
2	0	.980	.902	.810	.723	.640	.563	.490	.423	.360	.303	.250	.203	.160	.123	.090	.063	.040	.023	.010	.002
	1	.020	.095	.180	.255	.320	.375	.420	.455	.480	.495	.500	.495	.480	.455	.420	.375	.320	.255	.180	.095
	2	.000	.002	.010	.023	.040	.063	.090	.123	.160	.203	.250	.303	.360	.423	.490	.563	.640	.723	.810	.902
3	0	.970	.857	.729	.614	.512	.422	.343	.275	.216	.166	.125	.091	.064	.043	.027	.016	.008	.003	.001	.000
	1	.029	.135	.243	.325	.384	.422	.441	.444	.432	.408	.375	.334	.288	.239	.189	.141	.096	.057	.027	.007
	2	.000	.007	.027	.057	.096	.141	.189	.239	.288	.334	.375	.408	.432	.444	.441	.422	.384	.325	.243	.135
	3	.000	.000	.001	.003	.008	.016	.027	.043	.064	.091	.125	.166	.216	.275	.343	.422	.512	.614	.729	.857
4	0	.961	.815	.656	.522	.410	.316	.240	.179	.130	.092	.062	.041	.026	.015	.008	.004	.002	.001	.000	.000
	1	.039	.171	.292	.368	.410	.422	.412	.384	.346	.300	.250	.200	.154	.112	.076	.047	.026	.011	.004	.000
	2	.001	.014	.049	.098	.154	.211	.265	.311	.346	.368	.375	.368	.346	.311	.265	.211	.154	.098	.049	.014
	3	.000	.000	.004	.011	.026	.047	.076	.112	.154	.200	.250	.300	.346	.384	.412	.422	.410	.368	.292	.171
	4	.000	.000	.000	.001	.002	.004	.008	.015	.026	.041	.062	.092	.130	.179	.240	.316	.410	.522	.656	.815
5	0	.951	.774	.590	.444	.328	.237	.168	.116	.078	.050	.031	.019	.010	.005	.002	.001	.000	.000	.000	.000
	1	.048	.204	.328	.392	.410	.396	.360	.312	.259	.206	.156	.113	.077	.049	.028	.015	.006	.002	.000	.000
	2	.001	.021	.073	.138	.205	.264	.309	.336	.346	.337	.312	.276	.230	.181	.132	.088	.051	.024	.008	.001
	3	.000	.001	.008	.024	.051	.088	.132	.181	.230	.276	.312	.337	.346	.336	.309	.264	.205	.138	.073	.021
	4	.000	.000	.000	.002	.006	.015	.028	.049	.077	.113	.156	.206	.259	.312	.360	.396	.410	.392	.328	.204
	5	.000	.000	.000	.000	.000	.001	.002	.005	.010	.019	.031	.050	.078	.116	.168	.237	.328	.444	.590	.774
6	0	.941	.735	.531	.377	.262	.178	.118	.075	.047	.028	.016	.008	.004	.002	.001	.000	.000	.000	.000	.000
	1	.057	.232	.354	.399	.393	.356	.303	.244	.187	.136	.094	.061	.037	.020	.010	.004	.002	.000	.000	.000
	2	.001	.031	.098	.176	.246	.297	.324	.328	.311	.278	.234	.186	.138	.095	.060	.033	.015	.006	.001	.000
	3	.000	.002	.015	.042	.082	.132	.185	.236	.276	.303	.312	.303	.276	.236	.185	.132	.082	.042	.015	.002
	4	.000	.000	.001	.006	.015	.033	.060	.095	.138	.186	.234	.278	.311	.328	.324	.297	.246	.176	.098	.031
	5	.000	.000	.000	.000	.002	.004	.010	.020	.037	.061	.094	.136	.187	.244	.303	.356	.393	.399	.354	.232
	6	.000	.000	.000	.000	.000	.000	.001	.002	.004	.008	.016	.028	.047	.075	.118	.178	.262	.377	.531	.735
7	0	.932	.698	.478	.321	.210	.133	.082	.049	.028	.015	.008	.004	.002	.001	.000	.000	.000	.000	.000	.000
	1	.066	.257	.372	.396	.367	.311	.247	.185	.131	.087	.055	.032	.017	.008	.004	.001	.000	.000	.000	.000
	2	.002	.041	.124	.210	.275	.311	.318	.299	.261	.214	.164	.117	.077	.047	.025	.012	.004	.001	.000	.000
	3	.000	.004	.023	.062	.115	.173	.227	.268	.290	.292	.273	.239	.194	.144	.097	.058	.029	.011	.003	.000
	4	.000	.000	.003	.011	.029	.058	.097	.144	.194	.239	.273	.292	.290	.268	.227	.173	.115	.062	.023	.004
	5	.000	.000	.000	.001	.004	.012	.025	.047	.077	.117	.164	.214	.261	.299	.318	.311	.275	.210	.124	.041
	6	.000	.000	.000	.000	.000	.001	.004	.008	.017	.032	.055	.087	.131	.185	.247	.311	.367	.396	.372	.257
	7	.000	.000	.000	.000	.000	.000	.001	.001	.002	.004	.008	.015	.028	.049	.082	.133	.210	.321	.478	.698

Appendix II Tables

Table 4 continued

n	r	.01	.05	.10	.15	.20	.25	.30	.35	.40	.45	.50	.55	.60	.65	.70	.75	.80	.85	.90	.95
8	0	.923	.663	.430	.272	.168	.100	.058	.032	.017	.008	.004	.002	.001	.000	.000	.000	.000	.000	.000	.000
	1	.075	.279	.383	.385	.336	.267	.198	.137	.090	.055	.031	.016	.008	.003	.001	.000	.000	.000	.000	.000
	2	.003	.051	.149	.238	.294	.311	.296	.259	.209	.157	.109	.070	.041	.022	.010	.004	.001	.000	.000	.000
	3	.000	.005	.033	.084	.147	.208	.254	.279	.279	.257	.219	.172	.124	.081	.047	.023	.009	.003	.000	.000
	4	.000	.000	.005	.018	.046	.087	.136	.188	.232	.263	.273	.263	.232	.188	.136	.087	.046	.018	.005	.000
	5	.000	.000	.000	.003	.009	.023	.047	.081	.124	.172	.219	.257	.279	.279	.254	.208	.147	.084	.033	.005
	6	.000	.000	.000	.000	.001	.004	.010	.022	.041	.070	.109	.157	.209	.259	.296	.311	.294	.238	.149	.051
	7	.000	.000	.000	.000	.000	.000	.001	.003	.008	.016	.031	.055	.090	.137	.198	.267	.336	.385	.383	.279
	8	.000	.000	.000	.000	.000	.000	.000	.000	.001	.002	.004	.008	.017	.032	.058	.100	.168	.272	.430	.663
9	0	.914	.630	.387	.232	.134	.075	.040	.021	.010	.005	.002	.001	.000	.000	.000	.000	.000	.000	.000	.000
	1	.083	.299	.387	.368	.302	.225	.156	.100	.060	.034	.018	.008	.004	.001	.000	.000	.000	.000	.000	.000
	2	.003	.063	.172	.260	.302	.300	.267	.216	.161	.111	.070	.041	.021	.010	.004	.001	.000	.000	.000	.000
	3	.000	.008	.045	.107	.176	.234	.267	.272	.251	.212	.164	.116	.074	.042	.021	.009	.003	.001	.000	.000
	4	.000	.001	.007	.028	.066	.117	.172	.219	.251	.260	.246	.213	.167	.118	.074	.039	.017	.005	.001	.000
	5	.000	.000	.001	.005	.017	.039	.074	.118	.167	.213	.246	.260	.251	.219	.172	.117	.066	.028	.007	.001
	6	.000	.000	.000	.001	.003	.009	.021	.042	.074	.116	.164	.212	.251	.272	.267	.234	.176	.107	.045	.008
	7	.000	.000	.000	.000	.000	.001	.004	.010	.021	.041	.070	.111	.161	.216	.267	.300	.302	.260	.172	.063
	8	.000	.000	.000	.000	.000	.000	.000	.001	.004	.008	.018	.034	.060	.100	.156	.225	.302	.368	.387	.299
	9	.000	.000	.000	.000	.000	.000	.000	.000	.000	.001	.002	.005	.010	.021	.040	.075	.134	.232	.387	.630
10	0	.904	.599	.349	.197	.107	.056	.028	.014	.006	.003	.001	.000	.000	.000	.000	.000	.000	.000	.000	.000
	1	.091	.315	.387	.347	.268	.188	.121	.072	.040	.021	.010	.004	.002	.000	.000	.000	.000	.000	.000	.000
	2	.004	.075	.194	.276	.302	.282	.233	.176	.121	.076	.044	.023	.011	.004	.001	.000	.000	.000	.000	.000
	3	.000	.010	.057	.130	.201	.250	.267	.252	.215	.166	.117	.075	.042	.021	.009	.003	.001	.000	.000	.000
	4	.000	.001	.011	.040	.088	.146	.200	.238	.251	.238	.205	.160	.111	.069	.037	.016	.006	.001	.000	.000
	5	.000	.000	.001	.008	.026	.058	.103	.154	.201	.234	.246	.234	.201	.154	.103	.058	.026	.008	.001	.000
	6	.000	.000	.000	.001	.006	.016	.037	.069	.111	.160	.205	.238	.251	.238	.200	.146	.088	.040	.011	.001
	7	.000	.000	.000	.000	.001	.003	.009	.021	.042	.075	.117	.166	.215	.252	.267	.250	.201	.130	.057	.010
	8	.000	.000	.000	.000	.000	.000	.001	.004	.011	.023	.044	.076	.121	.176	.233	.282	.302	.276	.194	.075
	9	.000	.000	.000	.000	.000	.000	.000	.000	.002	.004	.010	.021	.040	.072	.121	.188	.268	.347	.387	.315
	10	.000	.000	.000	.000	.000	.000	.000	.000	.000	.000	.001	.003	.006	.014	.028	.056	.107	.197	.349	.599
11	0	.895	.569	.314	.167	.086	.042	.020	.009	.004	.001	.000	.000	.000	.000	.000	.000	.000	.000	.000	.000
	1	.099	.329	.384	.325	.236	.155	.093	.052	.027	.013	.005	.002	.001	.000	.000	.000	.000	.000	.000	.000
	2	.005	.087	.213	.287	.295	.258	.200	.140	.089	.051	.027	.013	.005	.002	.001	.000	.000	.000	.000	.000
	3	.000	.014	.071	.152	.221	.258	.257	.225	.177	.126	.081	.046	.023	.010	.004	.001	.001	.001	.000	.000
	4	.000	.001	.016	.054	.111	.172	.220	.243	.236	.206	.161	.113	.070	.038	.017	.006	.002	.001	.000	.000
	5	.000	.000	.002	.013	.039	.080	.132	.183	.221	.236	.226	.193	.147	.099	.057	.027	.010	.002	.000	.000

Table 4 continued

n	r	.01	.05	.10	.15	.20	.25	.30	.35	.40	.45	.50	.55	.60	.65	.70	.75	.80	.85	.90	.95
11	6	.000	.000	.000	.002	.010	.027	.057	.099	.147	.193	.226	.236	.221	.183	.132	.080	.039	.013	.002	.000
	7	.000	.000	.000	.000	.002	.006	.017	.038	.070	.113	.161	.206	.236	.243	.220	.172	.111	.054	.016	.001
	8	.000	.000	.000	.000	.000	.001	.004	.010	.023	.046	.081	.126	.177	.225	.257	.258	.221	.152	.071	.014
	9	.000	.000	.000	.000	.000	.000	.001	.002	.005	.013	.027	.051	.089	.140	.200	.258	.295	.287	.213	.087
	10	.000	.000	.000	.000	.000	.000	.000	.000	.001	.002	.005	.013	.027	.052	.093	.155	.236	.325	.384	.329
	11	.000	.000	.000	.000	.000	.000	.000	.000	.000	.000	.000	.001	.004	.009	.020	.042	.086	.167	.314	.569
12	0	.886	.540	.282	.142	.069	.032	.014	.006	.002	.001	.000	.000	.000	.000	.000	.000	.000	.000	.000	.000
	1	.107	.341	.377	.301	.206	.127	.071	.037	.017	.008	.003	.001	.000	.000	.000	.000	.000	.000	.000	.000
	2	.006	.099	.230	.292	.283	.232	.168	.109	.064	.034	.016	.007	.002	.001	.000	.000	.000	.000	.000	.000
	3	.000	.017	.085	.172	.236	.258	.240	.195	.142	.092	.054	.028	.012	.005	.001	.000	.000	.000	.000	.000
	4	.000	.002	.021	.068	.133	.194	.231	.237	.213	.170	.121	.076	.042	.020	.008	.002	.001	.000	.000	.000
	5	.000	.000	.004	.019	.053	.103	.158	.204	.227	.223	.193	.149	.101	.059	.029	.011	.003	.001	.000	.000
	6	.000	.000	.000	.004	.016	.040	.079	.128	.177	.212	.226	.212	.177	.128	.079	.040	.016	.004	.000	.000
	7	.000	.000	.000	.001	.003	.011	.029	.059	.101	.149	.193	.223	.227	.204	.158	.103	.053	.019	.004	.000
	8	.000	.000	.000	.000	.001	.002	.008	.020	.042	.076	.121	.170	.213	.237	.231	.194	.133	.068	.021	.002
	9	.000	.000	.000	.000	.000	.000	.001	.005	.012	.028	.054	.092	.142	.195	.240	.258	.236	.172	.085	.017
	10	.000	.000	.000	.000	.000	.000	.000	.001	.002	.007	.016	.034	.064	.109	.168	.232	.283	.292	.230	.099
	11	.000	.000	.000	.000	.000	.000	.000	.000	.000	.001	.003	.008	.017	.037	.071	.127	.206	.301	.377	.341
	12	.000	.000	.000	.000	.000	.000	.000	.000	.000	.000	.000	.001	.002	.006	.014	.032	.069	.142	.282	.540
15	0	.860	.463	.206	.087	.035	.013	.005	.002	.000	.000	.000	.000	.000	.000	.000	.000	.000	.000	.000	.000
	1	.130	.366	.343	.231	.132	.067	.031	.013	.005	.002	.000	.000	.000	.000	.000	.000	.000	.000	.000	.000
	2	.009	.135	.267	.286	.231	.156	.092	.048	.022	.009	.003	.001	.000	.000	.000	.000	.000	.000	.000	.000
	3	.000	.031	.129	.218	.250	.225	.170	.111	.063	.032	.014	.005	.002	.000	.000	.000	.000	.000	.000	.000
	4	.000	.005	.043	.116	.188	.225	.219	.179	.127	.078	.042	.019	.007	.002	.001	.000	.000	.000	.000	.000
	5	.000	.001	.010	.045	.103	.165	.206	.212	.186	.140	.092	.051	.024	.010	.003	.001	.000	.000	.000	.000
	6	.000	.000	.002	.013	.043	.092	.147	.191	.207	.191	.153	.105	.061	.030	.012	.003	.001	.000	.000	.000
	7	.000	.000	.000	.003	.014	.039	.081	.132	.177	.201	.196	.165	.118	.071	.035	.013	.003	.001	.000	.000
	8	.000	.000	.000	.001	.003	.013	.035	.071	.118	.165	.196	.201	.177	.132	.081	.039	.014	.003	.000	.000
	9	.000	.000	.000	.000	.001	.003	.012	.030	.061	.105	.153	.191	.207	.191	.147	.092	.043	.013	.002	.000
	10	.000	.000	.000	.000	.000	.001	.003	.010	.024	.051	.092	.140	.186	.212	.206	.165	.103	.045	.010	.001
	11	.000	.000	.000	.000	.000	.000	.001	.002	.007	.019	.042	.078	.127	.179	.219	.225	.188	.116	.043	.005
	12	.000	.000	.000	.000	.000	.000	.000	.000	.002	.005	.014	.032	.063	.111	.170	.225	.250	.218	.129	.031
	13	.000	.000	.000	.000	.000	.000	.000	.000	.000	.001	.003	.009	.022	.048	.092	.156	.231	.286	.267	.135
	14	.000	.000	.000	.000	.000	.000	.000	.000	.000	.000	.000	.002	.005	.013	.031	.067	.132	.231	.343	.366
	15	.000	.000	.000	.000	.000	.000	.000	.000	.000	.000	.000	.000	.000	.002	.005	.013	.035	.087	.206	.463
16	0	.851	.440	.185	.074	.028	.010	.003	.001	.000	.000	.000	.000	.000	.000	.000	.000	.000	.000	.000	.000
	1	.138	.371	.329	.210	.113	.053	.023	.009	.003	.001	.000	.000	.000	.000	.000	.000	.000	.000	.000	.000

Table 4 continued

n	r	.01	.05	.10	.15	.20	.25	.30	.35	.40	.45	.50	.55	.60	.65	.70	.75	.80	.85	.90	.95
												p									
16	2	.010	.146	.275	.277	.211	.134	.073	.035	.015	.006	.002	.001	.000	.000	.000	.000	.000	.000	.000	.000
	3	.000	.036	.142	.229	.246	.208	.146	.089	.047	.022	.009	.003	.001	.000	.000	.000	.000	.000	.000	.000
	4	.000	.006	.051	.131	.200	.225	.204	.155	.101	.057	.028	.011	.004	.001	.000	.000	.000	.000	.000	.000
	5	.000	.001	.014	.056	.120	.180	.210	.201	.162	.112	.067	.034	.014	.005	.001	.000	.000	.000	.000	.000
	6	.000	.000	.003	.018	.055	.110	.165	.198	.198	.168	.122	.075	.039	.017	.006	.001	.000	.000	.000	.000
	7	.000	.000	.000	.005	.020	.052	.101	.152	.189	.197	.175	.132	.084	.044	.019	.006	.001	.000	.000	.000
	8	.000	.000	.000	.001	.006	.020	.049	.092	.142	.181	.196	.181	.142	.092	.049	.020	.006	.001	.000	.000
	9	.000	.000	.000	.000	.001	.006	.019	.044	.084	.132	.175	.197	.189	.152	.101	.052	.020	.005	.000	.000
	10	.000	.000	.000	.000	.000	.001	.006	.017	.039	.075	.122	.168	.198	.198	.165	.110	.055	.018	.003	.000
	11	.000	.000	.000	.000	.000	.000	.001	.005	.014	.034	.067	.112	.162	.201	.210	.180	.120	.056	.014	.001
	12	.000	.000	.000	.000	.000	.000	.000	.001	.004	.011	.028	.057	.101	.155	.204	.225	.200	.131	.051	.006
	13	.000	.000	.000	.000	.000	.000	.000	.000	.001	.003	.009	.022	.047	.089	.146	.208	.246	.229	.142	.036
	14	.000	.000	.000	.000	.000	.000	.000	.000	.000	.001	.002	.006	.015	.035	.073	.134	.211	.277	.275	.146
	15	.000	.000	.000	.000	.000	.000	.000	.000	.000	.000	.000	.001	.003	.009	.023	.053	.113	.210	.329	.371
	16	.000	.000	.000	.000	.000	.000	.000	.000	.000	.000	.000	.000	.000	.001	.003	.010	.028	.074	.185	.440
20	0	.818	.358	.122	.039	.012	.003	.001	.000	.000	.000	.000	.000	.000	.000	.000	.000	.000	.000	.000	.000
	1	.165	.377	.270	.137	.058	.021	.007	.002	.000	.000	.000	.000	.000	.000	.000	.000	.000	.000	.000	.000
	2	.016	.189	.285	.229	.137	.067	.028	.010	.003	.001	.000	.000	.000	.000	.000	.000	.000	.000	.000	.000
	3	.001	.060	.190	.243	.205	.134	.072	.032	.012	.004	.001	.000	.000	.000	.000	.000	.000	.000	.000	.000
	4	.000	.013	.090	.182	.218	.190	.130	.074	.035	.014	.005	.001	.000	.000	.000	.000	.000	.000	.000	.000
	5	.000	.002	.032	.103	.175	.202	.179	.127	.075	.036	.015	.005	.001	.000	.000	.000	.000	.000	.000	.000
	6	.000	.000	.009	.045	.109	.169	.192	.171	.124	.075	.037	.015	.005	.001	.000	.000	.000	.000	.000	.000
	7	.000	.000	.002	.016	.055	.112	.164	.184	.166	.122	.074	.037	.015	.005	.001	.000	.000	.000	.000	.000
	8	.000	.000	.000	.005	.022	.061	.114	.161	.180	.162	.120	.073	.035	.014	.004	.001	.000	.000	.000	.000
	9	.000	.000	.000	.001	.007	.027	.065	.116	.160	.177	.160	.119	.071	.034	.012	.003	.000	.000	.000	.000
	10	.000	.000	.000	.000	.002	.010	.031	.069	.117	.159	.176	.159	.117	.069	.031	.010	.002	.000	.000	.000
	11	.000	.000	.000	.000	.000	.003	.012	.034	.071	.119	.160	.177	.160	.116	.065	.027	.007	.001	.000	.000
	12	.000	.000	.000	.000	.000	.001	.004	.014	.035	.073	.120	.162	.180	.161	.114	.061	.022	.005	.000	.000
	13	.000	.000	.000	.000	.000	.000	.001	.005	.015	.037	.074	.122	.166	.184	.164	.112	.055	.016	.002	.000
	14	.000	.000	.000	.000	.000	.000	.000	.001	.005	.015	.037	.075	.124	.171	.192	.169	.109	.045	.009	.000
	15	.000	.000	.000	.000	.000	.000	.000	.000	.001	.005	.015	.036	.075	.127	.179	.202	.175	.103	.032	.002
	16	.000	.000	.000	.000	.000	.000	.000	.000	.000	.001	.005	.014	.035	.074	.130	.190	.218	.182	.090	.013
	17	.000	.000	.000	.000	.000	.000	.000	.000	.000	.000	.001	.004	.012	.032	.072	.134	.205	.243	.190	.060
	18	.000	.000	.000	.000	.000	.000	.000	.000	.000	.000	.000	.001	.003	.010	.028	.067	.137	.229	.285	.189
	19	.000	.000	.000	.000	.000	.000	.000	.000	.000	.000	.000	.000	.000	.002	.007	.021	.058	.137	.270	.377
	20	.000	.000	.000	.000	.000	.000	.000	.000	.000	.000	.000	.000	.000	.000	.001	.003	.012	.039	.122	.358

Table 5 Poisson Probability Distribution

For a given value of λ, entry indicates the probability of obtaining a specified value of r.

r	λ .1	.2	.3	.4	.5	.6	.7	.8	.9	1.0
0	.9048	.8187	.7408	.6703	.6065	.5488	.4966	.4493	.4066	.3679
1	.0905	.1637	.2222	.2681	.3033	.3293	.3476	.3595	.3659	.3679
2	.0045	.0164	.0333	.0536	.0758	.0988	.1217	.1438	.1647	.1839
3	.0002	.0011	.0033	.0072	.0126	.0198	.0284	.0383	.0494	.0613
4	.0000	.0001	.0003	.0007	.0016	.0030	.0050	.0077	.0111	.0153
5	.0000	.0000	.0000	.0001	.0002	.0004	.0007	.0012	.0020	.0031
6	.0000	.0000	.0000	.0000	.0000	.0000	.0001	.0002	.0003	.0005
7	.0000	.0000	.0000	.0000	.0000	.0000	.0000	.0000	.0000	.0001

r	λ 1.1	1.2	1.3	1.4	1.5	1.6	1.7	1.8	1.9	2.0
0	.3329	.3012	.2725	.2466	.2231	.2019	.1827	.1653	.1496	.1353
1	.3662	.3614	.3543	.3452	.3347	.3230	.3106	.2975	.2842	.2707
2	.2014	.2169	.2303	.2417	.2510	.2584	.2640	.2678	.2700	.2707
3	.0738	.0867	.0998	.1128	.1255	.1378	.1496	.1607	.1710	.1804
4	.0203	.0260	.0324	.0395	.0471	.0551	.0636	.0723	.0812	.0902
5	.0045	.0062	.0084	.0111	.0141	.0176	.0216	.0260	.0309	.0361
6	.0008	.0012	.0018	.0026	.0035	.0047	.0061	.0078	.0098	.0120
7	.0001	.0002	.0003	.0005	.0008	.0011	.0015	.0020	.0027	.0034
8	.0000	.0000	.0001	.0001	.0001	.0002	.0003	.0005	.0006	.0009
9	.0000	.0000	.0000	.0000	.0000	.0000	.0001	.0001	.0001	.0002

r	λ 2.1	2.2	2.3	2.4	2.5	2.6	2.7	2.8	2.9	3.0
0	.1225	.1108	.1003	.0907	.0821	.0743	.0672	.0608	.0550	.0498
1	.2572	.2438	.2306	.2177	.2052	.1931	.1815	.1703	.1596	.1494
2	.2700	.2681	.2652	.2613	.2565	.2510	.2450	.2384	.2314	.2240
3	.1890	.1966	.2033	.2090	.2138	.2176	.2205	.2225	.2237	.2240
4	.0992	.1082	.1169	.1254	.1336	.1414	.1488	.1557	.1622	.1680
5	.0417	.0476	.0538	.0602	.0668	.0735	.0804	.0872	.0940	.1008
6	.0146	.0174	.0206	.0241	.0278	.0319	.0362	.0407	.0455	.0504
7	.0044	.0055	.0068	.0083	.0099	.0118	.0139	.0163	.0188	.0216
8	.0011	.0015	.0019	.0025	.0031	.0038	.0047	.0057	.0068	.0081
9	.0003	.0004	.0005	.0007	.0009	.0011	.0014	.0018	.0022	.0027
10	.0001	.0001	.0001	.0002	.0002	.0003	.0004	.0005	.0006	.0008
11	.0000	.0000	.0000	.0000	.0000	.0001	.0001	.0001	.0002	.0002
12	.0000	.0000	.0000	.0000	.0000	.0000	.0000	.0000	.0000	.0001

r	λ 3.1	3.2	3.3	3.4	3.5	3.6	3.7	3.8	3.9	4.0
0	.0450	.0408	.0369	.0334	.0302	.0273	.0247	.0224	.0202	.0183
1	.1397	.1304	.1217	.1135	.1057	.0984	.0915	.0850	.0789	.0733

Table 5 continued

					λ					
r	3.1	3.2	3.3	3.4	3.5	3.6	3.7	3.8	3.9	4.0
2	.2165	.2087	.2008	.1929	.1850	.1771	.1692	.1615	.1539	.1465
3	.2237	.2226	.2209	.2186	.2158	.2125	.2087	.2046	.2001	.1954
4	.1734	.1781	.1823	.1858	.1888	.1912	.1931	.1944	.1951	.1954
5	.1075	.1140	.1203	.1264	.1322	.1377	.1429	.1477	.1522	.1563
6	.0555	.0608	.0662	.0716	.0771	.0826	.0881	.0936	.0989	.1042
7	.0246	.2078	.0312	.0348	.0385	.0425	.0466	.0508	.0551	.0595
8	.0095	.0111	.0129	.0148	.0169	.0191	.0215	.0241	.0269	.0298
9	.0033	.0040	.0047	.0056	.0066	.0076	.0089	.0102	.0116	.0132
10	.0010	.0013	.0016	.0019	.0023	.0028	.0033	.0039	.0045	.0053
11	.0003	.0004	.0005	.0006	.0007	.0009	.0011	.0013	.0016	.0019
12	.0001	.0001	.0001	.0002	.0002	.0003	.0003	.0004	.0005	.0006
13	.0000	.0000	.0000	.0000	.0001	.0001	.0001	.0001	.0002	.0002
14	.0000	.0000	.0000	.0000	.0000	.0000	.0000	.0000	.0000	.0001

					λ					
r	4.1	4.2	4.3	4.4	4.5	4.6	4.7	4.8	4.9	5.0
0	.0166	.0150	.0136	.0123	.0111	.0101	.0091	.0082	.0074	.0067
1	.0679	.0630	.0583	.0540	.0500	.0462	.0427	.0395	.0365	.0337
2	.1393	.1323	.1254	.1188	.1125	.1063	.1005	.0948	.0894	.0842
3	.1904	.1852	.1798	.1743	.1687	.1631	.1574	.1517	.1460	.1404
4	.1951	.1944	.1933	.1917	.1898	.1875	.1849	.1820	.1789	.1755
5	.1600	.1633	.1662	.1687	.1708	.1725	.1738	.1747	.1753	.1755
6	.1093	.1143	.1191	.1237	.1281	.1323	.1362	.1398	.1432	.1462
7	.0640	.0686	.0732	.0778	.0824	.0869	.0914	.0959	.1002	.1044
8	.0328	.0360	.0393	.0428	.0463	.0500	.0537	.0575	.0614	.0653
9	.0150	.0168	.0188	.0209	.0232	.0255	.0280	.0307	.0334	.0363
10	.0061	.0071	.0081	.0092	.0104	.0118	.0132	.0147	.0164	.0181
11	.0023	.0027	.0032	.0037	.0043	.0049	.0056	.0064	.0073	.0082
12	.0008	.0009	.0011	.0014	.0016	.0019	.0022	.0026	.0030	.0034
13	.0002	.0003	.0004	.0005	.0006	.0007	.0008	.0009	.0011	.0013
14	.0001	.0001	.0001	.0001	.0002	.0002	.0003	.0003	.0004	.0005
15	.0000	.0000	.0000	.0000	.0001	.0001	.0001	.0001	.0001	.0002

					λ					
r	5.1	5.2	5.3	5.4	5.5	5.6	5.7	5.8	5.9	6.0
0	.0061	.0055	.0050	.0045	.0041	.0037	.0033	.0030	.0027	.0025
1	.0311	.0287	.0265	.0244	.0225	.0207	.0191	.0176	.0162	.0149
2	.0793	.0746	.0701	.0659	.0618	.0580	.0544	.0509	.0477	.0446
3	.1348	.1293	.1239	.1185	.1133	.1082	.1033	.0985	.0938	.0892
4	.1719	.1681	.1641	.1600	.1558	.1515	.1472	.1428	.1383	.1339
5	.1753	.1748	.1740	.1728	.1714	.1697	.1678	.1656	.1632	.1606
6	.1490	.1515	.1537	.1555	.1571	.1584	.1594	.1601	.1605	.1606
7	.1086	.1125	.1163	.1200	.1234	.1267	.1298	.1326	.1353	.1377

Table 5 continued

r	5.1	5.2	5.3	5.4	λ 5.5	5.6	5.7	5.8	5.9	6.0
8	.0692	.0731	.0771	.0810	.0849	.0887	.0925	.0962	.0998	.1033
9	.0392	.0423	.0454	.0486	.0519	.0552	.0586	.0620	.0654	.0688
10	.0200	.0220	.0241	.0262	.0285	.0309	.0334	.0359	.0386	.0413
11	.0093	.0104	.0116	.0129	.0143	.0157	.0173	.0190	.0207	.0225
12	.0039	.0045	.0051	.0058	.0065	.0073	.0082	.0092	.0102	.0113
13	.0015	.0018	.0021	.0024	.0028	.0032	.0036	.0041	.0046	.0052
14	.0006	.0007	.0008	.0009	.0011	.0013	.0015	.0017	.0019	.0022
15	.0002	.0002	.0003	.0003	.0004	.0005	.0006	.0007	.0008	.0009
16	.0001	.0001	.0001	.0001	.0001	.0002	.0002	.0002	.0003	.0003
17	.0000	.0000	.0000	.0000	.0000	.0000	.0001	.0001	.0001	.0001

r	6.1	6.2	6.3	6.4	λ 6.5	6.6	6.7	6.8	6.9	7.0
0	.0022	.0020	.0018	.0017	.0015	.0014	.0012	.0011	.0010	.0009
1	.0137	.0126	.0116	.0106	.0098	.0090	.0082	.0076	.0070	.0064
2	.0417	.0390	.0364	.0340	.0318	.0296	.0276	.0258	.0240	.0223
3	.0848	.0806	.0765	.0726	.0688	.0652	.0617	.0584	.0552	.0521
4	.1294	.1249	.1205	.1162	.1118	.1076	.1034	.0992	.0952	.0912
5	.1579	.1549	.1519	.1487	.1454	.1420	.1385	.1349	.1314	.1277
6	.1605	.1601	.1595	.1586	.1575	.1562	.1546	.1529	.1511	.1490
7	.1399	.1418	.1435	.1450	.1462	.1472	.1480	.1486	.1489	.1490
8	.1066	.1099	.1130	.1160	.1188	.1215	.1240	.1263	.1284	.1304
9	.0723	.0757	.0791	.0825	.0858	.0891	.0923	.0954	.0985	.1014
10	.0441	.0469	.0498	.0528	.0558	.0588	.0618	.0649	.0679	.0710
11	.0245	.0265	.0285	.0307	.0330	.0353	.0377	.0401	.0426	.0452
12	.0124	.0137	.0150	.0164	.0179	.0194	.0210	.0227	.0245	.0264
13	.0058	.0065	.0073	.0081	.0089	.0098	.0108	.0119	.0130	.0142
14	.0025	.0029	.0033	.0037	.0041	.0046	.0052	.0058	.0064	.0071
15	.0010	.0012	.0014	.0016	.0018	.0020	.0023	.0026	.0029	.0033
16	.0004	.0005	.0005	.0006	.0007	.0008	.0010	.0011	.0013	.0014
17	.0001	.0002	.0002	.0002	.0003	.0003	.0004	.0004	.0005	.0006
18	.0000	.0001	.0001	.0001	.0001	.0001	.0001	.0002	.0002	.0002
19	.0000	.0000	.0000	.0000	.0000	.0000	.0000	.0001	.0001	.0001

r	7.1	7.2	7.3	7.4	λ 7.5	7.6	7.7	7.8	7.9	8.0
0	.0008	.0007	.0007	.0006	.0006	.0005	.0005	.0004	.0004	.0003
1	.0059	.0054	.0049	.0045	.0041	.0038	.0035	.0032	.0029	.0027
2	.0208	.0194	.0180	.0167	.0156	.0145	.0134	.0125	.0116	.0107
3	.0492	.0464	.0438	.0413	.0389	.0366	.0345	.0324	.0305	.0286
4	.0874	.0836	.0799	.0764	.0729	.0696	.0663	.0632	.0602	.0573
5	.1241	.1204	.1167	.1130	.1094	.1057	.1021	.0986	.0951	.0916
6	.1468	.1445	.1420	.1394	.1367	.1339	.1311	.1282	.1252	.1221

Table 5 continued

					λ					
r	7.1	7.2	7.3	7.4	7.5	7.6	7.7	7.8	7.9	8.0
7	.1489	.1486	.1481	.1474	.1465	.1454	.1442	.1428	.1413	.1396
8	.1321	.1337	.1351	.1363	.1373	.1382	.1388	.1392	.1395	.1396
9	.1042	.1070	.1096	.1121	.1144	.1167	.1187	.1207	.1224	.1241
10	.0740	.0770	.0800	.0829	.0858	.0887	.0914	.0941	.0967	.0993
11	.0478	.0504	.0531	.0558	.0585	.0613	.0640	.0667	.0695	.0722
12	.0283	.0303	.0323	.0344	.0366	.0388	.0411	.0434	.0457	.0481
13	.0154	.0168	.0181	.0196	.0211	.0227	.0243	.0260	.0278	.0296
14	.0078	.0086	.0095	.0104	.0113	.0123	.0134	.0145	.0157	.0169
15	.0037	.0041	.0046	.0051	.0057	.0062	.0069	.0075	.0083	.0090
16	.0016	.0019	.0021	.0024	.0026	.0030	.0033	.0037	.0041	.0045
17	.0007	.0008	.0009	.0010	.0012	.0013	.0015	.0017	.0019	.0021
18	.0003	.0003	.0004	.0004	.0005	.0006	.0006	.0007	.0008	.0009
19	.0001	.0001	.0001	.0002	.0002	.0002	.0003	.0003	.0003	.0004
20	.0000	.0000	.0001	.0001	.0001	.0001	.0001	.0001	.0001	.0002
21	.0000	.0000	.0000	.0000	.0000	.0000	.0000	.0000	.0001	.0001

					λ					
r	8.1	8.2	8.3	8.4	8.5	8.6	8.7	8.8	8.9	9.0
0	.0003	.0003	.0002	.0002	.0002	.0002	.0002	.0002	.0001	.0001
1	.0025	.0023	.0021	.0019	.0017	.0016	.0014	.0013	.0012	.0011
2	.0100	.0092	.0086	.0079	.0074	.0068	.0063	.0058	.0054	.0050
3	.0269	.0252	.0237	.0222	.0208	.0195	.0183	.0171	.0160	.0150
4	.0544	.0517	.0491	.0466	.0443	.0420	.0398	.0377	.0357	.0337
5	.0882	.0849	.0816	.0784	.0752	.0722	.0692	.0663	.0635	.0607
6	.1191	.1160	.1128	.1097	.1066	.1034	.1003	.0972	.0941	.0911
7	.1378	.1358	.1338	.1317	.1294	.1271	.1247	.1222	.1197	.1171
8	.1395	.1392	.1388	.1382	.1375	.1366	.1356	.1344	.1332	.1318
9	.1256	.1269	.1280	.1290	.1299	.1306	.1311	.1315	.1317	.1318
10	.1017	.1040	.1063	.1084	.1104	.1123	.1140	.1157	.1172	.1186
11	.0749	.0776	.0802	.0828	.0853	.0878	.0902	.0925	.0948	.0970
12	.0505	.0530	.0555	.0579	.0604	.0629	.0654	.0679	.0703	.0728
13	.0315	.0334	.0354	.0374	.0395	.0416	.0438	.0459	.0481	.0504
14	.0182	.0196	.0210	.0225	.0240	.0256	.0272	.0289	.0306	.0324
15	.0098	.0107	.0116	.0126	.0136	.0147	.0158	.0169	.0182	.0194
16	.0050	.0055	.0060	.0066	.0072	.0079	.0086	.0093	.0101	.0109
17	.0024	.0026	.0029	.0033	.0036	.0040	.0044	.0048	.0053	.0058
18	.0011	.0012	.0014	.0015	.0017	.0019	.0021	.0024	.0026	.0029
19	.0005	.0005	.0006	.0007	.0008	.0009	.0010	.0011	.0012	.0014
20	.0002	.0002	.0002	.0003	.0003	.0004	.0004	.0005	.0005	.0006
21	.0001	.0001	.0001	.0001	.0001	.0002	.0002	.0002	.0002	.0003
22	.0000	.0000	.0000	.0000	.0001	.0001	.0001	.0001	.0001	.0001

Table 5 continued

r	9.1	9.2	9.3	9.4	λ 9.5	9.6	9.7	9.8	9.9	10
0	.0001	.0001	.0001	.0001	.0001	.0001	.0001	.0001	.0001	.0000
1	.0010	.0009	.0009	.0008	.0007	.0007	.0006	.0005	.0005	.0005
2	.0046	.0043	.0040	.0037	.0034	.0031	.0029	.0027	.0025	.0023
3	.0140	.0131	.0123	.0115	.0107	.0100	.0093	.0087	.0081	.0076
4	.0319	.0302	.0285	.0269	.0254	.0240	.0226	.0213	.0201	.0189
5	.0581	.0555	.0530	.0506	.0483	.0460	.0439	.0418	.0398	.0378
6	.0881	.0851	.0822	.0793	.0764	.0736	.0709	.0682	.0656	.0631
7	.1145	.1118	.1091	.1064	.1037	.1010	.0982	.0955	.0928	.0901
8	.1302	.1286	.1269	.1251	.1232	.1212	.1191	.1170	.1148	.1126
9	.1317	.1315	.1311	.1306	.1300	.1293	.1284	.1274	.1263	.1251
10	.1198	.1210	.1219	.1228	.1235	.1241	.1245	.1249	.1250	.1251
11	.0991	.1012	.1031	.1049	.1067	.1083	.1098	.1112	.1125	.1137
12	.0752	.0776	.0799	.0822	.0844	.0866	.0888	.0908	.0928	.0948
13	.0526	.0549	.0572	.0594	.0617	.0640	.0662	.0685	.0707	.0729
14	.0342	.0361	.0380	.0399	.0419	.0439	.0459	.0479	.0500	.0521
15	.0208	.0221	.0235	.0250	.0265	.0281	.0297	.0313	.0330	.0347
16	.0118	.0127	.0137	.0147	.0157	.0168	.0180	.0192	.0204	.0217
17	.0063	.0069	.0075	.0081	.0088	.0095	.0103	.0111	.0119	.0128
18	.0032	.0035	.0039	.0042	.0046	.0051	.0055	.0060	.0065	.0071
19	.0015	.0017	.0019	.0021	.0023	.0026	.0028	.0031	.0034	.0037
20	.0007	.0008	.0009	.0010	.0011	.0012	.0014	.0015	.0017	.0019
21	.0003	.0003	.0004	.0004	.0005	.0006	.0006	.0007	.0008	.0009
22	.0001	.0001	.0002	.0002	.0002	.0002	.0003	.0003	.0004	.0004
23	.0000	.0001	.0001	.0001	.0001	.0001	.0001	.0001	.0002	.0002
24	.0000	.0000	.0000	.0000	.0000	.0000	.0000	.0001	.0001	.0001

r	11	12	13	14	λ 15	16	17	18	19	20
0	.0000	.0000	.0000	.0000	.0000	.0000	.0000	.0000	.0000	.0000
1	.0002	.0001	.0000	.0000	.0000	.0000	.0000	.0000	.0000	.0000
2	.0010	.0004	.0002	.0001	.0000	.0000	.0000	.0000	.0000	.0000
3	.0037	.0018	.0008	.0004	.0002	.0001	.0000	.0000	.0000	.0000
4	.0102	.0053	.0027	.0013	.0006	.0003	.0001	.0001	.0000	.0000
5	.0224	.0127	.0070	.0037	.0019	.0010	.0005	.0002	.0001	.0001
6	.0411	.0255	.0152	.0087	.0048	.0026	.0014	.0007	.0004	.0002
7	.0646	.0437	.0281	.0174	.0104	.0060	.0034	.0018	.0010	.0005
8	.0888	.0655	.0457	.0304	.0194	.0120	.0072	.0042	.0024	.0013
9	.1085	.0874	.0661	.0473	.0324	.0213	.0135	.0083	.0050	.0029
10	.1194	.1048	.0859	.0663	.0486	.0341	.0230	.0150	.0095	.0058
11	.1194	.1144	.1015	.0844	.0663	.0496	.0355	.0245	.0164	.0106
12	.1094	.1144	.1099	.0984	.0829	.0661	.0504	.0368	.0259	.0176
13	.0926	.1056	.1099	.1060	.0956	.0814	.0658	.0509	.0378	.0271
14	.0728	.0905	.1021	.1060	.1024	.0930	.0800	.0655	.0514	.0387

Appendix II Tables

Table 5 continued

r	11	12	13	14	λ 15	16	17	18	19	20
15	.0534	.0724	.0885	.0989	.1024	.0992	.0906	.0786	.0650	.0516
16	.0367	.0543	.0719	.0866	.0960	.0992	.0963	.0884	.0772	.0646
17	.0237	.0383	.0550	.0713	.0847	.0934	.0963	.0936	.0863	.0760
18	.0145	.0256	.0397	.0554	.0706	.0830	.0909	.0936	.0911	.0844
19	.0084	.0161	.0272	.0409	.0557	.0699	.0814	.0887	.0911	.0888
20	.0046	.0097	.0177	.0286	.0418	.0559	.0692	.0798	.0866	.0888
21	.0024	.0055	.0109	.0191	.0299	.0426	.0560	.0684	.0783	.0846
22	.0012	.0030	.0065	.0121	.0204	.0310	.0433	.0560	.0676	.0769
23	.0006	.0016	.0037	.0074	.0133	.0216	.0320	.0438	.0559	.0669
24	.0003	.0008	.0020	.0043	.0083	.0144	.0226	.0328	.0442	.0557
25	.0001	.0004	.0010	.0024	.0050	.0092	.0154	.0237	.0336	.0446
26	.0000	.0002	.0005	.0013	.0029	.0057	.0101	.0164	.0246	.0343
27	.0000	.0001	.0002	.0007	.0016	.0034	.0063	.0109	.0173	.0254
28	.0000	.0000	.0001	.0003	.0009	.0019	.0038	.0070	.0117	.0181
29	.0000	.0000	.0001	.0002	.0004	.0011	.0023	.0044	.0077	.0125
30	.0000	.0000	.0000	.0001	.0002	.0006	.0013	.0026	.0049	.0083
31	.0000	.0000	.0000	.0000	.0001	.0003	.0007	.0015	.0030	.0054
32	.0000	.0000	.0000	.0000	.0001	.0001	.0004	.0009	.0018	.0034
33	.0000	.0000	.0000	.0000	.0000	.0001	.0002	.0005	.0010	.0020
34	.0000	.0000	.0000	.0000	.0000	.0000	.0001	.0002	.0006	.0012
35	.0000	.0000	.0000	.0000	.0000	.0000	.0000	.0001	.0003	.0007
36	.0000	.0000	.0000	.0000	.0000	.0000	.0000	.0001	.0002	.0004
37	.0000	.0000	.0000	.0000	.0000	.0000	.0000	.0000	.0001	.0002
38	.0000	.0000	.0000	.0000	.0000	.0000	.0000	.0000	.0000	.0001
39	.0000	.0000	.0000	.0000	.0000	.0000	.0000	.0000	.0000	.0001

Source: Extracted from William H. Beyer, ed., *CRC Basic Statistical Tables* (Cleveland, Ohio: The Chemical Rubber Co., 1971).

Table 6 Areas of a Standard Normal Distribution

The table entries represent the area under the standard normal curve from 0 to the specified value of z.

$z = 1.4$
$+ 0.08$
1.48

z	.00	.01	.02	.03	.04	.05	.06	.07	.08	.09
0.0	.0000	.0040	.0080	.0120	.0160	.0199	.0239	.0279	.0319	.0359
0.1	.0398	.0438	.0478	.0517	.0557	.0596	.0636	.0675	.0714	.0753
0.2	.0793	.0832	.0871	.0910	.0948	.0987	.1026	.1064	.1103	.1141
0.3	.1179	.1217	.1255	.1293	.1331	.1368	.1406	.1443	.1480	.1517
0.4	.1554	.1591	.1628	.1664	.1700	.1736	.1772	.1808	.1844	.1879
0.5	.1915	.1950	.1985	.2019	.2054	.2088	.2123	.2157	.2190	.2224
0.6	.2257	.2291	.2324	.2357	.2389	.2422	.2454	.2486	.2517	.2549
0.7	.2580	.2611	.2642	.2673	.2704	.2734	.2764	.2794	.2823	.2852
0.8	.2881	.2910	.2939	.2967	.2995	.3023	.3051	.3078	.3106	.3133
0.9	.3159	.3186	.3212	.3238	.3264	.3289	.3315	.3340	.3365	.3389
1.0	.3413	.3438	.3461	.3485	.3508	.3531	.3554	.3577	.3599	.3621
1.1	.3643	.3665	.3686	.3708	.3729	.3749	.3770	.3790	.3810	.3830
1.2	.3849	.3869	.3888	.3907	.3925	.3944	.3962	.3980	.3997	.4015
1.3	.4032	.4049	.4066	.4082	.4099	.4115	.4131	.4147	.4162	.4177
1.4	.4192	.4207	.4222	.4236	.4251	.4265	.4279	.4292	.4306	.4319
1.5	.4332	.4345	.4357	.4370	.4382	.4394	.4406	.4418	.4429	.4441
1.6	.4452	.4463	.4474	.4484	.4495	.4505	.4515	.4525	.4535	.4545
1.7	.4554	.4564	.4573	.4582	.4591	.4599	.4608	.4616	.4625	.4633
1.8	.4641	.4649	.4656	.4664	.4671	.4678	.4686	.4693	.4699	.4706
1.9	.4713	.4719	.4726	.4732	.4738	.4744	.4750	.4756	.4761	.4767
2.0	.4772	.4778	.4783	.4788	.4793	.4798	.4803	.4808	.4812	.4817
2.1	.4821	.4826	.4830	.4834	.4838	.4842	.4846	.4850	.4854	.4857
2.2	.4861	.4864	.4868	.4871	.4875	.4878	.4881	.4884	.4887	.4890
2.3	.4893	.4896	.4898	.4901	.4904	.4906	.4909	.4911	.4913	.4916
2.4	.4918	.4920	.4922	.4925	.4927	.4929	.4931	.4932	.4934	.4936
2.5	.4938	.4940	.4941	.4943	.4945	.4946	.4948	.4949	.4951	.4952
2.6	.4953	.4955	.4956	.4957	.4959	.4960	.4961	.4962	.4963	.4964
2.7	.4965	.4966	.4967	.4968	.4969	.4970	.4971	.4972	.4973	.4974
2.8	.4974	.4975	.4976	.4977	.4977	.4978	.4979	.4979	.4980	.4981
2.9	.4981	.4982	.4982	.4983	.4984	.4984	.4985	.4985	.4986	.4986
3.0	.4987	.4987	.4987	.4988	.4988	.4989	.4989	.4989	.4990	.4990
3.1	.4990	.4991	.4991	.4991	.4992	.4992	.4992	.4992	.4993	.4993
3.2	.4993	.4993	.4994	.4994	.4994	.4994	.4994	.4995	.4995	.4995
3.3	.4995	.4995	.4995	.4996	.4996	.4996	.4996	.4996	.4996	.4997
3.4	.4997	.4997	.4997	.4997	.4997	.4997	.4997	.4997	.4997	.4998
3.5	.4998	.4998	.4998	.4998	.4998	.4998	.4998	.4998	.4998	.4998
3.6	.4998	.4998	.4998	.4999	.4999	.4999	.4999	.4999	.4999	.4999

For values of z greater than or equal 3.70, use 0.4999 to approximate the shaded area under the standard normal curve.

Table 7 Student's *t* Distribution

Student's *t* values generated by Minitab Version 9.2

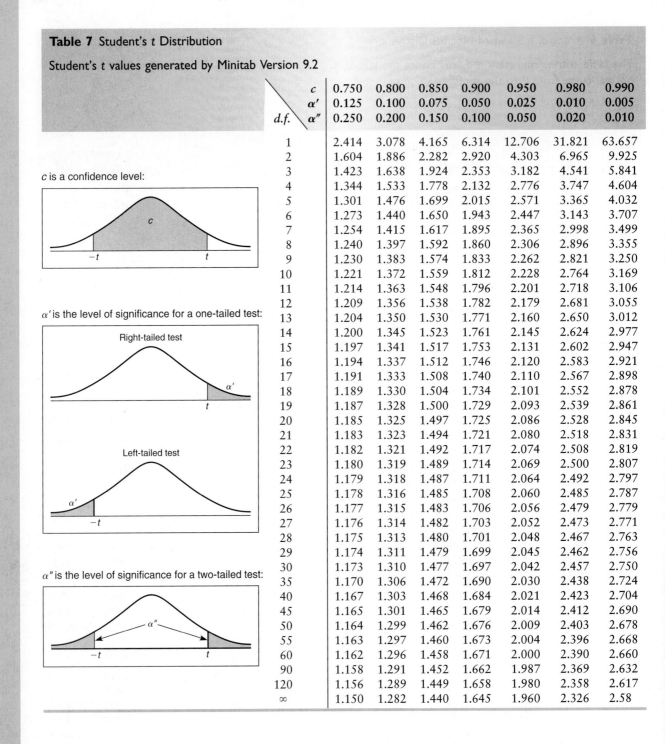

c is a confidence level:

α′ is the level of significance for a one-tailed test:

Right-tailed test

Left-tailed test

α″ is the level of significance for a two-tailed test:

d.f.	c α′ α″	0.750 0.125 0.250	0.800 0.100 0.200	0.850 0.075 0.150	0.900 0.050 0.100	0.950 0.025 0.050	0.980 0.010 0.020	0.990 0.005 0.010
1		2.414	3.078	4.165	6.314	12.706	31.821	63.657
2		1.604	1.886	2.282	2.920	4.303	6.965	9.925
3		1.423	1.638	1.924	2.353	3.182	4.541	5.841
4		1.344	1.533	1.778	2.132	2.776	3.747	4.604
5		1.301	1.476	1.699	2.015	2.571	3.365	4.032
6		1.273	1.440	1.650	1.943	2.447	3.143	3.707
7		1.254	1.415	1.617	1.895	2.365	2.998	3.499
8		1.240	1.397	1.592	1.860	2.306	2.896	3.355
9		1.230	1.383	1.574	1.833	2.262	2.821	3.250
10		1.221	1.372	1.559	1.812	2.228	2.764	3.169
11		1.214	1.363	1.548	1.796	2.201	2.718	3.106
12		1.209	1.356	1.538	1.782	2.179	2.681	3.055
13		1.204	1.350	1.530	1.771	2.160	2.650	3.012
14		1.200	1.345	1.523	1.761	2.145	2.624	2.977
15		1.197	1.341	1.517	1.753	2.131	2.602	2.947
16		1.194	1.337	1.512	1.746	2.120	2.583	2.921
17		1.191	1.333	1.508	1.740	2.110	2.567	2.898
18		1.189	1.330	1.504	1.734	2.101	2.552	2.878
19		1.187	1.328	1.500	1.729	2.093	2.539	2.861
20		1.185	1.325	1.497	1.725	2.086	2.528	2.845
21		1.183	1.323	1.494	1.721	2.080	2.518	2.831
22		1.182	1.321	1.492	1.717	2.074	2.508	2.819
23		1.180	1.319	1.489	1.714	2.069	2.500	2.807
24		1.179	1.318	1.487	1.711	2.064	2.492	2.797
25		1.178	1.316	1.485	1.708	2.060	2.485	2.787
26		1.177	1.315	1.483	1.706	2.056	2.479	2.779
27		1.176	1.314	1.482	1.703	2.052	2.473	2.771
28		1.175	1.313	1.480	1.701	2.048	2.467	2.763
29		1.174	1.311	1.479	1.699	2.045	2.462	2.756
30		1.173	1.310	1.477	1.697	2.042	2.457	2.750
35		1.170	1.306	1.472	1.690	2.030	2.438	2.724
40		1.167	1.303	1.468	1.684	2.021	2.423	2.704
45		1.165	1.301	1.465	1.679	2.014	2.412	2.690
50		1.164	1.299	1.462	1.676	2.009	2.403	2.678
55		1.163	1.297	1.460	1.673	2.004	2.396	2.668
60		1.162	1.296	1.458	1.671	2.000	2.390	2.660
90		1.158	1.291	1.452	1.662	1.987	2.369	2.632
120		1.156	1.289	1.449	1.658	1.980	2.358	2.617
∞		1.150	1.282	1.440	1.645	1.960	2.326	2.58

Table 8 Critical Values of Pearson Product-Moment Correlation, r

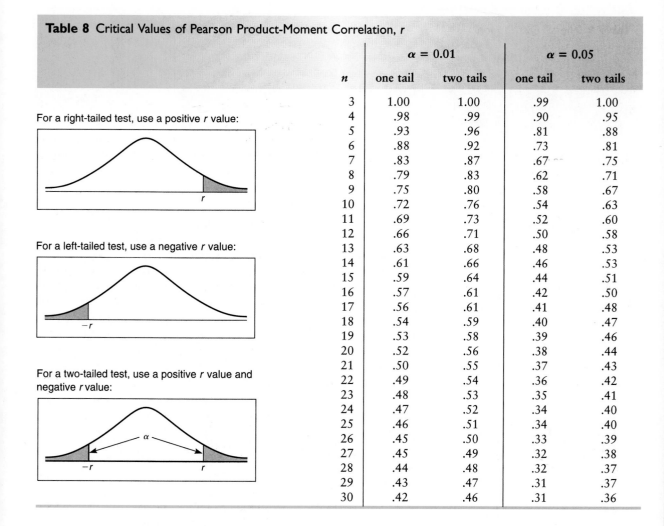

For a right-tailed test, use a positive r value:

For a left-tailed test, use a negative r value:

For a two-tailed test, use a positive r value and negative r value:

n	$\alpha = 0.01$ one tail	$\alpha = 0.01$ two tails	$\alpha = 0.05$ one tail	$\alpha = 0.05$ two tails
3	1.00	1.00	.99	1.00
4	.98	.99	.90	.95
5	.93	.96	.81	.88
6	.88	.92	.73	.81
7	.83	.87	.67	.75
8	.79	.83	.62	.71
9	.75	.80	.58	.67
10	.72	.76	.54	.63
11	.69	.73	.52	.60
12	.66	.71	.50	.58
13	.63	.68	.48	.53
14	.61	.66	.46	.53
15	.59	.64	.44	.51
16	.57	.61	.42	.50
17	.56	.61	.41	.48
18	.54	.59	.40	.47
19	.53	.58	.39	.46
20	.52	.56	.38	.44
21	.50	.55	.37	.43
22	.49	.54	.36	.42
23	.48	.53	.35	.41
24	.47	.52	.34	.40
25	.46	.51	.34	.40
26	.45	.50	.33	.39
27	.45	.49	.32	.38
28	.44	.48	.32	.37
29	.43	.47	.31	.37
30	.42	.46	.31	.36

Appendix II Tables

Table 9 The χ^2 Distribution

For d.f. ≥ 3

For d.f. = 1 or 2

d.f.\α	.995	.990	.975	.950	.900	.100	.050	.025	.010	.005
1	0.0^4393	0.0^3157	0.0^3982	0.0^2393	0.0158	2.71	3.84	5.02	6.63	7.88
2	0.0100	0.0201	0.0506	0.103	0.211	4.61	5.99	7.38	9.21	10.60
3	0.072	0.115	0.216	0.352	0.584	6.25	7.81	9.35	11.34	12.84
4	0.207	0.297	0.484	0.711	1.064	7.78	9.49	11.14	13.28	14.86
5	0.412	0.554	0.831	1.145	1.61	9.24	11.07	12.83	15.09	16.75
6	0.676	0.872	1.24	1.64	2.20	10.64	12.59	14.45	16.81	18.55
7	0.989	1.24	1.69	2.17	2.83	12.02	14.07	16.01	18.48	20.28
8	1.34	1.65	2.18	2.73	3.49	13.36	15.51	17.53	20.09	21.96
9	1.73	2.09	2.70	3.33	4.17	14.68	16.92	19.02	21.67	23.59
10	2.16	2.56	3.25	3.94	4.87	15.99	18.31	20.48	23.21	25.19
11	2.60	3.05	3.82	4.57	5.58	17.28	19.68	21.92	24.72	26.76
12	3.07	3.57	4.40	5.23	6.30	18.55	21.03	23.34	26.22	28.30
13	3.57	4.11	5.01	5.89	7.04	19.81	22.36	24.74	27.69	29.82
14	4.07	4.66	5.63	6.57	7.79	21.06	23.68	26.12	29.14	31.32
15	4.60	5.23	6.26	7.26	8.55	22.31	25.00	27.49	30.58	32.80
16	5.14	5.81	6.91	7.96	9.31	23.54	26.30	28.85	32.00	34.27
17	5.70	6.41	7.56	8.67	10.09	24.77	27.59	30.19	33.41	35.72
18	6.26	7.01	8.23	9.39	10.86	25.99	28.87	31.53	34.81	37.16
19	6.84	7.63	8.91	10.12	11.65	27.20	30.14	32.85	36.19	38.58
20	7.43	8.26	8.59	10.85	12.44	28.41	31.41	34.17	37.57	40.00
21	8.03	8.90	10.28	11.59	13.24	29.62	32.67	35.48	38.93	41.40
22	8.64	9.54	10.98	12.34	14.04	30.81	33.92	36.78	40.29	42.80
23	9.26	10.20	11.69	13.09	14.85	32.01	35.17	38.08	41.64	44.18
24	9.89	10.86	12.40	13.85	15.66	33.20	36.42	39.36	42.98	45.56
25	10.52	11.52	13.12	14.61	16.47	34.38	37.65	40.65	44.31	46.93
26	11.16	12.20	13.84	15.38	17.29	35.56	38.89	41.92	45.64	48.29
27	11.81	12.88	14.57	16.15	18.11	36.74	40.11	43.19	46.96	49.64
28	12.46	13.56	15.31	16.93	18.94	37.92	41.34	44.46	48.28	50.99
29	13.21	14.26	16.05	17.71	19.77	39.09	42.56	45.72	49.59	52.34
30	13.79	14.95	16.79	18.49	20.60	40.26	43.77	46.98	50.89	53.67
40	20.71	22.16	24.43	26.51	29.05	51.80	55.76	59.34	63.69	66.77
50	27.99	29.71	32.36	34.76	37.69	63.17	67.50	71.42	76.15	79.49
60	35.53	37.48	40.48	43.19	46.46	74.40	79.08	83.30	88.38	91.95
70	43.28	45.44	48.76	51.74	55.33	85.53	90.53	95.02	100.4	104.2
80	51.17	53.54	57.15	60.39	64.28	96.58	101.9	106.6	112.3	116.3
90	59.20	61.75	65.65	69.13	73.29	107.6	113.1	118.1	124.1	128.3
100	67.33	70.06	74.22	77.93	82.36	118.5	124.3	129.6	135.8	140.2

Table 10 The F Distribution, 5% (Roman Type) and 1% (Boldface Type) Points for the Distribution of F^*

$\alpha = 0.05$ F (in Roman Type)

$\alpha = 0.01$ F (in Boldface Type)

Degrees of Freedom for Numerator

Degrees of Freedom for Denominator	1	2	3	4	5	6	7	8	9	10	11	12	14	16	20	24	30	40	50	75	100	200	500	∞
1	161	200	216	225	230	234	237	239	241	242	243	244	245	246	248	249	250	251	252	253	253	254	254	254
	4052	4999	5403	5625	5764	5859	5928	5981	6022	6056	6082	6106	6142	6169	6208	6234	6258	6286	6302	6323	6334	6352	6361	6366
2	18.51	19.00	19.16	19.25	19.30	19.33	19.36	19.37	19.38	19.39	19.40	19.41	19.42	19.43	19.44	19.45	19.46	19.47	19.47	19.48	19.49	19.49	19.50	19.50
	98.49	99.01	99.17	99.25	99.30	99.33	99.34	99.36	99.38	99.40	99.41	99.42	99.43	99.44	99.45	99.46	99.47	99.48	99.48	99.49	99.49	99.49	99.50	99.50
3	10.13	9.55	9.28	9.12	9.01	8.94	8.88	8.84	8.81	8.78	8.76	8.74	8.71	8.69	8.66	8.64	8.62	8.60	8.58	8.57	8.56	8.54	8.54	8.53
	34.12	30.81	29.46	28.71	28.24	27.91	27.67	27.49	27.34	27.23	27.13	27.05	26.92	26.83	26.69	26.60	26.50	26.41	26.30	26.27	26.23	26.18	26.14	26.12
4	7.71	6.94	6.59	6.39	6.26	6.16	6.09	6.04	6.00	5.96	5.93	5.91	5.87	5.84	5.80	5.77	5.74	5.71	5.70	5.68	5.66	5.65	5.64	5.63
	21.20	18.00	16.69	15.98	15.52	15.21	14.98	14.80	14.66	14.54	14.45	14.37	14.24	14.15	14.02	13.93	13.83	13.74	13.69	13.61	13.57	13.52	13.48	13.46
5	6.61	5.79	5.41	5.19	5.05	4.95	4.88	4.82	4.78	4.74	4.70	4.68	4.64	4.60	4.56	4.53	4.50	4.46	4.44	4.42	4.40	4.38	4.37	4.36
	16.26	13.27	12.06	11.39	10.97	10.67	10.45	10.27	10.15	10.05	9.96	9.89	9.77	9.68	9.55	9.47	9.38	9.29	9.24	9.17	9.13	9.07	9.04	9.02
6	5.99	5.14	4.76	4.53	4.39	4.28	4.21	4.15	4.10	4.06	4.03	4.00	3.96	3.92	3.87	3.84	3.81	3.77	3.75	3.72	3.71	3.69	3.68	3.67
	13.74	10.92	9.78	9.15	8.75	8.47	8.26	8.10	7.98	7.87	7.79	7.72	7.60	7.52	7.39	7.31	7.23	7.14	7.09	7.02	6.99	6.94	6.90	6.88
7	5.59	4.74	4.35	4.12	3.97	3.87	3.79	3.73	3.68	3.63	3.60	3.57	3.52	3.49	3.44	3.41	3.38	3.34	3.32	3.29	3.28	3.25	3.24	3.23
	12.25	9.55	8.45	7.85	7.46	7.19	7.00	6.84	6.71	6.62	6.54	6.47	6.35	6.27	6.15	6.07	5.98	5.90	5.85	5.78	5.75	5.70	5.67	5.65
8	5.32	4.46	4.07	3.84	3.69	3.58	3.50	3.44	3.39	3.34	3.31	3.28	3.23	3.20	3.15	3.12	3.08	3.05	3.03	3.00	2.98	2.96	2.94	2.93
	11.26	8.65	7.59	7.01	6.63	6.37	6.19	6.03	5.91	5.82	5.74	5.67	5.56	5.48	5.36	5.28	5.20	5.11	5.06	5.00	4.96	4.91	4.88	4.86
9	5.12	4.26	3.86	3.63	3.48	3.37	3.29	3.23	3.18	3.13	3.10	3.07	3.02	2.98	2.93	2.90	2.86	2.82	2.80	2.77	2.76	2.73	2.72	2.71
	10.56	8.02	6.99	6.42	6.06	5.80	5.62	5.47	5.35	5.26	5.18	5.11	5.00	4.92	4.80	4.73	4.64	4.56	4.51	4.45	4.41	4.36	4.33	4.31
10	4.96	4.10	3.71	3.48	3.33	3.22	3.14	3.07	3.02	2.97	2.94	2.91	2.86	2.82	2.77	2.74	2.70	2.67	2.64	2.61	2.59	2.56	2.55	2.54
	10.04	7.56	6.55	5.99	5.64	5.39	5.21	5.06	4.95	4.85	4.78	4.71	4.60	4.52	4.41	4.33	4.25	4.17	4.12	4.05	4.01	3.96	3.93	3.91
11	4.84	3.98	3.59	3.36	3.20	3.09	3.01	2.95	2.90	2.86	2.82	2.79	2.74	2.70	2.65	2.61	2.57	2.53	2.50	2.47	2.45	2.42	2.41	2.40
	9.65	7.20	6.22	5.67	5.32	5.07	4.88	4.74	4.63	4.54	4.46	4.40	4.29	4.21	4.10	4.02	3.94	3.86	3.80	3.74	3.70	3.66	3.62	3.60
12	4.75	3.88	3.49	3.26	3.11	3.00	2.92	2.85	2.80	2.76	2.72	2.69	2.64	2.60	2.54	2.50	2.46	2.42	2.40	2.36	2.35	2.32	2.31	2.30
	9.33	6.93	5.95	5.41	5.06	4.82	4.65	4.50	4.39	4.30	4.22	4.16	4.05	3.98	3.86	3.78	3.70	3.61	3.56	3.49	3.46	3.41	3.38	3.36
13	4.67	3.80	3.41	3.18	3.02	2.92	2.84	2.77	2.72	2.67	2.63	2.60	2.55	2.51	2.46	2.42	2.38	2.34	2.32	2.28	2.26	2.24	2.22	2.21
	9.07	6.70	5.74	5.20	4.86	4.62	4.44	4.30	4.19	4.10	4.02	3.96	3.85	3.78	3.67	3.59	3.51	3.42	3.37	3.39	3.27	3.21	3.18	3.16
14	4.60	3.74	3.34	3.11	2.96	2.85	2.77	2.70	2.65	2.60	2.56	2.53	2.48	2.44	2.39	2.35	2.31	2.27	2.24	2.21	2.19	2.16	2.14	2.13
	8.86	6.51	5.56	5.03	4.69	4.46	4.28	4.14	4.03	3.94	3.86	3.80	3.70	3.62	3.51	3.43	3.34	3.26	3.21	3.14	3.11	3.06	3.02	3.00
15	4.54	3.68	3.29	3.06	2.90	2.79	2.70	2.64	2.59	2.55	2.51	2.48	2.43	2.39	2.33	2.29	2.25	2.21	2.18	2.15	2.12	2.10	2.08	2.07
	8.68	6.36	5.42	4.89	4.56	4.32	4.14	4.00	3.89	3.80	3.73	3.67	3.56	3.48	3.36	3.29	3.20	3.12	3.07	3.00	2.97	2.92	2.89	2.87
16	4.49	3.63	3.24	3.01	2.85	2.74	2.66	2.59	2.54	2.49	2.45	2.42	2.37	2.33	2.28	2.24	2.20	2.16	2.13	2.09	2.07	2.04	2.02	2.01
	8.53	6.23	5.29	4.77	4.44	4.20	4.03	3.89	3.78	3.69	3.61	3.55	3.45	3.37	3.25	3.18	3.10	3.01	2.96	2.89	2.86	2.80	2.77	2.75
17	4.45	3.59	3.20	2.96	2.81	2.70	2.62	2.55	2.50	2.45	2.41	2.38	2.33	2.29	2.23	2.19	2.15	2.11	2.08	2.04	2.02	1.99	1.97	1.96
	8.40	6.11	5.18	4.67	4.34	4.10	3.93	3.79	3.68	3.59	3.52	3.45	3.35	3.27	3.16	3.08	3.00	2.92	2.86	2.79	2.76	2.70	2.67	2.65

Table 10 continued

Degrees of Freedom for Numerator

Degrees of Freedom for Denominator	1	2	3	4	5	6	7	8	9	10	11	12	14	16	20	24	30	40	50	75	100	200	500	∞
18	4.41	3.55	3.16	2.93	2.77	2.66	2.58	2.51	2.46	2.41	2.37	2.34	2.29	2.25	2.19	2.15	2.11	2.07	2.04	2.00	1.98	1.95	1.93	1.92
	8.28	6.01	5.09	4.58	4.25	4.01	3.85	3.71	3.60	3.51	3.44	3.37	3.27	3.19	3.07	3.00	2.91	2.83	2.78	2.71	2.68	2.62	2.59	2.57
19	4.38	3.52	3.13	2.90	2.74	2.63	2.55	2.48	2.43	2.38	2.34	2.31	2.26	2.21	2.15	2.11	2.07	2.02	2.00	1.96	1.94	1.91	1.90	1.88
	8.18	5.93	5.01	4.50	4.17	3.94	3.77	3.63	3.52	3.43	3.36	3.30	3.19	3.12	3.00	2.92	2.84	2.76	2.70	2.63	2.60	2.54	2.51	2.49
20	4.35	3.49	3.10	2.87	2.71	2.60	2.52	2.45	2.40	2.35	2.31	2.28	2.23	2.18	2.12	2.08	2.04	1.99	1.96	1.92	1.90	1.87	1.85	1.84
	8.10	5.85	4.94	4.43	4.10	3.87	3.71	3.56	3.45	3.37	3.30	3.23	3.13	3.05	2.94	2.86	2.77	2.69	2.63	2.56	2.53	2.47	2.44	2.42
21	4.32	3.47	3.07	2.84	2.68	2.57	2.49	2.42	2.37	2.32	2.28	2.25	2.20	2.15	2.09	2.05	2.00	1.96	1.93	1.89	1.87	1.84	1.82	1.81
	8.02	5.78	4.87	4.37	4.04	3.81	3.65	3.51	3.40	3.31	3.24	3.17	3.07	2.99	2.88	2.80	2.72	2.63	2.58	2.51	2.47	2.42	2.38	2.36
22	4.30	3.44	3.05	2.82	2.66	2.55	2.47	2.40	2.35	2.30	2.26	2.23	2.18	2.13	2.07	2.03	1.98	1.93	1.91	1.87	1.84	1.81	1.80	1.78
	7.94	5.72	4.82	4.31	3.99	3.76	3.59	3.45	3.35	3.26	3.18	3.12	3.02	2.94	2.83	2.75	2.67	2.58	2.53	2.46	2.42	2.37	2.33	2.31
23	4.28	3.42	3.03	2.80	2.64	2.53	2.45	2.38	2.32	2.28	2.24	2.20	2.14	2.10	2.04	2.00	1.96	1.91	1.88	1.84	1.82	1.79	1.77	1.76
	7.88	5.66	4.76	4.26	3.94	3.71	3.54	3.41	3.30	3.21	3.14	3.07	2.97	2.89	2.78	2.70	2.62	2.53	2.48	2.41	2.37	2.32	2.28	2.26
24	4.26	3.40	3.01	2.78	2.62	2.51	2.43	2.36	2.30	2.26	2.22	2.18	2.13	2.09	2.02	1.98	1.94	1.89	1.86	1.82	1.80	1.76	1.74	1.73
	7.82	5.61	4.72	4.22	3.90	3.67	3.50	3.36	3.25	3.17	3.09	3.03	2.93	2.85	2.74	2.66	2.58	2.49	2.44	2.36	2.33	2.27	2.23	2.21
25	4.24	3.38	2.99	2.76	2.60	2.49	2.41	2.34	2.28	2.24	2.20	2.16	2.11	2.06	2.00	1.96	1.92	1.87	1.84	1.80	1.77	1.74	1.72	1.71
	7.77	5.57	4.68	4.18	3.86	3.63	3.46	3.32	3.21	3.13	3.05	2.99	2.89	2.81	2.70	2.62	2.54	2.45	2.40	2.32	2.29	2.23	2.19	2.17
26	4.22	3.37	2.98	2.74	2.59	2.47	2.39	2.32	2.27	2.22	2.18	2.15	2.10	2.05	1.99	1.95	1.90	1.85	1.82	1.78	1.76	1.72	1.70	1.69
	7.72	5.53	4.64	4.14	3.82	3.59	3.42	3.29	3.17	3.09	3.02	2.96	2.86	2.77	2.66	2.58	2.50	2.41	2.36	2.28	2.25	2.19	2.15	2.13
27	4.21	3.35	2.96	2.73	2.57	2.46	2.37	2.30	2.25	2.20	2.16	2.13	2.08	2.03	1.97	1.93	1.88	1.84	1.80	1.76	1.74	1.71	1.68	1.67
	7.68	5.49	4.60	4.11	3.79	3.56	3.39	3.26	3.14	3.06	2.98	2.93	2.83	2.74	2.63	2.55	2.47	2.38	2.33	2.25	2.21	2.16	2.12	2.10
28	4.20	3.34	2.95	2.71	2.56	2.44	2.36	2.29	2.24	2.19	2.15	2.12	2.06	2.02	1.96	1.91	1.87	1.81	1.78	1.75	1.72	1.69	1.67	1.65
	7.64	5.45	4.57	4.07	3.76	3.53	3.36	3.23	3.11	3.03	2.95	2.90	2.80	2.71	2.60	2.52	2.44	2.35	2.30	2.22	2.18	2.13	2.09	2.06
29	4.18	3.33	2.93	2.70	2.54	2.43	2.35	2.28	2.22	2.18	2.14	2.10	2.05	2.00	1.94	1.90	1.85	1.80	1.77	1.73	1.71	1.68	1.65	1.64
	7.60	5.42	4.54	4.04	3.73	3.50	3.33	3.20	3.08	3.00	2.92	2.87	2.77	2.68	2.57	2.49	2.41	2.32	2.27	2.19	2.15	2.10	2.06	2.03
30	4.17	3.32	2.92	2.69	2.53	2.42	2.34	2.27	2.21	2.16	2.12	2.09	2.04	1.99	1.93	1.89	1.84	1.79	1.76	1.72	1.69	1.66	1.64	1.62
	7.56	5.39	4.51	4.02	3.70	3.47	3.30	3.17	3.06	2.98	2.90	2.84	2.74	2.66	2.55	2.47	2.38	2.29	2.24	2.16	2.13	2.07	2.03	2.01
32	4.15	3.30	2.90	2.67	2.51	2.40	2.32	2.25	2.19	2.14	2.10	2.07	2.02	1.97	1.91	1.86	1.82	1.76	1.74	1.69	1.67	1.64	1.61	1.59
	7.50	5.34	4.46	3.97	3.66	3.42	3.25	3.12	3.01	2.94	2.86	2.80	2.70	2.62	2.51	2.42	2.34	2.25	2.20	2.12	2.08	2.02	1.98	1.96
34	4.13	3.28	2.88	2.65	2.49	2.38	2.30	2.23	2.17	2.12	2.08	2.05	2.00	1.95	1.89	1.84	1.80	1.74	1.71	1.67	1.64	1.61	1.59	1.57
	7.44	5.29	4.42	3.93	3.61	3.38	3.21	3.08	2.97	2.89	2.82	2.76	2.66	2.58	2.47	2.38	2.30	2.21	2.15	2.08	2.04	1.98	1.94	1.91
36	4.11	3.26	2.86	2.63	2.48	2.36	2.28	2.21	2.15	2.10	2.06	2.03	1.98	1.93	1.87	1.82	1.78	1.72	1.69	1.65	1.62	1.59	1.56	1.55
	7.39	5.25	4.38	3.89	3.58	3.35	3.18	3.04	2.94	2.86	2.78	2.72	2.62	2.54	2.43	2.35	2.26	2.17	2.12	2.04	2.00	1.94	1.90	1.87
38	4.10	3.25	2.85	2.62	2.46	2.35	2.26	2.19	2.14	2.09	2.05	2.02	1.96	1.92	1.85	1.80	1.76	1.71	1.67	1.63	1.60	1.57	1.54	1.53
	7.35	5.21	4.34	3.86	3.54	3.32	3.15	3.02	2.91	2.82	2.75	2.69	2.59	2.51	2.40	2.32	2.22	2.14	2.08	2.00	1.97	1.90	1.86	1.84
40	4.08	3.23	2.84	2.61	2.45	2.34	2.25	2.18	2.12	2.07	2.04	2.00	1.95	1.90	1.84	1.79	1.74	1.69	1.66	1.61	1.59	1.55	1.53	1.51
	7.31	5.18	4.31	3.83	3.51	3.29	3.12	2.99	2.88	2.80	2.73	2.66	2.56	2.49	2.37	2.29	2.20	2.11	2.05	1.97	1.94	1.88	1.84	1.81
42	4.07	3.22	2.83	2.59	2.44	2.32	2.24	2.17	2.11	2.06	2.02	1.99	1.94	1.89	1.82	1.78	1.73	1.68	1.64	1.60	1.57	1.54	1.51	1.49
	7.27	5.15	4.29	3.80	3.49	3.26	3.10	2.96	2.86	2.77	2.70	2.64	2.54	2.46	2.35	2.26	2.17	2.08	2.02	1.94	1.91	1.85	1.80	1.78
44	4.06	3.21	2.82	2.58	2.43	2.31	2.23	2.16	2.10	2.05	2.01	1.98	1.92	1.88	1.81	1.76	1.72	1.66	1.63	1.58	1.56	1.52	1.50	1.48
	7.24	5.12	4.26	3.78	3.46	3.24	3.07	2.94	2.84	2.75	2.68	2.62	2.52	2.44	2.32	2.24	2.15	2.06	2.00	1.92	1.88	1.82	1.78	1.75

Table 10 continued

Degrees of Freedom for Numerator

Degrees of Freedom for Denominator	1	2	3	4	5	6	7	8	9	10	11	12	14	16	20	24	30	40	50	75	100	200	500	∞
46	4.05 / 7.21	3.20 / 5.10	2.81 / 4.24	2.57 / 3.76	2.42 / 3.44	2.30 / 3.22	2.22 / 3.05	2.14 / 2.92	2.09 / 2.82	2.04 / 2.73	2.00 / 2.66	1.97 / 2.60	1.91 / 2.50	1.87 / 2.42	1.80 / 2.30	1.75 / 2.22	1.71 / 2.13	1.65 / 2.04	1.62 / 1.98	1.57 / 1.90	1.54 / 1.86	1.51 / 1.80	1.48 / 1.76	1.46 / 1.72
48	4.04 / 7.19	3.19 / 5.08	2.80 / 4.22	2.56 / 3.74	2.41 / 3.42	2.30 / 3.20	2.21 / 3.04	2.14 / 2.90	2.08 / 2.80	2.03 / 2.71	1.99 / 2.64	1.96 / 2.58	1.90 / 2.48	1.86 / 2.40	1.79 / 2.28	1.74 / 2.20	1.70 / 2.11	1.64 / 2.02	1.61 / 1.96	1.56 / 1.88	1.53 / 1.84	1.50 / 1.78	1.47 / 1.73	1.45 / 1.70
50	4.03 / 7.17	3.18 / 5.06	2.79 / 4.20	2.56 / 3.72	2.40 / 3.41	2.29 / 3.18	2.20 / 3.02	2.13 / 2.88	2.07 / 2.78	2.02 / 2.70	1.98 / 2.62	1.95 / 2.56	1.90 / 2.46	1.85 / 2.39	1.78 / 2.26	1.74 / 2.18	1.69 / 2.10	1.63 / 2.00	1.60 / 1.94	1.55 / 1.86	1.52 / 1.82	1.48 / 1.76	1.46 / 1.71	1.44 / 1.68
55	4.02 / 7.12	3.17 / 5.01	2.78 / 4.16	2.54 / 3.68	2.38 / 3.37	2.27 / 3.15	2.18 / 2.98	2.11 / 2.85	2.05 / 2.75	2.00 / 2.66	1.97 / 2.59	1.93 / 2.53	1.88 / 2.43	1.83 / 2.35	1.76 / 2.23	1.72 / 2.15	1.67 / 2.06	1.61 / 1.96	1.58 / 1.90	1.52 / 1.82	1.50 / 1.78	1.46 / 1.71	1.43 / 1.66	1.41 / 1.64
60	4.00 / 7.08	3.15 / 4.98	2.76 / 4.13	2.52 / 3.65	2.37 / 3.34	2.25 / 3.12	2.17 / 2.95	2.10 / 2.82	2.04 / 2.72	1.99 / 2.63	1.95 / 2.56	1.92 / 2.50	1.86 / 2.40	1.81 / 2.32	1.75 / 2.20	1.70 / 2.12	1.65 / 2.03	1.59 / 1.93	1.56 / 1.87	1.50 / 1.79	1.48 / 1.74	1.44 / 1.68	1.41 / 1.63	1.39 / 1.60
65	3.99 / 7.04	3.14 / 4.95	2.75 / 4.10	2.51 / 3.62	2.36 / 3.31	2.24 / 3.09	2.15 / 2.93	2.08 / 2.79	2.02 / 2.70	1.98 / 2.61	1.94 / 2.54	1.90 / 2.47	1.85 / 2.37	1.80 / 2.30	1.73 / 2.18	1.68 / 2.09	1.63 / 2.00	1.57 / 1.90	1.54 / 1.84	1.49 / 1.76	1.46 / 1.71	1.42 / 1.64	1.39 / 1.60	1.37 / 1.56
70	3.98 / 7.01	3.13 / 4.92	2.74 / 4.08	2.50 / 3.60	2.35 / 3.29	2.23 / 3.07	2.14 / 2.91	2.07 / 2.77	2.01 / 2.67	1.97 / 2.59	1.93 / 2.51	1.89 / 2.45	1.84 / 2.35	1.79 / 2.28	1.72 / 2.15	1.67 / 2.07	1.62 / 1.98	1.56 / 1.88	1.53 / 1.82	1.47 / 1.74	1.45 / 1.69	1.40 / 1.62	1.37 / 1.56	1.35 / 1.53
80	3.96 / 6.96	3.11 / 4.88	2.72 / 4.04	2.48 / 3.56	2.33 / 3.25	2.21 / 3.04	2.12 / 2.87	2.05 / 2.74	1.99 / 2.64	1.95 / 2.55	1.91 / 2.48	1.88 / 2.41	1.82 / 2.32	1.77 / 2.24	1.70 / 2.11	1.65 / 2.03	1.60 / 1.94	1.54 / 1.84	1.51 / 1.78	1.45 / 1.70	1.42 / 1.65	1.38 / 1.57	1.35 / 1.52	1.32 / 1.49
100	3.94 / 6.90	3.09 / 4.82	2.70 / 3.98	2.46 / 3.51	2.30 / 3.20	2.19 / 2.99	2.10 / 2.82	2.03 / 2.69	1.97 / 2.59	1.92 / 2.51	1.88 / 2.43	1.85 / 2.36	1.79 / 2.26	1.75 / 2.19	1.68 / 2.06	1.63 / 1.98	1.57 / 1.89	1.51 / 1.79	1.48 / 1.73	1.42 / 1.64	1.39 / 1.59	1.34 / 1.51	1.30 / 1.46	1.28 / 1.43
125	3.92 / 6.84	3.07 / 4.78	2.68 / 3.94	2.44 / 3.47	2.29 / 3.17	2.17 / 2.95	2.08 / 2.79	2.01 / 2.65	1.95 / 2.56	1.90 / 2.47	1.86 / 2.40	1.83 / 2.33	1.77 / 2.23	1.72 / 2.15	1.65 / 2.03	1.60 / 1.94	1.55 / 1.85	1.49 / 1.75	1.45 / 1.68	1.39 / 1.59	1.36 / 1.54	1.31 / 1.46	1.27 / 1.40	1.25 / 1.37
150	3.91 / 6.81	3.06 / 4.75	2.67 / 3.91	2.43 / 3.44	2.27 / 3.13	2.16 / 2.92	2.07 / 2.76	2.00 / 2.62	1.94 / 2.53	1.89 / 2.44	1.85 / 2.37	1.82 / 2.30	1.76 / 2.20	1.71 / 2.12	1.64 / 2.00	1.59 / 1.91	1.54 / 1.83	1.47 / 1.72	1.44 / 1.66	1.37 / 1.56	1.34 / 1.51	1.29 / 1.43	1.25 / 1.37	1.22 / 1.33
200	3.89 / 6.76	3.04 / 4.71	2.65 / 3.88	2.41 / 3.41	2.26 / 3.11	2.14 / 2.90	2.05 / 2.73	1.98 / 2.60	1.92 / 2.50	1.87 / 2.41	1.83 / 2.34	1.80 / 2.28	1.74 / 2.17	1.69 / 2.09	1.62 / 1.97	1.57 / 1.88	1.52 / 1.79	1.45 / 1.69	1.42 / 1.62	1.35 / 1.53	1.32 / 1.48	1.26 / 1.39	1.22 / 1.33	1.19 / 1.28
400	3.86 / 6.70	3.02 / 4.66	2.62 / 3.83	2.39 / 3.36	2.23 / 3.06	2.12 / 2.85	2.03 / 2.69	1.96 / 2.55	1.90 / 2.46	1.85 / 2.37	1.81 / 2.29	1.78 / 2.23	1.72 / 2.12	1.67 / 2.04	1.60 / 1.92	1.54 / 1.84	1.49 / 1.74	1.42 / 1.64	1.38 / 1.57	1.32 / 1.47	1.28 / 1.42	1.22 / 1.32	1.16 / 1.24	1.13 / 1.19
1000	3.85 / 6.66	3.00 / 4.62	2.61 / 3.80	2.38 / 3.34	2.22 / 3.04	2.10 / 2.82	2.02 / 2.66	1.95 / 2.53	1.89 / 2.43	1.84 / 2.34	1.80 / 2.26	1.76 / 2.20	1.70 / 2.09	1.65 / 2.01	1.58 / 1.89	1.53 / 1.81	1.47 / 1.71	1.41 / 1.61	1.36 / 1.54	1.30 / 1.44	1.26 / 1.38	1.19 / 1.28	1.13 / 1.19	1.08 / 1.11
∞	3.84 / 6.64	2.99 / 4.60	2.60 / 3.78	2.37 / 3.32	2.21 / 3.02	2.09 / 2.80	2.01 / 2.64	1.94 / 2.51	1.88 / 2.41	1.83 / 2.32	1.79 / 2.24	1.75 / 2.18	1.69 / 2.07	1.64 / 1.99	1.57 / 1.87	1.52 / 1.79	1.46 / 1.69	1.40 / 1.59	1.35 / 1.52	1.28 / 1.41	1.24 / 1.36	1.17 / 1.25	1.11 / 1.15	1.00 / 1.00

*From Biometrika Tables for Statisticians, Vol. I, by permission of the Biometrika Trustees.

Table 11 Critical Values for Spearman Rank Correlation, r_s

For a right- (left-) tailed test, use the positive (negative) critical value found in the table under significance level for a one-tailed test. For a two-tailed test, use both the positive and negative of the critical value found in the table under significance level for a two-tailed test, n = number of pairs.

	Significance level for a one-tailed test at			
	0.05	0.025	0.005	0.001
	Significance level for a two-tailed test at			
n	0.10	0.05	0.01	0.002
5	0.900	1.000		
6	0.829	0.886	1.000	
7	0.715	0.786	0.929	1.000
8	0.620	0.715	0.881	0.953
9	0.600	0.700	0.834	0.917
10	0.564	0.649	0.794	0.879
11	0.537	0.619	0.764	0.855
12	0.504	0.588	0.735	0.826
13	0.484	0.561	0.704	0.797
14	0.464	0.539	0.680	0.772
15	0.447	0.522	0.658	0.750
16	0.430	0.503	0.636	0.730
17	0.415	0.488	0.618	0.711
18	0.402	0.474	0.600	0.693
19	0.392	0.460	0.585	0.676
20	0.381	0.447	0.570	0.661
21	0.371	0.437	0.556	0.647
22	0.361	0.426	0.544	0.633
23	0.353	0.417	0.532	0.620
24	0.345	0.407	0.521	0.608
25	0.337	0.399	0.511	0.597
26	0.331	0.391	0.501	0.587
27	0.325	0.383	0.493	0.577
28	0.319	0.376	0.484	0.567
29	0.312	0.369	0.475	0.558
30	0.307	0.363	0.467	0.549

From G. J. Glasser and R. F. Winter, "Critical Values of the Coefficient of Rank Correlation for Testing the Hypothesis of Independence," *Biometrika, 48,* 444 (1961). Printed by permission of Biometrika Trustees.

Appendix III Answers and Key Steps to Odd-Numbered Problems

Chapter I

Section I.I

1. (a) Population: The responses to the question from all adults in the United States.
   (b) Sample: The responses from the 1261 adults.
3. (a) Population: Information about student fees from all colleges in the United States.
   (b) Sample: Information about student fees at the 30 colleges surveyed.
5. (a) Population: The time interval between the arrival of an insurance payment check and the time it clears for *all* checks received by the company from the five-state region.
   (b) Sample: The time interval between the arrival of the check and the time the check clears for the 32 payment checks in the sample.
7. (a) ratio (b) interval (c) nominal (d) ordinal (e) ratio (f) ratio
9. (a) Census, since ages of *all* members of both groups were used.
   (b) Experiment. The subjects were treated to determine level of pain tolerance.
   (c) Simulation. Computer images were used to model the relation between stride length and running efficiency.
   (d) Sampling. Gallup Chinese surveyed only a portion of the Chinese population.
11. (a) "Over the past few years" is likely to mean different time spans to people of different ages. "During the past 3 years" or "within the past 3 years" would be better.
    (b) The responses could well be different. If one considers the effects of other people running stop signs, the answer would likely be "yes." If a person recalls that he or she has inadvertently run stop signs, the answer is more likely to be "no."
    (c) Yes or no responses are likely to be unreliable. At certain times, such as for major sports events, the answer might be "yes." At other times, the same respondent could answer "no." Allowing a range of responses would probably produce more useful data.

Chapter Review Problems

1. Depends on article.
3. See text.
5. Possible directions on survey questions: Give height in inches, give age as of last birthday, give GPA to one decimal place, and so forth. Think about the types of responses you wish to have on each question.

Chapter 2

Section 2.1

1. See text.
3. Because the largest number has two digits, use groups of two digits in the random-number table. Select a starting place, and proceed until you have obtained six different numbers from 01 to 99. For instance, starting in column 1, line 5 produces the sample 06, 34, 87, 69, 38, 90. Different starting places will produce different samples.
5. Because the largest number has three digits, use groups of three digits in the random-number table. Select a starting place, and proceed until you have seven distinct numbers from 001 to 500. For instance, starting in column 1, line 4 produces the sample 315, 244, 397, 353, 086, 068, 084. Different starting places will produce different samples.
7. Use a random-number table to select four distinct numbers corresponding to people in your class.
   (a) Reasons may vary. For instance, the first four students may make a special effort to get to class on time.
   (b) Reasons may vary. For instance, four students who come in late might all be nursing students enrolled in an anatomy and physiology class that meets the hour before in a far-away building. They may be more motivated than other students to complete a degree requirement.
   (c) Reasons may vary. For instance, four students sitting in the back row might be less inclined to participate in class discussions.
   (d) Reasons may vary. For instance, the tallest students might all be male.
9. Since the largest number has two digits, read groups of two digits. Select a starting place in the random-number table, and proceed until you have six distinct numbers from 01 to 42. By starting in column 1 of row 11, we obtained the numbers 17, 13, 25, 29, 35, 06.
11. (a) Assign each sheep a distinct number from 1 to 250. Because the largest number has three digits, read groups of three digits from a random-number table. Select a starting place, and proceed until you have 15 distinct numbers from 001 to 250. Numbers included in the sample will vary according to the starting place and pattern for reading the table.
    (b) Because the largest number has four digits, read groups of four digits from a random-number table. Select a starting place, and proceed until you have 10 distinct numbers from 1024 to 8342. Numbers included in the sample will vary according to the starting place and pattern for reading the table.
    (c) Number the pieces of luggage as they come off the conveyor belt in the next 25 minutes. Use a random-number table to choose five distinct numbers that correspond to pieces of luggage. Numbers will vary according to the starting place and pattern for reading the table.
    (d) Give the survey to as many people as will take the time to complete the survey between 6 and 7 P.M. Number all the surveys obtained.

Use a random-number table to choose 12 distinct numbers corresponding to surveys. Note that the population you are sampling consists of survey data from people who are willing to complete surveys, not from everyone who comes to the shopping center during the designated time period.

13. Because the highest value on the face of a die has one digit, read single digits from a random-number table. Whenever a digit 1, 2, 3, 4, 5, or 6 occurs, record it and continue until you have 20 digits in the range 1 to 6 recorded. Notice that repetition of digits is required.

15. Since the largest number assigned to a card has two digits, read groups of two digits. Select a starting place in the random-number table, and proceed until you have five distinct numbers from 01 to 52. The sample is composed of the corresponding cards.

17. Since there are five possible outcomes for each question, read single digits from a random-number table. Select a starting place, and proceed until you have 10 digits from 1 to 5. Repetition is required. The correct answer for each question will be the letter choice corresponding to the digit chosen for that question.

19. (a) simple random sample
    (b) cluster sample
    (c) convenience sample
    (d) systematic sample
    (e) stratified sample

Section 2.2

1. Highest Level of Education and Average Annual Household Income (in thousands of dollars)

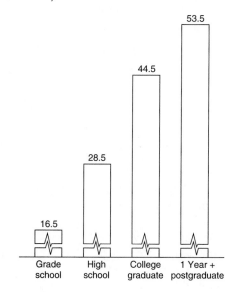

3. (a) Number of People Who Died in a Calendar Year from Listed Causes (Bar Graph)

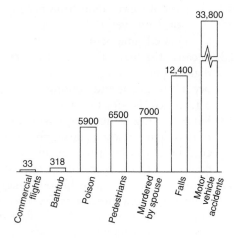

(b) Number of People Who Died in a Calendar Year from Listed Causes (Pareto Chart)

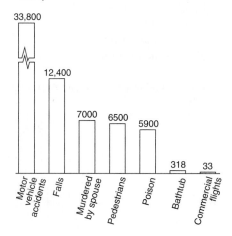

5. Where We Hide the Mess

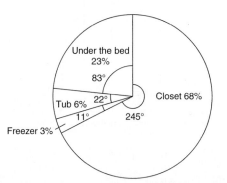

7. Type of Injury in PE Classes

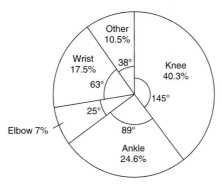

9. Percent of Households with Appliance

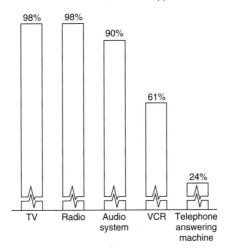

The information could not be put in a circle graph because some respondents have more than one of the designated appliances. Also notice that the percents do not total 100%.

11. U.S. Agricultural Land Owned by Foreign Interests

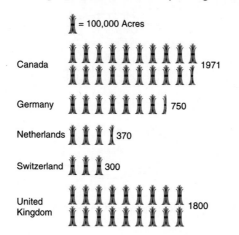

13. Personal Savings as a Percent of Disposable Income

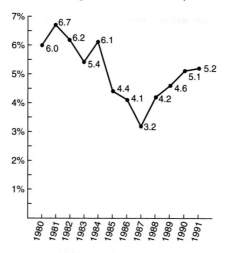

15. Cost of Long-Distance Telephone Calls per Minute (in constant 1993 figures)

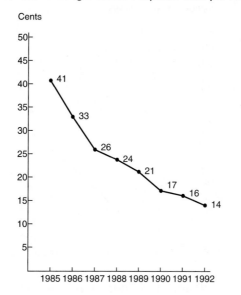

17. (a) The two graphs are bar graphs.

    (b) Revenue for the Consumer On-Line Information Industry (in billions of dollars)

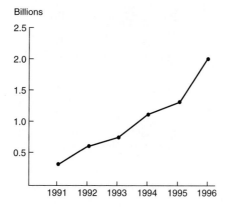

(c) Number of Subscribers for the Consumer On-Line Information Industry (in millions of subscribers)

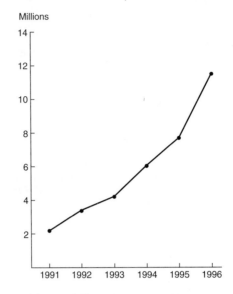

Section 2.3

1. (a) Class width = 49

(b)

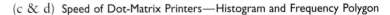

Speed of Dot-Matrix Printers					
Class Limits	Class Boundaries	Midpoint	Frequency	Relative Frequency	Cumulative Frequency
14– 62	13.5– 62.5	38	5	0.11	5
63–111	62.5–111.5	87	14	0.32	19
112–160	111.5–160.5	136	18	0.41	37
161–209	160.5–209.5	185	5	0.11	42
210–258	209.5–258.5	234	2	0.05	44

(c & d) Speed of Dot-Matrix Printers—Histogram and Frequency Polygon

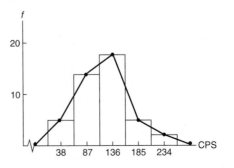

(e) Speed of Dot-Matrix Printers—Relative-Frequency Histogram

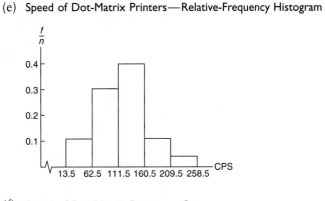

(f) Speed of Dot-Matrix Printers—Ogive

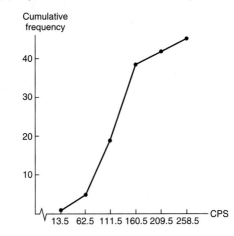

3. (a) Class width is 16.

(b)

Annual Tuition at Private Accredited U.S. Colleges (in hundreds of dollars)					
Class Limits	Class Boundaries	Midpoint	Frequency	Relative Frequency	Cumulative Frequency
38– 53	37.5– 53.5	45.5	9	0.184	9
54– 69	53.5– 69.5	61.5	11	0.225	20
70– 85	69.5– 85.5	77.5	8	0.163	28
86–101	85.5–101.5	93.5	8	0.163	36
102–117	101.5–117.5	109.5	4	0.082	40
118–133	117.5–133.5	125.5	6	0.122	46
134–149	133.5–149.5	141.5	3	0.061	49

(c & d) Annual Tuition at Private Accredited U.S. Colleges and Universities (in hundreds of dollars)—Histogram and Frequency Polygon

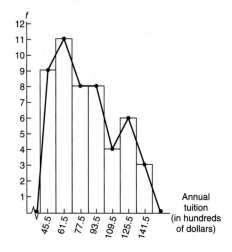

(e) Annual Tuition at Private Accredited U.S. Colleges and Universities (in hundreds of dollars)—Relative-Frequency Histogram

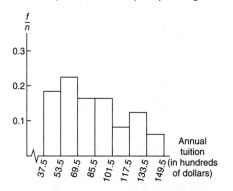

(f) Annual Tuition at Private Accredited U.S. Colleges (in hundreds of dollars)—Ogive

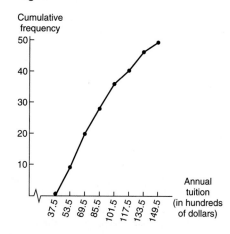

5. (a) Class width is 17.

(b)

Nurses' Night Workload					
Class Limits	Class Boundaries	Midpoint	Frequency	Relative Frequency	Cumulative Frequency
18– 34	17.5– 34.5	26	1	0.03	1
35– 51	34.5– 51.5	43	2	0.06	3
52– 68	51.5– 68.5	60	5	0.14	8
69– 85	68.5– 85.5	77	15	0.43	23
86–102	85.5–102.5	94	12	0.34	35

(c & d) Nurses' Night Workload—Histogram and Frequency Polygon

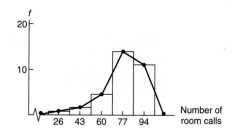

(e) Nurses' Night Workload—Relative-Frequency Histogram

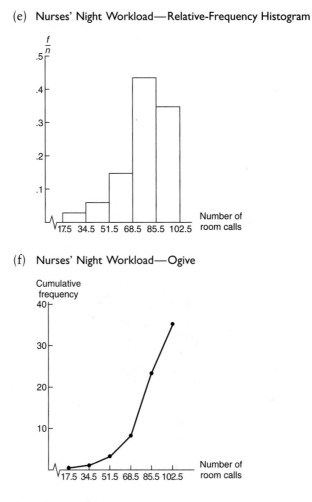

(f) Nurses' Night Workload—Ogive

7. (a) Class width is 6.

(b)

Age of Clothing Store Customers					
Class Limits	Class Boundaries	Midpoint	Frequency	Relative Frequency	Cumulative Frequency
16–21	15.5–21.5	18.5	9	0.300	9
22–27	21.5–27.5	24.5	5	0.167	14
28–33	27.5–33.5	30.5	4	0.133	18
34–39	33.5–39.5	36.5	4	0.133	22
40–45	39.5–45.5	42.5	3	0.100	25
46–51	45.5–51.5	48.5	4	0.133	29
52–57	51.5–57.5	54.5	1	0.033	30

(c & d) Age of Clothing Store Customers—Histogram and Frequency Polygon

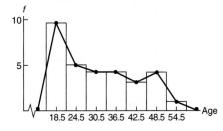

(e) Age of Clothing Store Customers—Relative-Frequency Histogram

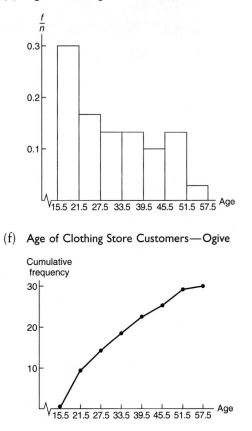

(f) Age of Clothing Store Customers—Ogive

9. (a)

Profit as a Percent of Sales—Food Companies (Class Width is 3)

Class	Frequency	Midpoint
−3−−1	2	−2
0− 2	16	1
3− 5	10	4
6− 8	9	7
9− 11	2	10

Profit as a Percent of Sales— Electronic Companies (Class Width is 5)

Class	Frequency	Midpoint
−6−−2	3	−4
−1− 3	13	1
4− 8	20	6
9− 13	7	11
14− 18	1	16

Profit as a Percent of Sales

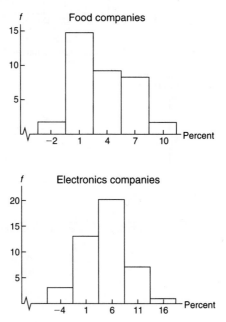

(b) Because the classes and class widths are different for the two company types, it is difficult to compare profits. We can notice that for the electronic companies the percentage of profits does extend as high as 18, while for the food companies the highest percent of profits is 11. On the other hand, some of the electronic companies also have greater losses than the food companies. Had we made the class limits the same for both company types, it would be easier to compare the data.

11. (a) The number of winning times of less than 7.15 seconds over 2 minutes is approximately 76 winning times. The percentage of winning times that are less than 7.15 seconds over 2 minutes is 76/92 = 83%.

    (b) The number of winning times less than 11.15 seconds over 2 minutes is 91, and the number less than 5.15 seconds over 2 minutes is 66. The number between 11.15 and 5.15 seconds is then 91 − 66 = 25 times between 2 minutes 5.15 seconds and 2 minutes 11.15 seconds. This represents 25/92, or about 27% of the winning times.

13. (a) Version 1 is skewed left; version 2 is uniform; version 3 is symmetrical; version 4 is bimodal; version 5 is skewed right.

    (b) Answers will vary.

15. (a) The first number in the list becomes 362, the second one becomes 428, and so forth.

    (b & c) Class width for whole-number data is 78. For the original data, it is 0.78.

Class Limits	Class Boundaries	Midpoint	Frequency
2.59–3.36	2.585–3.365	2.975	3
3.37–4.14	3.365–4.145	3.755	4
4.15–4.92	4.145–4.925	4.535	6
4.93–5.70	4.925–5.705	5.315	6
5.71–6.48	5.705–6.485	6.095	7
6.49–7.26	6.485–7.265	6.875	3

Prices to Develop Film

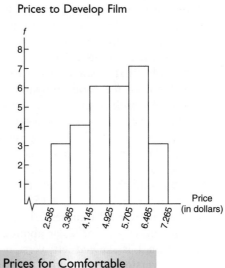

Section 2.4

1.

Prices for Comfortable Walking Shoes

Leaf Unit = $1
3 | 2 *represents $32*

4	0 6
5	0 2 5 5 5 8 8 9 9
6	0 0 0 2 5 5 9 9
7	0 0 6 8
8	
9	
10	9
11	0

Note: Leaves may be in any order.

Most of the data values are in the range from $50 to $70. The distribution is skewed right. There are no values between $80 and $100.

3.

Computer Store Connect Times

Leaf Unit = 1 minute
4 | 0 represents 40 minutes

```
0 | 3 5 5 7 8 8
1 | 0 0 2 2 2 2 4 5 5 5 5 6 6 7 7 7 8 8 8 9 9 9
2 | 0 0 1 1 2 4 5 5 6 6 7 9
3 | 0 0 1 1 3 7 7
4 | 0 2 3 7
5 | 1 7 8
6 | 1 1 1 2 5
7 | 2
```

Note: The leaves may be in any order

The distribution appears to be skewed right. The most heavily used time interval is 10 to 20 minutes. There are no gaps.

5.

Patient Dosage At Memorial Community Hospital

Leaf Unit = 1 pill
1 | 2 represents 12 pills
*Leaf digit is 0 through 4
•Leaf digit is 5 through 9

```
0* | 1 1 2 2 2 3 3 3 4 4 4
0• | 5 5 6 6 6 7 7 7 7 8 8 8 8 8 8 9 9 9 9 9 9
1* | 0 0 0 1 1 2 2 2 2 2 2 2 3 4
1• | 5 5 5
```

The number of pills most often prescribed ranges from 5 through 9. The distribution is generally symmetrical with a slight right skew. There are no gaps.

7.

Boston Marathon

Leaf Unit = 1 minute over 2 hours
1* | 2 represents 12 minutes over 2 hours

Years 1953–1972

0*	
0•	
1*	0 3 4
1•	5 5 6 7 8 8 8 8 9
2*	0 0 0 2 2 3 3
2•	5

Years 1973–1992

0*	
0•	7 8 8 8 8 9 9 9 9 9
1*	0 0 1 1 2 3 4 4
1•	6
2*	0
2•	

The two diagrams show that the winning times are decreasing. In 1953–1972, only three winners finished in less than 2 hours and 15 minutes. In 1973–1992, 18 winners finished in less than 2 hours and 15 minutes.

9.

Per Capita Energy Use by State

Leaf Unit = 100 million Btus
4 | 2 represents 420×10^7 Btu rounded to the nearest 10 million Btus

2	0 2 2 3 3 3 4 4 5 6 7 8 9
3	0 0 0 0 0 1 1 1 1 2 2 2 3 3 3 3 4 5 5 5 5 5 6 8 9 9
4	0 2 2 2 5 7
5	7
6	
7	8 9
8	
9	9

There are three exceptionally high values. Alaska uses 990, Wyoming 790, and Louisiana 780. One would expect Alaska to have a high energy use, especially in cold months.

Chapter Review Problems

1. (a) The graph is a Pareto chart showing which categories of companies have the strongest commitment to quality. This graph is a bar graph with the bars in order of decreasing frequency. The data come from a sample of 700 executives. The sample was probably a stratified sample with strata defined by the type of firm.

   (b) This graph is essentially a bar graph showing how many people go to work at different times. The bars are drawn as lines of workers. It also can be described as a pictogram, since each worker represents about 3 units. However, the diagram does not specify the unit measure for each picture of a worker, and fractional parts of workers are not shown. In addition, the picture of the worker varies, with some depicted as males and some as females. For these reasons, the diagram is closer to a bar graph than to a pictogram. The source of the data is the American Housing Survey. It is hard to tell what kind of survey this was. It may have been a simple random sample or a cluster sample.

   (c) This graph is a time plot of average points per game in college football for the years 1983–1992. The data are a time series of football statistics. The sample probably consists of all college football teams in the NCAA conference and as such is a census.

   (d) The graph is a bar graph showing the number of smoking-related deaths attributed to various medical conditions. Since the disease types are listed in decreasing order of cases, it also could be considered a Pareto chart. The source of the data is the Centers for Disease Control and Prevention. It is not clear whether this sample is the entire population of smoker deaths or a random sample of this population.

   (e) This graph is a pie chart showing which desserts are most frequently ordered in restaurants. The set of choices seems limited. The source of the data is a telephone and mail survey. This is probably a convenience sample consisting of people who are willing to respond to such a survey.

3. (a) 1991 Projected Government Revenues and Expenses

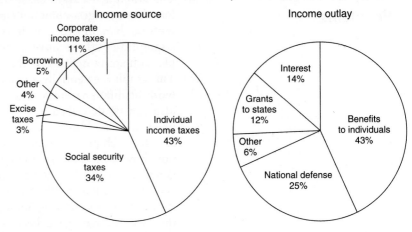

(b) Amount to be borrowed = 0.05 × 1233.3 billion = 61.67 billion.
(c) Net interest = 0.14 × 1233.3 billion = 172.66 billion.

5. (a) Assume that the x values are midpoints.

Earnings for Workers 15 Years of Age and Older (in thousands of dollars)

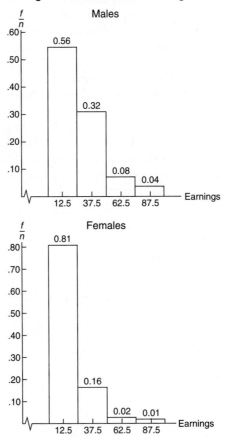

(b) Both distributions are skewed to the right. The distribution for females is more skewed. A much higher percentage of women workers is in the lowest earnings groups.

(c) Assuming that the x values are midpoints, we find that the upper boundary for the first class is halfway between the first two midpoints. The upper boundary for the first class is $(12.5 + 37.5)/2 = 25$. The class width is the distance between midpoints, so it is $37.5 - 12.5 = 25$.

Class Boundaries	Cumulative Relative Frequency for Males	Cumulative Relative Frequency for Females
0– 25	0.56	0.81
25– 50	0.88	0.97
50– 75	0.96	0.99
75–100	1.00	1.00

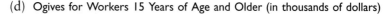
(d) Ogives for Workers 15 Years of Age and Older (in thousands of dollars)

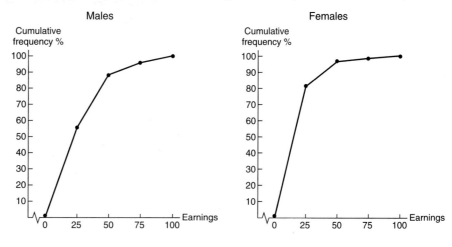

About 56% of males earn less than \$25,000. About 81% of females earn less than \$25,000.

7. (a) Completion of Educational Levels

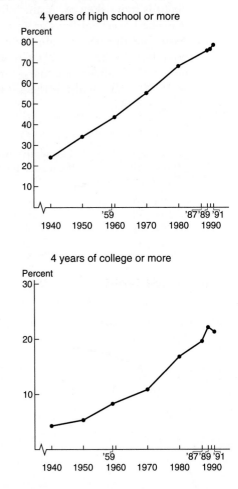

(b) The upward trend on the high school completion graph is generally steeper than that for the college completion graph. This probably reflects the fact that most people realize that completion of high school is essential for economic survival. It is harder to finish college. It is not surprising that the growth rate in the percentage of the population that finishes college should be less than the corresponding growth rate for high school completion. Both curves indicate that something is changing around 1987–1991.

9. (a) Patients between the ages of 64.5 and 84.5 are most frequent. About 35% of all patients are in this age bracket.

(b)

Age of Hospital Patients

Class Boundaries	Percentage
4.5–24.5	16%
24.5–44.5	28%
44.5–64.5	21%
64.5–84.5	35%

Percent of patients older than 44 years = 21% + 35% = 56%. Percent of patients 44 years old or younger = 16% + 28% = 44%.

11. (a)

Distribution of MVP Awards

Position	Frequency
Quarterbacks	14
Running backs	5
Wide receivers	3
Defensive ends	2
Defensive tackle	1
Linebacker	1
Safety	1

(b) Distribution of MVP Awards to Positions—Bar Graph

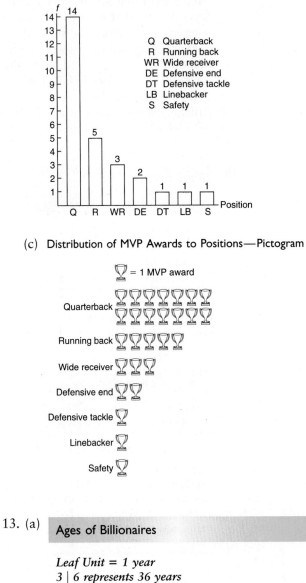

(c) Distribution of MVP Awards to Positions—Pictogram

13. (a)

Ages of Billionaires

Leaf Unit = 1 year
3 | 6 *represents 36 years*

```
3 | 3 3
4 | 1 1 3 3 4 4 5 6 6 6 9 9
5 | 0 0 0 1 2 3 3 4 5 7 8 8 8 8 9 9 9
6 | 0 0 1 1 3 3 4 4 5 5 6 6 6 6 7
7 | 0 0 1 1 2 3 3 3 4 5 6 6 7
8 | 0 0 1 3
9 | 0 3
```

(b) Class width $\doteq$ 9.

Class Limits	Class Boundaries	Midpoint	Frequency	Relative Frequency	Cumulative Frequency
33–41	32.5–41.5	37	4	0.06	4
42–50	41.5–50.5	46	13	0.20	17
51–59	50.5–59.5	55	14	0.22	31
60–68	59.5–68.5	64	15	0.23	46
69–77	68.5–77.5	73	13	0.20	59
78–86	77.5–86.5	82	4	0.06	63
87–95	86.5–95.5	91	2	0.03	65

Age Distribution of Billionaires—Histogram

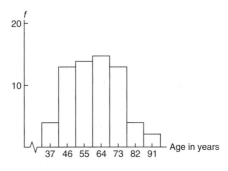

The histogram is skewed a little to the right.

(c) About 26% of the billionaires are 50 years old or younger.

Age Distribution of Billionaires—Ogive

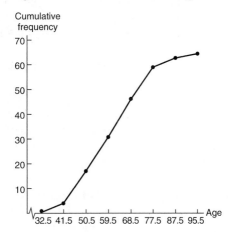

Chapter 3

Section 3.1

1. Mean = 156.33; median = 157; mode = 157. A gardener in Colorado should look at seed and plant descriptions to determine if the plant can thrive and mature in the designated number of frost-free days. The mean, median, and mode are all close. About half the locations have 157 or fewer frost-free days.

3. Mean = 21.36 cents/gal; median = 21 cents/gal; mode = 26 cents/gal.

5. (a) Mean = 15.5 points; median = 16.5 points; no mode.
   (b) Number of margins below the mean is 12; number of margins below the median is 13.
   (c) 5% trimmed mean = 14.9.

7. (a) Mean = 28.83 thousand dollars.
   (b) Median = 18.5 thousand dollars. The median best describes the salary of the majority of employees, since the mean is influenced by the high salaries of the president and vice president.
   (c) Mean = 17.3 thousand dollars; median = 17 thousand dollars.
   (d) Without the salaries for the two executives, the mean and the median are closer, and both reflect the salary of most of the other workers more accurately. The mean changed quite a bit, while the median did not, a difference that indicates that the mean is more sensitive to the absence or presence of extreme values.

9. (a) For the first week, mean = 14.57 meteoroids; median = 15 meteoroids; mode = 15 meteoroids.
   (b) For all nine nights, mean = 24.56 meteoroids; median = 15 meteoroids; mode = 15 meteoroids.
   (c) Extreme values affect the mean far more than they do the median or mode.

11. (a) Mean = 16.47; median = 17; mode = 16.
   (b) The mean is the arithmetic average. It is the sum of the data values divided by the number of data values. The median is the middle value when data are written in order. If there are an even number of values, it is the average of the two values on either side of the middle. The mode is the most frequently occurring number. The mean represents the average size of an elk herd. Every herd in the data is included. The median herd size represents the middle in the sense that there are as many herds larger than this value as there are herds smaller than this value. The mode is the most frequently occurring herd size. If you were to go looking for a herd of elk, this is the size herd you would most likely see.

13. (a) Mode
   (b) Mean, median, mode if it exists.
   (c) Mode if it exists; median, mean if 24-hour clock is used.

15. (a) If the largest data value is *replaced* by a larger value, the mean will increase because the sum of the data values will increase, but the num-

ber of them will remain the same. The median will not change. The same value will still be in the eighth position when the data are ordered.

(b) If the largest value is replaced by a value that is smaller (but still higher than the median), the mean will decrease because the sum of the data values will decrease. The median will not change. The same value will be in the eighth position in increasing order.

(c) If the largest value is replaced by a value that is smaller than the median, the mean will decrease because the sum of the data values will decrease. The median also will decrease because the former value in the eighth position will move to the ninth position in increasing order. The median will be the new value in the eighth position.

17. Answers will vary according to data collected.

Section 3.2

1. (a) Range $= 54$ deer/km^2; sample mean $\bar{x} = 20.9$ deer/km^2; sample variance $s^2 = 225.0$; sample standard deviation $s = 15.0$ deer/km^2.
   (b) CV $= 71.8$.
   (c) Since the standard deviation is about 72% of the mean, there is considerable variation in the distribution of deer from one part of the park to another.

3. (a) Range $= 10$ years.
   (b) Sample mean $\bar{x} = 6.57$ years.
   (c) Sample standard deviation $s = 3.51$ years.

5. (a) Range $= 43.3$ carats.
   (b) Population mean $\mu = 40.3$ carats.
   (c) Population standard deviation $\sigma = 14.8$ carats.

7. (a) Range $= \$143.0$; $\bar{x} = \$417.40$; $s = \$60.4$.
   (b) Range $= \$85.0$; $\bar{x} = \$249.0$; $s = \$33.1$.
   (c) The 13-inch sets have a lower average cost and sample standard deviation. For the 20-inch sets, CV $= 14.5$, and for the 13-inch sets, CV $= 13.3$. The relative price variation for the 13-inch sets is slightly smaller.

9. (a) $\bar{x} = 7.83$ lb; $s = 2.32$ lb; CV $= 29.6$; range $= 4.8$ lb.
   (b) $\bar{x} = 9.95$ lb; $s = 0.29$ lb; CV $= 2.9$; range $= 0.7$ lb.
   (c) The second line had more consistent performance, as reflected by the smaller standard deviation, the smaller coefficient of variation, and the range.

11. (a) 75% of the cycles should fall within 2 standard deviations of the mean: 6.67 to 15.35 years.
    (b) 93.8% of the cycles should fall within 4 standard deviations of the mean: 2.33 to 19.69 years.

13. (a) Use your calculator in statistics mode.

11. (a) $\bar{x}$ = 29 years; median = 26.5 years; mode = 27 years.
    (b) Range = 33 years; s = 11.06 years.
13. (a) It is possible for the range and the standard deviation to be the same. For instance, for data values that are all the same, such as 1, 1, 1, 1, 1, the range and standard deviation are both 0.
    (b) It is possible for the mean, median, and mode to be all the same. For instance, the data set 1, 2, 3, 3, 3, 4, 5 has mean, median, and mode all equal to 3. The averages can all be different, as in the data set 1, 2, 3, 3. In this case, the mean is 2.25, the median is 2.5, and the mode is 3.
15. Σw = 16, Σwx = 121, average = 7.56.

Chapter 4

Section 4.1

1. See text.
3. b, since 4.1 is greater than 1; d, since -0.5 is less than 0; h, since 150% is greater than 100% or 1.
5. $P(\text{success})$ = 33/35 = 0.94.
7. (a) $P(\text{mass mailing source})$ = 50/1000 = 0.05; $P(\text{help wanted ads source})$ = 140/1000 = 0.14; $P(\text{executive search firm source})$ = 110/1000 = 0.11; $P(\text{networking source})$ = 700/1000 = 0.70.
    (b) The probabilities add up to 1. They should because each job had exactly one of the four sources.
9. (a) $P(\text{best idea 6 A.M.}{-}12 \text{ noon})$ = 290/966 = 0.30; $P(\text{best idea 12 noon}{-}6 \text{ P.M.})$ = 135/966 = 0.14; $P(\text{best idea 6 P.M.}{-}12 \text{ midnight})$ = 319/966 = 0.33; $P(\text{best idea from 12 midnight}{-}6 \text{ A.M.})$ = 222/966 = 0.23.
    (b) The probabilities add up to 1. They should add up to 1 provided that the intervals do not overlap and each inventor chose only one interval. The sample space is the set of four time intervals.
11. (a) These events form a sample space. Every one in the survey gave a response that fell into one of the three categories: $P(\text{left alone})$ = 770/1000 = 0.77; $P(\text{waited on})$ = 160/1000 = 0.16; $P(\text{different treatment})$ = 70/1000 = 0.07.
    (b) $P(\text{not left alone})$ = 1 $-$ $P(\text{left alone})$ = 1 $-$ 0.77 = 0.23; $P(\text{not waited on})$ = 1 $-$ $P(\text{waited on})$ = 1 $-$ 0.16 = 0.84.
13. (a) The sample space consists of the values 1, 2, 3, 4, 5, 6. The outcomes are equally likely.
    (b) The probability of each outcome is 1/6, and the probabilities add up to 1.
    (c) There are 4 outcomes less than 5, so $P(\text{less than 5})$ = 4/6 = 2/3.
    (d) $P(5 \text{ or } 6)$ = 1/6 + 1/6 = 2/6 = 1/3.

Section 4.2

1. (a) $P(\text{orange or tan})$ = 0.15 + 0.05 = 0.20; yes, one M & M cannot be both orange and tan.
    (b) $P(\text{yellow or red})$ = 0.20 + 0.20 = 0.40; yes, one M & M cannot be both red and yellow.

(c) $P(not$ brown$) = 1 - 0.30 = 0.70$

3. (a) $P(ace\ or$ heart$) = \frac{4}{52} + \frac{13}{52} - \frac{1}{52} = \frac{16}{52} \approx 0.308$; no, one card is the ace of hearts.

 (b) $P(heart\ or$ red$) = \frac{13}{52} + \frac{26}{52} - \frac{13}{52} = \frac{26}{52} = 0.5$; no, all the hearts are also red cards.

 (c) $P(2\ or\ 10) = \frac{4}{52} + \frac{4}{52} = \frac{8}{52} \approx 0.154$; yes, no card is simultaneously a 2 and 10.

 (d) $P(not$ a diamond$) = 1 - 13/52 = 39/52 = 0.75.$

5. (a) Yes

 (b) $P(5$ on green and 3 on red$) = P(5) \cdot P(3) = (1/6)(1/6) = 1/36 \approx 0.028.$

 (c) $P(3$ on green and 5 on red$) = P(3) \cdot P(5) = (1/6)(1/6) = 1/36 \approx 0.028.$

 (d) $P(5$ on green and 3 on red$)$ or $(3$ on green and 5 on red$) = (1/36)$ $+ (1/36) = 1/18 \approx 0.056.$

7. (a) $P(sum\ of\ 6) = P(1\ and\ 5) + P(2\ and\ 4) + P(3\ and\ 3) + P(4\ and\ 2)$ $+ P(5\ and\ 1) = (1/36) + (1/36) + (1/36) + (1/36) + (1/36) = 5/36.$

 (b) $P(sum\ of\ 4) = P(1\ and\ 3) + P(2\ and\ 2) + P(3\ and\ 1) = (1/36)$ $+ (1/36) + (1/36) = 3/36$ or $1/12.$

 (c) $P(sum\ of\ 6\ or\ sum\ of\ 4) = P$ (sum of 6) $+ P$ (sum of 4) $= (5/36)$ $+ (3/36) = 8/36$ or $2/9$; yes.

9. (a) No, after the first draw the sample space becomes smaller and probabilities for events on the second draw change.

 (b) $P(ace$ on 1st and king on 2nd$) = P(ace) \cdot P(king,\ given$ ace$)$ $= (4/52)(4/51) = 4/663.$

 (c) $P(king$ on 1st and ace on 2nd$) = P(king) \cdot P(ace,\ given$ king$)$ $= (4/52)(4/51) = 4/663.$

 (d) $P(ace$ and king in either order$) = P(ace$ on 1st and king on 2nd$)$ $+ P(king$ on 1st and ace on 2nd$) (4/663) + (4/663) = 8/663.$

11. (a) Yes, replacement of the card restores the sample space and all probabilities for the second draw remain unchanged regardless of the outcome of the first card.

 (b) $P(ace$ on 1st and king on 2nd$) = P(ace) \cdot P(king) = (4/52)(4/52)$ $= 1/169.$

 (c) $P(king$ on 1st and ace on 2nd$) = P(king) \cdot P(ace) = (4/52)(4/52)$ $= 1/169.$

 (d) $P(ace$ and king in either order$) = P(ace$ on 1st and king on 2nd$)$ $+ (king$ on 1st and ace on 2nd$) = (1/169) + (1/169) = 2/169.$

13. (a) $P(6$ years or older$) = P(6-9) + P(10-12) + P(13$ and over$) = 0.27$ $+ 0.14 + 0.22 = 0.63.$

 (b) $P(12$ years or younger$) = P(2$ and under$) + P(3-5) + P(6-9)$ $+ P(10-12) = 0.15 + 0.22 + 0.27 + 0.14 = 0.78.$

 (c) $P(between\ 6\ and\ 12) = P(6-9) + P(10-12) = 0.27 + 0.14 = 0.41.$

 (d) $P(between\ 3\ and\ 9) = P(3-5) + P(6-9) = 0.22 + 0.27 = 0.49.$ The category 13 and over contains far more ages than the group 10–12. It is not surprising that more toys are purchased for this group, since there are more children in this group.

15. The information from James Burke can be viewed as conditional probabilities. $P(report$ lie, $given$ person is lying$) = 0.72$ and $P(report$ lie, $given$ person is not lying$) = 0.07.$

(a) P(person is not lying) = 0.90; P(person is not lying *and* polygraph reports lie) = P(person is not lying) × P(reports lie, *given* person not lying) = (0.90)(0.07) = 0.063 or 6.3%.

(b) P(person is lying) = 0.10; P(person is lying *and* polygraph reports lie) = P(person is lying) × P(reports lie, *given* person is lying) = (0.10)(0.72) = 0.072 or 7.2%.

(c) P(person is not lying) = 0.5; P(person is lying) = 0.5; P(person is not lying *and* polygraph reports lie) = P(person is not lying) × P(reports lie, *given* person not lying) = (0.50)(0.07) = 0.035 or 3.5%. P(person is lying *and* polygraph reports lie) = P(person is lying) × P(reports lie, *given* person is lying) = (0.50)(0.72) = 0.36 or 36%.

(d) P(person is not lying) = 0.15; P(person is lying) = 0.85; P(person is lying *and* polygraph reports lie) = P(person is not lying) × P(reports lie, *given* person is lying) = (0.15)(0.07) = 0.0105 or 1.05%. P(person is lying *and* polygraph reports lie) = P(person is lying) × P(reports lie, *given* person is lying) = (0.85)(0.72) = 0.612 or 61.2%.

17. (a) P(glasses *and* woman) = P(glasses) × P(woman, *given* glasses) = (0.56)(0.554) = 0.310.

(b) P(glasses *and* man) = P(glasses) × P(man, *given* glasses) = (0.56)(0.446) = 0.250.

(c) P(contacts *and* woman) = P(contacts) × P(woman, *given* contacts) = (0.036)(0.631) = 0.023.

(d) P(contacts *and* man) = P(contacts) × P(man, *given* contacts) = (0.036)(0.369) = 0.013.

(e) Since the preceding events are all disjoint, P(any one of the above) = 0.310 + 0.250 + 0.023 + 0.013 = 0.596; P(none) = 1 − 0.596 = 0.404.

19. (a) $P(A)$ = 1619/2525 = 0.641; $P(B)$ = 652/2525 = 0.258; $P(C)$ = 162/2525 = 0.064; $P(D)$ = 92/2525 = 0.036. These numbers mean that a college graduate is much more likely to have had an A grade average in high school than any other grade.

(b) P(1976) = 577/2525 = 0.229; P(1980) = 939/2525 = 0.372; P(1986) = 1009/2525 = 0.400. A college graduate is more likely to have graduated in 1986 than in 1980 or 1976.

(c) P(1976, *given* A) = 419/1619 = 0.259; P(1980, *given* A) = 593/1619 = 0.366; P(1986, *given* A) = 607/1619 = 0.375. A college graduate with an A average in high school is more likely to be a recent graduate.

(d) P(1976, *given* D) = 11/92 = 0.120; P(1980, *given* D) = 36/92 = 0.390; P(1980, *given* D) = 45/92 = 0.489. A college graduate with a D high school grade average is much more likely to have graduated recently than in the past. All the percentages increased over time, but the percentage of graduates having a D high school grade average increased much more rapidly than the percentage of college graduates with an A high school average.

(e) P(C, *given* 1976) = 24/577 = 0.042; P(C, *given* 1980) = 61/939 = 0.065; P(C, *given* 1986) = 77/1009 = 0.076. 1986 college graduates are more likely to have had a C high school grade average than college graduates from 1980 or 1976.

(f) $P(A \ or \ B) = 1619/2525 + 652/2525 = 2271/2525 = 0.8994$. The events are mutually exclusive.

(g) $P(B \ and \ 1976) = 123/2525 = 0.049$; $P(B \ and \ 1980) = 249/2525 = 0.099$; $P(B \ and \ 1986) = 280/2525 = 0.111$. More students are graduating each year. This could account for the increasing probabilities. However, the fraction of the 1986 class which had a B high school grade average is also rising.

(h) $P(B \ or \ 1976) = P(B) + P(1976) - P(B \ and \ 1976) = 652/2525 + 577/2525 - 123/2525 = 1106/2525 = 0.438$. No, these events are not mutually exclusive. $P(C \ or \ 1980) = P(C) + P(1980) - P(C \ and \ 1980) = 162/2525 + 939/2525 - 61/2525 = 1040/2525 = 0.412$. No, these events are not mutually exclusive.

21. (a) $P(Fa) = 364/653 = 0.557$; $P(Fa, \ given \ F) = 11/34 = 0.324$
$P(Fa, \ given \ S) = 353/619 = 0.570$.

(b) $P(F \ and \ Fa) = 11/653 = 0.017$.

(c) No.

(d) $P(S, \ given \ O) = 191/209 = 0.914$; $P(S, \ given \ N) = 75/80 = 0.938$.

(e) $P(S \ and \ Fa) = 353/653 = 0.541$; $P(S \ and \ O) = 191/653 = 0.292$.

(f) $P(S) = 619/653 = 0.948$; $P(S, \ given \ Fa) = 353/364 = 0.970$. No, the events S and Fa are not independent. The proportion of students among those in favor is different from the proportion of students in the college as a whole who favor the change.

(g) $P(Fa \ or \ O) = P(Fa) + P(O) = 364/653 + 209/653 = 0.877$. The events favor and oppose are mutually exclusive.

23. (a) $P(O) = 267/558 = 0.478$; $P(O, \ given \ L) = 73/283 = 0.258$
$P(O, \ given \ M) = 194/275 = 0.705$.

(b) $P(O \ and \ M) = 194/558 = 0.348$; $P(O \ or \ M) = P(O) + P(M) - P(O \ and \ M) = (267/558) + (275/558) - (194/558) = 0.624$.

(c) $P(R) = 291/558 = 0.522$; $P(R, \ given \ L) = 210/283 = 0.742$;
$P(R, \ given \ M) = 81/275 = 0.295$.

(d) $P(R \ and \ L) = 210/558 = 0.376$; $P(R \ or \ L) = P(R) + P(L) - P(R \ and \ L) = (291/558) + (283/558) - (210/558) = 0.652$.

(e) No; no.

25. (a) $P(A) = 697/1153 = 0.605$; $P(A, \ given \ G) = 406/511 = 0.795$
$P(A, \ given \ D) = 291/642 = 0.453$.

(b) $P(B) = 456/1153 = 0.395$; $P(B, \ given \ G) = 105/511 = 0.205$
$P(B, \ given \ D) = 351/642 = 0.547$.

(c) $P(G) = 511/1153 = 0.443$; $P(G, \ given \ A) = 406/697 = 0.582$
$P(G, \ given \ B) = 105/456 = 0.230$.

(d) $P(D) = 642/1153 = 0.557$; $P(D, \ given \ A) = 291/697 = 0.418$
$P(D, \ given \ B) = 351/456 = 0.770$.

(e) $P(G \ and \ A) = 406/1153 = 0.352$; $P(D \ or \ B) = P(D) + P(B) - P(D \ and \ B) = (642/1153) + (456/1153) - (351/1153) = 0.648$.

(f) No.

(g) No.

27. (a) $P(A) = 0.65$.   (b) $P(B) = 0.71$.   (c) $P(B,\ given\ A) = 0.87$.
    (d) $P(A\ and\ B) = P(A) \cdot P(B,\ given\ A) = (0.65)(0.87) \approx 0.57$.
    (e) $P(A\ or\ B) = P(A) + P(B) - P(A\ and\ B) = 0.65 + 0.71 - 0.57 = 0.79$.
    (f) $P(\text{not close}) = P(\text{profit 1st year } or \text{ profit 2nd year}) = P(A\ or\ B) = 0.79$; $P(\text{close}) = 1 - P(\text{not close}) = 1 - 0.79 = 0.21$.
29. (a) $P(A) = 0.08$.   (b) $P(B) = 0.08$.   (c) $P(B,\ given\ A) = 0.23$.
    (d) $P(A\ and\ B) = P(A) \cdot P(B,\ given\ A) = (0.08)(0.23) = 0.018$.
    (e) $P(A\ or\ B) = P(A) + P(B) - P(A\ and\ B) = 0.08 + 0.08 - 0.018 = 0.142$.
    (f) $P(\text{no claim}) = 1 - P(A\ or\ B) = 1 - 0.142 = 0.858$.
31. (a) $P(\text{TB } and \text{ positive}) = P(\text{TB})(\text{positive, } given \text{ TB}) = (0.04)(0.82) = 0.033$.
    (b) $P(\text{does not have TB}) = 1 - P(\text{TB}) = 1 - 0.04 = 0.96$.
    (c) $P(\text{no TB } and \text{ positive}) = P(\text{no TB})P(\text{positive, } given \text{ no TB}) = (0.96)(0.09) = 0.086$.

Section 4.3

1. (a) Outcomes for Tossing a Coin Three Times

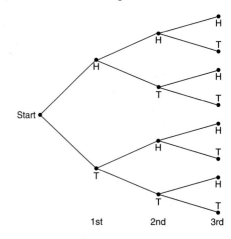

(b) 3
(c) $\frac{3}{8}$

3. (a) Outcomes for Drawing Two Balls (without replacement)

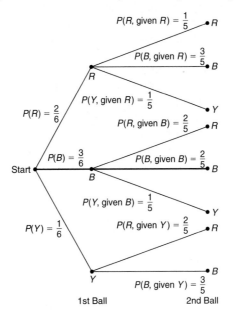

1st Ball   2nd Ball

(b) $P(R \ and \ R) = \frac{2}{6} \cdot \frac{1}{5} = \frac{1}{15}$

$P(R \ 1st \ and \ B \ 2nd) = \frac{2}{6} \cdot \frac{3}{5} = \frac{1}{5}$

$P(R \ 1st \ and \ Y \ 2nd) = \frac{2}{6} \cdot \frac{1}{5} = \frac{1}{15}$

$P(B \ 1st \ and \ R \ 2nd) = \frac{3}{6} \cdot \frac{2}{5} = \frac{1}{5}$

$P(B \ 1st \ and \ B \ 2nd) = \frac{3}{6} \cdot \frac{2}{5} = \frac{1}{5}$

$P(B \ 1st \ and \ Y \ 2nd) = \frac{3}{6} \cdot \frac{1}{5} = \frac{1}{10}$

$P(Y \ 1st \ and \ R \ 2nd) = \frac{1}{6} \cdot \frac{2}{5} = \frac{1}{15}$

$P(Y \ 1st \ and \ B \ 2nd) = \frac{1}{6} \cdot \frac{3}{5} = \frac{1}{10}$

5. (a) Choices for Three True/False Questions

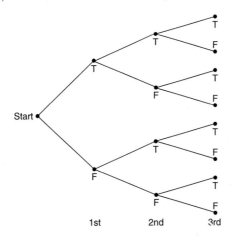

1st   2nd   3rd

(b) $\frac{1}{8}$

7. $4 \cdot 3 \cdot 2 \cdot 1 = 24$ ways
9. (a) $52 \cdot 52 = 2704$
   (b) $4 \cdot 4 = 16$
   (c) $16/2,704 = 0.006$
11. $4 \cdot 3 \cdot 3 = 36$
13. $P_{5,2} = (5!/3!) = 5 \cdot 4 = 20$
15. $P_{7,7} = (7!/0!) = 7! = 5040$
17. $C_{5,2} = (5!/(2!3!)) = 10$
19. $C_{7,7} = (7!/(7!0!)) = 1$
21. $15 \cdot 14 \cdot 13 = 2730$
23. (a) $8! = 40,320$
    (b) $8 \cdot 7 \cdot 6 \cdot 5 \cdot 4 = 6720$
25. $5 \cdot 4 \cdot 3 = 60$
27. $C_{15,5} = (15!/(5!10!)) = 3003$
29. (a) $C_{12,6} = (12!/(6!6!)) = 924$
    (b) $C_{7,6} = (7!/(6!1!)) = 7$
    (c) $7/924 = 0.008$

Section 4.4

1. (a) Discrete
   (b) Continuous
   (c) Continuous
   (d) Discrete
   (e) Continuous
   (f) Discrete
3. (a) Continuous
   (b) Discrete
   (c) Discrete
   (d) Continuous
   (e) Continuous
   (f) Discrete

5. (a)

x	1st	2nd	3rd	OT
$P(x)$	0.309	0.354	0.328	0.009

(b) Goals by Game Period for NHL 89–90

(c) Expected value = 2.04; this value tells us the period in which a goal selected at random is likely to fall on the average.

(d) Standard deviation = 0.82.

(e) A goal is most likely to be scored in the second period. P(goal not scored in second period) ≈ 1 − 0.354 = 0.646.

7. (a)

P(x)	36	37	38	39	40	41	42
P(x)	0.029	0.048	0.053	0.096	0.125	0.154	0.163

x	43	44	45
P(x)	0.135	0.120	0.077

(b)

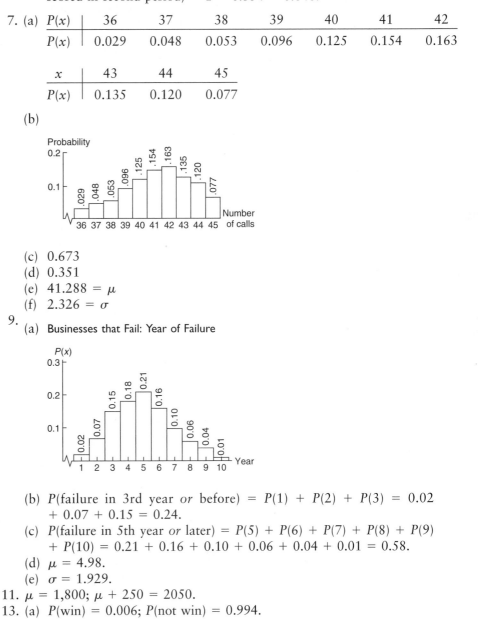

(c) 0.673

(d) 0.351

(e) 41.288 = μ

(f) 2.326 = σ

9.

(a) Businesses that Fail: Year of Failure

(b) P(failure in 3rd year *or* before) = P(1) + P(2) + P(3) = 0.02 + 0.07 + 0.15 = 0.24.

(c) P(failure in 5th year *or* later) = P(5) + P(6) + P(7) + P(8) + P(9) + P(10) = 0.21 + 0.16 + 0.10 + 0.06 + 0.04 + 0.01 = 0.58.

(d) μ = 4.98.

(e) σ = 1.929.

11. μ = 1,800; μ + 250 = 2050.

13. (a) P(win) = 0.006; P(not win) = 0.994.

(b) $14.88 = expected earnings; $25.12 = contribution.

Chapter Review Problems

1. (a)

x	0–4	5–9	10–14	15–19	20 +
$P(x)$	0.226	0.172	0.146	0.141	0.314

(b) P(at least 15 years old) $= 0.141 + 0.314 = 0.455$.

(c) P(between 5 and 14 years old) $= 0.172 + 0.146 = 0.318$.

(d) Expected age $= 12.7$ yr, standard deviation $= 7.8$ yr.

(e) Age of U.S. Commercial Aircraft

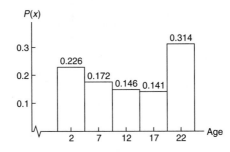

3. (a) If the first card is replaced, the outcomes are independent. Replacing the first card restores the original sample space. If the first card is not replaced, the outcomes are not independent, because removing the first card changes the sample space.

(b) P(heart *and* heart) $= (13/52)(13/52) = 0.063$.

(c) P(heart *and* heart) $= (13/52)(12/51) = 0.059$.

5. (a) Drop a fixed number of tacks and count how many land flat side down. Then form the ratio of the number landing flat side down to the total number dropped.

(b) Up, down.

(c) P(up) $= 160/500 = 0.32$; P(down) $= 340/500 = 0.68$.

7. (a) P(queen) $= 0.067$; P(bishop) $= 0.133$; P(knight) $= 0.133$; P(rook) $= 0.133$; P(pawn) $= 0.533$.

(b) $\mu = 2.599$.

(c) No.

9. (a)

x	0	1	2	3	4	5	6
$P(x)$	0.05	0.48	0.22	0.11	0.09	0.03	0.02

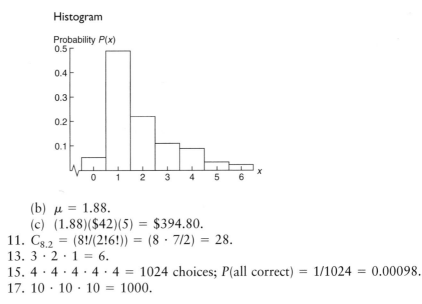

(b) $\mu = 1.88$.

(c) $(1.88)(\$42)(5) = \$394.80$.

11. $C_{8,2} = (8!/(2!6!)) = (8 \cdot 7/2) = 28$.

13. $3 \cdot 2 \cdot 1 = 6$.

15. $4 \cdot 4 \cdot 4 \cdot 4 \cdot 4 = 1024$ choices; P(all correct) $= 1/1024 = 0.00098$.

17. $10 \cdot 10 \cdot 10 = 1000$.

Chapter 5

Section 5.1

1. The experiment is binomial. A trial is a room call. Success $S =$ responds to a call within 3 minutes. Failure $F =$ responds to a call in more than 3 minutes. $n = 73$; $p = 0.8$; $q = 0.2$; $r = 62$.

3. The experiment is binomial. A trial consists of determining if one adult resident of Washington, D.C., is a lawyer. Success $S =$ a response that the person is a lawyer. Failure $F =$ response that the person is not a lawyer. $n = 15$; $p = 0.10$; $q = 0.90$; $r = 3$.

5. This is not a binomial experiment because there are more than two outcomes on each trial.

7. This is not a binomial experiment because the probability of drawing short straws changes.

9. This experiment is binomial with a range of r values. A trial is a check of a damage claim to see if the claimant is a single male under 25 years of age. Success is $S =$ finding claimant is a single male under 25 years of age. Failure is $F =$ finding claimant is not a single male under 25 years of age. $n = 619$; $p = 0.36$; $q = 0.64$; $r = 45, 46, 47, 48, 49, 50$.

11. The experiment is not binomial because the probability of success (wanting to spend Christmas vacation in a warm sunny place) p for college students may be different from p for people over 35 years old.

13. This is a binomial experiment. A trial consists of examining a home burglary report. Success $S =$ finding a record of a solved home burglary. Failure $F =$ finding a record of an unsolved home burglary. $n = 300$; $p = 0.14$, $q = 0.86$; r is all whole numbers between 0 and 40, including 0 and 40.

(a) $n = 3$; $P(r = 0) = 0.003$; $P(r > 1) = 0.939$.
(b) $n = 7$; $P(r \geqslant 3) = 0.999$ to 3 decimal places; $P(r = 7) = 0.321$.

17. A trial consists of counting the number of pups in a wolf den. Success = den contains five or more pups. Failure = den contains fewer than five pups. $n = 6$; $p = 0.75$; $q = 0.25$.
    (a) P(less than half successes) = $P(r < 3) = 0.037$.
    (b) $P(r \geqslant 4) = 0.831$.
    (c) $P(r = 6) = 0.178$.
    (d) $P(r = 0) = 0.000$ to three places after the decimal. If this happened, we would doubt that $p = 0.75$ in this region. If p were really 0.75, it is very unlikely that an occupied den would have no pups.

19. A trial consists of determining the kind of stone in a chipped stone tool.
    (a) $n = 11$. Success = obsidian. Failure = not obsidian. $p = 0.15$; $q = 0.85$; $P(r \geqslant 3) = 0.221$.
    (b) $n = 5$. Success = basalt. Failure = not basalt. $p = 0.55$; $q = 0.45$; $P(r \geqslant 2) = 0.869$.
    (c) $n = 10$. Success = neither obsidian nor basalt. Failure = either obsidian or basalt. The two outcomes, tool is obsidian or tool is basalt, are mutually exclusive. Therefore, P(obsidian *or* basalt) = 0.55 + 0.15 = 0.70. P(neither obsidian nor basalt) = $1 - 0.70 = 0.30$. Therefore, $p = 0.30$; $P(r \geqslant 4) = 0.350$.

21. A trial is noting the gender of the professor. Success = woman. Failure = man. $p = 0.30$; $q = 0.70$; $n = 5$.
    (a) $P(r = 0) = 0.168$.
    (b) $P(r = 5) = 0.002$.
    (c) $P(r \geqslant 1) = 0.471$.
    (d) $P(2 \leqslant r \leqslant 4) = 0.469$.

23. (a) They are the same.
    (b) They are the same.
    (c) $r = 1$.
    (d) The one headed by $p = 0.80$.

Section 5.3

1. (a) Binomial Distribution

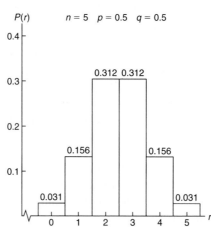

The distribution is symmetrical.

(b) Binomial Distribution

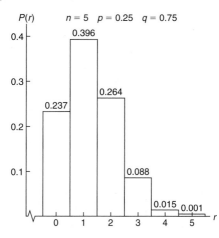

The distribution is skewed right.

(c) Binomial Distribution

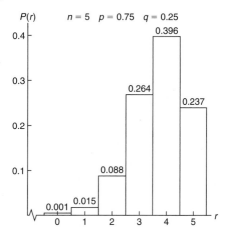

The distribution is skewed left.

(d) The distributions are mirror images of one another.

(e) The distribution would be skewed left for $p = 0.73$ because the more likely number of successes are to the right of the middle.

3. (a) Probability that a Senior Citizen Has High Blood Pressure

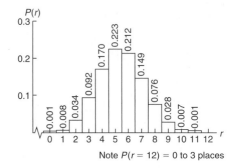

Note $P(r = 12) = 0$ to 3 places

(b) $\mu = np = 12(0.45) = 5.4$.

(c) $\sigma = \sqrt{npq} = \sqrt{12(0.45)(0.55)} = 1.723$.

5. (a) Binomial Distribution for Number of Address Found

$n = 6 \quad p = 0.70$

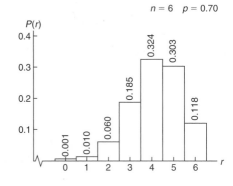

(b) $\mu = 4.2; \sigma = 1.122$.

(c) $n = 5$. Note that $n = 5$ gives $P(r \geq 2) = 0.97$.

7. (a) Binomial Distribution for Number of Illiterate People

$n = 7 \quad p = 0.20$

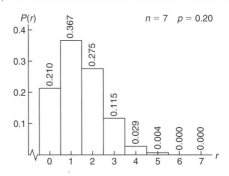

(b) $\mu = 1.4; \sigma = 1.058$.

(c) $n = 12$. Note that $n = 12$ gives $P(r \geq 7) = 0.98$, where success = literate and $p = 0.80$.

9. (a) Binomial Distribution for Number of Gullible Consumers

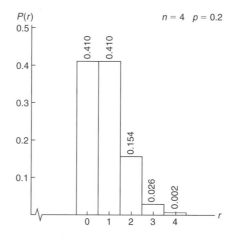

(b) $\mu = 2$; $\sigma = 1.225$.

(c) $n = 16$. Note that $n = 16$ gives $P(r \geqslant 1) = 0.99$.

11. $n = 20$ gives $P(r \geqslant 5) = 0.95$.

13. $P(r \geqslant 1) = 1 - P(r = 0)$. From the formula for the binomial distribution with $p = 0.1$ and $q = 0.9$, $P(r = 0) = C_{n,0}p^0 q^n = 1(0.1)^0(0.9)^n$. Therefore, $P(r \geqslant 1) = 1 - 0.9^n$. Computing this probability for various values of n shows that $n = 22$ is the smallest value for which $P(r \geqslant 1)$ is at least 0.90.

15. (a) $P(r = 0) = 0.410$; $P(r = 1) = 0.410$; $P(r = 2) = 0.154$; $P(r = 3) = 0.026$; $P(r = 4) = 0.002$.

(b) Binomial Distribution for Number of Prisoners Who Do Not Become Repeat Offenders

(c) $\mu = 0.8$; $\sigma = 0.8$.

(d) $n = 20$. Note that $n = 20$ gives $P(r \geqslant 2) = 0.93$.

17. $n = 4$ stations are necessary to be 98% certain. If 4 stations are used, the expected number of stations that will detect an enemy plane is $\mu = 2.6$.

19. $n = 6$ alarms are necessary to be 99% certain at least one alarm will go off. If 9 alarms are installed, the expected number that will sound is $\mu = 4.95$, or about 5.

21. We need $n = 10$ for $P(r \geq 6)$ to be greater than or equal 0.90 with $p = 0.75$. The expected number of successes is 6 players for 8 contacts.

Section 5.4

1. (a) $p = 0.77$; $P(n) = (0.77)(0.23)^{n-1}$.
   (b) $P(1) = 0.77$.
   (c) $P(2) = 0.1771$.
   (d) $P(3 \text{ or more tries}) = 1 - P(1) - P(2) = 0.0529$.

3. (a) $P(n) = (0.05)(0.95)^{n-1}$.
   (b) $P(5) = 0.0407$.
   (c) $P(10) = 0.0315$.
   (d) $P(n > 3) = 1 - P(1) - P(2) - P(3) = 1 - 0.05 - 0.0475 - 0.0451$
       $= 0.8574$.

5. (a) $P(n) = (0.71)(0.29)^{n-1}$.
   (b) $P(1) = 0.71$; $P(2) = 0.2059$; $P(n \geq 3) = 1 - P(1) - P(2) = 0.0841$.
   (c) $P(n) = (0.83)(0.17)^{n-1}$; $P(1) = 0.83$; $P(2) = 0.1411$; $P(n \geq 3)$
       $= 1 - P(1) - P(2) = 0.0289$.

7. (a) $P(n) = (0.30)(0.70)^{n-1}$.
   (b) $P(3) = 0.147$.
   (c) $P(n > 3) = 1 - P(1) - P(2) - P(3) = 1 - 0.300 - 0.210 - 0.147$
       $= 0.343$.

9. (a) $\lambda = (1.7/10) \times (3/3) = 5.1$ per 30-minute interval; $P(r) = (e^{-\lambda} \lambda^r)/r!$.
   (b) Using Table 5 in Appendix II with $\lambda = 5.1$, we find $P(4) = 0.1719$;
       $P(5) = 0.1753$; $P(6) = 0.1490$.
   (c) $P(r \geq 4) = 1 - P(0) - P(1) - P(2) - P(3) = 1 - 0.0061 - 0.0311$
       $- 0.0793 - 0.1348 = 0.7487$.
   (d) $P(r < 4) = 1 - P(r \geq 4) = 1 - 0.7487 = 0.2513$.

11. (a) For 1000 people, $\lambda = 16$ births; $\lambda = 8$ deaths.
    (b) By Table 5 in Appendix II, $P(10 \text{ births}) = 0.0341$; $P(10 \text{ deaths})$
        $= 0.0993$; $P(16 \text{ births}) = 0.0992$; $P(16 \text{ deaths}) = 0.0045$.
    (c) $\lambda(\text{births}) = (16/1000) \times (1500/1500) = 24$ per 1500 people.
        $\lambda(\text{deaths}) = (8/1000) \times (1500/1500) = 12$ per 1500 people.
        By the table, $P(10 \text{ deaths}) = 0.1048$; $P(16 \text{ deaths}) = 0.0543$. Since
        $\lambda = 24$ is not in the table, use the formula for $P(r)$ to find $P(10 \text{ births})$
        $= 0.00066$; $P(16 \text{ births}) = 0.02186$.
    (d) $\lambda(\text{births}) = (16/1000) \times (750/750) = 12$ per 750 people.
        $\lambda(\text{deaths}) = (8/1000) \times (750/750) = 6$ per 750 people.
        By Table 5 of Appendix II, $P(10 \text{ births}) = 0.1048$; $P(10 \text{ deaths})$
        $= 0.0413$; $P(16 \text{ births}) = 0.0543$; $P(16 \text{ deaths}) = 0.0003$.

13. (a) The Poisson distribution is a good choice for r because gale-force
        winds occur rather rarely. The occurrences are usually independent.
    (b) Interval of 108 hours $\lambda = (1/60) \times (108/108) = 1.8$ per 108 hours.
        Using Table 5 of Appendix II, we find that $P(2) = 0.2678$; $P(3)$
        $= 0.1607$; $P(4) = 0.0723$; $P(r < 2) = P(0) + P(1) = 0.1653 + 0.2975$
        $= 0.4628$.

(c) Interval of 180 hours $\lambda = (1/60) \times (180/180) = 3$ per 180 hours. Table 5 of Appendix II gives $P(3) = 0.2240$; $P(4) = 0.1680$; $P(5) = 0.1008$; $P(r < 3) = P(0) + P(1) + P(2) = 0.0498 + 0.1494 + 0.2240 = 0.4232$.

15. (a) The sales of large buildings are rare events. It is reasonable to assume that they are independent. The variable r = number of sales in a fixed time interval.
   (b) For a 60-day period, $\lambda = (8/275) \times (60/60) = 1.7$ per 60 days. By Table 5 of Appendix II, $P(0) = 0.1827$; $P(1) = 0.3106$; $P(r \geqslant 2) = 1 - P(0) - P(1) = 0.5067$.
   (c) For a 90-day period, $\lambda = (8/275) \times (90/90) = 2.6$ per 60 days. By Table 5 of Appendix II, $P(0) = 0.0743$; $P(2) = 0.2510$; $P(r \geqslant 3) = 1 - P(0) - P(1) - P(2) = 1 - 0.0743 - 0.1931 - 0.2510 = 0.4816$.

17. (a) The problem satisfies the conditions for a binomial experiment with small $p = 0.0018$ and large $n = 1000$. $np = 1.8$, which is less than 10, so the Poisson approximation to the binomial distribution would be a good choice. $\lambda = np = 1.8$.
   (b) By Table 5, Appendix II, $P(0) = 0.1653$; $P(r > 1) = 1 - P(0) - P(1) = 1 - 0.1653 - 0.2975 = 0.5372$.
   (c) $P(r > 2) = 1 - P(0) - P(1) - P(2) = 1 - 0.1653 - 0.2975 - 0.2678 = 0.2694$.
   (d) $P(r > 3) = 1 - P(0) - P(1) - P(2) - P(3) = 1 - 0.1653 - 0.2975 - 0.2678 - 0.1607 = 0.1087$.

19. (a) The problem satisfies the conditions for a binomial experiment with n large, $n = 175$, and p small. $np = (175)(0.005) = 0.875 < 10$. The Poisson distribution would be a good approximation to the binomial. $n = 175$; $p = 0.005$; $\lambda = np = 0.9$.
   (b) By Table 5 of Appendix II, $P(0) = 0.4066$.
   (c) $P(r \geqslant 1) = 1 - P(0) = 0.5934$.
   (d) $P(r \geqslant 2) = 1 - P(0) - P(1) = 0.2275$.

21. (a) $n = 100$; $p = 0.02$, $r = 2$; $P(2) = C_{100,2}(0.02)^2(0.98)^{98} = 0.2734$.
   (b) $\lambda = np = 2$; $P(2) = [e^{-2}(2)^2]/2! = 0.2707$.
   (c) The approximation is correct to two decimal places.
   (d) $n = 100$; $p = 0.02$; $r = 3$. By the formula for the binomial distribution, $P(3) = 0.1823$. By the Poisson approximation, $P(3) = 0.1804$. The approximation is correct to two decimal places.

Chapter Review Problems

1. (a)

   (b) $P(r \geqslant 6) = 0.966$.

(c) The expected number is $\mu = 8$.

(d) $\sigma = 1.26$.

3. $P(r < 2) = 0.000$ (to 3 decimal places). The data seem to indicate that the percent favoring the increase in fees is less than 85%.

5. (a) $P(r \geqslant 12) = 0.630$.

   (b) $P(r < 8) = P(r \leqslant 7) = 0.007$.

   (c) The expected number is $\mu = 12$.

7. (a)
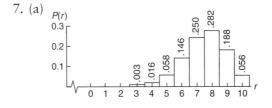

   (b) $P(r \geqslant 9) = 0.244$, $P(r \geqslant 1) = 0.999$.

   (c) The expected number is $\mu = 7.5$.

   (d) $\sigma = 1.37$.

9. The expected number is $\mu = 102$.

11. (a)
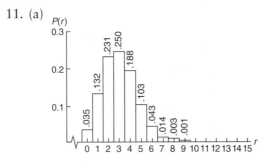

   (b) The expected number is $\mu = 3$, $\sigma = 1.55$.

   (c) $P(r \geqslant 3) = 0.602$, $P(r = 3) = 0.250$.

13. $P(r \leqslant 5) = 0.021$.

15. The expected number is $\mu = 325$.

17. (a) Coughs are a relatively rare occurrence. It is reasonable to assume that they are independent events, and the variable is the number of coughs in a fixed time interval.

   (b) $\lambda = 11$ coughs per minute; $P(r \leqslant 3) = P(0) + P(1) + P(2) + P(3)$ $= 0.000 + 0.002 + 0.0010 + 0.0037 = 0.0049$.

   (c) In a 30-second period, $\lambda = (11/1) \times (0.5/0.5) = 5.5$ coughs per 30-second period. $P(r \geqslant 3) = 1 - P(0) - P(1) - P(2) = 1 - 0.0041 - 0.0225 - 0.0618 = 0.9116$.

19. The loan-default problem satisfies the conditions for a binomial experiment. Moreover, p is small, n is large, and $np < 10$. Use of the Poisson approximation to the binomial distribution is appropriate. $n = 300$; p

$= 1/350 = 0.0029$, and $\lambda = np = 300(0.0029) = 0.86 \approx 0.9$; $P(r \geqslant 2)$
$= 1 - P(0) - P(1) = 1 - 0.4066 - 0.3659 = 0.2275$.

21. (a) Use the geometric distribution with $p = 0.5$. $P(n = 2) = (0.5)(0.5)$
$= 0.25$. As long as you toss the coin at least twice, it does not matter
how many more times you toss it. To get the first head on the second
toss, you must get a tail on the first and a head on the second.

(b) $P(n = 4) = (0.5)(0.5)^3 = 0.0625$; $P(n > 4) = 1 - P(1) - P(2) - P(3)$
$- P(4) = 1 - 0.5 - 0.5^2 - 0.5^3 - 0.5^4 = 0.0625$.

Chapter 6

Section 6.1

1. (a) No, it's skewed.
   (b) No, it crosses the horizontal axis.
   (c) No, it has three peaks.
   (d) No, the curve is not smooth.
3. Figure 6–20 has the larger standard deviation. The mean of Figure 6–20
   is $\mu = 10$. The mean of Figure 6–21 is $\mu = 4$.
5. (a) 50%
   (b) 68.2%
   (c) 99.7%
7. (a) 50%
   (b) 50%
   (c) 68.2%
   (d) 95.4%
9. (a) From 1207 to 1279
   (b) From 1171 to 1315
   (c) From 1135 to 1351
11. (a) $1.81 to $3.51
    (b) $0.96 to $4.36
    (c) $0.11 to $5.21
13. (a) Calculator verifies the results.
    (b) 6% to 13.6%
    (c) 2.2% to 17.4%
    (d) The growth rate, 17.4%, is more than 2 standard deviations above
        the mean. Since about 95% of the data lie within 2 standard devia-
        tions of the mean, only about 5% lie evenly distributed in the two
        tails. This means that about 2.5% of the growth rates are above the
        mean plus 2 standard deviations. A growth rate of over 13.6% is
        more than 1 standard deviation above the mean. We know that about
        68% of the data are within 1 standard deviation of the mean. The
        remaining 32% of the data are divided evenly between the two tails.
        Thus about 16% of the values are more than 1 standard deviation
        above the mean.
15. (a) 8.84 to 13.18 years
    (b) 6.67 to 15.35 years
    (c) 4.50 to 17.52 years

17. (a) Tri-County Bank Monthly Loan Request—First Year (Thousands of Dollars)

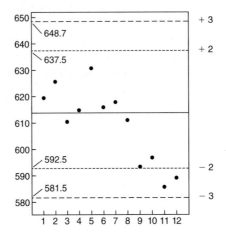

The process is out of control with type III warning signal, since 2 of 3 consecutive points are more than 2 standard deviations below the mean. The trend is down.

(b) Tri-County Bank Monthly Loan Requests—Second Year (Thousands of Dollars)

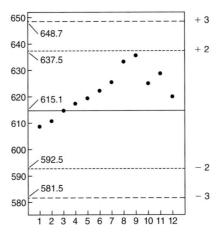

The process shows warning signal II, a run of nine consecutive points above the mean. It would say the economy is heating up.

19.   Visibility Standard Index

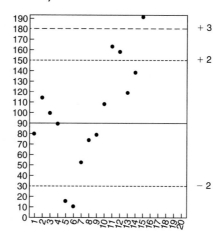

There is one point above 3σ. Thus control signal I indicates "out of control." Control signal III is present. There are two consecutive points below $\mu - 2\sigma$ and two consecutive points above $\mu + 2\sigma$. The out-of-control signals that cause the most concern are those above the mean. Special pollution regulations may be appropriate for those periods.

21.   Speeding Tickets on I-70 Between Vail and Glenwood Springs

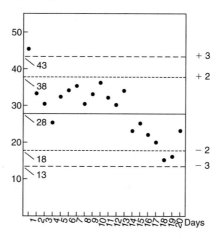

The number of tickets given on day 1 is more than 3 standard deviations above the mean (type I). All data values from day 5 to day 13 inclusive are on the same side of the mean (type II). Days 18 and 19 are both below $\mu - 2\sigma$ (type III).

Section 6.2

1. (a) Robert, Jan, and Linda each scored above the mean.
   (b) Joel scored on the mean.

(c) Susan and John scored below the mean.

(d) Robert, 172; Jan, 184; Susan, 110; Joel, 150; John, 134; Linda, 182.

3. (a) 0.75   (b) 0.00   (c) -0.83

   (d) -1.93 (e) 0.81   (f) -1.46

5. (a) $-4.00 < z < 4.00$ (b) $z < -1.6$ (c) $1.00 < z$

   (d) $81.75°F < x$ (e) $x < 63.5°F$ (f) $64°F < x < 81.25°F$

7. (a) $-1.77 < z$ (b) $z < 1.61$ (c) $-1.45 < z < 1.45$

   (d) $3706 < x < 5907$ (e) $x < 5615$ (f) $6000 < x$

   (g) A population of 2800 deer corresponds to a z value of -2.58. Data values this far below the mean occur less than 2.5% of the time. This would be an unusually low number. The population 6300 corresponds to a z value of 3.06. Fall deer populations are practically never that large. Such a population would be considered an unusually high population.

9. (a) $-1.00 < z$ (b) $z < -2.00$ (c) $-2.67 < z < 2.33$

   (d) $x < 4.4$ (e) $5.2 < x$ (f) $4.1 < x < 4.5$

   (e) A red blood cell count of 5.9 or higher corresponds to a standard z score of 3.67. Practically no data values occur this far above the mean. Such a count would be considered unusually high for a healthy female.

11. (a) RBC $z = -0.17$; WBC $z = -3.71$; HC $z = 2.00$; WBC is unusually low, with HC somewhat low and RBC normal.

   (b) RBC $z = -3.00$; WBC $z = -0.26$; HC $z = -1.50$; RBC is borderline low, with other readings normal.

   (c) RBC $z = 0.33$; WBC $z = -0.33$; HC $z = 3.40$; HC is unusually low, with other readings normal.

   (d) RBC $z = 3.67$; WBC $z = 2.57$; HC $z = 1.80$; RBC is unusually high. WBC is also on the high side, while HC is more normal.

13. (a) Although Walter sold less than Niko recently, he did better in comparison with the other salespeople in his district than Niko did.

   (b) $z = 1.67$ for Niko and $z = 2.54$ for Walter. Walter's z score is considerably farther above the mean than Niko's.

   (c) Promote Walter. He did better in comparison with other sales representatives in his district than Niko did.

Section 6.3

1. 0.4993	3. 0.4778	5. 0.8953	7. 0.3471
9. 0.0306	11. 0.5000	13. 0.0643	15. 0.0934
17. 0.8888	19. 0.6736	21. 0.4474	23. 0.2939
25. 0.6704	27. 0.3226	29. 0.8808	31. 0.5000
33. 0.0885	35. 0.4483	37. 0.8849	39. 0.8849

Section 6.4

1. $P(3 \leq x \leq 6) = P(-0.50 \leq z \leq 1.00) = 0.5328$

3. $P(50 \leq x \leq 70) = P(0.67 \leq z \leq 2.00) = 0.2286$

5. $P(8 \leq x \leq 12) = P(-2.19 \leq z \leq -0.94) = 0.1593$

7. $P(x \geq 30) = P(z \geq 2.94) = 0.0016$

9. $P(x \geq 90) = P(z \geq -0.67) = 0.7486$

11. 1.645
13. −1.41
15. −1.555
17. 1.41
19. ±2.33
21. (a) $P(x \geq 60) = P(z \geq -1) = 0.8413$
    (b) $P(x \leq 110) = P(z \leq 1) = 0.8413$
    (c) $P(60 \leq x \leq 110) = P(-1.00 \leq z \leq 1.00) = 2(0.3413) = 0.6826$
    (d) $P(x > 140) = P(z > 2.20) = 0.0139$
23. (a) $P(x > 675) = P(z > 1.75) = 0.0401$
    (b) $P(x < 450) = P(z < -0.50) = 0.3085$
    (c) $P(450 \leq x \leq 675) = P(-0.50 \leq z \leq 1.75) = 0.6514$
    (d) $P(x > 28) = P(z > 1.67) = 0.0475$
    (e) $P(x > 12) = P(z > -1.00) = 0.8413$
    (f) $P(12 \leq x \leq 28) = P(-1.00 \leq z \leq 1.67) = 0.7938$
25. (a) $P(x < 50 \text{ lb}) = P(z < -1.50) = 0.0668$
    (b) $P(x > 80 \text{ lb}) = P(z > 1.00) = 0.1587$
    (c) $P(50 \leq x \leq 80) = P(-1.50 \leq z \leq 1.00) = 0.7745$
27. (a) $P(650 \leq x \leq 815) = P(-1.62 \leq z \leq 2.31) = 0.9370$
    (b) $P(x \leq 600) = P(z \leq -2.81) = 0.0025$
    (c) $P(x \geq 800) = P(z \geq 1.95) = 0.0256$
29. (a) $P(2 \leq x \leq 6) = P(-1.88 \leq z \leq 0.63) = 0.7056$
    (b) $P(x \leq 1) = P(z \leq -2.50) = 0.0062$
    (c) $P(x \geq 10) = P(z \geq 3.13) = 0.0009$
31. (a) $P(x \leq 36) = P(z \leq -1.13) = 0.1292$
    They will have to replace about 13% of their batteries.
    (b) $z = -1.28$ or $x = 34.76$, or 35 months
33. (a) Approximately 95% of the data lies in the range of $19 - 9 = 10$ years. This range is also the range from $\mu - 2\sigma$ to $\mu + 2\sigma$. Therefore, $4\sigma = 10$ or $\sigma = 2.5$ years.
    (b) $P(x < 11) = P(z < -1.20) = 0.1151$
    (c) $P(x > 18) = P(z > 1.60) = 0.0548$
    (d) $z = -1.645$, $x = 9.9$ years
35. (a) $z = -2.33$; $x = 81$ months
    (b) $P(x \leq 84) = P(z \leq -1.62) = 0.0526$
37. (a) $P(x < 7200) = P(z < -1.60) = 0.0548$
    (b) $P(x > 8900) = P(z > 1.80) = 0.0359$
    (c) $P(7200 \leq x \leq 8900) = P(-1.60 \leq z \leq 1.80) = 0.9093$
    (d) $z = 1.28$; $x = 4.9$ hours after the doors open
    (e) $z = -1.04$; $x = 2.9$ hours after the doors open
    (f) The distribution for Friday would probably be different because many people work on Friday but have Saturday off.

Chapter Review Problems

1. (a) 0.4599
   (b) 0.4015
   (c) 0.0384

   (d) 0.0104
   (e) 0.0250
   (f) 0.8413
3. (a) 0.9821
   (b) 0.3156
   (c) 0.2977
5. (a) 1.645
7. $z = \pm 1.96$
9. (a) 0.89
   (b) 0
   (c) 0.2514
11. (a) 0.0013
   (b) 0.1587
   (c) 0.3413
13. (a) 0.9772
   (b) 17.3 hr
15. (a) 22 inches to 55.8 inches
   (b) 5.1 inches to 72.7 inches
17. (a) 0.5812
   (b) 0.0668
   (c) 0.0122

Chapter 7

Section 7.1

1. A set of measurements or counts either existing or conceptual. For example, the population of all ages of all people in Colorado; the population of weights of all students in your school; the population count of all antelope in Wyoming.
3. A numerical descriptive measure of a population, such as μ, the population mean; σ, the population standard deviation; σ^2, the population variance.
5. A statistical inference is a conclusion about the value of a population parameter. We will do both estimation and testing.
7. They help us visualize the sampling distribution by using tables and graphs that approximately represent the sampling distribution.
9. Sampling distributions help us evaluate the reliability of inferences about population parameters.

Section 7.2

1. (a) $\mu_{\bar{x}} = 15$; $\sigma_{\bar{x}} = 2.0$; $P(15 \leq \bar{x} \leq 17) = P(0 \leq z \leq 1.00) = 0.3413$
   (b) $\mu_{\bar{x}} = 15$; $\sigma_{\bar{x}} = 1.75$; $P(15 \leq \bar{x} \leq 17) = P(0 \leq z \leq 1.14) = 0.3729$
   (c) The standard deviation is smaller in part b because of the larger sample size. Therefore, the distribution about $\mu_{\bar{x}}$ is narrower in part b.
3. (a) No; the sample size is only 9 and so is too small.
   (b) Yes; the $\bar{x}$ distribution also will be normal with $\mu_{\bar{x}} = 25$; $\sigma_{\bar{x}} = 3.5/3$; $P(23 \leq \bar{x} \leq 26) = P(-1.71 \leq z \leq 0.86) = 0.7615$.

5. (a) $P(6 \leqslant \bar{x} \leqslant 7) = P(-1.69 \leqslant z \leqslant 2.53) = 0.9488$
    (b) $P(6 \leqslant \bar{x} \leqslant 7) = P(-2.39 \leqslant \bar{x} \leqslant 3.58) = 0.9914$
    (c) Yes.
7. (a) $P(\bar{x} \leqslant 19) = P(z \leqslant -1.20) = 0.1151$
    (b) $P(19 \leqslant \bar{x} \leqslant 21) = P(-1.20 \leqslant z \leqslant 0.65) = 0.6271$
    (c) $P(\bar{x} \geqslant 22) = P(z \geqslant 1.58) = 0.0571$
9. (a) $P(70 \leqslant x \leqslant 90) = P(-0.53 \leqslant z \leqslant 0.53) = 0.4038$
    (b) Since the x distribution is normal, the $\bar{x}$ distribution is also normal with mean \$80 and standard deviation \$6.008. $P(70 \leqslant \bar{x} \leqslant 90)$ $= P(-1.66 \leqslant z \leqslant 1.66) = 0.9030$.
    (c) We can't say anything about the distribution of $\bar{x}$ values unless the sample size is 30 or more. For samples of size 30 or more, we can say that the distribution is approximately normal with mean $\mu_{\bar{x}} = \$80$, $\sigma_{\bar{x}} = 19/\sqrt{n}$.
    (d) $P(70 \leqslant \bar{x} \leqslant 90) = P(-2.88 \leqslant z \leqslant 2.88) = 0.9960$
    (e) The probabilities increase as the standard deviation decreases. This is to be expected because the variation decreases with increasing sample size, resulting in a larger portion of the normal curve around the mean between 70 and 90.
11. (a) $P(x < 40) = P(z < -1.80) = 0.0359$; $P(x < 50) = P(z < -1.40)$ $= 0.0808$
    (b) Since the x distribution is approximately normal, the $\bar{x}$ distribution is approximately normal with mean 85 and standard deviation 17.678. $P(\bar{x} < 40) = P(z < -2.55) = 0.0054$; $P(\bar{x} < 50) = P(z < -1.98)$ $= 0.0239$
    (c) $P(\bar{x} < 40) = P(z < -3.12) = 0.0009$; $P(\bar{x} < 50) = P(z < -2.42)$ $= 0.0078$
    (d) $P(\bar{x} < 40) = P(z < -4.02) = 0.0001$; $P(\bar{x} < 50) = P(z < -3.13)$ $= 0.0009$.
13. (a) $P(x < 54) = P(z < -1.27) = 0.1020$
    (b) The expected number undernourished is 2200(0.1020), or about 224.
    (c) $P(\bar{x} \leqslant 60) = P(z \leqslant -2.99) = 0.0014$
    (d) $P(\bar{x} < 64.2) = P(z < 1.20) = 0.8849$. Since the sample average is above the mean, it is quite unlikely that the doe population is undernourished.
15. (a) $P(x < 35.5) = P(z < -0.63) = 0.2643$
    (b) $P(\bar{x} < 35.5) = P(z < -2.80) = 0.0026$
    (c) If the weight of only one car is less than 35.5 tons, we can't be sure the loader malfunctioned. There is about a 26% probability that it happened by chance. For the sample of 20 cars, we can be quite sure that the loader slipped out of adjustment if $\bar{x} < 35.5$ tons, since the probability of this happening by chance is less than 0.2%.
17. (a) Since there is no time between customer checkout, the total time for 30 customers to check out one after another will be the sum of the 30 individual times.

29. (a) Confidence interval for difference of means with large samples; -1.61 to -0.51.
    (b) Since the interval contains only negative numbers, at the 99% confidence level, 60-second ads received a higher average rating than 30-second ads received.
31. (a) Confidence interval for a difference of means with small samples. Using values of the means and standard deviations given in part a of Problem 30, the interval is from -3.1 to 1.3. Since the interval contains both negative and positive numbers, at the 90% confidence level there seems to be no difference in average age of professional football players in 1960 compared with 1992.
    (b) Shorter
33. (a) Confidence interval for a difference of proportions; -0.20 to 0.18
    (b) The interval contains both negative and positive values. At the 90% confidence level, we cannot detect a difference in the proportion of those who answer accurately in a face-to-face interview and those who answer accurately in a telephone interview.

Chapter 9

Section 9.1

1. See text.
3. No, if we fail to reject the null hypothesis, we have not proven it beyond all doubt. We have only failed to find sufficient evidence to reject it.
5. Class discussion or essay
7. (a) H_0: $\mu = 7.6$ million
   (b) H_1: $\mu \neq 7.6$ million
   (c) α is the probability of a type I error; that is, α is the probability of rejecting the null hypothesis when it is really true. Therefore, the probability that we make the wrong decision in rejecting H_0 is $\alpha = 0.01$. If the null hypothesis is really false and we fail to reject it, we have made a type II error.
   (d) We need the critical values and a critical region and an estimate $\bar{x}$ of the mean taken from a sample.
9. (a) H_0: $\mu = 8.7$ seconds
   (b) H_1: $\mu > 8.7$ seconds
   (c) H_1: $\mu < 8.7$ seconds
   (d) In part b the critical region is to the right of the mean, 8.7. In part c the critical region is to the left of the mean, 8.7.
   (e) We need the critical value and critical region for each part and an estimate $\bar{x}$ of the mean taken from a sample.
11. H_0: $\mu = 4$
    (a) H_1: $\mu < 4$
    (b) H_1: $\mu > 4$
    (c) H_1: $\mu > 4$

Section 9.2

1. H_0: $\mu = 16.4$; H_1: $\mu < 16.4$; left-tailed test; $z_0 = -2.33$; z value corresponding to $\bar{x}$ is $z = -2.44$. Since the sample test statistic falls to the left of the critical value in the critical region, we reject H_0. The storm seems to be retreating from its severe rating.

3. H_0: $\mu = 24.9$; H_1: $\mu \neq 24.9$; two-tailed test; $\pm z_0 = \pm 1.96$; z value corresponding to $\bar{x}$ is $z = 1.31$. Since the sample test statistic does not fall in the critical region, we fail to reject H_0. There is not enough evidence to conclude that the assembly time under the new system is different from that under the old system.

5. H_0: $\mu = 4.75$; H_1: $\mu > 4.75$; right-tailed test; $z_0 = 2.33$; z value corresponding to $\bar{x}$ is $z = 3.14$. Since the sample test statistic falls in the critical region, we reject H_0. It appears that the average tip Maureen received was greater than \$4.75.

7. H_0: $\mu = 10.2$; H_1: $\mu < 10.2$; left-tailed test; $z_0 = -1.645$; z value corresponding to $\bar{x}$ is $z = -1.52$. Since the sample test statistic does not fall in the critical region, we fail to reject H_0. There is not enough evidence to conclude that the average acceleration time for cars using premium gasoline is less than that for cars using regular.

9. H_0: $\mu = 7.62$; H_1: $\mu < 7.62$; left-tailed test; $z_0 = -2.33$; z value corresponding to $\bar{x}$ is $z = -3.49$. Since the sample test statistic falls in the critical region, we reject H_0. The average daily cost of owning a car for a college student seems to be less than the reported national average cost.

11. H_0: $\mu = 3.97$; H_1: $\mu \neq 3.97$; two-tailed test; $\pm z_0 = \pm 1.96$; z value corresponding to $\bar{x}$ is $z = 1.25$. Since the sample test statistic does not fall in the critical region, we fail to reject H_0. We do not have enough evidence to conclude that the mean age of deer in Mesa Verde National Park has changed since 1981.

13. H_0: $\mu = 1.43$; H_1: $\mu \neq 1.43$; two-tailed test; $\pm z_0 = \pm 1.96$; z value corresponding to $\bar{x}$ is $z = 1.26$. Since the sample test statistic does not fall in the critical region, we fail to reject H_0. There is not enough evidence to conclude that the population mean growth rate is different from the long-term average growth rate.

15. H_0: $\mu = 0.25$; H_1: $\mu > 0.25$; right-tailed test; $z_0 = 1.645$; z value corresponding to $\bar{x}$ is $z = 3.0$. Since the sample test statistic falls in the critical region, we reject H_0. The supplier's claim that the average amount of liquid is 0.25 gallon per can seems to be too low.

17. H_0: $\mu = 16{,}500$; H_1: $\mu > 16{,}500$; right-tailed test; $z_0 = 1.645$; z value corresponding the $\bar{x}$ is $z = 2.51$. Since the sample test statistic falls in the critical region, we reject H_0. It seems that the average startup cost is greater than \$16,500. The bank should consider lending more money.

19. (a) $c = 0.99$; a 99% confidence interval for μ is from 20.28 to 23.72; H_0 states $\mu = 20$, and 20 is not in the confidence interval, so we reject H_0.

    (b) $\pm z_0 = \pm 2.58$; z value corresponding to $\bar{x}$ is $z = 3.00$. Since the sample test statistic falls in the critical region, we reject H_0. This is the same conclusion we made in part a.

Section 9.3

1. (a) Since P value $> \alpha$, do not reject H_0.
   (b) Since P value $< \alpha$, reject H_0.
3. (a) Since P value $< \alpha$, reject H_0.
   (b) Since P value $< \alpha$, reject H_0.
5. (a) Since P value $> \alpha$, do not reject H_0.
   (b) Since P value $< \alpha$, reject H_0.
7. z value corresponding to $\bar{x}$ is $z = 2.78$; P value is in the right tail; P value $= P(z \geqslant 2.78) = 0.0027$; reject H_0 at both the 5% level and 1% level of significance.
9. z value corresponding to $\bar{x}$ is $z = -2.31$; P value is in the left tail; P value $= P(z \leqslant -2.31) = 0.0104$; reject H_0 at the 5% level; do not reject H_0 at the 1% level.
11. z value corresponding to $\bar{x}$ is $z = -1.18$; P value is in both tails; P value $= 2P(z \leqslant -1.18) = 0.2380$; do not reject H_0 at both the 5% and 1% levels of significance.
13. z value corresponding to $\bar{x}$ is $z = 2.23$; P value is in both tails; P value $= 2P(z \geqslant 2.23) = 0.0258$; reject H_0 at the 5% level; do not reject H_0 at the 1% level.

Section 9.4

1. $d.f. = 8$; $t_0 = -1.860$
3. $d.f. = 23$; $\pm t_0 = \pm 2.807$
5. $d.f. = 11$; $\pm t_0 = \pm 2.201$
7. (a) Mean and standard deviation round to results given.
   (b) H_0: $\mu = 4.8$; H_1: $\mu < 4.8$; left-tailed test; $d.f. = 5$; $t_0 = -2.015$. Using results of part a, the t value corresponding to $\bar{x}$ is $t = -4.06$. P value < 0.005. Since the sample test statistic falls in the critical region, we reject H_0. It seems that the population mean red blood count for this patient is lower than 4.8.
9. (a) Mean and standard deviation round to results given.
   (b) H_0: $\mu = 85$; H_1: $\mu \neq 85$; two-tailed test; $d.f. = 9$; $\pm t_0 = \pm 3.250$. Using results of part a, the t value corresponding to $\bar{x}$ is $t = 1.316$. $0.20 < P$ value < 0.25. Since the sample test statistic does not fall in the critical region, we fail to reject H_0. There is not enough evidence to conclude that this patient's average glucose level is different from that of healthy adults under age 50.
11. (a) Mean and standard deviation round to results given.
    (b) H_0: $\mu = 16.5$; H_1: $\mu \neq 16.5$; two-tailed test; $d.f. = 17$; $\pm t_0 = \pm 2.110$. Using results of part a, the t value corresponding to $\bar{x}$ is $t = 2.565$. $0.02 < P$ value < 0.05. The sample test statistic falls in the critical region so we reject H_0. The population average incubation time above 8000 feet seems to be different from 16.5 days.
13. (a) Mean standard deviation round to results given.
    (b) H_0: $\mu = 155.8$; H_1: $\mu \neq 155.8$; two-tailed test; $d.f. = 8$; $\pm t_0 = \pm 3.355$. Using results of part a, the t value corresponding to $\bar{x}$ is

$t = -2.824$. $0.02 < P$ value < 0.05. Since the sample test statistic does not fall in the critical region, do not reject H_0. There is not enough evidence to conclude that the average earnings for M.D.s practicing in rural communities in Nebraska is different from the average earnings of all M.D.s at the 1% level of significance.

15. (a) Mean and standard deviation round to results given.
    (b) H_0: $\mu = 1300$; H_1: $\mu \neq 1300$; two-tailed test; $d.f. = 9$; $\pm t_0 = \pm 3.250$. Using results of part a, the t value corresponding to $\bar{x}$ is $t = -2.714$. $0.02 < P$ value < 0.05. Since the sample test statistic does not fall in the critical region, do not reject H_0. There is not enough evidence to conclude that the population mean of tree ring dates is different from 1300 at the 1% level of significance.

17. (a) Mean and standard deviation round to results given.
    (b) H_0: $\mu = 77$; H_1: $\mu < 77$; left-tailed test; $d.f. = 19$; $t_0 = -1.729$. Using results of part a, the t value corresponding to $\bar{x}$ is $t = -0.630$; $0.125 < P$ value. Since the sample test statistic does not fall in the critical region, do not reject H_0. There is not enough evidence to conclude that the population mean life span for Honolulu residents is less than 77 years.

19. (a) Mean and standard deviation round to results given.
    (b) H_0: $\mu = 44.9$; H_1: $\mu < 44.9$; left-tailed test; $d.f. = 6$; $t_0 = -1.943$; t value corresponding to the $\bar{x}$ is $t = -2.131$; $0.025 < P$ value < 0.05. Since the sample test statistic falls in the critical region, we reject H_0 and conclude that the population mean startup cost for automobile paint shops in El Paso is less than 44.9 thousand dollars at the 5% level of significance.

Section 9.5

1. H_0: $p = 0.63$; H_1: $p \neq 0.63$; two-tailed test; $\pm z_0 = \pm 1.96$; z value corresponding to $\hat{p} = 0.7949$ is $z = 2.13$; P value $= 0.0332$. Since the sample test statistic falls in the critical region, we reject H_0. At the 5% level of significance we conclude that the population proportion of homeless people in Denver who agree with the statement is different from 63%.

3. H_0: $p = 0.25$; H_1: $p > 0.25$; right-tailed test; $z_0 = 2.33$; z value corresponding to $\hat{p} = 0.3288$ is $z = 1.55$; P value $= 0.0606$. Since the sample test statistic does not fall in the critical region, we fail to reject H_0. There is not enough evidence to conclude that the population proportion of high school drop-outs who have not had enough money to buy food at least once in the past year is greater than 25%.

5. H_0: $p = 0.77$; H_1: $p < 0.77$; left-tailed test; $z_0 = -2.33$; z value corresponding to $\hat{p} = 0.5556$ is -2.65; P value $= 0.0040$. Since the sample test statistic falls in the critical region, we reject H_0 and conclude at the 1% level of significance that the population proportion of driver fatalities related to alcohol in Kit Carson County is less than 77%.

7. H_0: $p = 0.47$; H_1: $p < 0.47$; left-tailed test; $z_0 = -2.33$; z value corresponding to $\hat{p} = 0.2787$ is $z = -2.99$; P value $= 0.0014$. Since the sample

test statistic falls in the critical region, we reject H_0. At the 1% level of significance we conclude that the population proportion of residents in Rangely who agree that there should be less grazing of cattle on public lands is less than 47%.

9. H_0: $p = 0.50$; H_1: $p < 0.50$; left-tailed test; $z_0 = -2.33$; z value corresponding to $\hat{p} = 10/34$ is -2.40; P value $= 0.0082$. Since the sample test statistic falls in the critical region, we reject H_0. It seems that the population proportion of female wolves is now less than 50% at the 1% level of significance.

11. H_0: $p = 0.29$; H_1: $p \neq 0.29$; two-tailed test; $\pm z_0 = \pm 1.96$; z value corresponding to $\hat{p} = 0.23$ is $z = -1.32$; P value $= 0.1868$. Since the sample test statistic does not fall in the critical region, we fail to reject H_0. There is not enough evidence to conclude that the population proportion of women who order from a catalogue and wear a size 8 shoe is different from 29%.

13. H_0: $p = 0.47$; H_1: $p > 0.47$; right-tailed test; $z_0 = 2.33$; z value corresponding to $\hat{p} = 490/1006$ is $z = 1.09$; P value $= 0.1379$. Since the sample test statistics does not fall in the critical region, we fail to reject H_0. There is not enough evidence to conclude that the population loyalty of Chevrolet owners is more than 47%.

15. H_0: $p = 0.65$; H_1: $p \neq 0.65$; two-tailed test; $\pm z_0 = \pm 1.96$; z value corresponding to $\hat{p} = 60/78$ is $z = 2.21$; P value $= 0.0272$. Since the sample test statistic falls in the critical region, we reject H_0. It seems that the proportion of office workers who decided to take their current job because of open communication with their supervisor is different from 65%.

17. H_0: $p = 0.94$; H_1: $p \neq 0.94$; two-tailed test; $\pm z_0 = \pm 2.58$; z value corresponding to $\hat{p} = 323/350 = -1.35$; P value $= 0.1770$. Since the sample test statistic does not fall in the critical region, we fail to reject H_0. There is not enough evidence to conclude that the proportion of on-time letters is different from 94%.

19. H_0: $p = 0.238$; H_1: $p > 0.238$; right-tailed test; $z_0 = 2.33$; z value corresponding to $\hat{p} = 178/610$ is $z = 3.12$; P value $= 0.0009$. Since the sample test statistic falls in the critical region, we reject H_0. It seems the population proportion of 18- to 22-year-olds in Biddford who are attending college is more than 23.8%.

Section 9.6

1. $\bar{d} = 0.44$; $s_d = 7.2$; H_0: $\mu_d = 0$; H_1: $\mu_d \neq 0$; two-tailed test; $d.f. = 4$; $\pm t_0 = \pm 4.604$. The t value corresponding to sample test statistic is $t = 0.137$; $0.25 < P$ value. Since the sample test statistic does not fall in the critical region, we fail to reject H_0. There is not enough evidence to conclude that there is any difference in the average number of people watching CBS Monday through Friday compared with those watching NBC at the 1% level of significance.

3. $\bar{d} = 12.6$; $s_d = 22.66$; H_0: $\mu_d = 0$; H_0: $\mu_d > 0$; right-tailed test; $d.f. = 4$;

$t_0 = 3.747$. The t value corresponding to the sample test statistic is $t = 1.243$. $0.125 < P$ value. Since the sample test statistic does not fall in the critical region, we fail to reject H_0. At the 1% level of significance we do not conclude that the peak wind gusts are higher in January than they are in April.

5. $\bar{d} = -1.15$; $s_d = 1.633$; H_0: $\mu_d = 0$; H_1: $\mu_d \neq 0$; two-tailed test; $d.f. = 11$; $\pm t_0 = \pm 2.201$. The t value corresponding to the sample test statistic is $t = -2.440$; $0.02 < P$ value < 0.05. Since the sample test statistic falls in the critical region, we reject H_0. At the 5% level of significance we have enough evidence to conclude that the average temperature in Buffalo is different from the average temperature during this period in Grand Rapids.

7. $\bar{d} = 6$; $s_d = 21.5$; H_0: $\mu_d = 0$; H_1: $\mu_d > 0$; right-tailed test; $d.f. = 7$; $t_0 = 1.895$. The t value corresponding to the sample test statistic is $t = 0.789$; $0.125 < P$ value. Since the sample test statistic does not fall in the critical region, we do not reject H_0. We do not have enough evidence to conclude that there are more inhabited houses than hogans on the Navajo Reservation.

9. $\bar{d} = 1.0$; $s_d = 5.24$; H_0: $\mu_d = 0$; H_1: $\mu_d \neq 0$; two-tailed test; $d.f. = 4$; $\pm t_0 = \pm 2.776$. The t value corresponding to the sample test statistic is $t = 0.427$; $0.25 < P$ value. Since the sample test statistic does not fall in the critical region, we do not reject H_0. There is not enough evidence to conclude that there is a difference in the number of service ware shards in subarea 1 and in subarea 2.

11. $\bar{d} = 9.286$; $s_d = 8.440$; H_0: $\mu_d = 0$; H_1: $\mu_d > 0$; right-tailed test; $d.f. = 6$; $t_0 = 1.943$. The t value correspnding to the sample test statistic is $t = 2.911$; $0.01 < P$ value < 0.025. Since the sample test statistic falls in the critical region, we reject H_0. We conclude at the 5% level of significance that the cigarette smokers' attitudes became less positive after the film.

13. $\bar{d} = -9$; $s_d = 7.43$; H_0: $\mu_d = 0$; H_1: $\mu_d \neq 0$; two-tailed test; $d.f. = 5$; $\pm t_0 = \pm 2.571$. The t value corresponding to the sample test statistic is $t = -2.967$; $0.02 < P$ value < 0.05. Since the sample test statistic falls in the critical region, we reject H_0. We conclude that the two tire brands show unequal wear.

15. $\bar{d} = 0.775$; $s_d = 1.0539$; H_0: $\mu_d = 0$; H_1: $\mu_d > 0$; right-tailed test; $d.f. = 7$; $t_0 = 2.998$. The t value corresponding to the sample test statistic is $t = 1.895$; $0.025 < P$ value < 0.05. Since the sample test statistic falls in the critical region, we reject H_0. At the 5% level of significance it seems that rats receiving larger rewards perform better on the ladder climb.

17. $\bar{d} = 10.5$; $s_d = 5.1672$; H_0: $\mu_d = 0$; H_1: $\mu_d < 0$; left-tailed test; $d.f. = 5$; $t_0 = 2.015$. The t value corresponding to the sample test statistic is $t = -4.977$. P value < 0.005. Since the sample test statistic falls in the critical region, we reject H_0. We conclude that the average heart rate 6 minutes after the test is higher than the average heart rate before the test.

19. $\bar{d} = 0.52$; $s_d = 0.4401$; H_0: $\mu_d = 0$; H_1: $\mu_d > 0$; use t distribution with d.f. = 5, $t_0 = 2.015$; $0.01 < P$ value < 0.025. Since the sample test statistic falls in the critical region, we reject H_0 and conclude that the average weeky sales dropped when the bonus system was discontinued at the 5% level of significance.

Section 9.7

1. H_0: $\mu_1 = \mu_2$; H_1: $\mu_1 > \mu_2$; right-tailed test with $z_0 = 2.33$. The z value corresponding to the sample test statistic $\bar{x}_1 - \bar{x}_2 = 0.7$ is $z = 4.22$. P value ≈ 0.0001. Since the sample test statistic falls in the critical region, we reject H_0 and conclude that, on average, 10-year-old children have more REM sleep than do 35-year-old adults.

3. H_0: $\mu_1 = \mu_2$; H_1: $\mu_1 > \mu_2$; right-tailed test with $z_0 = 2.33$. The z value corresponding to the sample test statistic $\bar{x}_1 - \bar{x}_2 = 13$ is $z = 3.50$. P value $= 0.0002$. Since the sample test statistic falls in the critical region, we reject H_0 and conclude that the mean pollution index for Englewood is less than that for Denver.

5. H_0: $\mu_1 = \mu_2$; H_1: $\mu_1 < \mu_2$; left-tailed test with $z_0 = -1.645$. The z value corresponding to the sample test statistic $\bar{x}_1 - \bar{x}_2 = -2.3$ is $z = -2.60$. P value $= 0.0047$. Since the sample test statistic falls in the critical region, we reject H_0 and conclude that the average sick leave for night workers is more than that for day workers.

7. H_0: $\mu_1 = \mu_2$; H_1: $\mu_1 \neq \mu_2$; two-tailed test with $\pm z_0 = \pm 1.96$. The z value corresponding to the sample test statistic $\bar{x}_1 - \bar{x}_2 = -1.4$ is $z = -0.11$. P value $= 0.9124$. Since the sample test statistic does not fall in the critical region, we do not reject H_0. There is virtually no evidence of any difference in the average scores of the two groups.

9. (a) The means and standard deviations round to the results given.
   (b) H_0: $\mu_1 = \mu_2$; H_1: $\mu_1 \neq \mu_2$; two-tailed test; d.f. = 29; $\pm t_0 = \pm 2.045$; $s = 2.6389$. The t value corresponding to the sample test statistic $\bar{x}_1 - \bar{x}_2 = 0.82$ is $t = 0.865$; $0.25 < P$ value. Since the sample test statistic does not fall in the critical region, we do not reject H_0. There is not enough evidence to conclude that the average number of cases of fox rabies is different in the two regions.

11. (a) The means and standard deviations round to the results given.
    (b) H_0: $\mu_1 = \mu_2$; H_1: $\mu_1 > \mu_2$; right-tailed test; d.f. = 18; $t_0 = 1.734$; $s = 18.172$. The t value corresponding to the sample test statistic $\bar{x}_1 - \bar{x}_2 = 17.17$ is $t = 2.102$; $0.01 < P$ value < 0.025. Since the sample test statistic falls in the critical region, we reject H_0 and conclude that the mean spending at restaurants at Key West is higher than it is at Fredericksberg at the 5% level of significance.

13. (a) The means and standard deviations round to the results given.
    (b) H_0: $\mu_1 = \mu_2$; H_1: $\mu_1 < \mu_2$; left-tailed test; d.f. = 20; $t_0 = -1.725$; $s = 2.592$. The t value corresponding the sample test statistic $\bar{x}_1 - \bar{x}_2 = -3.6$ is $t = -3.244$. P value < 0.005. Since the sample test statistic falls in the critical region, we reject H_0 and conclude that the average water temperature has increased.

15. (a) The means and standard deviations round to the results given.
    (b) H_0: $\mu_1 = \mu_2$; H_1: $\mu_1 \neq \mu_2$; two-tailed test; $d.f. = 12$; $\pm t_0 = \pm 3.055$; $s = 10.626$. The t value corresponding to the sample test statistic $\bar{x}_1 - \bar{x}_2 = -5.7$ is $t = -1.004$; $0.25 < P$ value. Since the sample test statistic does not fall in the critical region, we do not reject H_0. There is not sufficient evidence to conclude that the average number of emergency calls during the day differs from the average number at night.

17. Let $p_1 = $ proportion who agree in 1975 and $p_2 = $ proportion who agree in 1991; H_0: $p_1 = p_2$; H_1: $p_1 \neq p_2$; two-tailed test; $\pm z_0 = \pm 1.96$; $\hat{p} = 0.3436$. The z value corresponding to the sample test statistic $\hat{p}_1 - \hat{p}_2 = 0.0400$ is $z = 2.07$. P value $= 0.0384$. Since the sample test statistic falls in the critical region, we conclude that at the 5% level of significance the proportion of adults who agreed with the statement in 1991 is different from the proportion who agreed in 1975.

19. Let $p_1 = $ proportion who did not attend college and who believe in extraterrestrials and $p_2 = $ proportion who did attend college and who believe in extraterrestrials; H_0: $p_1 = p_2$; H_1: $p_1 < p_2$; left-tailed test; $z_0 = -2.33$; $\hat{p} = 0.42$. The z value corresponding to sample test statistic $\hat{p}_1 - \hat{p}_2 = -0.10$ is $z = -1.43$. P value $= 0.0761$. Since the sample test statistic does not fall in the critical region, we do not reject H_0. There is not enough evidence to conclude that the first proportion is less than the second.

21. Let $p_1 = $ proportion of cattle protected by vaccine A and $p_2 = $ proportion of cattle protected by vaccine B; H_0: $p_1 = p_2$; H_1: $p_1 \neq p_2$; two-tailed test; $\pm z_0 = \pm 2.58$; $\hat{p} = 0.8960$. The z value corresponding to the sample test statistic $\hat{p}_1 - \hat{p}_2 = -0.0729$ is $z = -3.26$. P value $= 0.0012$. Since the sample test statistic falls in the critical region, we reject H_0 and conclude that there is a difference in the proportion of cattle the two vaccines protect.

23. Let $p_1 = $ proportion of porpoises killed on a boat using nets without escape chutes, and let $p_2 = $ proportion killed on a boat using nets with escape chutes; H_0: $p_1 = p_2$; H_1: $p_1 > p_2$; right-tailed test; $z_0 = 2.33$; $\hat{p} = 0.0185$. The z value corresponding to the sample test statistic $\hat{p}_1 - \hat{p}_2 = 0.0283$ is $z = 5.6313$. P value ≈ 0.0001. Since the sample test statistic falls in the critical region, we reject H_0. There is strong evidence that the proportion of porpoises killed on boats using nets without safety chutes is higher than on the U.S. boats using nets with safety chutes.

25. Let $p_1 = $ percentage of bad fruit in Bartlett pears and $p_2 = $ percentage of bad fruit in LeConte pears; H_0: $p_1 = p_2$; H_1: $p_1 \neq p_2$; two-tailed test; $\pm z_0 = \pm 2.58$; $\hat{p} = 0.0529$. The z value corresponding to the sample test statistic $\hat{p}_1 - \hat{p}_2 = -0.0211$ is $z = -1.94$. P value $= 0.0524$. Since the sample test statistic does not fall in the critical region, we cannot reject H_0 at the 1% level of significance. We do not have enough evidence to conclude that the percentage of bad fruit in each of the two varieties is different.

Chapter Review Problems

1. Single mean, large sample; H_0: $\mu = 10.6$; H_1: $\mu \neq 10.6$; two-tailed test; $\pm z_0 = \pm 1.96$; z value corresponding to $\bar{x}$ is -4.00; P value ≈ 0.0002; reject H_0. The average number of miles driven in Chicago is different from the national average.

3. Difference of means, independent large samples; H_0: $\mu_1 = \mu_2$; H_1: $\mu_1 > \mu_2$; right-tailed test; $z_0 = 2.33$; z value corresponding to sample test statistic $\bar{x}_1 - \bar{x}_2 = 0.1$ is $z = 1.06$; P value $= 0.1446$; fail to reject H_0. We do not have enough evidence to conclude that Nippon tubes last longer.

5. Single mean, small sample; H_0: $\mu = 0.8$; H_1: $\mu > 0.8$; right-tailed test; d.f. $= 8$; $t_0 = 2.896$; t value corresponding to $\bar{x}$ is $t = 5.854$; P value < 0.005; reject H_0. The Toylot claim is too low.

7. Difference of means, independent small samples; H_0: $\mu_1 = \mu_2$; H_1: $\mu_1 > \mu_2$; right-tailed test; d.f. $= 22$; $t_0 = 2.508$; t value corresponding to $\bar{x}$ is $t = 3.106$; P value < 0.005; reject H_0. We can conclude that the yellow paint has less visibility after 1 year.

9. Single mean, large sample; H_0: $\mu = 19{,}800$; H_1: $\mu < 19{,}800$; left-tailed test; $z_0 = -1.645$; z value corresponding to $\bar{x}$ is $z = -4.00$; p value ≈ 0.0001; reject H_0. The average salary for the workers seems to be less than \$19,800.

11. Single proportion; H_0: $p = 0.20$; H_1: $p > 0.20$; right-tailed test; $z_0 = 1.645$; z value corresponding to $\hat{p} = 0.30$ is $z = 4.00$; P value ≈ 0.0001; reject H_0. It seems that the proportion of students who read the poetry magazine is greater than 20%.

13. Single mean, large sample; H_0: $\mu = 40$; H_1: $\mu > 40$; right-tailed test; $z_0 = 2.33$; z value corresponding to $\bar{x}$ is $z = 5.01$; P value < 0.0001; reject H_0. It seems that the mean number of matches per box is over 40.

15. Difference of means, small independent samples; H_0: $\mu_1 = \mu_2$; H_1: $\mu_1 \neq \mu_2$; two-tailed test; d.f. $= 28$; $\pm t_0 = \pm 2.048$; $s = 1.9097$; t value corresponding to sample test statistic $\bar{x}_1 - \bar{x}_2 = -0.4$ is $t = -0.5723$; $0.25 < P$ value; fail to reject H_0. There does not seem to be any difference.

17. Difference of means, small independent samples; H_0: $\mu_1 = \mu_2$; H_1: $\mu_1 < \mu_2$; left-tailed test; d.f. $= 20$; $t_0 = -2.528$; $s = 7.5249$; t value corresponding to sample test statistic $\bar{x}_1 - \bar{x}_2 = -6.3$ is $t = -1.956$; $0.025 < P$ value < 0.05; fail to reject H_0. At the 1% level of significance there is not enough evidence to conclude that the students who were given the sample problems did better.

19. Single mean, small sample; H_0: $\mu = 7$; H_1: $\mu \neq 7$; two-tailed test; d.f. $= 7$; $\pm t_0 = \pm 2.365$; t value corresponding to $\bar{x}$ is $t = 1.697$; $0.1 < P$ value < 0.15; fail to reject H_0. There is not enough evidence to conclude that the machine has slipped out of adjustment.

21. Paired difference test; H_0: $\mu_d = 0$; H_1: $\mu_d > 0$; right-tailed test; d.f. $= 5$; $t_0 = 3.365$; t value corresponding to $\bar{d} = 9.8333$ is $t = 6.066$; P value < 0.01; reject H_0. The experimental group did promote creative problem solving.

23. (a) The mean and standard deviation round to the given values.
    (b) Single mean, small sample; H_0: $\mu = 48$; H_1: $\mu < 48$; left-tailed test; $d.f. = 9$; $t_0 = -1.833$; t value of sample statistic is $t = -0.525$; $0.125 < P$ value; fail to reject H_0. There is not enough evidence to conclude that the average fuel injection system lasts less than 48 months.
25. (a) Fail to reject H_0 at $\alpha = 0.01$ level of significance.
    (b) Reject H_0 at $\alpha = 0.05$ level of significance.

Chapter 10

Section 10.1

1. Moderate or low linear correlation
3. High linear correlation
5. High linear correlation

7. (a) List Price and Best Price for Models of Oldsmobile Achieva (Thousands of Dollars)

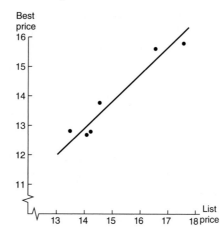

   (b) Just draw the line that you think best. In Section 10.2 you will learn how to get the equation for the line.
   (c) The linear correlation appears to be moderate.

9. (a) List Price and Best Price for Models of Dodge Dakota (Thousands of Dollars)

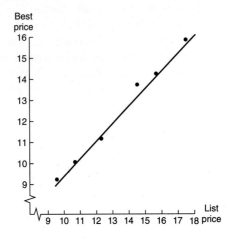

(b) Just draw the line that you think best. In Section 10.2 you will learn how to get the equation for the line.

(c) The linear correlation appears to be moderate.

11. (a) Change in Wages and in Consumer Prices in Various Countries (%)

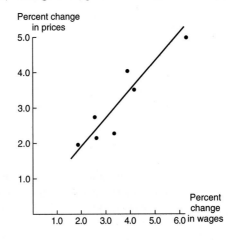

(b) Just draw the line that you think best. In Section 10.2 you will learn how to get the equation for the line.

(c) The linear correlation appears to be moderate.

13. (a) Sociology 110 Midterm versus Final Exam Scores

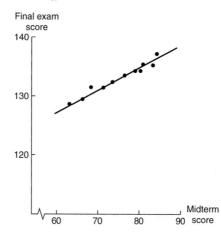

(b) Just draw the line that you think best. In Section 10.2 you will learn how to get the equation for the line.

(c) The linear correlation appears to be high.

15. (a) Unit Length on y Same as That on x

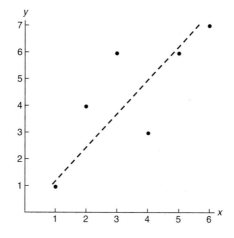

(b) Unit Length on y Twice That on x

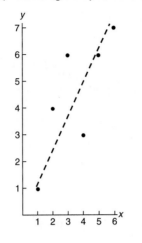

(c) Unit Length on y Half That on x

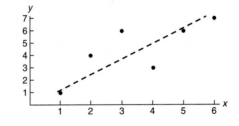

(d) The line in part b appears steeper than in part a, while the line in part c appears flatter than in part a. The slopes actually are all the same, but the lines look different because of the change in unit lengths on the y and x axes.

Section 10.2   *Note:* In this section and the next two, answers may vary slightly depending on how many significant digits are used throughout the calculations.

1. (a) Education and Income in Small Cities

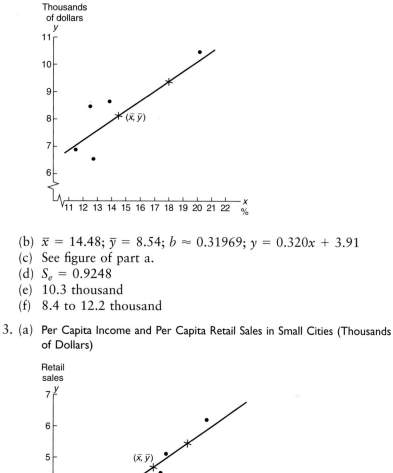

(b) $\bar{x} = 14.48$; $\bar{y} = 8.54$; $b \approx 0.31969$; $y = 0.320x + 3.91$
(c) See figure of part a.
(d) $S_e = 0.9248$
(e) 10.3 thousand
(f) 8.4 to 12.2 thousand

3. (a) Per Capita Income and Per Capita Retail Sales in Small Cities (Thousands of Dollars)

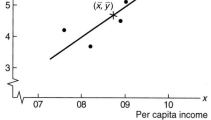

(b) $\bar{x} = 8.72$; $\bar{y} = 4.74$; $b \approx 0.966314$; $y = 0.966x - 3.69$
(c) See figure of part a.
(d) $S_e = 0.536832$
(e) 5.49 thousand
(f) 4.45 to 6.53 thousand

5. (a) List Price and Best Price for Dodge Dakota (Thousands of Dollars)

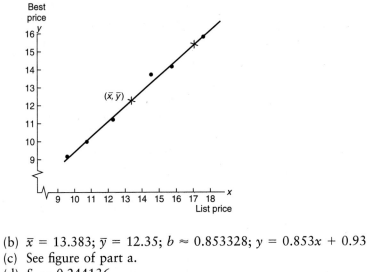

   (b) $\bar{x} = 13.383$; $\bar{y} = 12.35$; $b \approx 0.853328$; $y = 0.853x + 0.93$
   (c) See figure of part a.
   (d) $S_e = 0.244136$
   (e) 15.0 thousand
   (f) 14.2 to 15.8 thousand

7. (a) Absenteeism and Number of Assemblyline Defects

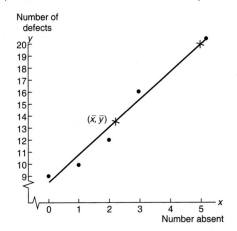

   (b) $\bar{x} = 2.2$; $\bar{y} = 13.4$; $b \approx 2.337838$; $y = 2.338x + 8.26$
   (c) See figure of part a.
   (d) $S_e = 0.877649$
   (e) 17.6
   (f) 14.3 to 20.9

9. (a) Cultural Affiliation and Elevation of Archaeological Sites

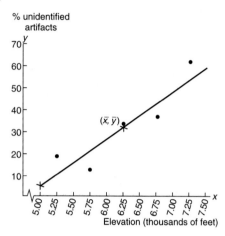

(b) $\bar{x} = 6.25$; $\bar{y} = 32.8$; $b \approx 22.0$; $y = 22.0x - 104.7$
(c) See figure of part a.
(d) $S_e = 8.996296$
(e) 38.3
(f) 24 to 52 (to nearest whole number) (Depending on how you round, the decimal parts of the interval endpoints will vary.)

11. (a) Advanced Ticket Sales and Hot Dog Sales (Thousands)

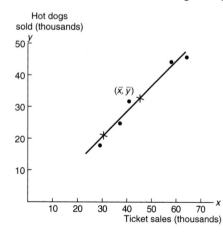

(b) $\bar{x} \approx 45.67$; $\bar{y} = 32.83$; $b \approx 0.80927$; $y = 0.809x - 4.12$
(c) See figure of part a.
(d) $S_e = 1.963789$
(e) 40.38
(f) 37.4 to 43.4

13. (a) Elevation and the Number of Frost-Free Days

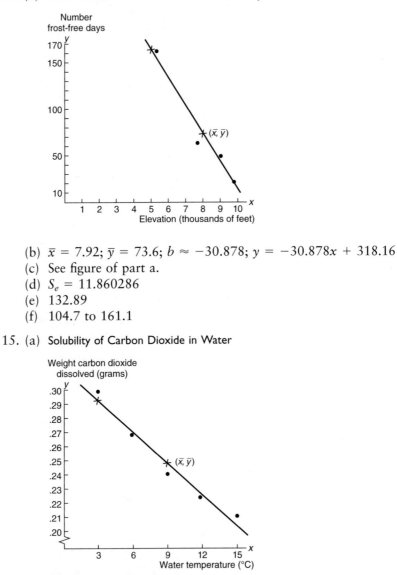

(b) $\bar{x} = 7.92$; $\bar{y} = 73.6$; $b \approx -30.878$; $y = -30.878x + 318.16$
(c) See figure of part a.
(d) $S_e = 11.860286$
(e) 132.89
(f) 104.7 to 161.1

15. (a) Solubility of Carbon Dioxide in Water

(b) $\bar{x} = 9.0$; $\bar{y} = 0.248$; $b \approx -0.00733$; $y = -0.00733x + 0.314$
(c) See figure in part a.
(d) $S_e = 0.006928$
(e) 0.241
(f) 0.223 to 0.259

Section 10.3   1. (a) No
                          (b) Increase in population

3. (a) No
   (b) Better medical treatment

5. (a) Percentage of 16- to 19-Year-Olds Not in School and Number of Violent Crimes per 1000

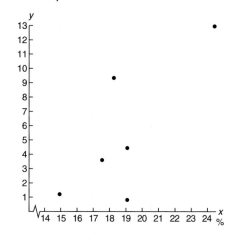

   (b) Closer to 1
   (c) $r = 0.764$; $r^2 = 0.584$; 58.4% explained; 41.6% unexplained

7. (a) Per Capita Income and Number of Medical Doctors per 10,000 Residents

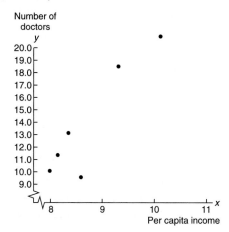

   (b) Closer to 1
   (c) $r = 0.934$; $r^2 = 0.872$; 87.2% explained; 12.8% unexplained

9. (a) Drivers' Ages and Fatal Accident Rate Due to Speeding

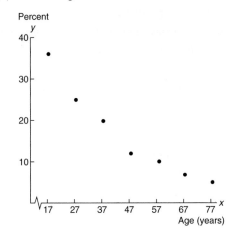

(b) Closer to -1
(c) $r = -0.959$; $r^2 = 0.920$; 92% explained; 8% unexplained

11. (a) List Price and Best Price for Models of Ford Ranger (Thousands of Dollars)

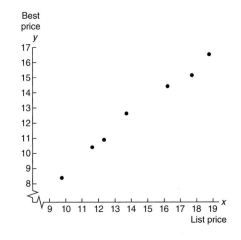

(b) Closer to 1
(c) $r = 0.994$; $r^2 = 0.988$; 98.8% explained; 1.2% unexplained

13. (a) Body Height and Bone Size

Body height
(inches)

Length of femur (inches)

(b) Closer to 1

(c) $r = 0.7061$; $r^2 = 0.499$; 49.9% explained; 50.1% unexplained

15. (a) The MI Money Supply and Passenger Car Sales

Millions
of cars

Tens of billions of dollars

(b) Closer to 1

(c) $r = 0.599$; $r^2 = 0.359$; 35.9% explained; 64.1% unexplained

Section 10.4

1. $H_0: \rho = 0$; $H_1: \rho > 0$. Critical value is 0.54. Because the observed sample statistic $r = 0.384$ does not fall in the critical region, we fail to reject H_0. At the 5% level, r is not significant. There is not enough evidence to conclude that there is a positive correlation between the time a movie has been running and its total revenue.

3. $H_0: \rho = 0$; $H_1: \rho > 0$. Critical value is 0.67. The sample statistic $r = 0.918$ falls in the critical region, so it is significant. We reject H_0 and conclude that there is a positive correlation between percentage change in wages and percentage change in consumer prices.

5. $H_0: \rho = 0$; $H_1: \rho < 0$. Critical value is -0.54. The sample statistic $r = -0.766$ falls in the critical region, so it is significant. We reject H_0 and conclude that there is a negative correlation between the number who finished college in 4 years and the death rate.

7. $H_0: \rho = 0$; $H_1: \rho > 0$. Critical value is 0.66. The sample statistic $r = 0.945$ falls in the critical region, so it is significant. We reject H_0 and conclude that there is a positive correlation between elevation and water content of snowpack.

9. $H_0: \rho = 0$; $H_1: \rho > 0$. Critical value is 0.54. The sample statistic $r = 0.982$ falls in the critical region, so it is significant. We reject H_0 and conclude that there is a positive correlation between list price and best price.

11. $H_0: \rho = 0$; $H_1: \rho > 0$. Critical value is 0.57. The sample statistic $r = 0.48$ does not fall in the critical region, so it is not significant. We cannot reject H_0. We do not have enough evidence to conclude that there is a positive correlation between the number of defects and the number of hours on the job.

Section 10.5

1. (a) Response variable is x_1. Explanatory variables are x_2, x_3, x_4.
   (b) 1.6 is the constant term; 3.5 is the coefficient of x_2; -7.9 is the coefficient of x_3; and 2.0 is the coefficient of x_4.
   (c) $x_1 = 10.7$
   (d) 3.5 units; 7 units; -14 units
   (e) $d.f. = 8$; $t = 1.860$; 2.72 to 4.28
   (f) $H_0: \beta_2 = 0$; $H_1: \beta_2 \neq 0$; $d.f. = 8$; $\pm t_0 = \pm 2.306$. The sample test statistic has $t = 8.35$. Since the sample test statistic falls in the critical region, we reject H_0. The explanatory variable x_2 should be included in the regression equation.

3. (a) Use the computer with given data points.
   (b) x_2 has greatest spread; x_3 has smallest spread.
   (c) x_2; yes; 95.78%; 94.20%
   (d) 97.66%
   (e) $x_1 = 30.997 + 0.861x_2 + 0.335x_3$; 3.35; 8.61
   (f) $H_0: \beta_2 = 0$; $H_1: \beta_2 \neq 0$; $d.f. = 8$; $\pm t_0 = \pm 2.306$. The sample test statistic has $t = 3.47$. Since the sample test statistic falls in the critical region, we reject H_0 and conclude that the coefficient of x_2 is not zero. $H_0: \beta_3 = 0$; $H_1: \beta_3 \neq 0$; $d.f. = 8$; $\pm t_0 = \pm 2.306$. The sample test statistic has $t = 2.557$. Since the sample test statistic falls in the critical region, we reject H_0 and conclude that the coefficient of x_3 is not zero.
   (g) $d.f. = 8$; $t = 1.860$; C.I. for β_2 is 0.40 to 1.32 C.I. for β_3 is 0.09 to 0.58.
   (h) 153.8; 148.3 to 159.4

5. (a) Use the computer with given data points.
   (b) x_4 has the largest spread; because of its large standard deviation; the fact that we are dividing by a large number.
   (c) x_4; 84.17%
   (d) 96.68%
   (e) $x_1 = 7.68 + 3.66x_2 + 7.62x_3 + 0.83x_4$; 7.62 million dollars
   (f) $H_0: \beta_2 = 0$; $H_1: \beta_2 \neq 0$; $d.f. = 6$; $\pm t_0 = \pm 2.447$. The sample test statistic has $t = 3.275$. Since the sample test statistic falls in the critical region, we reject H_0 and conclude that the coefficient of x_2 is not zero in the regression equation. $H_0: \beta_3 = 0$; $H_1: \beta_3 \neq 0$. The sample test statistic has $t = 4.599$. Since the sample test statistic falls in the critical region, we reject H_0 and conclude that the coefficient of x_3 is not zero. $H_0: \beta_4 = 0$; $H_1: \beta_4 \neq 0$. The sample test statistic has $t = 1.536$. Since the sample test statistic does not fall in the critical region, we cannot reject H_0. The coefficient of x_4 could be zero in the regression equation.
   (g) $d.f. = 6$; $t = 1.943$; C.I. for β_2 is 1.49 to 5.83; C.I. for β_3 is 4.40 to 10.84; C.I. for β_4 is -0.22 to 1.88.
   (h) 91.95; 77.56 to 106.33
   (i) 5.63; 4.21 to 7.04

Chapter Review Problems

1. (a)

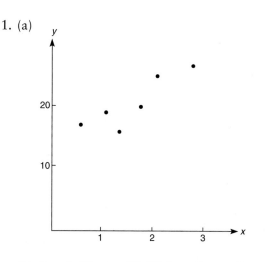

   (b) $\bar{x} = 1.53$; $\bar{y} = 20.67$; $b = 5$; $y = 5x + 13$
   (c) $r = 0.88$; $r^2 = 0.774$
   (d) $H_0: \rho = 0$; $H_1: \rho \neq 0$; critical values are -0.81 and 0.81. Because the sample statistic $r = 0.88$ falls in the critical region, we reject H_0. There seems to be a positive correlation at the 5% level of significance.

3. (a)

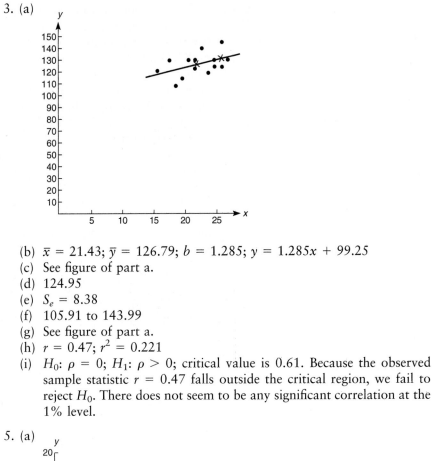

(b) $\bar{x} = 21.43$; $\bar{y} = 126.79$; $b = 1.285$; $y = 1.285x + 99.25$
(c) See figure of part a.
(d) 124.95
(e) $S_e = 8.38$
(f) 105.91 to 143.99
(g) See figure of part a.
(h) $r = 0.47$; $r^2 = 0.221$
(i) H_0: $\rho = 0$; H_1: $\rho > 0$; critical value is 0.61. Because the observed sample statistic $r = 0.47$ falls outside the critical region, we fail to reject H_0. There does not seem to be any significant correlation at the 1% level.

5. (a)

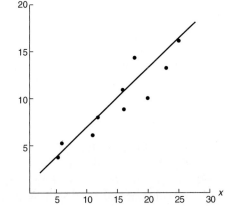

(b) $\bar{x} = 16.38$; $\bar{y} = 10.13$; $b = 0.554$; $y = 0.554x + 1.051$
(c) See line in figure of part a.
(d) 9.36
(e) $S_c = 1.73$

(f) 4.87 to 13.86

(g) $r = 0.91$; $r^2 = 0.828$

(h) H_0: $\rho = 0$; H_1: $\rho > 0$; critical value is 0.79. Because the observed sample statistic $r = 0.91$ falls in the critical region, we reject H_0.

Chapter 11

Section 11.1

1. H_0: job satisfaction and salary are independent; H_1: job satisfaction and salary are not independent; $\chi^2 = 8.91$, $\chi^2_{0.05} = 9.49$. Do not reject H_0 that they are independent.

3. H_0: age of adult and type of movie preferred are independent; H_1: age of adult and type of movie preferred are not independent; $\chi^2 = 3.62$; $\chi^2_{0.05} = 9.49$. Do not reject H_0. They are independent.

5. The cell in row 2 column 3 has expected frequency 4, which is too small for accurate results. The sample size should be increased.

7. H_0: total ticket sales and program offered are independent; H_1: total ticket sales and program offered are not independent; $\chi^2 = 1.87$; $\chi^2_{0.05} = 7.81$. Do not reject H_0 that they are independent.

9. H_0: party affiliation and dollars spent are independent; H_1: party affiliation and dollars spent are not independent; $\chi^2 = 2.17$; $\chi^2_{0.01} = 9.21$. Do not reject H_0. Party affiliation and dollars spent are independent.

Section 11.2

1. H_0: the distributions are the same; H_1: the distributions are different; $\chi^2 = 10.64$; $\chi^2_{0.01} = 9.21$. Reject H_0. The distributions are different.

3. H_0: the distributions are the same; H_1: the distributions are different; $\chi^2 = 1.23$; $\chi^2_{005} = 5.99$. Do not reject H_0. The distributions are the same.

5. H_0: the distributions are the same; H_1: the distributions are different; $\chi^2 = 25.32$; $\chi^2_{0.01} = 15.09$. Reject H_0. The distributions are different.

7. H_0: the distributions are the same; H_1: the distributions are different; $\chi^2 = 9.46$; $\chi^2_{0.01} = 16.81$. Do not reject H_0. The distributions are the same.

9. H_0: the distributions are the same; H_1: the distributions are different; $\chi^2 = 13.70$; $\chi^2_{0.01} = 15.09$. Do not reject H_0. The distributions are the same.

Section 11.3

1. (a) H_0: $\sigma^2 = 9$; H_1: $\sigma^2 < 9$; $\chi^2 = 9.23$; the critical value is $\chi^2_{0.95} = 13.09$. Because the observed value $\chi^2 = 9.23$ falls in the critical region, we reject H_0. The new shot has smaller variance of protection times.

   (b) $\chi^2_L = 9.26$; $\chi^2_U = 44.18$; $1.37 < \sigma < 2.99$.

3. (a) $\chi^2_U = 129.6$; $\chi^2_L = 74.22$; $72.60 < \sigma^2 < 126.77$

   (b) $8.52 < \sigma < 11.26$

5. H_0: $\sigma^2 = 0.15$; H_1: $\sigma^2 > 0.15$; $\chi^2 = 108.0$; the critical value is $\chi^2_{0.01} = 88.38$. Because the observed value $\chi^2 = 108.0$ falls in the critical region, we reject H_0. The variance is too large and the fan blades should be replaced.

7. (a) H_0: $\sigma^2 = 2.89$; H_1: $\sigma^2 \neq 2.89$; $\chi^2 = 54.50$; the critical values are 95.02 and 48.76. Because the observed value $\chi^2 = 54.50$ does not fall in the critical region, we do not reject H_0. The hormones have no effect on variance.

   (b) $\chi_U^2 = 90.53$; $\chi_L^2 = 51.74$; $1.74 < \sigma^2 < 3.04$

   (c) $1.32 < \sigma < 1.74$

9. (a) H_0: $\sigma^2 = 15$; H_1: $\sigma^2 \neq 15$; $\chi^2 = 20.02$; the critical values are 35.48 and 10.28. Because the observed value $\chi^2 = 20.02$ does not fall in the critical region, we do not reject H_0. There is no difference in variance.

   (b) $\chi_U^2 = 32.67$; $x_L^2 = 11.59$; $9.19 < \sigma^2 < 25.91$

   (c) $3.03 < \sigma < 5.09$

Section 11.4

1. (a) H_0: $\mu_1 = \mu_2 = \mu_3$; H_1: not all the means are equal

   (b–h)

Source of Variation	Sum of Squares	Degrees of Freedom	MS	F ratio	F critical val.	Test Decision
Between groups	32.847	2	16.424	4.678	4.26	Reject H_0
Within groups	31.60	9	3.511			
Total	64.447	11				

3. (a) H_0: $\mu_1 = \mu_2 = \mu_3$; H_1: not all the means are equal

   (b–h)

Source of Variation	Sum of Squares	Degrees of Freedom	MS	F ratio	F critical val.	Test Decision
Between groups	2.042	2	1.021	0.336	7.20	Do not reject H_0
Within groups	33.428	11	3.039			
Total	35.470	13				

5. H_0: $\mu_1 = \mu_2 = \mu_3 = \mu_4$
   H_1: not all the means are equal

Source of Variation	Sum of Squares	Degrees of Freedom	MS	F ratio	F critical val.	Test Decision
Between groups	238.225	3	79.408	4.611	3.29	Reject H_0
Within groups	258.340	15	17.223			
Total	496.565	18				

7. H_0: $\mu_1 = \mu_2 = \mu_3$
   H_1: not all the means are equal

Source of Variation	Sum of Squares	Degrees of Freedom	MS	F ratio	F critical val.	Test Decision
Between groups	80.133	2	40.067	0.374	3.88	Do not reject H_0
Within groups	1285.20	12	107.10			
Total	1365.33	14				

9. H_0: $\mu_1 = \mu_2 = \mu_3$
   H_1: not all the means are equal

Source of Variation	Sum of Squares	Degrees of Freedom	MS	F ratio	F critical val.	Test Decision
Between groups	422.00	2	211.00	5.271	4.26	Reject H_0
Within groups	360.25	9	40.028			
Total	782.25	11				

Chapter Review Problems

1. H_0: $\mu_1 = \mu_2 = \mu_3 = \mu_4$
   H_1: not all the means are equal

Source of Variation	Sum of Squares	Degrees of Freedom	MS	F ratio	F critical val.	Test Decision
Between groups	6149.75	3	2049.917	2.633	3.24	Do not reject H_0
Within groups	12454.80	16	778.425			
Total	18604.55	19				

3. (a) H_0: $\sigma^2 > 810000$; H_1: $\sigma^2 > 810000$; $\chi^2 = 65.54$; critical value is $\chi^2_{0.01} = 49.59$. Because the observed value $\chi^2 = 65.54$ is in the critical region, we reject H_0. The variance is more than claimed.
   (b) $\chi^2_U = 45.72$; $\chi^2_L = 16.05$; $1161147.4 < \sigma^2 < 3307642.4$
5. H_0: student grade and teacher rating are independent; H_1: student grade and teacher rating are not independent; $\chi^2 = 9.80$; $\chi^2_{0.01} = 16.81$. Do not reject H_0: they are independent.
7. H_0: the distributions are the same; H_1: the distributions are different: $\chi^2 = 33.93$; $\chi^2_{0.01} = 13.28$. Reject H_0: The distribution has changed.

Chapter 12

Section 12.1

1. Use μ_1 for new tip and μ_2 for old tip. H_0: $\mu_1 = \mu_2$; H_1: $\mu_1 > \mu_2$; right-tailed test; $z_0 = 1.645$. The z value for sample statistic $r = 0.75$ is $z = 1.73$. Since the sample test statistic falls in the critical region, we reject H_0 and conclude that the mean writing life of the new tip is longer than that of the old.
3. Use μ_1 for after lecture and μ_2 for before lecture. H_0: $\mu_1 = \mu_2$; H_1: $\mu_1 \neq \mu_2$; two-tailed test; $\pm z_0 = \pm 1.96$. The z value for sample statistic $r = 0.6250$ is $z = 1.00$. Since the sample test statistics does not fall in the critical region, we do not reject H_0. There is not enough evidence to conclude that the mean score before and after the lectures are different.
5. Use μ_1 for school A and μ_2 for school B. H_0: $\mu_1 = \mu_2$; H_1: $\mu_1 \neq \mu_2$; two-tailed test; $\pm z_0 = \pm 1.96$. The z value for sample statistic $r = 0.5833$ is $z = 0.58$. Since the sample test statistic does not fall in the critical region, do not reject H_0. There is not enough evidence to conclude that there is any difference in effectiveness in teaching reading at the two schools.
7. Use μ_1 for after hypnosis and μ_2 for before hypnosis. H_0: $\mu_1 = \mu_2$; H_1: $\mu_1 < \mu_2$; left-tailed test; $z_0 = -2.33$. The z value for the sample test statistic $r = 0.1875$ is $z = -2.50$. Since the sample test statistic falls in the critical region, reject H_0 and conclude the mean number of cigarettes

smoked per day after hypnosis is less than the mean number before hypnosis.

9. Use μ_1 for after birth and μ_2 for before labor; H_0: $\mu_1 = \mu_2$; H_1: $\mu_1 \neq \mu_2$; two-tailed test; $\pm z_0 = \pm 2.58$. The z value for the sample test statistic $r = 0.6429$ is $z = 1.07$. Since the sample test statistic does not fall in the critical region, we do not reject H_0. There is not enough evidence to conclude that there is a difference in the mean pulse rate of babies before and after birth.

11. Use μ_1 for 1985 and μ_2 for 1990; H_0: $\mu_1 = \mu_2$; H_1: $\mu_1 > \mu_2$; right-tailed test; $z_0 = 1.645$. The z value for the sample test statistic $r = 0.7857$ is $z = 2.14$. Since the sample test statistic falls in the critical region, we reject H_0. We conclude that the mean number of automobile deaths per 100 million vehicle miles is less in 1990 than it was in 1985.

Section 12.2

1. H_0: $\mu_1 = \mu_2$; H_1: $\mu_1 \neq \mu_2$; two-tailed test; $\pm z_0 = \pm 1.96$; $R = 82$; $\mu_R = 90$; $\sigma_R = 12.25$. The z value of sample rank R is $z = -0.65$. Since the sample test statistic does not fall in the critical region, we do not reject H_0. There is not enough evidence to conclude that there is a difference in performance.

3. H_0: $\mu_1 = \mu_2$; H_1: $\mu_1 \neq \mu_2$; two-tailed test; $\pm z = \pm 1.96$; $R = 80$; $\mu_R = 90$; $\sigma_R = 12.25$. The z value of sample rank R is $z = -0.82$. Since the sample test statistic does not fall in the critical region, we do not reject H_0. There is not enough evidence to conclude that the mean number of training sessions for the two methods are different.

5. H_0: $\mu_1 = \mu_2$; H_1: $\mu_1 \neq \mu_2$; two-tailed test; $\pm z = \pm 1.96$; $R = 66$; $\mu_R = 99$; $\sigma_R = 14.07$. The z value of sample rank R is $z = -2.35$. The sample test statistic falls in the critical region, so we reject H_0. It seems that the mean time to take the test in a competitive setting is different from that in a noncompetitive setting.

7. H_0: $\mu_1 = \mu_2$; H_1: $\mu_1 \neq \mu_2$; two-tailed test; $\pm z = \pm 2.58$; $R = 92$; $\mu_R = 90$; $\sigma_R = 12.25$. The z value of sample rank R is $z = 0.16$. Since the sample test statistic does not fall in the critical region, we do not reject H_0. There is not enough evidence to conclude that there is a difference.

9. H_0: $\mu_1 = \mu_2$; H_1: $\mu_1 \neq \mu_2$; two-tailed test; $\pm z = \pm 2.58$; $R_A = 78$; $\mu_R = 68$; $\sigma_R = 9.52$. The z value of sample rank $R_A = 1.05$. Since the sample test statistic does not fall in the critical region, we do not reject H_0. There is not enough evidence to conclude that there is a difference.

Section 12.3

1. H_0: $\rho_S = 0$; H_1: $\rho_S \neq 0$; $r_S = 0.682$; the critical values are 0.619 and -0.619. Because the observed value $r_S = 0.682$ falls in the critical region, we reject H_0 and conclude that there is a monotone relation (either increasing or decreasing).

3. H_0: $\rho_S = 0$; H_1: $\rho_S > 0$; $r_S = 0.571$; the critical value is 0.620. Because the observed value $r_S = 0.571$ falls in the acceptance region, we accept H_0 and conclude that there is no monotone relations between crowding and violence.

5.

Soldier	1	2	3	4	5	6	7
Humor rank	5	3	4	2	1	7	6
Aggressive rank	1	7	3	5	4	6	2
d	4	−4	1	−3	−3	1	4

$H_0: \rho_S = 0$; $H_1: \rho_S < 0$; $r_S = -0.214$; the critical value is 0.715. Because the observed value $r_S = -0.214$ falls in the acceptance region, we accept H_0 and conclude that there is no monotone relation.

7.

Cadet	1	2	3	4	5	6
Aptitude rank	8	1	7	3	11	3
Performance rank	7	1	8	4	10	2
d	1	0	−1	−1	1	1

Cadet	7	8	9	10	11
Aptitude rank	5	9	6	10	3
Performance rank	5	11	6	9	3
d	0	−2	0	1	0

$H_0: \rho_S = 0$; $H_1: \rho_S > 0$; $r_S = 0.955$; the critical value is 0.764. Because the observed value $r_S = 0.955$ falls in the critical region, we reject H_0 and conclude that there is a monotone increasing relation between aptitude rank and performance rank.

9.

City	1	2	3	4	5	6	7	8
Sales rank	6	7	1	8	3	2	5	4
Income rank	5	4	2.5	8	6	1	7	2.5
d	1	3	−1.5	0	−3	1	−2	1.5

$H_0: \rho_S = 0$; $H_1: \rho_S \neq 0$; $r_S = 0.661$; the critical value is 0.881. Because the observed value $r_S = 0.661$ falls in the acceptance region, we accept H_0 and conclude that there is no monotone relation.

Chapter Review Problems

1. $H_0: \mu_1 = \mu_2$; $H_1: \mu_1 \neq \mu_2$; two-tailed test; $\pm z = \pm 1.96$; $R = 107$; $\mu_R = 110$; $\sigma_R = 14.20$. The z value of sample rank R is $z = -0.21$. Since the sample test statistic does not fall in the critical region, we do not reject H_0. There is not enough evidence to show a difference in means.

3. $H_0: \mu_1 = \mu_2$; $H_1: \mu_1 > \mu_2$; right-tailed test; $z = 2.33$. The z value of sample test statistic $r = 0.77$ is $z = 1.95$. Since the sample test statistic does not fall in the critical region, we do not reject H_0. There is not enough evidence to conclude that the mean sales improved after advertising.

5. $H_0: \rho_S = 0$; $H_1: \rho_S > 0$; critical value is 0.600. Because the observed value $r_S = 0.617$ falls in the critical region, we reject H_0 and conclude that there is a monotone increasing relation in the ranks.

Index

Frequently Used Formulas

n = sample size N = population size f = frequency

Chapter 2

Class Width = $\dfrac{\text{high} - \text{low}}{\text{number classes}}$ (increase to next integer)

Class Midpoint = $\dfrac{\text{upper limit} + \text{lower limit}}{2}$

Lower boundary = lower boundary of previous class
+ class width

Chapter 3

Sample mean $\bar{x} = \dfrac{\Sigma x}{n}$

Population mean $\mu = \dfrac{\Sigma x}{N}$

Weighted average = $\dfrac{\Sigma xw}{\Sigma w}$

Range = largest data value − smallest data value

Sample standard deviation $s = \sqrt{\dfrac{\Sigma(x - \bar{x})^2}{n - 1}}$

Computation formula $s = \sqrt{\dfrac{SS_x}{n - 1}}$ where

$SS_x = \Sigma x^2 - \dfrac{(\Sigma x)^2}{n}$

Population standard deviation $\sigma = \sqrt{\dfrac{\Sigma(x - \mu)^2}{N}}$

Sample variance s^2

Population variance σ^2

Sample Coefficient of Variation $CV = \dfrac{s}{\bar{x}} \cdot 100$

Sample mean for grouped data $\bar{x} = \dfrac{\Sigma xf}{n}$

Sample standard deviation for grouped data

$s = \sqrt{\dfrac{\Sigma(x - \bar{x})^2 f}{n - 1}}$

Chapter 4

Probability of the complement of event A
$P(\text{not } A) = 1 - P(A)$

Multiplication rule for independent events
$P(A \text{ and } B) = P(A) \cdot P(B)$

General multiplication rules
$P(A \text{ and } B) = P(A) \cdot P(B, \text{given } A)$
$P(A \text{ and } B) = P(B) \cdot P(A, \text{given } B)$

Addition rule for mutually exclusive events
$P(A \text{ or } B) = P(A) + P(B)$

General addition rule
$P(A \text{ or } B) = P(A) + P(B) - P(A \text{ and } B)$

Permutation rule $P_{n,r} = \dfrac{n!}{(n - r)!}$

Combination rule $C_{n,r} = \dfrac{n!}{r!(n - r)!}$

Mean of a discrete probability distribution $\mu = \Sigma x P(x)$

Standard deviation of a discrete probability distribution

$\sigma = \sqrt{\Sigma(x - \mu)^2 P(x)}$

Chapter 5

For Binomial Distributions

r = number of successes; p = probability of success;
$q = 1 - p$

Binomial probability distribution $P(r) = \dfrac{n!}{r!(n - r)!} p^r q^{n-r}$

Mean $\mu = np$

Standard deviation $\sigma = \sqrt{npq}$

Geometric Probability Distribution

n = number of trial on which first success occurs
$P(n) = p(1 - p)^{n-1}$

Poisson Probability Distribution

λ = mean number of successes over given interval
$P(\lambda) = \dfrac{e^{-\lambda} \lambda^r}{r!}$

Chapter 6

Raw score $x = z\sigma + \mu$

Standard score $z = \dfrac{x - \mu}{\sigma}$

Chapter 7

Mean of $\bar{x}$ distribution $\mu_{\bar{x}} = \mu$

Standard deviation of $\bar{x}$ distribution $\sigma_{\bar{x}} = \dfrac{\sigma}{\sqrt{n}}$

Standard score for $\bar{x}$ $\quad z = \dfrac{\bar{x} - \mu}{\sigma/\sqrt{n}}$

Chapter 8

Confidence Interval

for $\mu (n \geqslant 30)$

$$\bar{x} - z_c\frac{\sigma}{\sqrt{n}} < \mu < \bar{x} + z_c\frac{\sigma}{\sqrt{n}}$$

for $\mu (n < 30)$

$$d.f. = n - 1$$

$$\bar{x} - t_c\frac{s}{\sqrt{n}} < \mu < \bar{x} + t_c\frac{s}{\sqrt{n}}$$

for $p (np > 5 \text{ and } nq > 5)$

$$\hat{p} - z_c\sqrt{\frac{\hat{p}(1 - \hat{p})}{n}} < p < \hat{p} + z_c\sqrt{\frac{\hat{p}(1 - \hat{p})}{n}} \text{ where } \hat{p} = r/n$$

for difference of means $(n_1 \geqslant 30 \text{ and } n_2 \geqslant 30)$

$$(\bar{x}_1 - \bar{x}_2) - z_c\sqrt{\frac{\sigma_1^2}{n_1} + \frac{\sigma_2^2}{n_2}} < \mu_1 - \mu_2 < (\bar{x}_1 - \bar{x}_2)$$
$$+ z_c\sqrt{\frac{\sigma_1^2}{n_1} + \frac{\sigma_2^2}{n_2}}$$

for difference of means $(n_1 < 30 \text{ and/or } n_2 < 30 \text{ and } \sigma_1 \approx \sigma_2)$

$$d.f. = n_1 + n_2 - 2$$

$$(\bar{x} - \bar{x}_2) - t_c s\sqrt{\frac{1}{n_1} + \frac{1}{n_2}} < \mu_1 - \mu_2 < (\bar{x}_1 - \bar{x}_2)$$
$$+ t_c s\sqrt{\frac{1}{n_1} + \frac{1}{n_2}}$$

where $s = \sqrt{\dfrac{(n_1 - 1)s_1^2 + (n_2 - 1)s_2^2}{n_1 + n_2 - 2}}$

for difference of proportions

where $\hat{p}_1 = r_1/n_1; \hat{p}_2 = r_2/n_2; \hat{q}_1 = 1 - \hat{p}_1; \hat{q}_2 = 1 - \hat{p}_2$

$$(\hat{p}_1 - \hat{p}_2) - z_c\sqrt{\frac{\hat{p}_1\hat{q}_1}{n_1} + \frac{\hat{p}_2\hat{q}_2}{n_2}} < p_1 - p_2 < (\hat{p}_1 - \hat{p}_2)$$
$$+ z_c\sqrt{\frac{\hat{p}_1\hat{q}_1}{n_1} + \frac{\hat{p}_2\hat{q}_2}{n_2}}$$

Sample Size for Estimating

means $n = \left(\dfrac{z_c\sigma}{E}\right)^2$

proportions

$n = p(1 - p)\left(\dfrac{z_c}{E}\right)^2$ with preliminary estimate for p

$n = \dfrac{1}{4}\left(\dfrac{z_c}{E}\right)^2$ without preliminary estimate for p

Chapter 9

Sample Test Statistics for Tests of Hypotheses

for $\mu (n \geqslant 30)$ $\quad z = \dfrac{\bar{x} - \mu}{\sigma/\sqrt{n}}$

for $\mu (n < 30); d.f. = n - 1$ $\quad t = \dfrac{\bar{x} - \mu}{s/\sqrt{n}}$

for p $\quad z = \dfrac{\hat{p} - p}{\sqrt{pq/n}}$ where $q = 1 - p$

for paired differences d $\quad t = \dfrac{\bar{d} - \mu_d}{s_d/\sqrt{n}}$ with $d.f. = n - 1$

difference of means large sample

$$z = \frac{(\bar{x}_1 - \bar{x}_2) - (\mu_1 - \mu_2)}{\sqrt{\dfrac{\sigma_1^2}{n_1} + \dfrac{\sigma_2^2}{n_2}}}$$

difference of means small sample with $\sigma_1 \approx \sigma_2$;
$d.f. = n_1 + n_2 - 2$

$$t = \frac{(\bar{x}_1 - \bar{x}_2) - (\mu_1 - \mu_2)}{s\sqrt{\dfrac{1}{n_1} + \dfrac{1}{n_2}}}$$

where $s = \sqrt{\dfrac{(n_1 - 1)s_1^2 + (n_2 - 1)s_2^2}{n_1 + n_2 - 2}}$

difference of proportions

$$z = \frac{\hat{p}_1 - \hat{p}_2}{\sqrt{\dfrac{\bar{p}\bar{q}}{n_1} + \dfrac{\bar{p}\bar{q}}{n_2}}} \text{ where } \bar{p} = \frac{r_1 + r_2}{n_1 + n_2}; \bar{q} = 1 - \bar{p};$$

$\hat{p}_1 = r_1/n_1; \hat{p}_2 = r_2/n_2$